# LEGAL
# FOUNDATIONS
# OF NURSING
# PRACTICE

## Irene A. Murchison, R.N., B.S., M.A.

Nursing Consultant, Legal Areas of Nursing Practice; formerly Professor of Nursing and Chairman of Graduate Faculty in Nursing, University of Colorado School of Nursing, Boulder and Denver; Assistant Director, National League for Nursing, New York City; Professor of Nursing and Director of the Division of Nursing, Loretto Heights College, Loretto, Colorado; Director of Nursing Education and Licenses, Colorado Board of Nursing, Denver


## Thomas S. Nichols, A.B., M.S., L.L.B.

Member of the Bar of the State of Colorado

# LEGAL

# FOUNDATIONS

# OF NURSING

# PRACTICE

THE MACMILLAN COMPANY

COLLIER-MACMILLAN LIMITED, LONDON

*First Printing*

Library of Congress catalog card number: 69-15093

THE MACMILLAN COMPANY, NEW YORK
866 Third Avenue, New York, New York 10022

COLLIER-MACMILLAN CANADA, LTD., TORONTO, ONTARIO

*Printed in the United States of America*

To my family
I. A. M.

To my father and mother
T. S. N.

# Preface

It was the belief of the authors in the writing of this book that law is a behavioral science–oriented discipline and, as such, its study by the professional nurse will add another dimension to the social and behavioral sciences now a significant part of her undergraduate and graduate curriculum. With this as the focus, the book takes on added meaning for the student of nursing when she sees law as a study of human conduct, as a social force for change, and a means of ordering society. In common with related behavioral sciences, the law is concerned with norms of human conduct and has developed its unique method of establishing norms as a basis for dealing with social deviancy.

The nurse is continually engaged in broadening the scope and depth of her understanding of human conduct in an increasingly complex society. She must learn to cope with the problems of the day both within and outside her profession. The study of law as it impinges on nursing practice offers a challenge to select and apply from another related discipline relevant information that will add to her professional competency and the breadth of her social concerns. Thus, the purposes of the authors in writing the book were:

To introduce the subject of law as a means of social and political control that will be meaningful for a citizen and a professional practitioner, in an increasingly complex society.

To familiarize the nurse with the body of substantive law applicable to her professional practice.

To stimulate an awareness of the law regarding nursing continually being evolved through judicial decisions, with a principal aim of identifying and avoiding those situations from which litigation is apt to arise, for the prevention of litigation is as pertinent as preventive medicine. When the nurse is aware of the legal framework of her practice, she can make intelligent choices in full recognition of the consequences of her decisions.

To present judicial decisions, not only to enable the nurse to consider the outcome for the individual or group of nurses concerned, but also to enable her to seek the image the court holds of the nurse as a professional practitioner and to examine this image in terms of expectations of society for the nurse and the goals of the profession for its practitioners.

## Plan of the Book

The book attempts to encourage critical thinking through its analytical orientation. It is designed to assist the teacher, the student, and the practitioner of nursing in the study of nursing jurisprudence and to assist the lawyer and the nurse when they collaborate in teaching. It is planned to be used as a text in formal course work, to be used for independent study and for study by nursing service groups in continuing education programs, and for various types of nursing practitioners and members of related disciplines.

Chapter 1 is a general introduction to the law; it offers basic information for the student of nursing, and others, as citizens and as members of a helping profession. It lays a foundation for a clear understanding of the subject matter to follow.

Each subsequent chapter can be used as a part of a complete course or as source material for the integration of legal principles into a related area of patient care. For example, the concept of the reasonable man could be made an integral part of the teaching of the care of the adult or chronically ill, or the legal area of child battering could be included in the teaching of child care in community agencies and institutions.

The format is the same in each chapter. A case unrelated to nursing is presented to open the discussion of the substantive law; the case serves as a foundation for the rest of the section, which attempts to give the reader a knowledge of the particular legal concept quite apart from any application to nursing. Immediately following the general discussion of the law, the inter-relation of law and nursing in the given area is discussed. Examples are provided, but they are important only as examples; they will have served their purpose if they prompt teacher and student to seek others in related areas of nursing practice.

The third part of each section is entitled "Notes." The method is borrowed and somewhat modified from textual materials of the law. The purpose is to provide material enabling the student to examine in depth a topic related to the preceding material, or to present an opposing point of view. Those Notes taken directly from the literature are preceded by explanatory material or questions aimed at encouraging the reader in independent critical reasoning and decision making.

At this point, the assumption is that the reader has a sufficient grasp of the topic under discussion to move to the reading of a case and to analyze the judicial reasoning. Examination of the judicial reasoning process is designed to enable the student to identify the crucial facts in a case which lead to the application of the legal principles involved. Throughout the book opportunity is given for the nurse to continue to develop beginning skills in legal reasoning, skills that could have broad implications for her in fields other than the particular subject matter of law.

Following the presentation of full cases, a series of case summaries are presented. The purpose is to encourage the student to develop skills in independent analysis of cases and to identify through these additional examples the types of situation that have potential for litigation. These are presented sufficiently completely to stand alone for discussion or to challenge the student, particularly the graduate student, to read the full case as a basis for a creative analytical exercise.

The listing of recommended source material for each section is consistent with the belief of the authors that the purpose of the book is to provide a substantive foundation from a closely related discipline that will enable the nurse to develop a rationale for the legal aspects of her practice. On this premise, the bibliography offers further opportunities to explore the thinking of writers in the field of law. Some selections are made from medical literature and related disciplines to show divergent points of view or variations that may occur in the treatment of the same topic by members of related disciplines. References to nursing literature are limited, for it is assumed that this source material is easily accessible to the reader.

I. A. M.
T. S. N.

# Acknowledgments

The writers would like to express appreciation to our friends and colleagues who have encouraged us in the preparation of this book and specifically to express our gratitude to:

Loretta Ford, R.N., Ed.D., Professor of Public Health Nursing, University of Colorado School of Nursing; Patricia Vander Leest, R.N., Ph.D., Professor of Nursing, Wichita State University; Robert Amundson, Ph.D., Professor of Sociology and Anthropology, Loretto Heights College; faculty and library staff, University of Colorado School of Law; faculty and library staff, University of Denver School of Law; faculty, Division of Nursing, Loretto Heights College; faculty, School of Nursing, University of Colorado; nursing service and medical librarian, St. Luke's Hospital; nursing service, Denver General Hospital staff, Denver Visiting Nurse Service, Department of Health and Hospitals; professional nurse staff, and Colorado Board of Nursing; Gayle A. Nichols.

I. A. M.

T. S. N.

# Contents

xiii

## Part Three

## Social Consequences of Deliberate Acts— Intentional Torts

## Part Four

## Sanctions and Social Justice in the Criminal Law Process—Criminal Law

## Part Five

## Social Concern for Safety of Professional Practice—Board of Nursing, an Administrative Agency

# Analytical Contents

Notes

(1) HISTORY OF LAW   28
Wormser, R., *The Law : The Story of Lawmakers and the Law We Live
By*, 16–20 (New York: Simon & Schuster, Inc.,1949)   29
(2) SYNTHESIS OF THE SOCIAL AND BEHAVIORAL SCIENCES INTO A LEGAL
DECISION   31
Fahr, S., and Ojemann, R., *The Use of Social and Behavioral Science
Knowledge in Law*, 48 Iowa L. Rev. 59, 63–64 (1962)   31

Cases: *Rochin v. California*, 342 U.S. 165 (1952)   33

## Chapter Two

## Evidence   37

FUNCTION OF EVIDENCE   37

TYPES OF EVIDENCE   39

RULES OF EVIDENCE   39
   Relevancy   39      Opinion   40      Hearsay   41

MEDICAL RECORDS AS EVIDENCE   43
   Medical Record as a Business Record   43      Scope and Objectivity
   of Medical Record   44      Legal Uses of Medical Records   46

EXPERT TESTIMONY   49
   Medical and Professional Nurse Witness   51

PRIVILEGED COMMUNICATIONS   54
   Medical Privilege   56

Notes

(1) CONSPIRACY OF SILENCE   59
(2) EVALUATION OF EVIDENCE BY JUDGE AND JURY   61
Prosser, W. L., *Handbook of the Law of Torts*, 191 (2nd ed., St. Paul:
West Publishing Co., 1955)   62

Cases: *Ostrowski v. Mockridge*, 242 Minn. 265, 65 N.W.2d 185 (1954)   63

Cases for Further Analysis: *Williams v. Alexander*, 309 N.Y. 283,
129 N.E.2d 417 (1955)   68      *General Benevolent Ass'n v. East Fowler*,
210 Miss. 578, 50 So.2d 137 (1951)   69      *Polsca v. East River Mgmt.
Corp.*, 160 N.Y.S.2d 658 (App. Div. 1957)   69

Recommended Source Material   70

# Part Two

# Social Consequences of Inadvertence —Unintentional Torts

# Chapter Three

# Standard of Care  77

Chapter Four
Legal Duty    120

## Chapter Five

## Causation   171

# Chapter Six
# Res Ipsa Loquitur    205

# Chapter Seven
# Vicarious Liability    233

# Part Three
# Social Consequences of Deliberate Acts
# —Intentional Torts

## Chapter Eight
## Intended Interference with the Person   281

# Part Four
# Sanctions and Social Justice in the Criminal
# Law Process—Criminal Law

Chapter Nine
Criminal Law   327

# Part Five

# Social Concern for Safety of Professional Practice—Board of Nursing, an Administrative Agency

## Chapter Ten

# Appendixes

**Part One**

---

# Law, A Force for Social Control

# Chapter One

# The American Legal System

Nursing and law are both disciplines primarily concerned with the conduct of man. Each discipline seeks to understand man's behavior. Each acknowledges a common foundation of behavioral sciences essential to comprehend his actions and the varying social means used to structure those actions.

The study of law and its synthesis into nursing practice begins with an analysis of a situation of human interaction drawn from real life, an event which disturbs the ordered fabric of our society, in other words, a socially disturbing event. The various behavioral sciences, and the law, each brings a different perspective to bear upon the analysis of the fact pattern of the disturbing event, and it is hypothesized how the members of the respective disciplines would respond to the situation, descriptively and by actual intervention designed to direct or modify the lives of the participants.

In subsequent sections of the text, an opportunity is afforded for detailed analysis of the interaction of law and nursing which, when coupled with an application of behavioral science principles, can augment the nurse's understanding of man and his conduct and thus add another dimension to her nursing practice.

## A Socially Disturbing Event

John, age 12, and Edward, age 9, were shining shoes in a crowded neighborhood of a large metropolitan city. Both boys came from broken homes and lived in a slum area in the city where they were proud members of the most powerful minority group gang in the neighborhood. John had a history of juvenile delinquency and had once spent six months in Juvenile

Hall for truancy. He was the leader of the two and much admired by Edward. They were not making much money on this particular morning of March 1, 1968, and together they thought of a plan to rob an old man, for they needed money and also wanted to impress the other members of their gang with their courage and cleverness in evading the law. They followed the old man to his hotel; Edward stayed outside and the older boy went to the old man's room and asked for a drink of water. When the man brought it to him, the boy grabbed him and struck him with a shoe brush. The boy knocked the man to the floor, a knife was held to his throat by Edward, who had rejoined John, and together the two boys beat the man up badly, and took his wallet containing $13. The boys then left him and in a secluded spot they divided the money, reserving a portion for their contribution to the funds of the gang.

The victim was taken to the City General Hospital where it was found that he had a fractured jaw and a knife cut under his chin and that he was severely bruised about the face and head. He became progressively worse. Within a few days he lost consciousness and remained unconscious for a month, when he died.

Let us examine this disturbing event as it might be viewed by each of several behavioral scientists and a lawyer. In using examples to illustrate the particular point of view which would distinguish one discipline from the other, care is taken in the analysis of the facts to avoid confusing correlation with actual cause. For example, it would not follow because the boys came from broken homes that this was the cause of their juvenile delinquency.

PSYCHOLOGY

In this body of facts, the psychologist and the social psychologist focus on the behavior of the individual, his physiological make-up, his emotions, drives, motives, heredity, attitudes, and numerous other complex individual characteristics that may be constitutional or environmental in origin. He would see the behavior of the two boys as abnormal from the perspective of the larger society, although it might be considered acceptable in the framework of the subculture and values espoused by the boys. After this analysis the psychologist might advise testing and programs of action to deal in some therapeutic manner with the boys.

SOCIOLOGY

The sociologist in his examination of the facts would be primarily concerned with group behavior, the family, and the primary group relationships within the gang. He might see the facts surrounding the crime as an outcome of persuasive forces operating within a gang in which nonnormative behavior was sanctioned. He would analyze the cooperative method of the planning of the brutal act and the possibility of group pressure that led to the fair division of the money. Further consideration would lead him to look to the socioecological variables bearing on the adaptation of the individual to the environment in which he lives. For example, would these boys have engaged in this kind of behavior had they been living in a middle-class suburban area? His plan of action would lead him to study the gang as a contraculture association, the slum area in which the boys lived, and the family influences tenuous as they might have been.

ANTHROPOLOGY

The anthropologist views the conduct of John and Edward as a part of the totality of human behavior. His channel for operation is the culture which serves as a filter through which human conduct can be examined, for everything which man learns or acquires is reflected in his culture. In his analysis of the culture he would note the cherished values, manifest or latent, as they are reflected in the basic social institutions of the family, government, religion, education, and economy. Certain theories concerning the relationship between the subculture and expected behavior pattern might be germane in relation to these particular facts. For example, the opportunity structure is not the same for the subculture in which the boys operated as for the middle class. Since laws reflect middle-class values, any "definition of the situation" which runs counter to middle-class institutional mores will put these boys in conflict with the law.

LAW

In his analysis of the facts the lawyer would regard the actions of the boys as socially prohibited conduct and would think in terms of the legal processes available to ensure the best interests of society and of the children. He would seek such sanctions as might be imposed for the safety of the public. His course of action might lead to his consideration of correctional institutions available to the juvenile court. Such institutions might offer programs of rehabilitation including psychotherapy, constructive work, and education, and might offer the simultaneous advantages of isolating the boys from society and providing therapeutic treatment and re-education to values of group living, which would adequately prepare them to return to society as productive citizens. Thus, the law would draw from the several behavioral sciences and would respond to socially disruptive actions in such a way as to exert a positive force for social control.

## The Existence and Nature of Law

Every society must face the imperative of selection in developing its culture. Every society ultimately arrives at a limited body of norms, conformity to which is expected of its members. Adaptation to the norms is rewarded and deviation from the norms is penalized.

While laws are legal norms, they are also institutionalized mores and therefore are social norms. Law is an aspect of social control and represents social norms reinforced by legal sanctions. Every legal system is based on certain cultural assumptions and it is the function of substantive law to translate basic cultural postulates into social action by making decisions concerning whether a particular action is or is not in conformity with the basic assumptions underlying the culture.

Thus, law is unquestionably a major instrument in the development and maintenance of cultures. If, therefore, the legal norms of any society are understood, appreciated, and respected, it is essential to know as much as possible about the cultural basis upon which it rests. The social and behavioral sciences can contribute much to a better understanding of law, and to the process of orderly and beneficial change in legal norms.

Laws may arise from the tribal councils ("legislatures" in modern terms). They may arise from pronouncements of the family patriarch or matriarch. They may come from the pronouncements of the high priest, the medicine man, the rabbi, or the guru. They may be mild or severe, fair or oppressive, reasoned or irrational. Every culture and every society, from prehistory to the present day, possesses a form and structure because of a complex mixture of rules, regulations, religious convictions and fears, ethical standards, material desires, and needs. We can think of this mixture as the "laws" of a society. Clearly, there is no single meaning for the term "law." In this most general sense, the laws of a society are simply the sum total of the myriad pressures, requirements, and psychological factors on various levels, together with the interaction of personalities that characterize daily living in any society and that control or influence conduct. In this sense, "law" is the concern of many disciplines. Sociologists will analyze the forces brought into being by the varied needs of the group as a whole; psychologists will consider the effect on the individual of the social forces; anthropologists will attempt to see the culture as a reflection of man's interaction to these rules.

Laws take many forms, and all of these forms may have a profound influence on the life of society. In many primitive societies, the social "laws" of family relationship strictly control who may marry whom. Similarly, in primitive societies, as indeed in some modern societies, the status and occupation of the parents may largely determine the status and occupational opportunities available to the children. Religious tenets, too, may strongly affect daily life. For example, Brahmin societies in India developed, in accordance with their religious beliefs, a caste system to a highly refined degree, and at least until recent days, the possibility of movement from one to another was nonexistent. Under such a system, personal freedom as we know it is inhibited, and the culture established within such limits looks strange and different to a foreign eye. Dietary laws, based on religious principle, are important. The prohibitions of the Hindu religion on the use of certain meat for food have an impact upon the urgent social problems of potential famine.

## Function of Laws in Society

From the purely practical view, it is obvious that the existence of laws of varying kinds complicates to some degree the life of each individual in a given society. What then is the purpose of laws? Behavior that is directly or indirectly inhibited is, to the extent of the inhibition, not free behavior. One might, therefore, inquire whether the existence of societal laws is necessary to the effective, continuing operation of that society. Philosophically, a society operating without laws is an anarchical one, and anarchy, from time to time, is advocated as a Utopian solution to the ills of a society grown complex and perhaps cumbersome. Nonetheless, it appears that no successful society of any complexity bases its legal or political system upon anarchy. To a greater or lesser degree, nearly every known society does operate under rules and regulations developed and promulgated by the society itself.

The reason for the law's existence has been put in these terms [Hoebel, E. A., *The Law of Primitive Man*, 275–76 (Cambridge: Harvard University Press, 1954)]:

Law performs certain functions essential to the maintenance of all but the very most simple societies.

The first is to define relationships among the members of a society, to assert what activities are permitted and what are ruled out, so as to maintain at least minimal integration between the activities of individuals and groups within the society.

The second is derived from the necessity of taming naked force and directing force to the maintenance of order. It is the allocation of authority and the determination of who may exercise physical coercion as a socially recognized privilege-right, along with the selection of the most effective forms of physical sanction to achieve the social ends that the law serves.

The third is the disposition of trouble cases as they arise.

The fourth is to redefine relations between individuals and groups as the conditions of life change. It is to maintain adaptability.

Purposive definition of personal relations is the primary law-job. Other aspects of culture likewise work to this end, and, indeed, the law derives its working principles (jural postulates) from postulates previously developed in the nonlegal spheres of action. However, the law's important contribution to the basic organization of society as a whole is that the law specifically and explicitly defines relations. It sets the expectancies of man to man and group to group so that each knows the focus and the limitations of its demand-rights on others, its duties to others, its privilege-rights and powers as against others, and its immunities and liabilities to the contemplated or attempted acts of others. This is the "bare-bones job," as Karl Llewellyn likes to call it. It is the ordering of the fundamentals of living together.

No culture has a specific starting point in time; yet in the operation of the first function it is as though men were getting together and saying to each other, "Look here! Let's have a little organization here or we'll never get anywhere with this mess! Let's have a clear understanding of who's who, what we are to do, and how we are going to do it!" In its essence it is what the social-contract theorists recognized as the foundation of social order.

Laws may benefit society and encourage its growth, or they may inhibit it. One can assume that the matters most important to a given society will find recognition in the creation of laws relating to those concerns, whether the laws be written or unwritten. The most socially destructive acts, as viewed from within the society, will be prohibited—most societies find it necessary to impose prohibitions upon the unrestrained slaughter of their members by one another—whereas the socially constructive acts will be encouraged in different ways by the legal structure. An example of a law designed to encourage constructive acts can be found in our own history. In the middle 1800's, it was thought desirable to encourage population growth along the western frontier. Laws were therefore passed giving free land to any who chose to occupy it. This, presumably, had the effect of stimulating the expansion and growth of the country.

The judgment of the lawmakers who create formal laws for the benefit of society may be wisely or unwisely exercised. In pluralistic complicated societies such as our own, what is "best" for society as a whole is an elusive notion. Society may make a mistake and promulgate laws that end as veritable cancers eating into its structure and ultimately destroying it, or weakening it to such an extent that other forces bring about destruction. A theoretical instance of this kind of destructive law is found in the Marxist view of the capitalistic system. Marxism, at least in its pristine form, sees a capitalistic democratic system as bringing about its own destruction. Marx reasoned that the capitalistic rule-making class would so overreach itself as to bring about violent revolution, with the result that the rule-making class itself would be eliminated. Marx' theories have not yet proved to be accurate, because he failed to recognize the capacity of the system for orderly change, and failed to foresee that capitalism would of its own accord deal with many of the social evils that it brought into being.

Laws may have unexpected or unanticipated effects, which are undesirable in themselves, or which undercut the law's original purpose. An oft-cited instance is the series of laws in eighteenth-century England imposing death penalties for petty theft and other minor crimes. Guilt or innocence in England then as now was determined by a jury, and the effect of such extreme penalties was that juries refused to convict persons charged with these crimes, however convincing the evidence of their guilt. Therefore, instead of these laws preventing crime, they resulted in the thieves going entirely unpunished.

Whether effective or ineffective, however, laws fulfill the function in society of regulating behavior. The function of laws might be described as the regulation of behavior toward the end of fulfilling society's needs as those needs are perceived by the society itself.

As social needs change with time and circumstance, the laws themselves may vary. At any given time, therefore, the laws from differing cultures will reflect the needs and demands of that culture, and likewise, the needs of any one culture will vary in time, as the society is born, ages, and matures. It is virtually a truism that, in modern times, the societies in which we live have increased enormously in complexity and that the problems to be dealt with, either within or without the law, have developed, altered, and assumed an entirely different character from that of one hundred years ago. Consequently our laws, in one way or another, must take into account these varying needs or we would have laws designed for the nineteenth century attempting to solve the problems of the twentieth century. The legal system applicable to a rural, agrarian economy needs extensive modification before it will be effective in an urbanized industrial society. For example, in the late nineteenth century, Judge Oliver Wendell Holmes, Jr., decided in a case before him that the driver of an automobile who failed to stop his car at a railroad crossing, and get out and peer up and down the tracks was acting negligently. Such a rule of law simply has no place in today's world and, indeed, has been changed.

## Criminal Law and Civil Law

One of the great divisions in any system of law is found in the distinction between the laws governing the relationship between the individual and his society as a whole and the laws governing relationships strictly among individual members of the society. In American law, the former is termed the "criminal" law and the latter the "civil" law. Criminal laws are designed to protect all members of society from undesirable and detrimental forms of conduct. They are blanket prohibitions, which attempt to prevent or inhibit disruptive acts. Civil laws, on the other hand, regulate private disputes and seek to provide ways to resolve such controversies peaceably and fairly.

The criminal law and the civil law are not mutually exclusive. The categories do not divide human conduct, but the law. Behavior may be dealt with in both systems; a robbery, for instance, can lead to the state punishing the thief under the criminal law and to his victim seeking return of his property under the civil law.

CRIMINAL LAW

Criminal cases arise from the efforts of the state to compel obedience to its laws. They come about when someone is accused of violating one or more laws, for which the state will impose a sanction, or punishment. Criminal law enforcement is largely the job of the government. Government employees, i.e., police, watch for violations and arrest suspects. Government investigators gather evidence for the prosecuting attorney. The prosecuting attorney, a government official, presents the case against the accused. If convicted, the accused criminal will be incarcerated in a government prison; sometimes, the government in its wisdom will take all that he has, his life. The state's involvement stems from the belief that the criminal law is concerned with protecting the whole of society from disruptive conduct.

The criminal law performs four functions: the first is to deter potential violators through the inducement of a fear of the sanctions that will be imposed. Second, the sanctions imposed have the effect of restraining members of society who have demonstrated their inability to comply with society's rules and regulations. One who has stolen may steal again and confining him to prison protects society from his theft, at least for the period of his confinement. Third, the criminal law in its broad scope, together with the penal system, should perform a rehabilitative function, and do what is necessary by way of psychological or occupational training or therapy to enable the criminal to return to society to become a useful member thereof rather than a menace. Last, it seems that a penalty imposed by the criminal law carries with it a sense of collective revenge. Each member of society may experience an element of gratification when a person convicted of a brutal murder is hanged, or when the confirmed thief or other criminal is sent to prison for a long term, even for his entire life. Although it may be questioned whether in an enlightened society such a consideration should legitimately form a part of the motive for enacting criminal statutes, nevertheless it seems undeniable that such a motive has existed for many years; witness the social nature of the public hangings of an earlier day in this country, in England, and in some periods of our Western history.

CIVIL LAW

Civil laws, on the other hand, deal with private disputes where the persons involved are unable or unwilling to resolve their controversies by themselves, and therefore must resort to the courts. Thus, when one person does not fulfill the terms of a contract, or fails to repay a loan, society through the civil law provides a means for adjustment of differences. Except when it is itself a party to a civil dispute, the state rarely becomes directly involved. It does not seek out violations; it does not gather evidence; it does not prosecute. All this is left to the individuals concerned; civil matters are initiated by private parties who seek redress for wrongs done to them, either in the form of monetary payments or by some order of the court directing someone to do or refrain from doing certain things. For example, a homeowner may sue a nearby factory because of the fumes coming from the factory smokestack, and he may request both that compensation be paid for the damage to his property and that the factory be directed by the court to stop producing fumes. The coercive power of the state becomes active in civil disputes only to enforce the decrees or judgments of its courts after the dispute between the two parties has been decided.

There are three basic functions of our civil law. The first is to provide a means for the peaceable settlement of disputes. This is done by establishing court systems, which provide a somewhat calmer arena for battle than the back alley. In this way, the state prohibits the settlement of private quarrels by strife, and at the same time provides an alternate procedure. Second, the civil law must see that disputes are settled in a manner consonant with right and justice. In other words, it must see that fair, consistent, and impartial results are achieved. Our system of substantive laws prescribes the general principles governing what the outcome of civil disputes shall be. Thus, the law provides that you must pay for any damage if you carelessly drive your car into your neighbor's fence. Third, the law must ensure that the courts' judgments and decrees are honored. To accomplish this, the state establishes mechanisms for punishing those who disobey court decrees and for ensuring, insofar as possible, that the compensation the court system has determined should be paid is in fact paid to the victim of a wrong. Here the coercive power of the state enters the civil proceeding, for to effect the workings of the court system and to see that money judgments are paid to those entitled to them, the state will seize and sell the wrongdoer's property on behalf of the victim and will prevent the wrongdoer, through force if need be, from resisting.

## Statutory Law and Common Law

STATUTORY LAW

Another way in which the American system of laws can be subdivided is between statutory law and common law. Statutory law consists of written enactments of the Congress of the United States, the various state legislatures, and other legislative bodies found at lower levels in the governmental scheme. The Congress works on the national level; the state legislatures produce statutes with statewide effect; counties, townships, and municipalities all have their legislative bodies.

These enactments are the work of representatives elected at regular intervals in every state and political subdivision. These laws represent the collective wisdom as to what is good and beneficial for the people whom the legislators represent. Generally, they are enacted by majority vote of the legislature, with such controls as the state sees fit to establish with respect to gubernatorial veto and approval by a second house or chamber of the legislative body.

The statutes are written, published, made available to the public, and are binding upon every person. They are formalized, precisely drafted to cover particular situations, and often codified in regular or organized form. They regulate the multitudinous affairs of the populace in our country, reaching to the regulation of many, many diverse kinds of activities, in many, many ways. Their enforceability does not depend upon the knowledge of the terms by any person. Every citizen is subject to the command of the statute regardless of his ignorance thereof. They are, or purport to be, nondiscriminatory, and blind to status, wealth, color, or creed.

CRIMINAL AND REGULATORY STATUTES

Basically, legislative enactments fall into one of two major categories: criminal statutes and regulatory statutes. Although at times the dividing line is fuzzy, in general criminal statutes are those that prohibit conduct and impose sanctions, usually a fine or imprisonment or both, for those apprehended and convicted of a violation of the terms. Criminal statutes regulate many types of activity, from murder and armed robbery to overtime parking. They may be promulgated by Congress, by the state legislature, by city council, or by village board. Those accused of violations may be tried in the federal courts, in the state courts, or before justices of the peace. Criminal statutes have one thing in common: they are based upon the theory that the way to regulate conduct that is deemed by the legislature to be undesirable is to impose sanctions upon those who engage in forbidden activity.

The regulatory statutes deal with problems of policy and allocation of the resources available to the legislature. Thus, appropriations bills devised by legislatures or legislative bodies are based upon decisions of those elected representatives as to how much money is required for various areas of governmental concern. The legislature considers, upon the evidence before it derived from such investigation as the legislators care to undertake, whether a greater share of the available resources shall be allocated to highways or to schools, for guns or for butter, and how many dollars the public interest requires to be allocated to each. Similarly, statutes establishing governmental departments or agencies such as boards of nursing, reflect a legislative determination that additional governmental activity is needed in certain areas. Statutes can and do regulate businesses in many ways. From licensing provisions for small businesses to intricate and complex regulation of entire industries, such as the air travel industry or the securities industry, these regulatory statutes reflect the legislative decision that the public interest is protected by such regulations.

Thus, the regulatory statutes do not impinge directly upon behavior; no one is arrested, fined, or imprisoned for violation of them. Nevertheless, they have great impact upon society as a whole, and direct impact upon those persons who are subject to their terms.

COMMON LAW

What we term "common law" is essentially judge-made law. It is the aggregate of the results of a series of decisions of judges in individual cases; it generally deals with matters upon which the statutes are silent. It is the voice of history. The term "common" law refers to the general applicability of this body of law to everyone; all of us are equally subject to its rules. The common law has enormous influence upon the daily conduct of affairs and business. No statute says that contracts entered between individuals are enforceable; that is left to the common law. No statute says that the person who negligently harms another is responsible for the financial losses of the injured person; the common law does that. No statute says that a promissory note obtained by fraud and deceit is unenforceable; again, that is the function of the common law.

The common law is nowhere explicitly set forth in writing, but is the accumulated result of thousands and thousands of legal decisions that have been handed down in America and England through the years. That is, it comes from the fact that through the hundreds of years of English and American history, the courts have dealt with situations of human conflict that recur time and time again. Over this span of time, rules have evolved that best lead to that fairness, consistency, and impartiality we described as a function of the civil law.

The manner in which common law emerges as a social force is perhaps best illustrated by example. Mr. A is sitting one day on his front porch, when a truck of a painter stops in front of his house, a man gets out with ladder, paint brush, and paint, and begins to paint Mr. A's house. Mr. A does not know the painter, has had no contact with him or his company, and has not ordered the painting done in any way. In fact, the basis for the painter's painting Mr. A's house is that he is mistaken about the address of a house he was in fact hired to paint, and is painting Mr. A's house under the mis-apprehension that Mr. A's house is the right one. Mr. A says nothing, but permits the painter to continue until the house is glossy and resplendent in its new coat of paint. Mr. A's pleasure in his newly painted house is, however, diminished when he receives a bill from the painter for an amount fair for the work actually done. Upon Mr. A's refusal to pay, the painter sues him and the judge is faced with the decision (let us assume for the first time) as to whether the law will impose upon Mr. A a duty to pay for the unordered paint job, under the circumstances outlined here. Assume that the judge decides that Mr. A is obligated to pay for the paint job. In this decision of the judge one finds the beginnings of the common law. The next time a similar situation is presented to the same judge, he will decide the same way. The next time the same question is presented to a different judge, he too will follow the earlier decision, so that basic tenets of fairness—that persons in similar circumstances are treated similarly—may be fulfilled.

In time, and it may be a long time, enough judges in enough courts in enough similar situations will have decided that Mr. A, or someone similarly situated, is obligated to pay, that the obligation to pay under such circumstances may be said to be a firmly established legal obligation. No legislature has ever considered the matter; certainly the Constitution says nothing about it. Nevertheless, it may, under these circumstances, be said with considerable certainty that people whose houses are painted in the situation described here do not receive a windfall, but rather must give the painter fair compensation.

This example further illustrates an important aspect of the common law, namely, that a precedent, once established, will be followed so that a uniformity of administration of the law may be achieved. Thus, when any judge is faced with a question to decide, it is important to him to know how that question was decided earlier in identical or similar situations. At times he may concern himself more with uniformity in the law than with what appears to be a just result in the particular case at hand. What if the houseowner is very poor, and the painter is very rich? In a way, it imposes a real hardship upon a needy

Mr. A to pay for something he never wanted in the first place and would not have dreamed of ordering for himself. Nevertheless, every judge is concerned with the long-range implications of his decision in the case before him, and he must in the interest of the maintenance of the system and the predictability of legal results impose that hardship on Mr. A.

The adherence to precedent goes further, and it is sometimes said that a judge *must* follow an earlier decision if the facts in that case were identical to those before him. The principle is called the principle of *stare decisis*. The principle is an important one, but it can be seen that the principle may conflict with the need for a flexible system able to adjust to new demands, unexpected situations, and social change. Important as the principle is, therefore, an enlightened system will permit it to yield in those cases calling for different decisions in light of new situations. The most renowned student of the common law, Oliver Wendell Holmes, Jr., describes this characterization of the common law in these famous words [Holmes, O. W., Jr., *The Common Law*, 1 (Boston: Little, Brown and Company, 1881)]:

> The life of the law has not been logic: it has been experience. The felt necessities of the time, the prevalent moral and political theories, intuitions of public policy, avowed or unconscious, even the prejudices which judges share with their fellow-men, have had a good deal more to do than the syllogism in determining the rules by which men should be governed. The law embodies the story of a nation's development through many centuries, and it cannot be dealt with as if it contained only the axioms and corollaries of a book of mathematics. In order to know what it is, we must know what it has been, and what it tends to become.

### The Constitution of the United States

The United States of America has a constitutional government. Behind this simple statement and familiar concept rest legal and governmental considerations of the greatest complexity. The Constitution of the United States is a document drafted by representatives from the states and formally agreed to and ratified by every state. It is a product of men of great learning, men with deep understanding of political theory and philosophy, and men who pondered over the political problems of their day and were willing to build new structures on ancient foundations in an attempt to bring about the solution to these problems.

It became effective on March 4, 1789. From that day to this, the terms and conditions set forth in the Constitution have been at the center of our laws, and every law passed by every state or by Congress since that date has been enacted and interpreted in light of our Constitution.

The Constitution established a three-part, or tripartite, government consisting of the legislative branch, the judicial branch, and the executive branch. At the same time, it delineated the powers of each branch and fixed limits to those powers. The establishment of the legislative branch, the executive branch, and the judicial branch is familiar to all of us from our first contact with American history, and from day-to-day associations with the government. The system whereby the members of Congress are elected by direct vote, and the exercise by the federal government of its power to coin money, to establish post offices, to raise and support armies, to provide and maintain a navy, are all matters taken for granted by all of us, but which find their ultimate basis in the Constitution.

Parts of the Constitution are in this day and age the subject of much current interpretation and application in new situations. Beginning in the middle 1950's, the Supreme Court of the United States, exercising the judicial powers given by the Constitution, set in motion powerful forces directed toward the elimination of racial discrimination as a sociological fact in the United States. Under the Constitution, boundaries are set for permissible conduct. Every day, attorneys are appointed for indigent persons accused of crime, in furtherance of the constitutional rights of those accused of crime. These and many other aspects of law and of daily life positively show the influence of the Constitution.

Thus although the Constitution was drafted in the late 1700's, it is a viable force today and a prime bulwark of individual liberties. Our Constitution has been found by our society to possess those attributes of constancy with flexibility that are essential to the effectiveness of a law, in varying times, for a society of great complexity and constantly varying composition. In this sense, at least from a short-term perspective of history, the Constitution has demonstrated itself to be an exceptionally workable instrument, protecting the high value of individual liberty and social welfare and providing at the same time effective governmental framework.

The Constitution, moreover, is supreme throughout our United States, and every other law or activity is subordinate to it and its prohibitions. No state can pass and enforce laws that transgress the mandates of the Constitution. This is an accepted fact today, but in the early days of our nation political controversies swirled around the subservience of the states and their laws to the newly formed and newly executed Constitution. The Constitution can, after all, be viewed as a surrender of power by the states to a centralized government. However, many of the states did not desire to surrender power or at least did not desire to surrender power in certain ways. Therefore, a highly significant and important event occurred in 1807, when the United States Supreme Court finally decided that state laws in contravention of the

Constitution were invalid even in the state that passed them. This decision contributed greatly to the power of a national government, and helped make possible the welding of the solid and formidable structure of the United States as we know it today. It should be kept in mind in the discussions of other types of laws that follow that, ultimately, any law is valid only to the extent that it does not contravene one or more of the Constitution's prohibitions.

## Structure of Court Systems in America

Broadly speaking, our system of courts is divided into two main divisions, the courts created by the authority of the various states, and the courts created by Congress, known as federal courts. Sitting as a reviewing court for decisions of both of these major court systems is the Supreme Court of the United States.

The state courts are created by state legislatures, and include many different kinds of courts. Principally, there will be a court of general jurisdiction handling all types of civil disputes between private citizens, and the criminal cases that arise for violations of the state criminal statutes. There are variations from state to state, but generally there will be additional courts, including municipal courts, which handle minor traffic violations, and probate courts, which handle the administration of wills and decedents' estates. Other specialized courts may be created such as small claims courts, handling minor civil disputes, and juvenile courts, handling matters involving children. In addition, each state has one or more appellate courts sitting in review of the decisions of its subsidiary courts.

It is in the state courts that the great bulk of litigation is centered. These courts administer the laws promulgated by the various states and therefore will operate under differing rules, depending upon the enactments of the particular state concerned. For the ordinary citizen faced with a litigation problem either in civil or criminal aspects, the state courts will be the forum to which he will look for a decision on his controversy.

The federal courts, generally speaking, administer the laws promulgated by the Congress of the United States. The jurisdiction of the federal courts is derived from Article III of the Constitution, which expressly provides for the creation of federal courts to hear certain types of controversies. Chief among these are the controversies arising under federal law, both civil and criminal. The federal courts have exclusive jurisdiction of claims arising under federal laws, such as antitrust cases and securities legislation cases.

Unless there is a particular federal interest or law involved in a dispute, the federal courts have no power to hear it. Thus, when members of the local citizenry get into a legal fracas, the state courts, not the federal courts, will hear their case. However, another exceedingly important aspect of the federal courts' jurisdiction confers upon them the power to hear civil controversies when the antagonists are from different states. To some degree, therefore, the jurisdiction of the federal courts and the state courts overlap, and a litigant in civil cases may have a choice of the court in which he pursues his case. It is important to the administration of justice that the selection of courts not determine the outcome of litigation, but rather that the outcome be determined in accordance with the applicable law and principles of justice. Therefore, the rule has been developed that federal courts must apply the law of the state in which they sit to the end that the outcome in federal courts would be the same as if the case had been tried in state court.

Another principal area with which federal courts are concerned is violation of the federal criminal statutes. In general, it may be said that to constitute a federal crime some act of a character involving more than one state, or particular federal interest, must be involved. Thus, although it is not a federal crime to steal a car, it is a federal crime to transport that vehicle across state lines, and upon so doing, the thief will violate both state and federal laws and may be prosecuted in either federal or state courts, depending upon the authorities who apprehend him. Likewise, acts such as taxation fraud, international espionage, certain types of narcotics crimes when more than one state becomes involved, improper use of the mails, and fraud in connection with interstate sales of securities run afoul of the federal statutes and are prosecuted in the federal courts rather than state courts.

In the federal system there is one intermediate appellate court, known as the Court of Appeals, which hears appeals from the decisions of federal district courts. In addition, there are a number of special courts created by Congress to handle particular problems, federal in nature. These include the Court of Claims, which hears cases involving breach of contract with the United States; the Court of Customs and Patent Appeals, which has jurisdiction of cases involving patents and customs regulations; and the Tax Court, which reviews tax matters.

The Supreme Court of the United States has appellate jurisdiction in both federal and state matters. With respect to decisions from the state supreme courts, its review generally consists of determining whether or not the actions of those courts were in violation of the Constitution; it will ordinarily not review questions of state law that are not of particular importance outside the state. Even this aspect of the Supreme Court's appellate jurisdiction, i.e., the right to review state court decisions to determine their conformity with the Constitution of the United States, was in the early days of the republic a difficult and controversial issue. Many persons, in those days, felt strongly that the states were of the nature of independent political bodies that had not surrendered any of their sovereignty to the federal Supreme Court. The early political battles centering around this aspect of the Supreme Court jurisdiction were exceedingly important in terms of unifying the republic generally and in settling that the decisions of the Supreme Court superseded those of the state court. Although it is now unquestioned that this jurisdiction is firmly established, review of state court decisions by the Supreme Court of the United States is still a hotly emotional issue and many persons still take a position opposing Supreme Court review of what they consider to be state affairs.

The Supreme Court has a great deal of discretion in determining which cases it shall hear, and is charged with the responsibility of accepting only those cases that have a nationwide and universal interest, and applicability to all citizens. Because the Supreme Court sits as a court of last resort over both state and federal courts, it is the final interpreter of the Constitution; in a very real sense, the Constitution means what the Supreme Court says it means.

In the last analysis, each of us as citizens looks to the courts of the state in which we live finally to determine disputed questions of state law, and to the Supreme Court of the United States finally to determine disputed questions of federal law, and disputed questions of construction of the Constitution itself. The function of the United States Supreme Court in interpreting the Constitution is a meaningful and difficult one. Recent years have seen a number of alterations and innovations in the standards set by the Supreme Court for constitutional behavior of state governments in respect to segregation in schools and other public areas, and in respect to police activity in apprehending criminals, and in crime detection and punishment. To the extent that the Supreme Court applies the Constitution to control police behavior, for example, every arrest made by every policeman throughout the country must be in accordance with Supreme Court standards, or the suspect will ultimately go free. Each of us is affected by these decisions, and each of us has the duty to uphold and support them.

## Court Mechanics and Procedures

### FUNCTION OF PROCEDURAL RULES

Lawsuits are structured affairs. They are conducted from beginning to end in accordance with written rules, promulgated generally by the supreme court of each state, and in the case of federal courts, by the Supreme Court of the United States. The necessity for rules is self-evident; the kinds of disputes that can arise between citizens is limited only by the number of the citizens themselves. An endless variety of problems and disputes comes before the courts, and without a set of governing regulations, the management and orderly resolutions of these disputes would be impossible. The courts have two overriding functions: first, to resolve disputes between parties in a way consistent with the applicable law and principles of justice, and second, to accomplish this in a time that will make any relief granted meaningful. It is an attribute of fairness that the results in two similar cases be the same, and not dependent merely upon the whims of the judge or jury, or upon transient considerations that unwarrantedly benefit undeserving litigants at the expense of others. Procedural rules help to further this goal. The volume of court business is so great that orderly handling is mandatory if cases are to be disposed of with dispatch. Morever, as a general proposition one of the two parties who is brought into court will be interested in deferring the moment of truth for as long as possible, and the courts must therefore establish time schedules for the various steps of the proceedings; otherwise the entire judicial system could be thwarted.

With these functions in mind, let us look at the sequence of events in a typical civil case. In its broad aspects, the course of a civil action can be traced through five distinct procedures or steps. These are (1) the filing of a document called a *complaint* by a person called the *plaintiff* who contends that his legal rights have been infringed by the conduct of one or more other persons called *defendants*; (2) the written response of the defendants accused of having violated the legal rights of the plaintiff, termed an *answer*; (3) pretrial activities of both parties designed to elicit all the facts of the situation, termed *discovery*; (4) the *trial* of the case, in which all the relevant facts are presented to the judge or jury for decision; and (5) *appeal* from a decision by a party who contends that the decision was wrongly made.

Each of these steps in turn is governed by detailed rules, and the conduct of all these steps must be in accordance with the rules. The discussion which follows is based upon the rules applicable in all the federal courts; these rules or their equivalent have been adopted also in a number of states.

INITIATION OF CASE BY COMPLAINT

A complaint is a document that will normally be drafted by the plaintiff's attorney. It will be prepared by the attorney after consultation with his client, and after consideration by the attorney and the client of the nature of the act complained of, what legal rules may have been violated, and what damages have been suffered by the plaintiff as a result of the violation. The complaint is filed in the court, and thereby the action is initiated. A copy of the complaint must be given to the defendant, thus providing him with notice that a lawsuit has been instigated against him by the plaintiff.

The complaint is designed primarily to serve two related functions. It provides the defendant with formal notification that someone is complaining of his acts, and it tells him in greater or lesser detail what those acts were. Normally, of course, a defendant will readily recognize the acts upon which the complaint is based. For example, if an automobile accident is involved, it will be only the rare case where the defendant is not fully aware that the accident occurred, and that someone or someone's property was injured or damaged, or at least that someone was in a position to allege that they had been damaged. The questions of who was at fault in the accident, how much the damages are, and whether or not there is any reason why the plaintiff should not recover are generally the contested questions.

RESPONSE OF DEFENDANT BY ANSWER

Once having been served with a complaint, a defendant has no choice. Regardless of how unfair or unjustified he may feel the complaint to be, he must respond, for if he fails to respond and ignores the complaint altogether, the courts will presume that plaintiff's complaint is true and grant the plaintiff the relief he requested. Because the relief requested will often be an award of substantial sums of money, which award may be satisfied involuntarily out of defendant's property, a defendant will nearly always respond to the complaint to prevent or forestall the confiscation of his property. His response will be to admit or deny the various allegations by plaintiff. Thus, in the ordinary accident case, the defendant is likely to admit readily that an accident occurred, at the place and at the time alleged by plaintiff. The defendant is much less likely to agree to plaintiff's characterization of the accident as having been the fault of defendant, and therefore, he will normally deny such an allegation. In addition to a denial that he was not the one at fault, the defendant will also set forth any reasons why the plaintiff should not recover. Examples of reasons why recovery might not be allowed would be that plaintiff had already been compensated by the defendant, that the action was not brought within the time required by law after the accident happened, that the plaintiff was at fault as well as the defendant, and any one of a number of other defenses, termed *affirmative defenses*.

PRETRIAL PREPARATION BY DISCOVERY

It is the experience and conviction of those concerned with the American court system—lawyers, judges, and scholars alike—that in litigated controversies, justice is best served by a full disclosure by both sides of all the facts in their possession, in advance of the actual trial. That is to say, permitting one party to surprise the other at the trial with important facts is not a good way to achieve the fairest results. True, the one who, by concealment, is able to spring the surprise may gain a tactical advantage, but the courts do not sit to award judgments or verdicts in favor of the cleverest party or the ablest attorney. They sit to analyze a transaction or event in detail, to ascertain the truth, and to reach a fair decision based on all the facts. Therefore, rules are established whereby each side may discover facts known to the other side that bear upon the matter at hand. The courts require one party at the instance of the other to submit to an oral examination, called a *deposition* and conducted by an attorney. In this examination he may be asked all manner of questions relating to the transaction at issue, and these questions and answers will be recorded mechanically and typed into a transcript of the proceeding. Thus, the party will have placed on record his version of events, and will have done so under oath.

Taking a deposition is an effective device in developing the full truth of any matter. It permits both sides to know what the witness's version of an event will be at trial, and thus both sides have equal opportunity to find corroborating evidence or evidence to refute it. Although a witness can substantially change his story, he will have to provide a convincing explanation for his switch; if he fails, the truth of his testimony will be suspect.

Another discovery technique is found in the provisions for written interrogatories, under which either side may ask the other a number of questions in writing, to be answered in writing under oath, about the facts of the case. In addition, each party may be required to surrender for inspection to the other side documents and records in its possession that bear upon the matter at hand. Thus, if the action centers around a contract in which the activities of the business are at issue, that business may be required to open its files and records to the opposing side. All this is done in the interest of bringing to light all the relevant facts, for it is in this way that truth is more likely to emerge.

THE RESOLUTION OF THE ISSUES BY TRIAL

The crucial stage in any lawsuit is the trial of the action. At the trial, witnesses will testify as to what they saw, heard, or know about the matters at issue. They will be subject to cross-examination, which means that the attorneys for the side opposing the witness' position have an opportunity to question him to find the true basis for his knowledge, or his opportunity to see or hear. The evidence having been presented to the judge or to the jury, it is then made the subject of decision. Thus, it may be shown that someone was driving at a certain rate of speed on a slippery road and from these facts the triers of fact will determine whether or not negligence was involved. Similarly, it might be shown in a case involving injury to a patient that a nurse administered treatment in accordance with a particular written instruction by a doctor. A number of results might follow from this simple statement of facts, depending upon whether the instructions were clear or the implentation of the procedure was faulty. The conclusions are for the jury to finally determine from the facts presented to it.

Each party in turn presents the facts in accordance with the rules of evidence. These rules of evidence are unwritten rules, developed as part of the common law over a long period of time. They are designed to prohibit any facts from coming before the court that are not properly authenticated and based upon first-hand information, and that are not germane to the matter at hand. Thus, it is forbidden to parties to a lawsuit to prove facts by having someone testify that someone else told him that fact so-and-so was true. It is necessary for that other person to come in and to testify that fact so-and-so is true, thereby exposing any inadequacies in his abilities to interpret what he has seen or in his abilities to observe, to show that he has an interest in fact so-and-so, or otherwise to reflect upon the true character of his statement. Likewise, documents used as evidence must be shown to be genuine before they will be permitted.

Trials are usually conducted before a judge and a jury. The jury's responsibility is to determine the facts and to reach an ultimate conclusion based upon these facts. To illustrate, suppose A sues B for damages for a collision at an intersection, and each accuses the other of having gone through a red light. Which one actually went through the light is a question of fact, to be decided solely by the jury, on the basis of their evaluation of the evidence presented.

The judge's function is to present the law to the jury in the form of what are called *instructions*. The instructions consist of an explanation by the judge of the law applicable in the case at hand, and are given by the judge at the end of the presentation of the evidence, and before the jury retires to consider its verdict. In these instructions, the court will tell the jury what the law requires by way of factual elements that the jury must find to be present before they can render a verdict for a plaintiff, or find a defendant guilty of a crime. For example, in a criminal trial instructions on the law would consist of a description and explanation of what acts had to be proved before the jury could find that a crime had been committed. Thus, in a trial of a person accused of illegal transportation of a stolen car across state lines, the jury might be told that a crime would consist of (1) driving a car from one state to another, and (2) knowing or having reason to believe it was stolen. The jury would then be responsible for determining whether these factors were adequately proved in the case being tried, that is, whether the car in fact was driven across state lines and whether the defendant knew or should have known of its contraband character.

### REVIEW OF THE DECISION BY APPEAL

Human nature being what it is, even when a judge or jury renders a decision, the losing party often believes that that decision was erroneous. To afford the greatest possible protection against mistaken verdicts, any party aggrieved has the right to appeal his case to a higher court. The erroneous result may be because such verdicts were based upon misinterpretations or errors of law, or upon prejudice of one kind or another. As we have seen, in the federal system following a decision by the trial court the case appealed will go to the Court of Appeals, then, if a further review is sought, to the Supreme Court. In many state courts, a similar course would ensue after trial; that is, first an appeal would be taken to an intermediate appellate court, followed by a final appeal to the highest court if the judgment is still thought to be unsatisfactory.

However, the issues on an appeal are somewhat different from those presented at trial. An appellate court does not retry a case or hear all the evidence again. In the absence of a showing of gross error, an appellate court will not reconsider whether or not the factual issues were wrongly resolved or certain facts were wrongly found by the judge or jury; they will consider primarily errors of law, and review the proceedings in the trial court to see that no misunderstandings or mistaken impressions have occurred. The refusal of appellate courts to reconsider factual findings is based upon the premises that the judge and the jury have the opportunity to see and evaluate the credibility of witnesses and the impression they have made through their testimony. The court of appeals, reviewing only a printed record of what occurred, does not have that same ability to sense untruthfulness in a witness. Therefore, an appellate court will not normally reverse a decision on the grounds that one person rather than another was believed. If Mr. A says that he saw Mr. X running from a bank with a gun and a sack of money in his hand, and Mr. X says that he was elsewhere at the time, and the jury finds Mr. X guilty of robbing the bank, on appeal Mr. X will be hard pressed to induce an appellate court to overturn the jury's determination that it was in fact Mr. X running from the bank. The judgment whether to believe Mr. A or Mr. X is the jury's alone, to be made at the time of trial, not on appeal.

The appellate court will examine the record, however, to see if there is any evidence to sustain the verdict. A verdict based upon prejudice will not be permitted to stand, just as a verdict implementing a wrong rule of law will not be permitted to stand. The basic distinction must always be kept in mind, than an appellate court generally sits to review questions of law, and not questions of fact, and that the findings of fact made by a judge or jury based upon an evaluation of all the testimony and evidence, will not be overturned on appeal unless they are clearly erroneous. This distinction emphasizes the great importance of the discovery process, whereby means are available to both parties to obtain all the facts. Thus, if the parties present all the facts they can present to the jury and fail to persuade the jury of their position, it is imminently fair that they must abide by an adverse verdict just as they would have had the benefit of a verdict in their favor. They will not later be heard to say on appeal that they wish they had presented more facts or different facts.

## PROBLEMS OF PROOF IN LITIGATION

In every trial, the elements of liability must be established by the plaintiff before there can be recovery by him. These elements are established by the evidence, that is, by the proof of facts. We will discuss the problems of proof in terms of negligence: however, the principles are applicable to all types of cases.

In any case involving negligence or breach of duty, the jury has a two-step analysis to make. First, it must determine what the actual conduct of the various participants was in fact, and it must determine whether the conduct was negligent. There may or may not be disputes over what the conduct was. For instance, in an automobile accident case, one witness may testify that the car was speeding down the wrong side of the road, whereas another witness may say that the car was driving slowly in its own lane. Or the situation may be even simpler, with the driver of one car testifying he gave a turn signal and another driver denying that such a signal was made. When a conflict in the evidence occurs, the jury must determine what happened before they can evaluate the conduct in the light of the law as given them in the judge's instructions.

Once a conclusion about the facts has been reached, the jury must turn its attention to the question of whether the conduct was negligent. Thus, if the jury should conclude that a car was driving on the wrong side of the road, it may have to evaluate whether this was negligent in the light of a claim that the car swerved to avoid a child who darted into its path, or that it swerved to avoid a cat, or a cardboard box, or a small rock. In other words, the jury invariably must grapple with the problem of measuring the proven conduct against the hypothetical standard set by the law.

PROOF OF FACTS

Let us analyze what we mean when we say a fact is "proved." Generally speaking, a fact may be proved directly or it may be proved circumstantially. Direct proof is normally based upon an actual observation by a witness. If an issue in a case is who started a fire, the fact might be established directly, by A testifying that he saw B light a cigarette and discard the match into a pile of dry leaves, which caught fire. Another type of direct proof is based upon what is called "real" evidence, rather than upon testimonial evidence. If the issue in a case is whether a person had on a red jacket, the red jacket itself, if offered as a part of the proof, would be real evidence, not depending upon testimony for its primary impact. In our sample case of fire-building, the remains of a match, if offered, would be real evidence tending to corroborate the testimony.

The same conclusion, that B started a fire, might be proved circumstantially. For example, one witness might testify that he saw B smoking a cigarette, a second witness that no one but B was near the leaves, and a third that B had offered him a match to light his pipe. Such evidence is termed circumstantial because the existence of the primary fact is inferred from other facts, or from the surrounding circumstances that are themselves subject to direct proof.

The reasoning process in the use of circumstantial evidence is that the existence of one or more known facts increases the probability that another fact is true. To put it another way, we say that proof of certain facts warrants a conclusion that other facts were also true. How do we know whether this inference is warranted? As put by a noted authority [Prosser, W. L., *Law of Torts*, 200 (St. Paul: West Publishing Co., 2nd ed. 1955)]:

> The inference, or reasoning, must be based on the evidence given and the background of common human experience. It may be strong or weak, depending entirely on the facts. Defense counsel in criminal cases have long made us familiar with the weaknesses of some kinds of circumstantial evidence; but there is still no man who would not accept dog tracks in the mud against the sworn testimony of a hundred eye-witnesses that no dog has passed by.*

Note, too, that inferential processes are at work even in the acceptance of the most direct evidence. When we accept a witness' testimony that an event occurred, we infer from the manner in which he tells the story, from his appearance, from a lack of motive to lie, and so on, that he is telling the truth and not fabricating a tale. We infer that he was in possession of his faculties, that he uses words in the same sense we do, and that he correctly identified

* Reprinted with permission of West Publishing Company.

the persons involved. So the line between direct and circumstantial evidence is never completely clear; always some inferences are drawn, and there are some facts not capable of direct proof upon which the validity of the so-called direct proof depends.

## BURDEN OF PROOF

Every trial begins with a clean slate. Neither the judge nor the jury has any knowledge or information concerning the dispute that has brought the parties to the courtroom. There is an existing state of affairs, a *status quo*, that the instigator of the suit wants changed. The plaintiff, in other words, wants the defendants' property, and he seeks to invoke the mighty power of the state to get it. Further, it may be assumed that the defendant will not give it up willingly; had he been willing, the parties would have compromised and settled their differences without the expense and inconvenience of a formal trial.

Unless the plaintiff is successful in convincing the judge and jury of the justice of his cause, the *status quo* will remain. If plaintiff has been injured, he will remain uncompensated; he will bear the loss himself. What should be required of the plaintiff in order that the *status quo* be changed? What quantum of evidence should the law require him to produce to persuade the jury in his favor? Which party should be required to introduce evidence on particular issues? The answers to some of these questions are dealt with by the legal doctrines termed *burden of proof*.

The basic rule in a civil case is simple: the plaintiff must show, by a *preponderence of the evidence*, that he has a right to recover from the defendant. And since he is the one who accuses, the plaintiff is the one required at the outset to produce, or go forward with, the evidence. These two aspects of what is required of a plaintiff are both summed up in the rule that "the plaintiff has the burden of proof."

The first aspect—that the plaintiff must prove his case by the greater weight, called preponderance of the evidence—comes into play at the end of a trial, when all the evidence is before the jury. At that point, the plaintiff wins if and only if the jury believes that the plaintiff's evidence outweighs defendant's. If, after considering everything, the jury is unable to decide the truth of the matter, they are duty-bound to decide for the defendant. The plaintiff has failed to meet his burden of proof. His is "the risk of non-persuasion." Similarly, if defendant's proof outweighs the plaintiff's, he is entitled to the jury's verdict in his favor.

The second way in which the phrase "burden of proof" is used pertains to the issue of who must offer evidence. At the opening of a trial, the plaintiff must go forward with some evidence; otherwise, the existing situation will remain undisturbed. There may come a point in the trial, however, when the plaintiff has proved enough to entitle him to a judgment. Under these circumstances, the defendant, unless he is content to lose, must offer counterevidence, and weaken or contradict plaintiff's factual showing, or offer evidence of an unrelated reason why plaintiff has no right to recover. Thus, in a suit for money owed, a plaintiff may testify that the defendant agreed orally to pay him for drilling a well on defendant's property, that he drilled the well and has not been paid. If defendant offered no further evidence, plaintiff would be entitled to a verdict; to avoid such a verdict defendant must go forward with proof of facts which will exonerate him, or with refutation of facts offered by the plaintiff. He may deny making an agreement, or claim that the well was improperly drilled. He may contend that plaintiff was paid, or that the well was drilled on the wrong property. Any of these, if believed by the jury, would warrant the conclusion that plaintiff was not entitled to a verdict. In other words, defendant met his burden of going forward with the evidence, and when he does this it is up to the jury to decide the case.

## NOTES

The following section adapts, with certain modifications, the method followed in textbooks in the various fields of law. The purpose of the notes as they appear throughout the book is to provide a means for the student to examine in depth some of the subjects and ideas discussed in a more general fashion earlier and to introduce the student to differing points of view on related topics.

The notes add materially to the content of the text and it is hoped they offer the challenge of reading in a related field with significant implications for nursing and that they will stimulate the reader to a more critical and analytical approach to her practice.

## (1)  History of Law

The history of the evolution of law is a miniature history of the human race. Philosophers, religious and military leaders, dictators, and even fanatics have all played a part. When the history of the law is viewed as a reflection of man's social thought and action, it takes on added meaning. Professor Wormser discusses the development of a judicial system and the part vengeance has played from primitive times. The reader should compare the idea of primitive vengeance with that of present-day objectives of the criminal law, discussed in Chapter 9.

**Wormser, R., *The Law: the Story of Lawmakers and the Law We Live By*, 16–20 (New York: Simon & Schuster, Inc., 1949)** \*

VENGEANCE

Man did not develop legislative machinery until comparatively recently. There was no need for doing so. Legal customs accommodated themselves easily enough to change in social views. This is illustrated most readily by the changes in the treatment of vengeance. In the Bible, in Exodus xxi, the chapter following that containing the Ten Commandments, is the following:

. . . thou shalt give life for life,
Eye for eye, tooth for tooth, hand for hand, foot for foot,
Burning for burning, wound for wound, stripe for stripe,

indicating that, when these words were written, the Jews were in a state of primitive tribal law and yet at least one stage from barbarism.

At first the group had had no interest at all in the problem of revenge; if someone put out your eye, you went off and waylaid him and knocked his brains out, or kidnaped his wife, or stole his children. But there came a time when it was felt that revenge should not be allowed to go too far. If your eye was put out, you had a right to put out the eye of the offender but not to hack off his arm in addition. It is this stage in development which the eye-for-an-eye rule of the Old Testament reflects. About this time we find the beginnings of a judicial system, for there had to be some way of determining how much revenge you were entitled to. Then chiefs and headmen began to make an effort to reduce the slaughter within the group and to prevent manhunts and clan feuds. They would get the disputants together and try to induce a compromise, a voluntary form of arbitration in which the matters at issue were the right to get personal revenge, and how that revenge should be satisfied.

There was another factor in revenge which developed some law. It is almost a reflex action to want revenge on the object which hurt you. If you stumble over a chair, you kick it. The primitive felt this sort of urge clearly, and he wanted revenge not only against the man who did him an injury but also against the *thing* which did it. He was often willing, strange as it may seem, to forgo revenge against the person if he could get revenge against the thing. In the Old Testament if an ox gored a man to death the ox must be stoned to death, and his flesh might not be eaten. Under the Roman law an animal who did an injury must be given up and the owner was then not responsible for damages. In England, under Edward I, if a man fell out of a tree the tree was made *deodand*—in the language of Blackstone, "an accursed thing." If he were drowned in a well, the well had to be filled up, as *deodand*. The *deodand* concept carried on into modern law, for, in British criminal cases, even in this century, the article with which a man was killed was appraised in the indictment and forfeited to the king. The thing which did the deed was accursed, and the injured party (or the king in his stead) had the right to revenge against it. And so, in our own admiralty law, if a ship does you an injury, you "libel" or attach, and actually sue, the ship.

Our system of granting damages probably came about through this idea of revenge against the object which did the damage. Instead of delivering that object, the owner made a stipulated payment, either in money or in cattle or some other medium of exchange, buying off the right of revenge. Regular scales of payment became the vogue. But there were limitations on this composition system. Certain injuries—murder and rape, for instance—could not be settled by payment of a fine; the family was still entitled to its personal revenge.

Obviously, with damages some sort of court became necessary. This was not yet a true court in our sense, deciding facts and applying law. It was merely a medium for limiting the right of blood feud; the court was just a peacemaker; it might still be ignored and its decision violated, but it became more and more difficult to repudiate the decision of a peacemaking court. As the chief, who usually acted as the court or presided over it, grew more powerful, it became less likely that his judgment would be ignored. Moreover, the idea of the "king's peace" came along. The chief or king had the right to have peace in his tribe or in his domain, and he could impose a fine on anyone who broke the peace. The chief could even impose a more dreaded penalty, banishment, or outlawry. Thus the group, acting through its executive, began to protect itself against breaches of the peace; but it was still not "punishing" a wrongdoer, in the sense that we punish a criminal. At least, it was not conscious of doing punishment.

Sometimes a feud was ended by leaving it to the gods to decide who was right. Trial by battle was one method. The theory was that the righteous would win. Another method was to make the disputants take a fearful oath; everybody was satisfied that the perjurer would be punished from on high. Often "compurgators" were sworn as well, members of the family or friends of the litigants, who would also be subject to the revenge of the gods if they swore falsely. Trial by ordeal had behind it the same idea, that the gods would save the righteous and punish the evildoer. If the accused succumbed to the ordeal—if his hand burned in the fire, or if he drowned when thrown into the water—that proved his guilt. . . .

Much of the law of the Torah is taken up with torts, as might be expected in any primitive or semiprimitive system. A tort is an injury to a person or his property for which he may sue. You commit a tort when you hit someone in the jaw. If you walk over another's land without his permission, or beat his dog, that is a tort. And if you libel or slander a man, that is a tort also. As the Jews were pastoral and agricultural, many of the rules of tort law had to do with domesticated animals and with the fields. For example, "If a man shall steal an ox or a sheep, and kill it, or sell it; he shall restore five oxen for an ox, and four sheep for a sheep." Or, "If a man shall cause a field or vineyard to be eaten, and shall put in his beast, and shall feed in another man's field: of the best of his own field, and of the best of his own vineyard, shall he make restitution."

All the tort law in the Torah is not primitive. It is provided that, if an ox gore a man or woman, "the ox shall be surely stoned, and his flesh shall not be eaten; but the owner of the ox shall be quit." However, "if the ox were wont to push with his horn in time past, and it hath been testified to his owner, and he hath not kept him in," then, if the ox gore someone to death, the owner, as well as the ox, is to be put to death. Note that the ox is put to death. This may be a hangover of some superstitious idea—that the offending animal is a thing possessed—or it may derive merely from the simple primitive desire for revenge against things which injure. Such explanations have been given by jurists. On the other hand, the ox may have been killed just as a vicious dog might now be exterminated. Note that a man is not held responsible if he does not know that his ox is dangerous; but if a man has an ox which is known to be likely to gore, he is held accountable for anything that happens. It took most of humanity a long while to understand the concept of negligence, and here we have it stated in an Old Testament law.

## (2) Synthesis of the Social and Behavioral Sciences into a Legal Decision

In the socially disturbing event brought about by John and Edward as described in the introduction to this chapter, the meaning of the facts was discussed as they might be viewed by members of each of several disciplines in the behavioral science field, and various modes of action were analyzed. Fahr and Ojemann mention some ways the courts have made practical use of the knowledge drawn from the fields of the behavioral sciences. From this article and your own background knowledge in this field develop your analysis and course of action, considering the interests of society and the individual.

**Fahr, S., and Ojemann, R.,** *The Use of Social and Behavioral Science Knowledge in Law,* **48 Iowa L. Rev. 59, 63–64 (1962)** *

Social and behavioral scientists and lawyers have long recognized that the law is concerned with, and is also in turn very deeply affecting, concepts of behavior and of society which these sciences are in the process of investigating. Consequently there have been from time to time attempts not only to incorporate the attitudes of science in certain areas but, what is more, to adopt the findings of scientists. There is not room enough in an article of this length to begin to document completely this trend toward explicit recognition of such science findings in legal affairs. But, to mention a few areas involved, they would include criminal law from arrest through final disposition; the law of the family; the law regarding large economic concentrations; and many others. In fact, since law in the end always deals with human beings, there would seem to be almost no area in which the influence and the findings of the social and behavioral sciences might not be used to explain and improve the law in its daily operation upon the members of our society.

Some progress has been made in the acceptance of this point of view by lawyers. For example, we are used to seeing the trained social service worker or probation officer in and around the courts. In anti-trust actions, not only the government but also the corporations under attack employ the factual findings and the arguments of economics as a major part of their cases. When the United States Supreme Court reversed a long-standing position on segregation of the races, it relied in part upon evidence drawn from areas such as education and sociology. Many other examples could be cited to show that in fact there has been considerable acceptance of the techniques and conclusions of all the areas of inquiry we group under the heading of Social and Behavioral Science. . . .

* Reprinted with permission of the *Iowa Law Review* and the authors.

## II. SOCIAL SCIENCE "FINDINGS" AND THE LAW

## A. Examples of Present Application

In social science knowledge there are some statements of relationships that are based on a large number of observations with fairly refined measures. For example, the statement that a given form of behavior may develop in many different ways and that one cannot judge from its overt appearance alone how it developed is based on a large number of careful observations of a great variety of behavior in different settings. Thus, when an adolescent is brought before a court on a charge of stealing, an attempt to prevent that behavior from occurring again by levying a fine and letting it go at that or by adding a verbal reprimand may do nothing as far as the basic forces which produced the behavior are concerned. For example, suppose a child has stolen some clothes from a store. Suppose that he has worried about the quality of his clothes and that he had been the subject of ridicule because of them. If the motive behind the theft was to get clothes that would meet with the approval of his associates the need for finding methods of solving the problem of self-respect still remains after the fine has been paid. Unless he can find another method to solve the basic problem, perhaps with the help of someone such as his parents, a teacher, the judge, a social worker or a clergyman, the problem will continue to bother him and he may try stealing again. He knows it is against the law but he feels trapped.

If it be argued that there is not time in the first appearance of an offender in court to make a detailed study of the probable causes of his behavior and that the court is hypothesizing that a stern reminder is all he needs, we could accept the first fine. But if the behavior appears again it would seem strong evidence that the fine and whatever else was administered did not meet the basic problem and therefore a careful analysis should be ordered.

In considering a juvenile case, a court will normally rely heavily upon such officials attached to the court as probation officers, social service workers, sometimes physicians or psychologists and will often render judgment heavily influenced by social science findings. Suppose a certain hypothetical delinquent has shown a pattern of violence coupled with "gang" associations, and suppose a person trained in dynamic psychiatry after careful study of the case suggests that these symptoms represent an attempt to satisfy a form of "herd" activity (the "desire to belong") often found in adolescence, and that punishment will not satisfy this strong psychological need. Confinement may throw our offender into a group association as in a "training school," but such an association is usually only temporary and will be dissolved when the offender leaves the training school. Consequently, our psychiatrist will argue, we can hope for recovery (or reformation) only if we can channel this "desire" into socially permissible activities. Recommendations along these lines will be received by the court in the process of rendering judgment.

Or let us move from the criminal, or pseudocriminal, area to the field of family law. Very often in a divorce case in which children are involved a court will hear evidence as to the effect of the marital situation and possible divorce upon the children. Often such evidence will come from a physician, sometimes from the family, acquaintances or welfare workers. The court evaluates it finally, and decides accordingly.

# CASES

This is the first of numerous cases to follow. It offers an opportunity to apply to an actual situation principles and legal theory from the foregoing content of the preceding chapter. Questions at the end of the case aim to guide a critical analysis of the case. Turn to the Constitution printed in the Appendix *infra*, p. 450, and think about Amendments V and XIV in relation to Mr. Rochin's situation. In the main, do these constitutional guarantees serve an ultimate good?

### *Rochin v. California,* 342 U.S. 165 (1952)*

Mr. Justice Frankfurter delivered the opinion of the Court.

Having "some information that [the petitioner here] was selling narcotics," three deputy sheriffs of the County of Los Angeles, on the morning of July 1, 1949, made for the two-story dwelling house in which Rochin lived with his mother, common-law wife, brothers, and sisters. Finding the outside door open, they entered and then forced open the door to Rochin's room on the second floor. Inside they found petitioner sitting partly dressed on the side of the bed, upon which his wife was lying. On a "night stand" beside the bed the deputies spied two capsules. When asked "Whose stuff is this?" Rochin seized the capsules and put them in his mouth. A struggle ensued, in the course of which the three officers "jumped upon him" and attempted to extract the capsules. The force they applied proved unavailing against Rochin's resistance. He was handcuffed and taken to a hospital. At the direction of one of the officers a doctor forced an emetic solution through a tube into Rochin's stomach against his will. This "stomach pumping" produced vomiting. In the vomited matter were found two capsules which proved to contain morphine.

Rochin was brought to trial before a California Superior Court, sitting without a jury, on the charge of possessing "a preparation of morphine" in violation of the California Health and Safety Code, 1947, § 11,500. Rochin was convicted and sentenced to sixty days' imprisonment. The chief evidence against him was the two capsules. They were admitted over petitioner's objection, although the means of obtaining them was frankly set forth in the testimony by one of the deputies, substantially as here narrated.

On appeal, the District Court of Appeal affirmed the conviction, despite the finding that the officers "were guilty of unlawfully breaking into and entering defendant's room and were guilty of unlawfully assaulting and battering defendant while in the room," and "were guilty of unlawfully assaulting, battering, torturing and falsely imprisoning the defendant at the alleged hospital." 101 Cal App2d 140, 143, 225 P2d 1, 3. One of the three judges, while finding that "the record in this

* Cases and authorities cited by the court in all cases in this text are omitted, without indication of the omission, unless inclusion of the cited material adds to the clarity of the opinion.

case reveals a shocking series of violations of constitutional rights," concurred only because he felt bound by decisions of his Supreme Court. These, he asserted, "have been looked upon by law enforcement officers as an encouragement, if not an invitation, to the commission of such lawless acts." Ibid. The Supreme Court of California denied without opinion Rochin's petition for a hearing. Two justices dissented from this denial, and in doing so expressed themselves thus: ". . . a conviction which rests upon evidence of incriminating objects obtained from the body of the accused by physical abuse is as invalid as a conviction which rests upon a verbal confession extracted from him by such abuse. . . . Had the evidence forced from the defendant's lips consisted of an oral confession that he illegally possessed a drug . . . he would have the protection of the rule of law which excludes coerced confessions from evidence. But because the evidence forced from his lips consisted of real objects the People of this state are permitted to base a conviction upon it. [We] find no valid ground of distinction between a verbal confession extracted by physical abuse and a confession wrested from defendant's body by physical abuse." 101 Cal App2d 143, 149, 150, 225 P2d 913, 917, 918.

This Court granted certiorari, because a serious question is raised as to the limitations which the Due Process Clause of the Fourteenth Amendment imposes on the conduct of criminal proceedings by the States.

In our federal system the administration of criminal justice is predominantly committed to the care of the States. The power to define crimes belongs to Congress only as appropriate means of carrying into execution its limited grant of legislative powers. US Const Art 1, § 8, cl 18. Broadly speaking, crimes in the United States are what the laws of the individual States make them, subject to the limitations of Art 1 § 10[1], in the original Constitution, prohibiting bills of attainder and ex post facto laws, and of the Thirteenth and Fourteenth Amendments. . . .

However, this Court too has its responsibility. Regard for the requirements of the Due Process Clause "inescapably imposes upon this Court an exercise of judgment upon the whole course of the proceedings [resulting in a conviction] in order to ascertain whether they offend those canons of decency and fairness which express the notions of justice of English-speaking peoples even toward those charged with the most heinous offenses."

These standards of justice are not authoritatively formulated anywhere as though they were specifics. Due process of law is a summarized constitutional guarantee of respect for those personal immunities which, as Mr. Justice Cardozo twice wrote for the Court, are "so rooted in the traditions and conscience of our people as to be ranked as fundamental," or are "implicit in the concept of ordered liberty."

The Court's function in the observance of this settled conception of the Due Process Clause does not leave us without adequate guides in subjecting State criminal procedures to constitutional judgment. In dealing not with the machinery of government but with human rights, the absence of formal exactitude, or want of fixity of meaning, is not an unusual or even regrettable attribute of constitutional provisions. Words being symbols do not speak without a gloss. On the one hand the gloss may be the deposit of history, whereby a term gains technical content. Thus the requirements of the Sixth and Seventh Amendments for trial by jury in the Federal courts have a rigid meaning. No changes or chances can alter the content of the verbal symbol of "jury"—a body of twelve men who must reach a unanimous conclusion if the verdict is to go against the defendant. On the other hand, the gloss of some of the verbal symbols of the Constitution does not give them a fixed technical content. It exacts a continuing process of application. . . .

The vague contours of the Due Process Clause do not leave judges at large. We may not draw on our merely personal and private notions and disregard the limits that bind judges in their judicial function. Even though the concept of due process of law is not final and fixed, these limits are derived from considerations that are fused in the whole nature of our judicial process. These are considerations deeply rooted in reason and in the compelling traditions of the legal profession. The Due Process Clause places upon this Court the duty of exercising a judgment, within the narrow confines of judicial power in reviewing State convictions, upon interests of society pushing in opposite directions.

Due process of law thus conceived is not to be derided as resort to a revival of "natural law." To believe that this judicial exercise of judgment could be avoided by freezing "due process of law" at some fixed stage of time or thought is to suggest that the most important aspect of constitutional adjudication is a function for inanimate machines and not for judges, for whom the independence safeguarded by Article 3 of the Constitution was designed and who are presumably guided by established standards of judicial behavior. Even cybernetics has not yet made that haughty claim. To practice the requisite detachment and to achieve sufficient objectivity no doubt demands of judges the habit of self-discipline and self-criticism, in certitude that one's own views are incontestable and alert tolerance toward views not shared. But these are precisely the presuppositions of our judicial process. They are precisely the qualities society has a right to expect from those entrusted with ultimate judicial power. . . .

Applying these general considerations to the circumstances of the present case, we are compelled to conclude that the proceedings by which this conviction was obtained do more than offend some fastidious squeamishness or private sentimentalism about combatting crime too energetically. This is conduct that shocks the conscience. Illegally breaking into the privacy of the petitioner, the struggle to open his mouth and remove what was there, the forcible extraction of his stomach's contents—this course of proceeding by agents of government to obtain evidence is bound to offend even hardened sensibilities. They are methods too close to the rack and the screw to permit of constitutional differentiation.

It has long since ceased to be true that due process of law is heedless of the means by which otherwise relevant and credible evidence is obtained. This was not true even before the series of recent cases enforced the constitutional principle that the States may not base convictions upon confessions, however much verified, obtained by coercion. These decisions are not arbitrary exceptions to the comprehensive right of States to fashion their own rules of evidence for criminal trials. They are not sports in our constitutional law but applications of a general principle. They are only instances of the general requirement that States in their prosecutions respect certain decencies of civilized conduct. Due process of law, as a historic and generative principle, precludes defining, and thereby confining, these standards of conduct more precisely than to say that convictions cannot be brought about by methods that offend "a sense of justice." See Mr. Chief Justice Hughes, speaking for a unanimous Court in Brown v. Mississippi, 297 US 278, 285, 286, 80 L ed 682, 686, 687, 56 S Ct 461. It would be a stultification of the responsibility which the course of constitutional history has cast upon this Court to hold that in order to convict a man the police cannot extract by force what is in his mind but can extract what is in his stomach.

To attempt in this case to distinguish what lawyers call "real evidence" from verbal evidence is to ignore the reasons for excluding coerced confessions. Use of involuntary verbal confessions in State criminal trials is constitutionally obnoxious not only because of their unreliability. They are inadmissible under the Due Process Clause even though statements contained in them may be independently established as true. Coerced confessions offend the community's sense of fair play and decency. So here, to sanction the brutal conduct which naturally enough was condemned by the court whose judgment is before us, would be to afford brutality the cloak of law. Nothing would be more calculated to discredit law and thereby to brutalize the temper of a society.

In deciding this case we do not heedlessly bring into question decisions in many States dealing with essentially different, even if related, problems. We therefore put to one side cases which have arisen in the State courts through use of modern methods and devices for discovering wrongdoers and bringing them to book. It does not fairly represent these decisions to suggest that they legalize force so brutal and so offensive to human dignity in securing evidence from a suspect as is revealed by this record. Indeed the California Supreme Court has not sanctioned this mode of securing a conviction. It merely exercised its discretion to decline a review of the conviction. All the California judges who have expressed themselves in this case have condemned the conduct in the strongest language.

We are not unmindful that hypothetical situations can be conjured up, shading imperceptibly from the circumstances of this case and by gradations producing practical differences despite seemingly logical extensions. But the Constitution is "intended to preserve practical and substantial rights, not to maintain theories."

On the facts of this case the conviction of the petitioner has been obtained by methods that offend the Due Process Clause. The judgment below must be Reversed.

Mr. Justice Minton took no part in the consideration or decision of this case.

ANALYSIS

1. In what way did Mr. Rochin contend that he had been wronged?

2. On what basis could the Court say that the community mores were offended by the police conduct when Mr. Rochin was in fact guilty? How could the police officer be held as in the wrong when he successfully apprehended the criminal?

3. The Court, in admonishing the police through their decision, might deter future officers under similar circumstances. Is this desirable?

4. Suppose the police officer had forced Mr. Rochin to submit to being fingerprinted; would this have offended "canons of decency"? What is the difference between the taking of fingerprints and the taking of the evidence from Mr. Rochin?

# Chapter Two

---

# Evidence

### Function of Evidence

Evidence is the data that are assembled in a lawsuit for presentation to the triers of fact—judge or jury—so that they may ascertain the "truth" about a particular event and, further, once the "truth" is ascertained, that the legal consequences arising out of the event may be determined. Evidence, therefore, provides the means by which facts and events are proved or disproved.

The data are presented at the trial stage of litigation. Through the law of evidence, certain limits are set on the presentation of such data. This area of the law consists of an elaborate and complex set of rules, which specify what is required before the trier of fact (judge or jury) will be permitted to consider a particular piece of evidentiary matter; these rules specify, in other words, whether particular data are admitted as evidence, or whether it will be excluded. If the prerequisites for admissibility are met, the evidence will be admitted; if the prerequisites are not shown to exist, the evidence will be excluded. For example, before a personal letter is admitted, the law of evidence requires that it be established that the signature is genuine. If such a showing is not made, the letter will normally be excluded.

A fundamental question arises, therefore, at the outset of a discussion of what these rules are, and that is: Why have any rules at all? Why not permit each party to tell his story in any way he pleases? Why should a person who seeks compensation for an injury, or a person who stands accused of crime, or a person against whom a claim is asserted, be limited in any way in establishing his claim or his defense? Is he not the best judge of what can best establish his position? A moment's reflection calls to mind several reasons why there must be restrictions upon the use of evidentiary materials.

First, it must be understood that a lawsuit determines responsibility for wrongs, and determines it on the basis of a pre-existing definition of what constitutes a wrong and what does not. Therefore, only matters tending to show the existence and consequences of a particular wrong are properly considered, and not facts unrelated to the claimed wrong, no matter how strongly those facts might influence the trier of fact to relieve the wrongdoer of responsibility. Thus, in theory, when someone is accused of the theft of a loaf of bread, he may not make known the fact that his children were hungry, because this does not aid the determination of whether he committed the theft.

Second, some types of data have certain inherent weaknesses in their probative value, and are excluded on this basis. Thus, confessions induced by real or threatened physical coercion are excluded because the risk of inaccuracy is great. That is, an incriminating statement made after a result of a beating, or under the spectre of physical or emotional trauma, lacks probative force because under such stresses most persons would make such statements whether or not they were true.

Third, some evidence is not permitted because the risk of undue prejudice outweighs the probative value. For example, when an accused is on trial for burglary, it generally cannot be shown that he has been convicted before of other crimes. The reasoning is that the fact of the earlier convictions will render the trier of fact too susceptible to the view that the accused is guilty of the crime charged, not on the basis of the evidence at hand, but merely because of his former transgressions.

Fourth, some evidence is not heard because to permit it would have an adverse effect on relationships the law protects. Thus, an attorney cannot be compelled to testify about conversations with his client, because to do so would tend to undermine the relationship. See *infra*, p. 55.

Fifth, orderly administration of our court system requires that trial be concluded within a reasonable time, so that all those who invoke the judicial system can be accommodated. If there were no limitations on extraneous material, trials could continue for as long as someone could be found to speak. Ultimately, the system would produce unjust results.

The law of evidence, which permits some data to be considered and other to be excluded, represents an effort to achieve the ultimate aim of determining truth and dispensing justice. A general rationale of evidentiary regulation is stated by Morgan, McGuire, and Weinstein [Morgan, E. M., McGuire, J. M., and Weinstein, J. B., *Cases and Material on Evidence*, 1 (Brooklyn: The Foundation Press, Inc., 4th ed., 1957)]:

> Evidence is produced at a trial so that an impartial trier can decide how an event occurred. Time is irreversible, events unique, and any reconstruction of the past at best an approximation. As a result of this lack of certainty about what happened, it is inescapable that the trier's conclusions be based upon probabilities. The odds of his arriving at truth in any case are reduced not only by limits of time and energy but by the nature of our procedural system and collateral policies, such as those excluding privileged testimony. Fundamental, then, is acceptance of the fact that the

results of adjudication are imperfect, that the rules represent a pragmatic attempt to come as reasonably close to the truth as the law's resources permit.

## Types of Evidence

Data that can legitimately form the basis for a judgment come in an infinite variety of forms. The type of evidence commonly associated with a trial is testimonial evidence, which consists of the oral statements of witnesses in open court, under oath and subject to cross-examination. Such testimony can cover the complete range of subject matter with which the suit is concerned. It can be a narrative of events, a report of direct observation, or an expert opinion. It can be positive or negative, for the defense or for the prosecution. It may relate to a link in a chain of evidence, or it may determine the entire controversy. Many rules of evidence find their most frequent and significant application to the testimony of witnesses.

Evidence may also consist of an object that plays a primary role in the cause, such as a vial of narcotics, bloody clothing, or a gun. Frequently termed "real evidence," such items are often highly probative and valuable to the trier of fact, and are perfectly valid as evidence. A very important category of evidence of this type is documentary evidence. In many situations, the documentary record of an act or transaction lies at the heart of any controversy and therefore is of great importance in a just allocation of legal responsibility. Business litigation almost invariably involves numerous writings of various kinds, and lawsuits involving medical practitioners often include consideration of records, reports, and documents. In summary, the law of evidence sets out general rules that apply equally to real and testimonial evidence, to documents and photographs, and to every other piece of data. It also deals specifically with many aspects of the use of documents and likewise treats in detail various facets of oral testimony. The sum total of these rules therefore largely determines the course of a trial and has a significant impact on the outcome.

## Rules of Evidence

### RELEVANCY

The fundamental requirement of any evidence—real, documentary, testimonial, or any other—is that it relate to the matters at issue in a trial, and have probative value on one side or the other. If some fact logically tends to prove or disprove some proposition before the court, it is relevant. By contrast, if the fact does not make more likely either the truth or the falsity of the proposition, that is, if it has no bearing whatsoever on any issue, it is not relevant. Once the determination of relevancy is made and a basic connection established, the trier of fact will be permitted to consider it in reaching his decision, unless the evidence is excluded for some other reason, such as a failure to establish authenticity or genuineness.

Any evidence may be directed toward a primary issue in the case, e.g., an eyewitness testifies to the commission of the actual act constituting a crime, or it may be directed at one event in a chain of evidence that circumstantially establishes a crucial point, e.g., when a witness testifies he saw the defendant near the scene of a crime. The test of relevancy is satisfied in either case.

OPINION

One of the notable characteristics of our system of evidence is that it demands that the information presented to the trier of fact be the most reliable sort available. Therefore, it has long been the rule in our courts that a witness will be permitted to testify to an observable fact if and only if he had an opportunity to observe and did in fact observe the event to which he testifies. This rule excludes testimony based upon conjecture, upon information received from another person, and, therefore, excludes testimony constituting an opinion, even though such an opinion may be of the sort upon which action is based in everyday life and that is formed from a variety of sources, including some first-hand observation. The law seeks, insofar as possible, to obtain raw data; it prefers the specific to the general, the particular to the abstract. Testimony that a man "smelled of liquor" and was "reeling" is preferred to a bare statement that the man was "drunk."

The theory of this evidentiary rule is easy to understand, but its application is at times most difficult. In the first place, what is fact and what is opinion is based upon a distinction without a clear dividing line. One man's fact is another man's opinion. If a witness testifies that the car was being driven down the left side of the road and was weaving back and forth, he has testified to a "fact." On the other hand, if he testifies that the car was being carelessly driven, he has merely given an "opinion," or a "conclusion." The latter testimony is not admissible, whereas the former clearly is.

Opinions are excluded in part because in the limited atmosphere of a courtroom too little is known about the probity of a witness. Everyone is familiar with some persons whose opinions are highly valued and regarded as entirely reliable. On the other hand, everyone has acquaintances, too, whose opinions are generally discounted and not respected. The jury has no personal knowledge of the witnesses and therefore is in no position to judge the weight to be attached to any particular witness' opinion. Therefore, except in one class of cases, that of expert testimony, opinions are not permitted.

HEARSAY

One of the great problems of devising rules for proving facts centers in the use of hearsay testimony. Hearsay evidence, as defined by a leading authority, is oral testimony or written evidence [McCormick, C. T., *Handbook of the Law of Evidence*, 460 (St. Paul: West Publishing Company, 1954)]:

... of a statement made out of court, such statement being offered as an assertion to show the truth of matters asserted therein, and thus resting for its value upon the credibility of the out-of-court asserter.

Generally speaking, hearsay testimony is not admissible in a trial. To illustrate, when the issue in a case is whether A was present at a particular time and place, and B proposes to testify that C told B that A was present, B's testimony would be excluded as hearsay because it would offer C's out-of-court statement to prove that A was present.

Clearly, in everyday affairs we very often give great credence to hearsay statement. If A says, "B says it's raining," we take an umbrella outside without doubting for an instant that it is raining. Moreover, hearsay is believed and relied upon in serious matters as well as trivial, for we frequently believe statements to be true even though they are related to us by someone whom we know to be without actual knowledge. When a day nurse reports to a doctor that "the patient was restless during the night and complained of pain," the doctor will base his actions upon that report in spite of his awareness that the nurses who in fact observed the patient are not actually the ones giving the report.

Why, then, is hearsay excluded from the courtroom? Several reasons have been advanced, all supporting to a greater or lesser extent the idea that hearsay statements are too unreliable to serve as a basis for imposing or denying legal liability. It is said that the out-of-court statement lacks the strength the in-court testimony gains by the solemn oath; that the dangers of misreporting are too great; and that the statement would be admitted without the person adversely affected thereby having the right to cross-examine the person making it. The latter affords the primary justification for the general prohibition against hearsay testimony. Long experience of the courts has shown that cross-examination can demonstrate the fallibility in the ability of witnesses to remember, to observe accurately, and to speak objectively with sufficient frequency that its lack with respect to hearsay statements can significantly impede the judicial quest for truth.

The rule against hearsay, however, is subject to a long list of exceptions; that is, there are many instances in which hearsay testimony *is* admitted by the courts. In general, these exceptions constitute particular situations in which hearsay is thought to have considerable reliability, and in which, therefore, the reasons for exclusion lose some of their force. No attempt will be made here to catalog all the numerous exceptions; the following will serve to illustrate a few of them.

A significant type of statement that is admitted even though it is hearsay is a "declaration against interest." Here, evidence of a statement made out of court will be received when it can be shown that the statement was against the pecuniary interest of the declarant. Thus, witness A may be permitted to testify, for example, to an out-of-court statement by B, that B told A that B did not own certain property, or that B owed money. The rationale of admitting this evidence, contrary to the general rule that excludes such testimony, is that the statement was made under circumstances such that B's statement has a special reliability, and, therefore, the need for cross-examination of B is not so important. Thus, in the example given, the special reliability stems from the fact that people do not normally make statements that are to their disadvantage unless such statements are true. The probative value of reliable statements is sufficiently great that they should be available to the judge or jury, in spite of the fact that they partake of some of the disadvantages of hearsay testimony.

Another area of special reliability arises from what are termed "dying declarations." In some types of cases, statements made by one who is conscious of his impending death are admissible even though they are hearsay, the theory being based upon an ancient feeling that deathbed utterances are likely to be free of falsehood.

The third important exception to the rule prohibiting use of hearsay as testimony relates to the use of written business records. Every business of any complexity keeps more or less elaborate records of various kinds of its day-to-day operations. These records often play a significant part in litigation. If a written record is offered to prove the truth of the matter asserted in that record, it is clearly hearsay and subject to all the weaknesses of hearsay; e.g., the recorder is not under oath nor is he subject to cross-examination. However, business records have that special quality of reliability that we have seen above is likely to lead to an exception to the hearsay rule and to the admission of hearsay as valid evidence. The details of the rule surrounding the admission of business records are complicated, and we will make no attempt to study them in detail. The more liberal jurisdictions require only that some showing of regularity of entry be made and that the person who made the entry not be readily available. Upon such showing, these courts would permit the trier of fact to consider the records as part of the evidence. Other states have narrower rules and impose more stringent requirements upon admissibility. However, it seems clear that both reason and the modern trend of case law is toward liberality of admission of such records, and this trend has been fostered by many jurisdictions that have enacted statutes tending to simplify the introduction in evidence of the normal business record.

## Medical Records as Evidence

### MEDICAL RECORD AS A BUSINESS RECORD

Sound reasons have been offered to explain the fallibility of the out-of-court assertion but, at times, so reliable are the facts reported that to exclude them as evidence would be to impede justice. Such is the case with numerous business records, of which the medical record is a prime example. The medical record may vary widely both in content and in the place where it is assembled, but there are certain characteristics common to all and these, when compared to business records, offer striking similarities.

What are some of these similarities? Health care facilities are business enterprises and as such their records are kept in the regular course of business. These records consist of original entries made contemporaneously with the transaction as recorded and the contents are within the personal knowledge of those engaged in the delivery of some phase of patient care. The entry is made by the person having knowledge of the event or by a third person who, in the course of his employment, is responsible for recording the transaction. Use of the medical record to refresh the memory of the witness does not fall within the hearsay rule; both the record and the witness are available for examination by counsel.

As in the case of business records, if the medical record as such is offered as evidence when the truth of the facts reported in the record rests on the out-of-court asserter for their credibility, objection to their admission as evidence would be based on the contention that the record was hearsay. If the objection were overruled, the statements made on the record would be admitted and would have to stand or fall on their own merit, which would effectively deny counsel the privilege of cross-examination of the author of the entries that might throw a new light on the evidence being presented to the jury. An objection to a medical record as hearsay was made in *Melton v. St. Louis Public Service Co.*, 363 Mo. 474, 251 S.W.2d 663 (1952), in which an action was brought by a pedestrian for injuries sustained in a collision with a moving streetcar. The defendant introduced into evidence the record of the St. Louis City Hospital, which stated that on admission the patient was conscious and rational and had explained "that he had walked into the front corner of a moving streetcar." The record continued that he was knocked down and suffered an injury to his right leg and left thoracic region. The plaintiff objected to admission of the record on the ground that the Uniform Business Records as Evidence Law did not apply to hospital records, and, furthermore, that parts of the records were conclusions and hearsay. The Missouri court rejected this contention and stated that the term "business" could mean any kind of business, profession, occupation, calling, or operation of institutions, whether they are intended for profit or not.

Ordinarily the truth of hearsay statements would be subject to question in a trial, but the weaknesses of hearsay do not necessarily carry over to the medical record, for the sole reason for assembling the record in the first place is to be of value as a truthful account of patient conduct, laboratory findings, diagnostic tests, and so on, which in itself gives a sense of reliability. Its day-to-day use further confirms that, in terms of the patient's safety and welfare, it is considered a personal and accurate record.

However, when the statements made in the record are objectionable on grounds other than hearsay and information contained in the record lies at the heart of the legal dispute, the court has been known to reject the record as proof.

*New York Life Ins. Co. v. Taylor*, 79 App.D.C. 66, 147 F.2d 297 (D.C.Cir. 1945), was an action for payment of double indemnity where the issue was whether the cause of death was an accident or suicide. The trial court had admitted, under the business records exception to the hearsay rule, psychiatric diagnoses in the deceased's medical record which tended to show that he was suicidal. In reversing a decision based on a finding of suicide, the appellate court stated that:

Regularly recorded facts as to the patient's condition or treatment on which the observations of competent physicians would not differ are of the same character as records of sales or payrolls. Thus a routine examination of a patient on admission to a hospital stating that he had no external injuries is admissible. An observation that there was a deviation of the nasal septum is admissible. . . . But the records before us are not of that character. The diagnosis of a psychoneurotic state involves conjecture and opinion. It must, therefore, be subjected to the safeguard of cross examination of the physician who makes it.

### SCOPE AND OBJECTIVITY OF MEDICAL RECORD

The nature and the length of a medical record can vary from a comprehensive family health and welfare record to a report of a single treatment for a minor injury in an emergency service. Most frequently, it is a complex, diversified series of documents that of necessity must be a combination of facts and opinions. A typical hospital record begins with sociological data, followed by the history that identifies the patient, and gives an account, as told by the patient, of the injury or illness that led to the particular condition. When this portion of the record is accurately made, in the regular course of hospital practice by a qualified person, it normally meets the requirement for admission into evidence, for it is sufficient to support the proposition that the statement is that of the narrator.

The record made of the physical examination should report facts as observed and avoid opinions and the use of value judgment words such as "negative," "normal," or "satisfactory." The diagnosis, often the focal point in the legal consideration of the record, is a subjective judgment, but, within the record itself, factual material can usually be found to support the conclusion, e.g., the history, the physical findings, the results of laboratory tests, and exploratory procedures. The section of the medical chart that includes the medical orders, the treatment sheet, the nurses' notes, and the physician's progress record fulfills a threefold purpose: it is a plan of action, a day-to-day log of action taken, and a series of notations bearing on the results of the action. So integrated are these three phases in good patient care that the report may be of evidentiary value not only for its content but also to reflect communication, or lack of it, between the members of the medical team.

In any type of health care facility where the nurse is employed, her records are subject to review if a dispute arises or a claim is made bearing on the care the nurse has given the patient. The nurse's notes, although interspersed throughout the record, in the aggregate may offer a useful body of evidence when properly made, and again they may be silent on vital points in dispute. Probably the most common error made by the nurse in entering her notes, and one that decreases the value of the record when offered to the court, is to report value judgments, opinions, or conclusions instead of factual observations. For example, a nurse who examines a child in an emergency room should not chart "appears to have been beaten." Rather, she should record the bruises and other observable signs of violence and leave the inferences of what happened to the proper authorities.

A nurse who observes and records the condition of an arm after a cast has been applied should not chart "cast too tight, fingers uncomfortable." Rather, she should record "fingers blue and cold," or "patient states there is lack of feeling."

In recording behavior of patients on a psychiatric ward, instead of recording "patient withdrawn," the nurse should state that the patient sat alone in his room all day. Instead of recording that the patient was "hallucinating," the chart should indicate that "the patient, with his ear to the wall, carried on a conversation with a person whom he addressed as his booking agent."

Hygienic practices may be reported as "has refused a bath for three days."

A public health nurse, on a home visit, should note on her record the hourly interval and the amount of the feedings, as reported to her by the mother, instead of recording that "the baby is filling out well," or "diet adequate."

If called upon to report an accident for an insurance claim, the nurse's record should not state that the patient fell down stairs, rather "patient stated that she caught her heel, pitched forward and fell four steps."

There has been some confusion among nurses about the value of the medical record as a legal document. A major misconception is that when a record is not used or is denied admission into evidence, it is a reflection upon the quality of techniques used in reporting and assembling the record. Counsel for the plaintiff or for the defendant may choose not to offer a record as evidence because it may not serve a purpose or it might even have an adverse effect. Likewise, it may be rejected by the court because it does not bear on the issues in the case. It is true that when a record is carelessly assembled, however desirable its use as evidence, it is not of a quality to present to the court.

A medical chart is not a self-authenticating document. When a chart is to be offered as evidence, it must be identified in the court by the person who kept the record, or one who knows how it was kept. This requirement is usually fulfilled by the hospital administrator or the chief custodian of the records who testifies as to how it was assembled and verifies it to be the record of the patient under consideration.

LEGAL USES OF MEDICAL RECORDS

Instances are numerous in which the chart has potential utility in suits, or threats of suits, as a source of medical evidence; five differing types of circumstances will serve to illustrate:

*First*, to settle accident and personal injury claims. The chart may be of value in its report of the findings of the physical condition of the patient on admission, the length of the period of hospitalization, and the nature of the treatment—all as a basis for the determination of the extent of the injuries. The medical prognosis may be of assistance in assessing the damages. When the chart is used under these circumstances, neither the hospital, the physician, nor the nurse would normally be a party to the suit, nor would they have a direct interest in the outcome. An example of the use of the record in potential litigation of this type, reported to one of the authors, arose when the record of a public health nurse was used to support an insurance claim on a baby who died a few months after the policy was issued. The agent for the insurance company, in the course of evaluating the company's liability on its policy, was given access to and reviewed for the insurance company the record of the physical examination in the clinic and the subsequent home visits by the nurse, all of which indicated that the baby was in good health at the time the policy was issued. Similarly, in child relinquishment cases or cases of suspected child abuse, the record used at trial or by an investigating agency might be used as evidence of unexplained injuries, malnutrition, child left in the home with younger children, or that the mother failed to follow the medical or nursing instructions or meet clinic appointments.

*Second*, to show a series of events leading to an injury, and whether the conduct of the physician or the nurse shared in bringing it about, either singly or together. In other words, in such cases the report of patient care has a distinct bearing on the complaint of the injury. Under these circumstances, the chart would be offered as evidence tending to prove or disprove that negligence caused the harm. In the case of *Mundt v. Alta Bates Hosp.*, *infra*, p. 162, the chart was introduced into evidence and the nurse's notes, both factual and opinion, were significant items of proof for the plaintiff, as, "calf edematous and firm" and "right leg on pillows, appears edematous." Although the nurse testified that she had observed an increase in the size of the leg and its progressive deterioration, these observations were not recorded. The decision, in which the nurse was held liable, was based on a lack of affirmative action on the part of the nurse, which may have started through her initial failure to record.

*Third*, to show failure to utilize information available on the chart, and that the patient suffered because of this failure. A chart is an operative tool which guides nursing practice; its misuse or failure to be used may be all that is necessary as evidence of proof of negligence. For example, a patient on admission reported that she was allergic to penicillin; this was noted on the chart, but as the chart became more and more voluminous, the notation was lost sight of, and the patient was given the drug and died as a consequence. When the chart was admitted into evidence at the trial, it was clear that both the physician and the nurse had failed to utilize highly pertinent information contained in the record [*Recent Case, Med. Sci. Law*, 4:286 (1964)].

*Fourth*, to show failure to transmit information from one department to another. When the chart is sent with the patient to an ancillary department, it should be complete as to history, provisional diagnosis, and any warning symptoms to guide others in safeguarding the patient. In *Favalora v. Aetna Cas. & Sur. Co.*, 144 So.2d 544 (La. App. 1962), a roentgenologist was held liable for failure to recognize the likelihood of his patient fainting. The patient had a history of fainting and this history was dictated on the admission record but was not sent to the ward. The radiologist made no effort to ascertain the history, even though the chart did not provide it. During the x-ray examination, the patient fainted and fell, fracturing her hip, which required an open reduction. This aggravated a pre-existing condition, and caused an embolism requiring surgery, which was followed by a kidney infection.

The court also found negligence on the part of the nurse in failing to secure a clinical history of the plaintiff and entering it in the space reserved on the requisition slip for this specific purpose. Had she done so, the court said, the radiologist would have been alerted to the circumstances surrounding the diagnostic tests, and would have been aware of the danger of fainting spells. As to this aspect of the case, two questions could be raised: was the break in communications between the admitting office and the ward due to hospital policy rather than an act of inadvertence on the part of the nurse and what was the nurse's responsibility when the history was not sent from the admission office?

*Fifth*, to show failure to write clear medical orders. A discussion of medical orders and their interpretation by the nurse will be undertaken shortly. Sufficient to note at this point is the case of *Norton v. Argonaut Ins. Co., infra*, p. 189, where two significant errors occurred, each of which contributed to the death of a baby. The first was that the physician failed to write on the chart that he had told the mother to continue giving the medication. The second error was that in writing the order for the drug (which would have amounted to a second dose) he failed to indicate the mode of administration.

An overall judicial attitude toward hospital charts is shown in *Globe Indem. Co. v. Reinhart*, 152 Md. 439, 137 Atl.43 (1927), where the Supreme Court of Maryland made a forceful statement concerning their value:

The question here presented is whether evidence represented by the hospital chart contains a sufficient guaranty of its truthfulness. We are of the opinion that it does. It is a record required by hospital authorities to be made by one whose duty it is to correctly make the entries therein contained.

So far as the hospital is concerned, there could be no more important record than the chart which indicates the diagnosis, the condition, and treatment of patients. This record is one of the important advantages incident to hospital treatment, for it not only records for the use of the physician or surgeon what he himself observes during the time he is with the patient, but also records at short intervals the symptoms, condition, and treatment of the patient during the whole time of the physician's absence. Upon this record the physician depends in a large measure to indicate and guide him in the treatment of any given case. Long experience has shown that the physician is fully warranted in depending on the reliability and trustworthiness of such a record. It is difficult to conceive why this record should not be reliable. There is no motive for the person whose duty it is to make entries, to do other than record them correctly and accurately. On the other hand, there is the strongest reason why he should: First, because of the great responsibility, he knowing that the treatment of the patient depends largely upon this record, and, if it be incorrect, it may result, and probably will result, in the patient's failure to receive proper medical or surgical treatment, which failure might be followed by serious consequences or even death. Second, the entrant must realize and appreciate that his position is dependent upon the accuracy with which the record is made. Third, as was stated in Tindall, C. J., in Poole v. Dicas 1. Bing. (N.C.) 649: "It is easier to state what is true than what is false; the process of invention implies trouble in such a case unnecessarily incurred."

The legal value of a properly kept medical record is indisputable, but its value in every case depends on continuing emphasis on the quality, objectivity, pertinency, and accuracy of recording, for which, in all instances, the nurse has vast responsibility.

## Expert Testimony

A witness testifying in court is generally called upon to state what he saw or what he heard, the assumption being that the witness has organic, moral, and mental powers to give an accurate statement of fact. The jury, a group of average people, is presumed fully capable of understanding and dealing with these facts. However, there are times when facts alone are not sufficient as a basis for the jury's determination and it becomes necessary to secure the testimony of one whose experience enables him to illuminate the ideas underlying the facts. The testimony of such a witness is called expert testimony.

Expert testimony is offered for the consideration of the court and jury as an opinion, and is of value because of the specific experience and expertise of the witness as distinguished from matters of general experience common to every member of the community. Such testimony is permitted and encouraged in those areas where the jurors have no experience or knowledge upon which to base a decision as to whether a given practice or fact or act was reasonable or unreasonable, correct or incorrect, negligent or not negligent, or met or failed to meet standards of the community. In other words, the expert is permitted to draw inferences the jury would not be competent to draw.

Thus, before permitting expert testimony, the court must make a determination as to whether a particular subject is one that the ordinary jury could not be expected to decide without the benefit of someone's opinion. Examples of situations where the jury is not qualified to make a judgment without the aid of an expert are questions of value, questions as to whether an act performed by a medical specialist was in accordance with the standards of the community, questions of proper accounting techniques, and interpretations of chemical and physical tests performed.

The use of the skilled witness to give expert testimony reaches far into the past. At first it was viewed simply as an aid to the court placing the witness in an almost parallel position to the jury. In 1493, in a case concerning the paternity of a child, several physicians testified and gave scientific reasons [Wigmore, J. H., *Evidence* 3rd ed., Vol. 7, § 1917, 3 (Boston: Little, Brown and Company, 1940)]:

The court held here that it might well be as the physicians had affirmed; . . . and so the Court delivered to the jury that the said Elizabeth, who was born forty weeks and more after the death of the said Edmund Andrews, might well be the daughter of said Edmund.

In determining who may give expert testimony two classes of experience are considered: first, experience of a person who has acquired knowledge on a particular topic through occupational experience—the kind directly obtained in the course of some occupation or livelihood, and at the same time is sufficiently removed from experience of the average citizen to make it difficult for a lay jury to analyze without the aid of expert testimony; second, experience acquired through systematic training involving the study of a body of knowledge forming a branch of some science or art. There is no sharp line between experience and training; in most instances a person will have both. Indeed, in the broad category of experience are included many facets of training—the continual use of faculties, habit, and practice of the occupation, special study, professional training—which produce a fitness for the person to answer the question in point. For example, a police physician of experience could testify concerning characteristics of a blood stain, its probable age, and its color, whereas one with scientific background of a pathologist could also testify on the constituents of the blood stain and equate the findings with normal human blood.

Expert testimony may be given from first-hand knowledge of the material facts and inferences drawn from these facts. A geologist who sampled a claim could report his findings and testify that in his opinion the ore was rich in uranium and that it would be practical to work the property. Expert testimony need not be based on direct knowledge, however. When the expert has no first-hand knowledge of the situation and has made no investigation of the facts, he may also give testimony: the way then to secure the benefit of his scientific skill is to assume facts, state them as a premise, and ask him to give his opinion or inference in view of the factual assumptions. A question to an expert, so phrased, is known as a hypothetical question. This form is accepted by the courts when the assumed facts are based on the evidence.

For example, consider a case where the issue is whether the collapse of a building wall was due to faulty construction or to other causes. Clearly, the lay-juror will not know generally the effect of various construction methods and will need the assistance of an expert in evaluating the allegedly negligent conduct. Of course, experts are not generally standing about waiting for walls to collapse so that they can give their opinions as to the cause. The hypothetical question is an effective device for providing evidence in such a case. A hypothetical question might be framed to an expert witness along these lines:

Assume that the wall was built on a certain type soil (which would be described), assume the wall was built of specified materials and in a certain fashion (which would be described), assume that after the collapse certain facts were observable (which would be described). Do you, Mr. Civil Engineer, have an opinion as to whether the collapse of the wall was due to the manner of construction? What is that opinion, and why?

As another illustration, A. was driving a truck down the highway when he collided with a passenger car, and three of the car's occupants were killed. A pint whiskey bottle, nearly empty, was found in A.'s truck. A. was taken to the hospital where a sample of blood was taken; subsequent laboratory analysis showed. 0.17 per cent blood alcohol content. The question might be asked of the expert toxicologist:

Q: At what point in the blood alcohol level do the reactions of the average person become substantially impaired?

A: At about 0.15 per cent.

Q: Do you have an opinion as to the fitness of a person to drive an automobile who has a blood alcohol content of 0.17 per cent?

A: I do.

Q: What is that opinion?

A: Such a person is incapable of properly handling a motor vehicle, and is not in a physical condition to drive.

MEDICAL AND PROFESSIONAL NURSE WITNESS

We have seen how the rules of evidence have gradually evolved from the need for an orderly system to settle disputes with maximum impartiality and accuracy. In this process, the witness is the key figure in reporting what he saw or heard. We have also seen that when the subject is such that the jury could not be expected to make an informed decision on the facts, expert opinion becomes necessary. What actually happened in a particular instance may be clear in its picture of the facts, but what made it wrong or legally significant may require the opinion of a qualified person in the field of science, business, or one of the professions. For example, the description of a superficial head injury may be factual and entirely within the comprehension of the jury, but the opinion that the force of the blow that produced this injury also led to a fracture at the base of the brain and was the cause of death, coming from a properly qualified medical expert witness, would add significantly to the information available to the jury. It is for this reason that personal injury and malpractice cases often cannot be settled without the expert medical witness who is able to draw inferences from the facts as presented.

The use of the medical expert to clarify highly technical issues has long been recognized by the law. The professional nurse is a relative newcomer to the field; however, she can anticipate that her legal role as a witness will be extended as her body of knowledge increases and as her responsibilities for complex practices in health care are extended. As one in possession of direct evidence, the nurse might be asked as a witness in a personal injury or malpractice case to give factual testimony of her observations, e.g., concerning the condition of the patient on admission, and that he was babbling and could not recall his name; and to testify that the blood on the shirt she had removed was directly over the stab wound in the chest. Similarly she might be asked to identify a material object such as a bloody knife that she had found in the clothing she had removed from the patient on admission.

At times, the nurse might be called upon to offer circumstantial evidence that could be combined with other evidence to support inferences of misconduct, for example, that the patient, who was a narcotic addict, was visited by his wife and shortly thereafter lapsed into sound sleep followed by coma and death.

In contrast with factual testimony or circumstantial evidence, the field of expert testimony is quite a different matter and one of increasing importance to the nurse. It is common practice for the physician to testify on subjects that fall within the province of the medical field and to offer his opinion on questions in this area. Similarly when the subject of nursing is under legal consideration, the nurse, as the expert witness, is best qualified to testify.

In every instance, the competency of the expert is relative in that his expertise must bear directly on the topic under discussion. In malpractice actions, the determination as to whether the expert should be drawn from the field of medicine or nursing should be based on the capacity of the individual to speak in those areas in which he is qualified.

In general, the fields in which the physician is competent to testify will vary widely from those of the nurse. The physician may be called upon for his opinion regarding the accuracy of the diagnosis that was made, the prevailing practice concerning therapeutic measures undertaken, the cause of death, and any factors in the medical conduct of the case that may have contributed to the outcome. In a distinctly different vein, when the nurse is called as an expert witness she may be asked to give her opinion regarding the quality of the nursing care that was given, the way in which the nurse functioned as a skilled observer, the propriety of the nursing judgment, the validity of decisions made as based on utilization of scientific principles, or the skill with which the nursing activities were carried out.

Although there are differences in the contribution the physician can make as an expert witness as compared to that of the nurse, these are differences of content and do not bear on the actual procedure followed by the courts in admitting the testimony of either expert into evidence. Since the analogy is direct in the legal principles followed, the term "medical expert witness" will be used interchangeably to mean either the physician or the nurse.

The party offering the testimony of the medical expert witness to the court must show that the witness is qualified to speak to the subject at hand. To establish these qualifications, the witness will testify concerning his occupation, preparation, experience, and present position, specialization, familiarity with the area under discussion through preparation, practice, or both, membership in professional organizations, research and writing, and any other pertinent qualifications. The trial court then determines whether the particular witness has the desired qualification and, subject to review for abuse of discretion, the judge's decision stands.

As an illustration, in *Joseph v. W. H. Groves Latter Day Saints Hosp.* 65 Utah 724, 318 P.2d 330 (1957), an action was brought for wrongful death on the alleged ground that the hospital had negligently administered a transfusion of incompatible blood to the deceased. The plaintiff contended that a nurse who cared for the deceased could not express an opinion that the patient was given good care. The objection was that the existence or nonexistence of good care was the central issue to be decided by the jury and that permitting the nurse expert to give her opinion on the ultimate question would constitute an invasion of the province of the jury. The objection was overruled, and the court stated:

Where the subject of inquiry is in a field beyond the knowledge generally possessed by laymen, one properly qualified therein may be permitted to testify to his opinion as an expert. If opinion evidence is such that it will aid the jury in understanding their problems and lead them to the truth as to disputed issues of fact, it is competent and admissible irrespective of whether it bears directly upon the ultimate fact the jury is to determine.

In specific cases there frequently exists in the practice of medicine a legitimate divergence of opinion in such matters as a differential diagnosis, causation, extent of disability, and prognosis. It may well be that medical experts for the plaintiff and for the defendant will differ, because the sum total of medical knowledge exceeds the capacity of one physician. It is unrealistic to expect medical testimony invariably to agree nor would justice be served if the courts did not encourage individual freedom of expression. When nursing or nursing practice is an issue, the position of nurse expert witnesses might be analogous to that of physicians and a divergence of opinion could be anticipated.

In common with other experts, the medical witness may be examined or cross-examined on the validity of his opinion, the accuracy of his observations, his credibility, and any possible interest or bias he might have in the outcome of the trial. Valuable as the expert witness is in the settlement of disputes, problems arise. Medical science is not an exact science and many times it is difficult for the witness to give an unqualified answer. Therefore, the courts accept answers based on a reasonable degree of medical certainty.

Another difficulty of the expert system lies in the possibility of the jury's distrust of the witness in the belief that his testimony is biased in favor of the party calling him, and it is certainly true that an expert's opinion is valuable only to the extent it is objective and dispassionate. Lord Macmillan [Macmillan, A. B., *Law and Other Things*, 250 (London: Crown Press, 1937)] warns:

> Of one thing I am certain, and that is no scientific man ought ever to become a partisan to a side; he may be the partisan of an opinion of his own science, if he honestly entertains it; but he ought never to accept a retainer to advocate in evidence a particular view merely because it is the view which is in the interests of the party who has retained him to maintain. To do so is to prostitute science and to practice a fraud on the administration of justice.

## Privileged Communications

Generally speaking, the ability of a litigant to obtain evidence favorable to his case is not dependent upon the voluntary cooperation of the people who were in a position to observe a matter relevant to the lawsuit, or who have possession of material records, documents, or physical objects. Through a power that has long been incident to the judicial process, called the subpoena power, any party to a lawsuit is entitled to have any persons he designates to appear at the trial and testify on his behalf. This right vested in the litigant has the force of law; persons who are properly given notice to appear must appear, upon pain of being punished for contempt of court. This means that all of us, in our capacities as private citizens, are subject to being called as witnesses in any case, and being forced to reveal all the information in our possession, however reluctant we are to do so.

The need for such a power in the courts is based upon the theory that truth in litigation will best emerge through full and complete disclosure of all relevant facts. No barrier, such as the mere unwillingness of a person to testify voluntarily, can be allowed to impede the search for truth. It goes against our grain to think that the winner in a judicial contest would in fact have been the loser had all the facts been known. Therefore, we give each party the weapons to obtain all the facts that they deem essential. Therefore, if the full facts are not brought to the attention of the jury or the court, the fault lies with the litigants and not with the tools available to them or with the judicial system itself.

Like most legal rules, the general one just stated has its exceptions. Under these exceptions, when a proper set of circumstances exists, the law will protect certain information and facts from disclosure, even though the factual matters suppressed might have a significant bearing upon the outcome of litigation. Thus it is the law that the government may not be compelled to disclose state and military secrets, even where their materiality to a lawsuit is clear. The overall disadvantages to society of disclosure of information of this character is said by the courts to outweigh the interest that society has in stimulating the full disclosure necessary to accurate resolution of lawsuits. The process is one of balancing the competing interests; clearly there are disadvantages to either rule. If state secrets are to be disclosed at the instance of litigants in the name of truth, the ill effects on the state might be considerable, and ultimately extend to the point where the system itself would break down. On the other hand, exclusion of state and military secrets, when relevant, potentially leads to erroneous and therefore unfair judgments in lawsuits. Which of these policies has the greater weight is clearly a matter of individual opinion. The courts, however, have struck this particular balance in favor of the state's interest, and against that of the litigants.

Another instance where information is excluded, even though it might have significant bearing on the truth of a particular matter before the court, lies in testimony from one accused of crime, which testimony would or might tend to prove the state's case against him. Known as the privilege against self-incrimination, the accused's right to remain silent derives from the Fifth Amendment of the Constitution, which states that "no person . . . shall be compelled in any criminal case to be a witness against himself." Thus, a criminal defendant can never be called to the witness stand by the prosecuting attorney and asked whether or not he committed a crime.

Still another type of information that is excluded even though it might be probative is communications between husband and wife. This privilege is based upon the idea that the relationship between a married couple is sacrosanct and not subject to probing into what transacts between the husband and wife in the privacy of their marital state.

Another type of privilege recognized by the court is that between the attorney and his client. This privilege prevents the attorney from disclosing, without the client's consent, any communication obtained from his client in his capacity as a legal advisor. The policy underlying the attorney-client privilege is to enable the client to speak freely to his attorney, in order that the attorney can best advise him of the strengths or weaknesses of his case or other legal problems. In fairness to his client, the attorney should have all available information if the client is to receive complete and honest advice.

MEDICAL PRIVILEGE

In many states today, there is like privilege for communications that take place between the patient and his doctor and likewise between the patient and other medical personnel. The reasons given for the grant of a privilege to the medical profession are, first, that if the patient knows that his confidence may be divulged he will hesitate to get needed medical aid, or will be reluctant to reveal the full facts to the treating physician, and, second, that this permits physicians and other medical practitioners to carry out their ethical obligation against disclosure of a patient's confidence. One of the most significant features of the physician-patient privilege is that it belongs to the patient and not to the physician. It is the patient and not the medical practitioner who is entitled to protection from disclosure of his secrets.

However, the privilege is not universally recognized, but exists only in those states where a statutory provision has been enacted prohibiting the physician from disclosing information given to him by the patient unless the patient consents. Without such a statute, the physician can be compelled, without regard for his ethical commitment, like anyone else, to tell from the witness stand what he has seen or heard from his patient when he was under his care. When a statute exists, his lips are sealed. Thus, in an action for a personal injury, the defendant can normally not call the plaintiff's doctor who treated the plaintiff shortly after the injury and question him about the nature and the extent of plaintiff's injuries. Even though the physician might be in a position to say that at the time there were no discernible injuries, and even though such testimony could bear significantly on the fairness or justice of the plaintiff's claim, in states that have statutes granting physicians privilege, his patient may claim the privilege and prevent the doctor from testifying.

The power of the privilege is seen in the case of *Harpman v. Devine*, 130 Ohio St. 1, 10 N.E.2d 776 (1957). There, the plaintiff sued the owner of a building for heavy damages, charging that glass from a window broken because of defendant's negligence hit the plaintiff. He testified that prior to the accident, his general condition was "very good," but that after the accident he had suffered loss of weight, severe and chronic headaches, failing eyesight, insomnia, facial paralysis, and inability to walk normally. He admitted that he had consulted various physicians before the accident. The defendant called one of those doctors to testify that the plaintiff was suffering from anemia before the accident ever happened, but the court refused to allow the doctor's evidence "in view of the very delicate and confidential nature of the relation." The defendant was thereby prevented from establishing a very plausible alternative explanation for the plaintiff's condition.

In some thirty states, statutes implementing the privilege for medical practitioners have been passed. However, there is wide variation in the terms of the statutes and generalizations as to the provisions of all statutes are difficult. Consequently, anyone concerned with the protection of confidential information provided by law must find his answer in the statute of the particular state and not in general principles. The statutes vary as to type of relationships that are within the privilege, e.g., physician-patient or nurse-patient. They also vary as to what conduct by the patient constitutes a waiver of the privilege, and what circumstances will lead to its termination.

The sense of professional honor or ethical consideration which prompts physicians to keep their patients' secrets is not involved where the patient wills otherwise. The law does not recognize that obligation as a reason to keep the matter confidential, or to keep it from seeing the light of day in a trial where it may be helpful to a resolution of the issues on a just basis. Nevertheless, physicians may well feel that maintaining silence in order to protect the confidential physician-patient relationship is of tremendous importance. Consider the competing policies involved in the following situation, quoted by Z. Chafee [*Privileged Communications: Is Justice Served or Obstructed by Closing the Doctor's Mouth on the Witness Stand?* 52 Yale L.J. 607, 615 (1943)]:*

While Dillinger, the former Public Enemy No. 1, was fleeing from prison, he went to Dr. May to be treated for gunshot wounds incurred during his escape. Was Dr. May ethically bound as a physician to preserve secrecy or was he under a duty as a citizen to notify the police? In fact, he neglected to inform the police of his ministrations and was consequently imprisoned two years for harboring a fugitive wanted under a federal warrant. The *Lancet* commented that "colleagues in every country will applaud his action in not betraying a professional trust." (1934). 226 *Lancet* 1183. Not many laymen are likely to join in the applause.

Do you think it would be relevant to consider how many persons were murdered by Dillinger in the interval between his visit to Doctor May and his subsequent recapture? Is the incident described an extreme one or are there many situations in which justice is impeded by a statutory provision that prevents the physician from revealing facts known to him, unless the patient consents?

With respect to communications directed by patients to nurses either in the presence of a physician or to them in their professional capacity, there is a decided split of authority.

In some states, the statutes themselves expressly extend to nurses a privilege for communications. Thus, the New York statute provides:

* Reprinted by permission of The Yale Law Journal Company and Fred B. Rothman & Company from *The Yale Law Journal,* Vol. 52, p. 607.

A person duly authorized to practice physic or surgery, or dentistry, or a professional or registered nurse, or licensed practical nurse, shall not be allowed to disclose any information which she acquired in attending a patient in a professional capacity . . .

With such a statute, the situation is clear and patient's communications to nurses will be kept confidential and she will not and cannot be compelled to disclose them in court, unless the patient consents.

In cases in approximately seven states it has been decided that a nurse who is acting as an employee or an assistant of the physician cannot be compelled to testify as to communications made by the patient to her. Under these decisions, the patient's privilege extends to communications to the nurse on the theory that she is acting as the physician's assistant, and in furtherance of the medical treatment to be given to the patient by the doctor. As stated by the court in *Williams v. State*, 65 Okla. Crim. 336. 86 P.2d 1015 (1939):

It is often necessary for those who assist the doctor as a nurse or attendant to be present at conversations between the patient and doctor, and little good would be served, if the lips of the doctor could be sealed by statute as to conversations, but the nurse or attendant might testify to all that was said and everything that was done. The purpose of the law was to protect the right of privacy, and while its scope should not be unduly extended, its very intention might be completely thwarted by the admission of this character.

A contrary line of cases holds that the nurse *can be compelled* to testify as to patients' communications made to her in the presence of a doctor. The general theory of the latter line of cases is that the physician-patient privilege is defined by statute, that it impedes the search for truth, and that it should not be extended beyond the narrow limits established by the legislature.

The nurse's privilege in the absence of statute was considered in *Southwest Metals Co. v. Gomez*, 4 F.2d 215 (9th Cir. 1925). There a coal miner claimed damages under a workman's compensation statute for injury to his eye, occurring in the course of his employment when he was picking rock with a bar and dust or rock fell into his eye, leading to infection and ultimately to loss of vision. The miner testified that the day after the accident, certain doctors had removed dirt from his eye. The defendant called the physicians, apparently to disprove plaintiff's statement that they had removed dirt from the eye, but the court held that their testimony was properly excluded on the grounds that it was privileged. Defendant then called a nurse who had assisted the physician but her testimony was also excluded at the trial, on the privilege ground. On appeal, the court reversed the exclusion of the nurse's testimony and said that she should have been required to testify. The statute establishing a physician-patient privilege did not specifically mention nurses, and on this ground, the court held her testimony admissible. The court said:

> If public policy demands that the privilege of the physician and surgeon should be extended to nurses and other attendants who are neither physicians nor surgeons, the change should be made by the Legislature, not by judicial construction.

As with physicians, the nurse's ethical obligation yields to the law's search for truth. The *Code of Ethics for Nurses, infra,* p. 468, states as one of its provisions:

> The nurse safeguards the individual's right to privacy by judicially protecting information of a confidential nature, sharing only that information relevant to his care.

Nevertheless, in the interpretation of the *Code* it is recognized that the legal obligation of the nurse may require her to divulge confidential information:

> Occasionally, the nurse may be obligated to give testimony in court in relation to confidential information about a patient. Under these circumstances, she should obtain legal counsel before testifying in order to be fully informed as to her rights and responsibilities in relation to both her patient and herself.

## NOTES

### (1) Conspiracy of Silence

The existence of a "conspiracy of silence" among physicians who are loath to testify against other physicians in malpractice actions is a problem recognized mutually by the professions of law and medicine [Louisell, D. A., and Williams, H. T., *Trial of Medical Malpractice Cases,* ¶ 18.04 (New York: Matthew Bender & Co., 1968)]. Group loyalty is not unique to the medical profession; a sense of professional loyalty doubtless deters the lawyer, the scientist, and the architect as well from testifying against their respective colleagues. With the medical profession, however, the problem is more acute, for medical practice co-mingles with the processes of law more frequently than do other disciplines. Malpractice cases are increasing in number and are becoming more complex as multiple parties, each perhaps with his own insurance carrier, become involved in the settlement of disputes.

Attorneys contend that expert medical testimony in malpractice cases is difficult to secure and physicians, to a lesser degree, acknowledge this to be true. However, this is not due to an arbitrary position the medical profession has taken nor is it done deliberately to impede the settlement of just claims.

Why then does the physician not wish to testify? One reason may be that suits or threats of suits are thought to damage the reputation of the defendant physician. Members of the profession are aware of this and are loath to participate in litigation, particularly when the question of negligence is a close one and the error in practice so debatable that, regardless of medical competence, it might well have happened to any doctor. Another serious deterrent to testimony in malpractice cases is that to hold a physician liable for a breach of duty, it must be established that the physician's conduct did not meet the standard of care in the locality in which he was practicing. This puts the medical witness in the position of testifying against a colleague with whom he may be closely associated. The reluctance stemming from close working relationships may be diminishing as the courts are gradually becoming less rigid on the locality requirement because of improved standards of medical education and the ease of interchange of medical knowledge and are becoming more willing to consider an expert from a distant but similar locality. Therefore, there is a wider field for the choice of the medical witness. Still another reason that members of the medical profession are reluctant to appear in court is that they may not feel at home in the legal process of decision making. In his practice the physician may work with a medical team or call in a consultant for whom he has profound respect and together they strive for accuracy in the diagnosis and the treatment of the patient. When the physician is confronted with the highly structured environment of the courtroom, the adversary method, the jury system, and the restraints of the rules of evidence, he is many times at a loss to know how to deal with the situation. He is uncomfortable in this process, which appears to him to be a battle in the manipulation of the truth and one in which there is an attempt to confuse him and even to question his veracity. It may also appear that each opposing party has sought medical opinion to support his particular claim, which to him undermines the credibility of his testimony and creates an unfavorable climate for both of the medical witnesses. At times it seems that physicians and lawyers become antagonistic when they confront each other on the opposite sides of a claim, although there usually is no conflict in the desire to seek justice but only in the methods employed.

On occasion, the courts have expressed the broad view that malpractice cases fail to come to a fair conclusion simply because the plaintiff's attorney is unable to secure a qualified medical witness. Illustrative of this point of view is the case of *Steiginga v. Thron*, 30 N.J. Super. 423, 105 A.2d 10 (1954). In an action founded on a charge of malpractice on the part of the defendant physician, the plaintiffs sought an adjournment of the trial because of the refusal of the expert witness to testify. In granting the adjournment, the court stated that in its opinion:

. . . the only expert witness retained on the plaintiff's behalf, had, without warrant and without further notice, declined on "second thought" to testify against a "brother practitioner." This, even though, as it is said, he then reiterated the respects wherein the defendant had been negligent. . . . The circumstances of the case must be looked at in the light of—the matter is of sufficient public concern to call for plain speaking—a shocking unethical reluctance on the part of the medical profession to accept its obligations to society and its profession in an action for malpractice. . . . A charge of malpractice is a serious and emburdening charge upon a professional man, but it is not answered by an attempt to throttle justice.

This "conspiracy of silence" is not an insurmountable problem, if its correction is viewed as a joint responsibility of both law and medicine. Some long-range solutions have been proposed that recognize that the time to develop an objective point of view necessary for collaboration is before problems are encountered in actual practice. Various plans are being followed to encourage interdisciplinary communication of law and medical students, e.g., courses in legal medicine, seminars held jointly to encourage free discussion, moot court in which the students of law and medicine play the roles they will later assume in actual practice. For current practitioners interdisciplinary committees appointed by the professional organizations have worked together on problems of malpractice action. The plan being tried in several states of making available to the court a panel of medical experts should also have its effect in breaking the "conspiracy of silence."

Medical knowledge can bring a distinct contribution to the administration of justice and every means to bring this about should be a mutual concern of both law and medicine. The members of the nursing profession share with other disciplines the problem of divided loyalties when asked to give expert testimony in malpractice cases. Because the nurse's position in this respect is analogous to that of the physician, she may need to give thought, if she has any reluctance to testify, to the social consequences of her refusal. As she grows in her knowledge of the law as it relates to nursing, and in her understanding that justice is the goal of the litigation process, she will see that when an unavoidable mistake occurs and an injury to the patient results, then in fairness, the patient should be compensated in a just and reasonable manner; and the nurse should be aware that she has an ethical obligation to assist in the process of seeking such a settlement.

## (2) Evaluation of Evidence by Judge and Jury

The following discussions present fundamental legal principles on how evidence is to be weighed. Reconsider this Note at the conclusion of chapters that follow.

Prosser, W. L., *Handbook of the Law of Torts,* 191 (2nd ed. St. Paul: West Publishing Co., 1955) *

The existence of negligence in a particular case often is said to be a mixed question of law and fact. By this it is meant, not only that both the court and the jury have an important part to play in the determination of the issue, and that separate functions are assigned to each, but further, that these functions to some extent overlap, and that it is not easy to fix any definite line of demarcation. It is said also that the court must decide questions of law, and the jury questions of fact. But this means little or nothing until some method of classification is provided, by which "law" may be distinguished from "fact"; and the division of functions between court and jury is a matter rather of historical origins and present policy than of any such definitions.

The issue of negligence presents at least five more or less distinct questions, as to which the court and the jury have separate parts to play in reaching a decision. These are as follows:

1. The sufficiency of the evidence to permit a finding of the facts. Before any duty, or any standard of conduct may be set, there must first be proof of facts which give rise to it; and once the standard is fixed, there must be proof that the actor has departed from it. If it be assumed that the driver of an automobile approaching a visible intersection will be required to moderate his speed, there is still the question whether the intersection was visible, and whether he did in fact slow down. These are purely questions of fact, and within the recognized province of the jury as the triers of fact. But over such questions of fact the courts always have reserved a preliminary power of decision, as to whether the issue shall be submitted to the jury at all. If the evidence is such that no reasonably intelligent man would accept it as sufficient to establish the existence of a fact essential to negligence, it becomes the duty of the court to remove the issue from the jury, and to nonsuit the plaintiff, or direct a verdict for the defendant, or even to set aside a verdict once rendered. Less frequently, the evidence may be so overwhelming that no reasonable man could fail to accept the fact as proved; and the court must then direct the jury accordingly. This is, of course, merely a part of the general law of evidence, and in this respect negligence cases do not differ from any other cases where essential facts must be proved.

2. The weight of the evidence as establishing the facts. Once it is determined that reasonable men may differ as to whether a fact has been proved, the probative value of the evidence, and the conclusion to be drawn from it, lies in the hands of the jury. They must not only decide as to the credibility of the testimony, but draw or refuse to draw any inferences from the testimony as to which there may be reasonable difference of opinion. In this respect again, negligence cases do not differ from any others.

3. The existence of a duty. In other words, whether, upon the facts in evidence, such a relation exists between the parties that the community will impose a legal obligation upon one for the benefit of the other—or, more simply, whether the interest of the plaintiff which has suffered invasion was entitled to legal protection at the hands of the defendant. This is entirely a question of law, to be determined by reference to the body of statutes, rules, principles and precedents which make

* Reprinted with permission of West Publishing Company.

up the law; and it must be determined only by the court. It is no part of the province of a jury to decide whether a manufacturer of goods is under any obligation for the safety of the ultimate consumer, or whether the Long Island Railroad is required to protect Mrs. Palsgraf from fireworks explosions. A decision by the court that, upon any version of the facts, there is no duty, must necessarily result in judgment for the defendant. A decision that, if certain facts are found to be true, a duty exists, leaves open the other questions now under consideration.

4. The general standard of conduct. As has been said before, this is the necessary complement of duty. In negligence cases, once a duty is found, the duty, in theory at least, always requires the same standard of conduct, that of a reasonable man under the same or similar circumstances—except perhaps in those jurisdictions where statutory or common law modifications have recognized "degrees" of care, and a higher or lower standard in particular cases. Since the standard is a legal rule, from which the jury are not free to deviate, it is a matter of law, and is to be applied by the court. Almost invariably this application takes the form of an instruction to the jury declaring, briefly or more fully, a formula such as that of the reasonable man of ordinary prudence. There is room for considerable skepticism as to how far such instructions are understood by the average jury, or have any weight with them, but they represent the attempt, so far as is reasonably possible, to enlighten the layman's ignorance of the law, and to impose a social, rather than an individual standard.

5. The particular standard of conduct. Since it is impossible to prescribe definite rules in advance for every combination of circumstances which may arise, the details of the standard must be filled in in each particular case. The question then is what the reasonable man would have done under the circumstances. Under our system of procedure, this question is to be determined in all doubtful cases by the jury, because the public insists that its conduct be judged in part by the man in the street rather than by lawyers, and the jury serves as a shock-absorber to cushion the impact of the law. The question usually is said to be one of fact, but it should be apparent that the function of the jury in fixing the standard differs from that of the judge only in that it cannot be reduced to anything approaching a definite rule.

# CASES

The following case is presented for study against the background of legal discussion on the subject of *evidence*. In answering the questions that follow the case, return to the foregoing theory and seek applications of the content to this particular case.

## Ostrowski v. Mockridge, 242 Minn. 265, 65 N.W. 2d 185 (1954)

Thomas Gallagher, Justice.
Two actions, one by Lucille M. Ostrowski and one by Albin I. Ostrowski, her husband, for damages arising out of an automobile accident which occurred June

30, 1948. Defendant admitted responsibility for the accident, and the only issue for determination was the extent of damages sustained by each plaintiff.

The cases were tried together. The jury returned a verdict for Lucille M. Ostrowski in the sum of $12,000 for injuries sustained, and $3,000 for Albin I. Ostrowski covering damages to automobile, loss of wife's services, and medical expenses paid or incurred. This is an appeal from an order denying defendant's subsequent motions for a new trial.

On appeal it is contended that the trial court erred (1) in failing to grant defendant's motions for a mistrial because of several references in Lucille M. Ostrowski's testimony to "the insurance company"; (2) in receiving over objection memorandum covering part of Lucille M. Ostrowski's employment record furnished by her employer; and (3) in sustaining objections to testimony of Dr. Albert J. Lenarz and Mrs. Albert J. Lenarz called by defendant on the ground of privilege. It is also contended that the verdicts are so excessive as to indicate passion and prejudice on the part of the jury.

The accident occurred June 30, 1948, near the village of Rice. The following morning Lucille M. Ostrowski, who was then pregnant, visited the office of Dr. Albert J. Lenarz, physician at Browerville, for treatment for injuries sustained therein. Dr. Lenarz examined her in the presence of her husband and in the presence of Mrs. Lenarz who was acting as his nurse.

The same day plaintiffs commenced a five-day trip from Browerville to California where they lived. Lucille M. Ostrowski testified that on this trip her back, neck, right arm, and face gave her considerable pain; that at Salt Lake City she suffered a miscarriage; that after her arrival in California because of continued pain due to the accident she was required to be treated repeatedly by physicians there and was forced to be absent from her employment on numerous occasions; and that such pain and treatments continued at intervals to the date of trial. . . .

During the trial defendant called upon Dr. Albert J. Lenarz for testimony with respect to his examination of plaintiff immediately after the accident. Plaintiff's objection to his testimony on the ground of privilege was sustained. Defendant thereupon offered to prove by him that when Lucille was examined on July 1, 1948, she had told him that she was one or two weeks past her period and was possibly pregnant; that he had examined her and found no visible sign of any bodily injury; and that in June 1950 she had called upon him for treatment for a sore throat and had made no reference then to injuries sustained in the accident. Objection to this offer was likewise sustained on the ground of privilege.

Defendant then called Mrs. Albert J. Lenarz, wife of Dr. Lenarz, who was present in the capacity of a nurse in Dr. Lenarz' office at the time he treated plaintiff immediately following the accident. Objections to her testimony and to an offer to provide evidence similar to that offered on behalf of Dr. Lenarz were sustained on the ground of privilege.

Prior to the foregoing Lucille had referred to her call upon Dr. Lenarz immediately after the accident and had testified that he had prescribed certain pills for her. On cross-examination she had referred to her second call at his office in June 1950. Her counsel, in cross-examining Dr. Sprafka, physician called by defendant, as the basis for a hypothetical question had stated: Assuming that "next day a. m. saw Dr. Lenarz because she felt shaky, ached all over back and shoulders and was getting pain in right side and Dr. recommended X-ray, but she said she had to leave for

Los Angeles and had not time. . . ." A number of other physicians called by her testified as to her physical condition. It is defendant's contention that the above testimony and references, as well as the fact that her husband was present when she was examined by Dr. Lenarz, in effect constituted a waiver of her right to claim privilege with respect to the testimony of either Dr. or Mrs. Lenarz. . . .

With reference to the exclusion of the testimony of Dr. Lenarz on the ground of privilege, M.S.A. § 595.02(4) provides:

A licensed physician or surgeon shall not, without the consent of his patient, be allowed to disclose any information or any opinion based thereon which he acquired in attending the patient in a professional capacity. . . .

And that:

. . . no oral or written waiver of the privilege hereinbefore created shall have any binding force or effect except that the same be made upon the trial or examination where the evidence is offered or received;

Defendant contends that plaintiff waived the privileged character of her conversations with and treatment by Dr. Lenarz by submitting testimony as to her disabilities and by furnishing testimony of other medical experts with reference thereto. We have held to the contrary in a number of cases.

As stated in the Polin case, 159 Minn. 412, 199 N.W. 87:

. . . Defendants insist that plaintiff waived the right to invoke this statute . . . by testifying concerning such injuries and the treatment given. The legislature has not seen fit to say that such acts shall operate as a waiver. . . . This court, in accordance with the weight of authority, has adopted the rule that bringing an action, unless it be against the physician himself for malpractice, or testifying concerning the injuries sustained and the treatment received unless such testimony relates to communications made to the physician or questions the propriety of his treatment, is not a waiver of the privilege.

Here Lucille's only reference to her consultation with Dr. Lenarz was that because of pain and discomfort after the accident she visited Dr. Lenarz who gave her some medicine which she took and some orders which she obeyed. Any further information with reference thereto was brought out through cross-examination by defendant's counsel. Her husband, who was present at the consultation, testified that after looking her over Dr. Lenarz gave his wife some prescriptions. The basis for a hypothetical question submitted by Lucille's counsel to Dr. Sprafka called by defendant referred only to a prescription Dr. Lenarz had given to Lucille. In our opinion these vague and indefinite references to the call upon Dr. Lenarz would not come within the waiver contemplated by § 595.02(4).

Previous decisions cited by defendant are not in conflict with this conclusion. In Burke v. Chicago & N. W. Ry. Co., 131 Minn. 209, 154 N.W. 960, plaintiff's doctor had testified without objection for some time, the privilege being claimed only when his testimony became unfavorable to plaintiff. In Maas v. Midway Chevrolet Co., 219 Minn. 461, 18 N.W.2d 233, the patient was held to have waived the privilege by calling his physician to the stand. In Doll v. Scandrett, 201 Minn. 316, 276 N.W. 281, and Leifson v. Henning, 210 Minn. 311, 298 N.W. 41, in each of which two physicians had made a unitary examination of plaintiff, we held plaintiff's submission of the testimony of one of such examiners constituted a waiver of the privilege as to the other. It is clear that all such situations are quite distinct from the facts claimed as constituting waiver in the instant case.

3. As to Mrs. Albert J. Lenarz, we are of the opinion that the privilege claimed should extend to her. Clearly she was acting in the capacity as agent for Dr. Lenarz at the time of his examination of Lucille. Obviously any communications which were transmitted to Dr. Lenarz in her presence were made for the purpose of treatment and privileged under the statute. The fact that they were overheard by the nurse would not, in our opinion, take from them their privileged character. We can conceive of a different result had the nurse in attendance not been an agent or employee of the examining physician, as was the case in First Trust Co. v. Kansas City Life Ins. Co., 8 Cir., 79 F.2d 48.

It is true the authorities on the question appear to be divided. A number of courts hold that the statutory privilege does not exclude the testimony of a nurse attending the physician. Other courts have permitted such testimony where it appears the information sought to be elicited was acquired from sources separate and distinct from action in concert with a physician against whom the claim of privilege is made. On the other hand, some jurisdictions take the view that the privilege extends by implication to nurses or attendants who are employees or acting under the direction of the physician examining or treating the patient. In our opinion, the latter view to a greater extent carries out the intent and purport of the statute creating privilege. . . .

We do not feel that $12,000 as an award for the injuries and damages sustained by Lucille was so excessive as to indicate passion and prejudice. This covered lost wages, loss of future earnings, and pain and suffering, as well as permanent injuries. At the time of the accident she was 25 years of age and was "very healthy." As a result of the accident she sustained injuries to her neck and back which were severe and permanent. In addition, shortly thereafter she suffered a miscarriage. Subsequent thereto she has had frequent medical treatment for her back, neck, and arm, taking "shots" to relieve pain therein. For approximately six months thereafter to a large extent she lost control of her right arm, a condition recurring approximately every three months to date and continuing for about an hour at such intervals. She has been treated two or three times a week by doctors. Her back bothers her constantly, even when she is lying down, and particularly when she is working. She has taken phenobarbital and codeine for the relief of her pain, which she complained of since the day of the accident. She has seen doctors at least twice a week for the four and one-half year period preceding the trial. She has taken medical treatment from an orthopedist prescribing therapy in an effort to relieve her pain and regain the full use of her limbs. She has taken treatments involving traction and has purchased a mechanical device which she uses daily for this purpose. Relief from this source or as the result of heat lamps extends only for approximately a three-hour period. She can no longer perform her regular housework, and her duties with reference thereto are limited to sweeping and washing dishes. Relatives who either lived with her or nearby have performed most of her housework.

Testimony would support a finding that since the accident she has lost approximately 1,000 hours from her employment at an average hourly rate of $1.27 for a total loss in excess of $1,270.

Medical testimony submitted indicated that as a result of the accident she suffered a concussion and whip-snap injury to her neck which caused the vertebrae therein to be jerked apart; that her present disability is due to a continuing disturbance resulting in a neuralgic pain radiating over the back of her head; that in court reverses a judgment for defendants and a new trial is ordered.

## commended Source Material

### XTS

wling, N., Patterson, E., and Powell, R., *Materials for Legal Method* (Mineola, N.Y.: The Foundation Press, Inc., 1952).
.ebensen, H., *You, the Expert Witness*; and *You, the Medical Witness* (Chicago: Callaghan & Company, 1962).
Louisell, D., and Williams, H., *The Parenchyma of Law*, 1–229 (Rochester: Professional Publications, 1960).
McCormick, C., *Cases and Materials on the Law of Evidence* (St. Paul: West Pub. Co., 3rd ed., 1956).
Pollack, E., *Fundamentals of Legal Research* (Mineola, N.Y.: The Foundation Press, Inc., 2nd ed., 1962).
Stetler, C., Stetler, J., and Moritz, A., *Doctor, Patient and the Law*, 209–247 (St. Louis: C. V. Mosby Co., 4th ed., 1962).
Wormser, R., *The Law; The Story of the Lawmakers and the Law We Live By* (New York: Simon & Schuster, Inc., 1949).

### PERIODICALS

Appel, J., *Law as a Social Science in the Undergraduate Curriculum*, 10 J. Legal Ed. 485 (1958).
Hale, W., *Hospital Records as Evidence*, 14 S. Cal. L. Rev. 99 (1941).
Mills, R., Hidden Dangers of Hospital Chart, *Hosp. Med.* 34: 11, June, 1965.
Note, *Hospital—Failure to Keep Clear Records*. 4 Law & Sci. 286 (1964).
Note, *Opinion Entry Problems in Medical Records*, 19 Baylor L. Rev. 122 (1967).
Note, *Medical Practice and the Right to Privacy*, 43 Minn. L. Rev. 943 (1959).
Scott, A., *Introduction to Law*, 50 Law Lib. J. 464 (1957).
Wallace, J., *An Excursion into the Affinities Between Law and the Behavioral Sciences*, 18 J. Legal Ed. 43 (1965).

addition she sustained a strain to the structures of her lower back, particularly in the region of the lumbosacral joint and the right sacroiliac synchondrosis; that the involvement of her right arm indicated an injury to the brachial plexus; and that her injuries are permanent and will result in a substantial loss of her future earning capacity. When these factors are considered, the conclusion is inescapable that we are lacking in authority to interfere with the jury's award as above described.

6. As to the $3,000 awarded Albin I. Ostrowski, it does not appear excessive. Evidence was submitted as to his liability for the cost of medical treatment required by his wife as a result of the accident extending over a four and one-half year period and for the medicine and drugs required in connection therewith. In view of the permanent nature of his wife's injuries, it is probable that his liability for expenses of this kind will continue for a long period of time in the future. There was also evidence that his wife sustained the loss of 75 percent of her capacity to do the ordinary and regular household work and that this condition was permanent. We do not feel that the jury's award for such losses was so excessive as to require our interference therewith.

The order appealed from is affirmed.

Affirmed.

### ANALYSIS

1. In brief what were the facts of the situation and why was the case appealed? What were the three ways in which it was said that the trial court erred?

2. The subject of privilege received considerable attention. What mention was made of the nurse as the doctor's assistant and the effect it had on her testimony in court? Of the principles regarding privilege discussed in the text, which ones were helpful in a better understanding of this case?

## CASES FOR FURTHER ANALYSIS

The following are summaries of cases that are related to the subject matter of the immediately preceding chapter. Similar summaries appear at the end of each chapter. The reader should study and analyze these cases, and decide whether they correctly apply legal principles to the medical situation with which they deal, and correctly formulate legal doctrine for those situations. This independent analysis should be patterned after the analysis found in the text after each full case.

For example, in *Williams v. Alexander* the court seemed to believe that the history of an accident did not have a place of importance in the medical history. Upon reading this summary, the reader should ponder the correctness of the court's view, how it happened to reach such a conclusion, and decide what medical and nursing implications are present in this judicial attitude.

Consider whether you would agree with the view of the court that the hospital record narrating the nature of the accident was not germane to diagnosis or treatment. If not, cite similar instances when such a report might be of evidentiary value to the court.

### Williams v. Alexander, 309 N.Y. 283, 129 N.E.2d 417 (1955)

This case was an action for personal injuries sustained in an automobile accident, in which the defendant claimed that the car in which he had been driving had been struck from behind by another car and propelled forward upon the plaintiff, and the plaintiff contended that defendant had entered an intersection without reducing his speed and ran into him. At the trial, plaintiff introduced a hospital record to prove what his injuries had been and what treatment he had received. The defendant then introduced the same hospital records in which it appeared that the plaintiff had stated to a physician that he was crossing the street and an automobile ran into another automobile that was at a standstill, causing the latter to run into him. The plaintiff denied making any such statement and the doctor who had recorded it was not called. On appeal, the court considered the question of whether the recorded statement of the plaintiff was admissible under the New York statutes. The court refers to the general rule that business records are admissible, even though they technically are hearsay, because of the fact that they are the routine entries in a day-to-day business operation, and that it is to the interest of the person making the entry that they are truthful and accurate as can be. The court recognizes that it is this element of trustworthiness that justifies admission of the record or writing without the need to call all the persons who have had a hand in preparing it.

However, in this case, the court reverses the judgment for the defendant and holds that the hospital record was wrongly admitted. The court says that the business of a hospital is to diagnose and treat patients' ailments and that the only purpose of the record is to record those acts and occurrences that relate to the diagnosis, prognosis, or treatment or are otherwise helpful to an understanding of the medical or physical aspects of plaintiff's hospitalization. The court says that the mere narration of the nature of the accident causing the injury is not germane to diagnosis or treatment in this case. The court recognizes that, although under some circumstances it might assist the treating doctors to know how an injury had been brought about, it was irrelevant whether this particular patient had been hit by one car under its own power or because it had been struck from behind by another car. That being so, the court said, entries purporting to give the particulars of the accident and that would serve no medical purpose could not be regarded as having been made in the regular course of the hospital's business. The court went on to say that although the particulars might be a natural subject of the doctor's curiosity, neither the

inquiries nor the response properly belonged in the rec... the regular course of the hospital's business.

### General Benevolent Ass'n v. East Fowler, 210 Miss. 578, (1951)

In an action for negligence of the hospital nurses, the cour... jury verdict for a hospital patient. The plaintiff had become ill wi... and among other treatments her doctor had prescribed intravenous... of glucose every 24 hours. The glucose infusions were given by nurs... four-day period. The plaintiff showed that when she entered the hos... left arm was in a normal condition, but when she was discharged it v... colored, swollen, and painful. After she left the hospital, the site of the inj... continued to be tender, swollen, and painful and developed a strong unpl... odor. Four days after leaving the hospital several doctors in succession tr... her and the last found a broken hypodermic needle about one-half inc... length in her arm. The needle was 25 gauge in size, and the testimony sho... that this size needle was used only for infusion of narcotics and other high... liquid substances, or for administration of glucose to children by doctors. Th... evidence was that 20-gauge needles were used for infusion in adults. At th... trial, the hospital records were introduced, and all six nurses who had... administered the infusions testified that they had not observed the broken needle and that they had never seen an infusion needle broken.

On this circumstantial evidence, the court said that the plaintiff was entitled to go to the jury, and that those facts were sufficient to warrant an... inference that the needle was inserted and broken off in the arm by the act o... the nurses in the hospital, or that the nurses had been negligent in failing t... ascertain that the needle had broken there and in failing to remove it, or bot... and also warranted an inference that one of the nurses had used the wrong s... of needle.

### Polsca v. East River Mgmt. Corp., 160 N.Y.S.2d 658 (App. Div.) (19

The opinion in full in this case is as follows:

The refusal of the trial court to receive in evidence portions of a h... record relating to prior diagnosis of swollen ankle and severe headach... error, particularly in view of plaintiff's claim that she had never had p... trouble with her feet and that her swollen ankles and persistent headac... the result of the accident upon which this suit was based. Hospital... which relate to diagnosis, prognosis or treatment or which are otherv... ful to the understanding of the medical aspects of the hospitalizatic... missible in evidence.

addition she sustained a strain to the structures of her lower back, particularly in the region of the lumbosacral joint and the right sacroiliac synchondrosis; that the involvement of her right arm indicated an injury to the brachial plexus; and that her injuries are permanent and will result in a substantial loss of her future earning capacity. When these factors are considered, the conclusion is inescapable that we are lacking in authority to interfere with the jury's award as above described.

6. As to the $3,000 awarded Albin I. Ostrowski, it does not appear excessive. Evidence was submitted as to his liability for the cost of medical treatment required by his wife as a result of the accident extending over a four and one-half year period and for the medicine and drugs required in connection therewith. In view of the permanent nature of his wife's injuries, it is probable that his liability for expenses of this kind will continue for a long period of time in the future. There was also evidence that his wife sustained the loss of 75 percent of her capacity to do the ordinary and regular household work and that this condition was permanent. We do not feel that the jury's award for such losses was so excessive as to require our interference therewith.

The order appealed from is affirmed.

Affirmed.


ANALYSIS

1. In brief what were the facts of the situation and why was the case appealed? What were the three ways in which it was said that the trial court erred?

2. The subject of privilege received considerable attention. What mention was made of the nurse as the doctor's assistant and the effect it had on her testimony in court? Of the principles regarding privilege discussed in the text, which ones were helpful in a better understanding of this case?


## CASES FOR FURTHER ANALYSIS

The following are summaries of cases that are related to the subject matter of the immediately preceding chapter. Similar summaries appear at the end of each chapter. The reader should study and analyze these cases, and decide whether they correctly apply legal principles to the medical situation with which they deal, and correctly formulate legal doctrine for those situations. This independent analysis should be patterned after the analysis found in the text after each full case.

For example, in *Williams v. Alexander* the court seemed to believe that the history of an accident did not have a place of importance in the medical history. Upon reading this summary, the reader should ponder the correctness of the court's view, how it happened to reach such a conclusion, and decide what medical and nursing implications are present in this judicial attitude.

Consider whether you would agree with the view of the court that the hospital record narrating the nature of the accident was not germane to diagnosis or treatment. If not, cite similar instances when such a report might be of evidentiary value to the court.

### Williams v. Alexander, 309 N.Y. 283, 129 N.E.2d 417 (1955)

This case was an action for personal injuries sustained in an automobile accident, in which the defendant claimed that the car in which he had been driving had been struck from behind by another car and propelled forward upon the plaintiff, and the plaintiff contended that defendant had entered an intersection without reducing his speed and ran into him. At the trial, plaintiff introduced a hospital record to prove what his injuries had been and what treatment he had received. The defendant then introduced the same hospital records in which it appeared that the plaintiff had stated to a physician that he was crossing the street and an automobile ran into another automobile that was at a standstill, causing the latter to run into him. The plaintiff denied making any such statement and the doctor who had recorded it was not called. On appeal, the court considered the question of whether the recorded statement of the plaintiff was admissible under the New York statutes. The court refers to the general rule that business records are admissible, even though they technically are hearsay, because of the fact that they are the routine entries in a day-to-day business operation, and that it is to the interest of the person making the entry that they are truthful and accurate as can be. The court recognizes that it is this element of trustworthiness that justifies admission of the record or writing without the need to call all the persons who have had a hand in preparing it.

However, in this case, the court reverses the judgment for the defendant and holds that the hospital record was wrongly admitted. The court says that the business of a hospital is to diagnose and treat patients' ailments and that the only purpose of the record is to record those acts and occurrences that relate to the diagnosis, prognosis, or treatment or are otherwise helpful to an understanding of the medical or physical aspects of plaintiff's hospitalization. The court says that the mere narration of the nature of the accident causing the injury is not germane to diagnosis or treatment in this case. The court recognizes that, although under some circumstances it might assist the treating doctors to know how an injury had been brought about, it was irrelevant whether this particular patient had been hit by one car under its own power or because it had been struck from behind by another car. That being so, the court said, entries purporting to give the particulars of the accident and that would serve no medical purpose could not be regarded as having been made in the regular course of the hospital's business. The court went on to say that although the particulars might be a natural subject of the doctor's curiosity, neither the inquiries nor the response properly belonged in the record designed to reflect the regular course of the hospital's business.

### General Benevolent Ass'n v. East Fowler, 210 Miss. 578, 50 So.2d 137 (1951)

In an action for negligence of the hospital nurses, the court affirmed a jury verdict for a hospital patient. The plaintiff had become ill with gastritis, and among other treatments her doctor had prescribed intravenous injections of glucose every 24 hours. The glucose infusions were given by nurses over a four-day period. The plaintiff showed that when she entered the hospital her left arm was in a normal condition, but when she was discharged it was discolored, swollen, and painful. After she left the hospital, the site of the injections continued to be tender, swollen, and painful and developed a strong unpleasant odor. Four days after leaving the hospital several doctors in succession treated her and the last found a broken hypodermic needle about one-half inch in length in her arm. The needle was 25 gauge in size, and the testimony showed that this size needle was used only for infusion of narcotics and other highly liquid substances, or for administration of glucose to children by doctors. The evidence was that 20-gauge needles were used for infusion in adults. At the trial, the hospital records were introduced, and all six nurses who had administered the infusions testified that they had not observed the broken needle and that they had never seen an infusion needle broken.

On this circumstantial evidence, the court said that the plaintiff was entitled to go to the jury, and that those facts were sufficient to warrant an inference that the needle was inserted and broken off in the arm by the act of the nurses in the hospital, or that the nurses had been negligent in failing to ascertain that the needle had broken there and in failing to remove it, or both, and also warranted an inference that one of the nurses had used the wrong size of needle.

### Polsca v. East River Mgmt. Corp., 160 N.Y.S.2d 658 (App. Div.) (1957)

The opinion in full in this case is as follows:

The refusal of the trial court to receive in evidence portions of a hospital record relating to prior diagnosis of swollen ankle and severe headaches was error, particularly in view of plaintiff's claim that she had never had previous trouble with her feet and that her swollen ankles and persistent headaches were the result of the accident upon which this suit was based. Hospital records which relate to diagnosis, prognosis or treatment or which are otherwise helpful to the understanding of the medical aspects of the hospitalization are admissible in evidence.

The court reverses a judgment for defendants and a new trial is ordered.

## Recommended Source Material

TEXTS

Dowling, N., Patterson, E., and Powell, R., *Materials for Legal Method* (Mineola, N.Y.: The Foundation Press, Inc., 1952).

Liebensen, H., *You, the Expert Witness*; and *You, the Medical Witness* (Chicago: Callaghan & Company, 1962).

Louisell, D., and Williams, H., *The Parenchyma of Law*, 1–229 (Rochester: Professional Publications, 1960).

McCormick, C., *Cases and Materials on the Law of Evidence* (St. Paul: West Pub. Co., 3rd ed., 1956).

Pollack, E., *Fundamentals of Legal Research* (Mineola, N.Y.: The Foundation Press, Inc., 2nd ed., 1962).

Stetler, C., Stetler, J., and Moritz, A., *Doctor, Patient and the Law*, 209–247 (St. Louis: C. V. Mosby Co., 4th ed., 1962).

Wormser, R., *The Law ; The Story of the Lawmakers and the Law We Live By* (New York: Simon & Schuster, Inc., 1949).

PERIODICALS

Appel, J., *Law as a Social Science in the Undergraduate Curriculum*, 10 J. Legal Ed. 485 (1958).

Hale, W., *Hospital Records as Evidence*, 14 S. Cal. L. Rev. 99 (1941).

Mills, R., Hidden Dangers of Hospital Chart, *Hosp. Med.* 34: 11, June, 1965.

Note, *Hospital—Failure to Keep Clear Records*. 4 Law & Sci. 286 (1964).

Note, *Opinion Entry Problems in Medical Records*, 19 Baylor L. Rev. 122 (1967).

Note, *Medical Practice and the Right to Privacy*, 43 Minn. L. Rev. 943 (1959).

Scott, A., *Introduction to Law*, 50 Law Lib. J. 464 (1957).

Wallace, J., *An Excursion into the Affinities Between Law and the Behavioral Sciences*, 18 J. Legal Ed. 43 (1965).

# Part Two

---

# Social Consequences of Inadvertence—Unintentional Torts

## Accidents as a Social Problem

The unfortunate propensity of the human race to have accidents creates a continuing social problem of great magnitude and importance. Accidents, with their consequent injuries, are a part of societal living, and it is doubtless the case that total elimination of accidents is a practical impossibility. In a society as diverse as our own, as highly industrialized, as heavily concentrated, and as easily mobile, the possibility of injuries from accidents is very great. It is demonstrable that the economic and social costs of accidents over a period of time is staggering in monetary terms. It has been estimated, for example, by the National Safety Council, that the direct economic cost of accidents in the year 1965 was $18 billion. Accidental death took more lives during World War II than the war itself. Four fifths of the persons accidentally killed have twenty years of productive life before them, and in 1965 alone a million years of productive effort were wiped out by automobile accidents.

In addition to human suffering, both physical and emotional, which is inevitably associated with serious accidents, there are economic losses, both direct and indirect. Direct economic loss to an accident victim as a consequence of an accident may come about in several ways, depending upon the nature and severity of the injury. First, there is loss of wages or salary during the period of convalescence, and there are the medical and hospital expenses essential for recovery. Second, there are handicaps of a permanent nature, which result in loss of earning ability or loss of future increases in earnings. Third, there may be disability that not only creates a loss of income but also gives rise to continuing expenses and liabilities. Thus, in a home in which the breadwinner is injured and disabled, not only do the members of his family have to find alternate sources of income for support, but sufficient income has to be generated to pay continuing medical expenses. Fourth, there are the pain and suffering inevitably incident to any serious injury.

Any serious injury brings with it indirect losses as well. For example, a business may have to incur expenses for training individuals to replace the injured worker, administrative expenses in worker turnover must be borne, and loss of key personnel in a business is always accompanied by lowered business efficiency, hence less income. There may be tradesmen who have advanced credit to a person or family and who do not get paid because the family source of income is cut off; hospital bills frequently remain unpaid in cases of injury, which results in the hospital bearing a part of the loss caused by injury. There is also the substantial physical and emotional suffering that attends injury and that is visited on family and friends as well as the victim.

Who bears these losses? Clearly, unless the injured party or his family receive payments or other compensation from some source, they will bear the loss themselves. Because accidents are likely to strike anyone at anytime, pure chance will determine the victims, and the losses will be distributed willy-nilly, depending upon the accident victim's relationship to his family and his community and upon his independent resources and means. However, if methods exist for providing the victims with recompense for their losses, the loss will be shifted to whomever is finally determined to be responsible for actually paying for the losses. It is the methods for allocating these losses that we will now consider.

## Society's Means for Allocating Accident Losses

The allocation of these losses is the general province of the tort law. Tort law deals with a wide variety of civil wrongs in which someone, through socially unreasonable conduct, has harmed another. It sets the legal standard for ascertaining the fault, for fixing the blame for the fault, and for measuring the economic loss stemming from accidental and unintentional injury.

The overriding objective of the tort law is to provide a means for compensating those injured by the wrongful conduct of another. It is not primarily designed to punish or penalize, although it may indirectly do so. It seeks, by awarding money damages, to restore a *status quo* insofar as possible, by placing the injured party in a position equivalent to that he had before the tort was committed.

Tort law has a deterrent or preventive function as well. It proceeds, in part, upon the premise that the allocation of monetary responsibility to a particular class of persons for certain types of injuries will tend to influence that class to take steps to avoid such injuries. For example, holding railroads responsible for all accidents at crossings not adequately marked will tend to influence them to erect warning signs to avoid such liability. Presumably, the number of railroad crossing accidents will be reduced as a result. Thus, the tort law formulates its rules with a view toward promoting socially desirable conduct and inhibiting socially undesirable conduct.

It is wise to keep in mind, however, the words of leading authorities in this field [Harper, F., and James, F., *The Law of Torts*, Vol. 2, 743, (Boston: Little, Brown & Company, 1956)]:

> It is well to note that tort law is by no means the only device for social control in the accident problem. We may be kept from unreasonably dangerous conduct, for instance, by the urge for self-preservation, by fear of criminal fines and penalties, by licensing regulations, or by attitudes built up through education and by non-legal social and economic pressures, as well as by fear of tort liability. Compensation of the accident victim, by the same token, may be brought about through private or public insurance with which the tort-feasor had nothing to do. . . . The civil law of torts, in other words, cannot alone solve the accident problem. We should not expect it to. Rather we should realize that it is only one of a number of complex variables within the field and we should try to evaluate it, to the extent we can, in its full context. This will call for careful weighing and balancing, but the difficulties of the task should not be shirked.*

### THE FAULT PRINCIPLE

The primary method in force in our country today of allocating the financial responsibility for accidents is through the judicial process whereby recourse to the courts is had, or threatened, by an injured party against the one who has allegedly caused his injury. That is, the allocation of loss in any particular matter is fixed by a judge or jury in the process of litigation, or, without actually going to court, the parties involved determine the allocation based upon their prediction of what the result of litigation would be.

The person who is involved in a traffic violation, the shopkeeper who fails to remove ice from his sidewalk, the worker who carelessly handles dangerous machinery, the nurse who fails to read the warning on the wrapper of a new drug, or the orderly who is unduly aggressive in restraining a patient, all

* Reprinted with permission of Little, Brown & Co.

engage in socially undesirable conduct that may lead to injury and tragedy, and ultimately to the courts. Such wrongful acts are called "torts"; a tort may be defined as one person's civil or private conduct that is wrongful to another and that injures the second person, either physically, mentally, or economically. Recovery through the judicial process for torts is based upon the fault principle, i.e., *one who through his own fault injures another should be required to bear the resulting financial loss*. When allocation is based upon individual fault, recourse to the courts will often become necessary to make the fundamental determination: who, if anyone, was at fault in a particular circumstance resulting in injury. Human nature being what it is, the fault issue is frequently hotly disputed, and, in the field of torts, the court's role is that of an impartial tribunal determining the allocation of loss by deciding the fault question. In such a case, the entire loss may be shifted to the perpetrator of the wrong through a court case in which a judgment is rendered against the defendant for monetary damages or through the threat of such a court case. The fault that is alleged to give rise to the responsibility for bearing all costs of injury, however great, is generally the fault of negligent conduct. Cases are relatively rare where a deliberate wrong has been inflicted, although, as we shall see, in those cases as well, the wrongdoer is expected to bear the full loss.

Accidents through fault in the medical field, although constituting a relatively small percentage of cases in which injury results from negligence, are the principal area of concern of nurses and doctors. A patient injured on the operating table through an improper or negligent act of a surgeon or nurse is, of course, equally the victim of accident as is the person injured in an automobile collision. In neither case is injury intended, but in both cases it is brought about by a failure to act responsibly. Negligence in the medical field has received the special name of "malpractice." The law governing malpractice cases in its overall outline is the same law that governs motor vehicle and all other types of accident cases arising from an alleged negligence or misconduct. We will examine the principles of law in detail, with an emphasis upon their application to the medical field.

STRICT LIABILITY

In some situations, one who injures another must bear the loss even though his conduct was in no way negligent or improper. Rather than predicating liability on fault, or breach of duty, the law holds him responsible because of the nature of the conduct. This kind of legal liability is termed *strict* or *absolute* liability and applies generally to extremely hazardous activities where the risks of injury are great even without negligence. Instances of such extrahazardous activities are blasting operations, collection of water or other materials that if released are apt to cause widespread damage, and the keeping of dangerous animals. In these situations, and others, if injury results to another, the liability is absolute, without regard to the fault principle.

Under this rule, if one chooses to keep a rattlesnake as a companion and it escapes and bites a neighbor, there is no need for the neighbor to show that the escape was due to fault or negligence; there is strict liability for the harm resulting from the escape of dangerous creatures. Similarly, when a building contractor uses dynamite, if as a result of the explosions the entire population of a nearby chicken farm dashes itself against the walls of the henhouse, the contractor must pay, on a strict liability theory.

The social philosophy of strict liability is supported by reasoning that the one engaging in the dangerous activities is best able to guard against injury to others, and best able to protect their financial interest by carrying appropriate insurance or some analogous device. Because he knows in advance of his potential liability, he is in a position to take steps to insure against it.

## WORKMEN'S COMPENSATION

Although the tort law is the most frequent tool for resolving disputes in general, in the field of industrial accidents another means of dealing with the accident problem has developed: the workmen's compensation statutes. These statutes establish a system of social insurance that pays compensation to victims of industrial accidents for injuries occurring in the course of employment. Payments for such injuries are financed by a contribution program participated in both by the employer and the employee, and thus all share to a degree the cost of such accidents. Generally, the rates that any employer must pay depend upon the past history of accidents in his particular business or his particular type of business. Because the employer sets the prices for his product at such a level that his costs of doing business—including his payments for workmen's compensation—will be recovered, the public as a whole ultimately bears the cost of industrial accidents.

The significant feature of this system of compensation is that recovery by a workman for his injury is in no way made dependent upon fault of any other person or lack of fault of his own. If it is shown that injury has been incurred in the course of employment, the worker will not have to bear the loss; it will be shifted to a degree to the employer and to the public using the employer's product or services.

# Chapter Three

---

# Standard of Care

We have examined the broad outline of what has been termed "the accident problem" in society, within the general confines of accidental injury, and determined that the problem is principally one of providing compensation for accident victims on a just basis.

We now begin our detailed study of the judicial process of fixing responsibility upon those more or less directly responsible for the injury on the basis of fault.

In injuries unintentionally caused, the ultimate issue is whether the conduct causing the injury is such that it justifies the imposition of the loss upon the actor; the resolution of this question is based upon whether the actor was negligent in his conduct. Negligent conduct may be defined as conduct that falls below the standard society expects that its members will attain to avoid injury to others. It is not the actor's thoughts, but his deeds alone that are scrutinized. Acts carried out with the utmost indifference or carelessness are not rendered negligent merely because of the egregious character of the act. If such acts are, objectively viewed, within the range tolerated by society, liability will not be imposed. Similarly, an act can be negligent though carried out with the greatest concern and worry on the part of the doer; if the conduct is defective, the actor will be held liable.

Given that a primary task of the law is to determine fault, how is this determination to be accomplished? In other words, what standard is to be used to determine whether certain conduct is or is not negligent? This section will consider the delineation of that standard.

Mr. Menlove built a haystack near the boundary of his farm and quite close to Mr. Vaughn's cottage. Over a period of several weeks, Menlove received repeated warnings that the temperature in the haystack was rising and that there was a substantial risk that the entire stack would burst into flames. He did not think, however, that there was any danger and failed to remove the stack or take any precaution. Mr. Menlove's optimistic view turned out to be sadly in error when the haystack did in fact burst into flame. The flames spread and completely consumed Mr. Vaughn's cottage. Vaughn filed suit, claiming that Menlove had failed to use the reasonable caution a prudent man would exercise under the circumstances prevailing. Mr. Menlove contended that he had acted in good faith and to the best of his judgment, and should not be responsible for the misfortune of not possessing the highest order of intelligence.

The court decided that Mr. Menlove was required by the law to act prudently, that a good faith decision would not absolve him from liability for imprudent conduct, and that Mr. Vaughn was entitled to recover from Mr. Menlove the value of his destroyed property [*Vaughn v. Menlove*, 3 Bing (N.C.) 468, 132 Eng. Rep. 490 (1837)].

## The Reasonable Man

Because society attaches great weight to a determination that conduct is or is not negligent, it is clear that as objective and fair a standard as possible must be established for the measurement of that conduct. Therefore, for purposes of measuring conduct, an imaginary man has been created by the common law and applied in the thousands upon thousands of contested cases that have come before the courts. This being is called "the reasonably prudent man." He has the imperfections of the race, to be sure. His judgment is not perfect; his foresight is limited; he has average courage and average caution. He does not stand out, but, equally important, he does not fall below the crowd in any of his attributes. *His hypothetical conduct is the standard against which all others' conduct is judged.* Conduct that does not reach that standard is negligent conduct; conduct that would be engaged in by a reasonably prudent man in a particular situation is nonnegligent conduct. If negligent conduct causes injury to another, the law requires the person guilty of such conduct to bear the financial losses suffered by the injured party. It is not enough that a person uses his own best judgment, as Mr. Menlove found; where the exercise of that judgment leads to injury to another, it must reach the level of the reasonable man.

Whether someone has violated the standard of the reasonable man in a particular case depends upon the circumstances existing at the time and place the questioned behavior occurred. The reasonable man is placed in the position of the doer, and in the doer's external environment. If it was raining at the relevant time, it is a reasonable man's behavior in the rain that affords the measure; if it was dark, his behavior in the dark. The standard does not require the blind to see or the deaf to hear, but only that persons behave in a reasonable way in relation to their environment.

The use of this standard falls within the province of the jury. In any matter reaching the courts, it will be the jury that considers the conduct of the defendant in the case and makes the final evaluation of that conduct when compared with that of the reasonable man. It is the jury that determines whether conduct is or is not negligent. *Negligence consists of a failure to act as a reasonably prudent man would act under the same or similar circumstances as faced by the defendant.* The jury will be told by the judge, in the judge's instructions, that it should consider whether the defendant's conduct was that of a reasonably prudent man. If the jury believes that it was, it will find no negligence; if the jury believes it was not, it will find negligence to exist.

The courts have analyzed many types of conduct in terms of whether it meets the reasonable man standard. Not infrequently, someone accused of negligence attempts to show that his conduct conformed to that of all others in similar situations, arguing that what he did was therefore not unreasonable. This argument has generally been unsuccessful. The reasoning is illustrated by a statement of a renowned jurist, Judge Learned Hand, in *The T. J. Hooper*, 60 F.2d 737 (2d Cir. 1932). In that decision, a tugboat in coastal waters was towing barges, which were sunk by a sudden storm. The owner of the barges sued the tugboat company, alleging that its failure to equip the tugs with radios led to failure to hear weather bureau reports warning of the storm. The tugboat company's answer was that it was the custom and practice of barge lines not to carry radios, and therefore its failure to do so did not constitute negligence. In holding the defendant tugboat owner liable, Judge Hand said:

... [I]n most cases reasonable prudence is in fact common prudence; but strictly it is never its measure; a whole calling may have unduly lagged in the adoption of new and available devices. It never may set its own tests, however persuasive be its usages. Courts must in the end say what is required; there are precautions so imperative that even their universal disregard will not excuse their omission.

Another question is: to what degree will knowledge of certain facts be held to be an attribute of the reasonable man, so that lack of knowledge on the part of a defendant becomes negligence. Clearly, a person will be charged with such knowledge as he actually possesses, without regard to whether that knowledge is part of the intellectual equipment of the imaginary reasonable man. If a man has knowledge of dangerous highway conditions, or a hole in the floor, he must take account of this knowledge in his conduct; he cannot with impunity say to himself that the prudent man would not know these facts, and therefore that they can be disregarded.

A further point should be noted. One of the things a man may know is his own ignorance, and this in itself may often be found to call for precautions against possible but unknown danger. Thus, one who finds himself in a strange dark hallway must take precautions against possible "obstructions to his passage and pitfalls to his feet." [Harper, F., and James, F., *The Law of Torts*, Vol. 2, 908, (Boston: Little, Brown & Company, 1956).]*

In commonplace affairs, the reasonable man standard readily suffices, for all society can be held to have certain skills, knowledge, intelligence, and physical prowess. But what of the specialist who fails to perform to the standard expected of one of his expertise, where that expertise is far beyond the level of the average man? The answer is clear: the specialist must reach at least the level expected of those practicing the specialty; like the ordinary man, he is held to the standards of the community, except that instead of the world at large, his is a community of specialists. This requirement is based upon a twofold premise. First, the professional man is in the business of selling his services, his knowledge, and his skill. People come to him because he has fostered the belief that he possesses the requisite skills, and it follows that he should be held to the possession of such skills in the event a person is injured in the course of his professional activities. Second is the direct application of the reasonable man standard. Inasmuch as it would be unreasonable for a layman to perform an appendectomy because of the risk of harm, such an operation becomes reasonable only if the actor possesses the skills and knowledge required for carrying out the operation with reasonable safety.

The need to evaluate professional conduct inheres in the medical accident or malpractice case, and there, as with other professional or specialized activities, a refined standard emerges. In such fields, special knowledge requires special responsibility. Formerly, and to a large extent today, the special knowledge required for a professional was said to be that prevailing in the geographic community in which he worked, and frequently this community would be narrowly defined, as the village, town, or city where the matters complained of occurred.

Thus what would be recognized as acceptable practice in one locality might not be true of another, for there all practitioners could be guilty of a lag in advancing their standards. This legal doctrine of judging conduct according to current practice in a local community is yielding to a number of social forces. The current standards of preparation of practitioners in most medical fields is clearly defined and the competencies expected are the same whether he is practicing in an isolated area or in a densely populated one. Statutory laws that require licensing to practice define conduct without regard for any area in the particular jurisdiction. National and state accrediting agencies exert a force in prescribing standards of performance against which the courts can view the conduct of the individual practitioner. All of these together with a more mobile

* Reprinted with permission of Little, Brown & Co.

population, ease of communication, and speedy means of transporting patients to well-equipped medical centers have served to minimize the importance of local practice in a local area.

## The Professional Practitioner

Although the hypothetical actions of the reasonably prudent man may be used as a means of measuring conduct, his actions provide only a guide and a measure that are by no means fixed. A person assumes several roles in the course of daily living; for each of these varied roles the standard of the reasonable man can be applied. The nurse as an ordinary citizen would be held to the conduct of a reasonable man in the driving of her car, in being a safe neighbor, in her ownership of property, and so on. When, however, a person offers her services as a professional nurse, the measure used is that of the specialist who is held to an entirely different standard of conduct because of those specialized knowledges and skills that enable her to practice her profession. It is her conduct as related to her practice and the reasonableness of this conduct in terms of the standards of her profession that is of concern.

The legal liability of the nurse is not a new development, nor has there in recent years been a radical shift of the basic framework of the law within which her practice falls. In fact, the fundamental legal doctrines of negligence and malpractice are the same in assessing the conduct of the nurse who burned the patient with a hot-water bottle as for the one who administered an intravenous injection of a drug without full knowledge of its action, or for the one who attempted to defibrillate a heart with knowledge only of the mechanics of the procedure.

Although there has been no change of legal doctrine, the advances of medical science have been accompanied by radically new developments in nursing practice which require careful legal evaluation. As the nurse assumes increased responsibility for complex acts requiring greater skill, she should be aware that the boundaries of reasonable conduct are shifting. Indeed, were a nurse to harm a patient today, she could well be held to a level of knowledge of medical science and medical practice unknown a generation ago.

Concomitant with increasingly complex nursing practice is the continual realignment of the functions of the professional nurse and the physician. While this has ever been the case, at this time boundaries of responsibility are shifting at a more rapid rate because of increased demands for health services, because of the far greater complexity of medical care, and because of a dearth of qualified practitioners on all levels to provide this care. It is significant that in a period of rapid transition, as is taking place, the identical procedure performed on a patient may be the practice of medicine when done by a physician or the practice of professional nursing when carried out by a nurse. Should harm come to the patient, it is easy to see that those who fall within this gray zone of responsibility are highly vulnerable for suit. In the event of legal action, questions would inevitably arise concerning the standard of conduct for the reasonably prudent practitioner of nursing. Within this standard, did the conduct under question fall within the scope of nursing practice? Did the nurse have both knowledge and skill necessary to perform the act? If she did not, should she have had it? What was her legal authority, from statutory or case law, for doing what she did?

We may turn first to those questions concerning the sphere and scope of nursing practice. The delineation of these boundaries is a *nursing* decision and one that requires a continuing examination of the nature of nursing, the needs of society, and the part the nurse will have in the delivery of health services, both today and tomorrow. Once the nursing profession has accepted a function, as one falling within the sphere of nursing, then each nurse who carries out that function must obtain the systematic instruction needed for her to acquire the necessary knowledge and skill to support her practice. In its analysis of the nature of nursing, a real danger lies in the profession's being swayed by the urgency of the situation and assuming tasks on the basis of expediency and then allowing them to fall into current practice. Such an informal means of extending the scope of nursing would leave the nurse with scant legal support if an injury should occur to the patient.

Where does the nursing profession turn for legal support enabling it to move with social and scientific change in extending the scope and sphere of nursing practice? Two legal sources are available: statutory law and common law.

In every American jurisdiction, the statute governing the practice of nursing defines professional nursing in broad general terms which permits the practice to advance into areas of increasing difficulty, provided it can be shown that the newly assumed nursing function is predicated upon the ability to draw upon a knowledge of physical, biological, and social sciences. Thus, at the same time that the general statutory definition permits an expanding role for the nurse, it is also limiting in another sense, for it requires more than proficiency in a skill and allows the practice of that skill only when it is supported by the necessary knowledge of underlying science. Society looks to the professional person to do safely those acts he undertakes to do and the limitation of this statutory definition of nursing is a sound legal safeguard.

Common law is essentially judge-made law. Many of the cases which follow throughout this text demonstrate the increasingly high level of responsibility to which the practitioner of nursing is being held by the courts today. It is through these decisions that the nursing profession can examine the view of the courts regarding the standards derived from statute or practice, or lack of them, that the nurse has to support her practice. At times, common law decisions are the first to interpret nursing practice in areas not specifically defined by statutory law. It then becomes the responsibility of the profession to examine this decision in terms of the expectations of society for the practitioner and the goals of the profession. If the profession decides that a particular decision points the way to nursing practice for the future, it may mean that the statute regulating the practice of nursing will need reconsideration.

As the nursing profession continues to delineate its place as a part of the health team, the legal foundation for its functioning must be redefined to support and move with change. Questions having legal implications for the shifting role of the nurse deserve repeated study: When the nurse extends the periphery of her practice, what are her legal safeguards? What statements made by the profession might serve as legal support for an evolving standard of the reasonable and prudent practitioner in the field of nursing? What is the function of statutory law in establishing the standard of the reasonable and prudent practitioner? Is there a legal as well as professional obligation for continuing education? If the law has lagged, how may this lag affect the delivery of safe nursing service to the public? In litigated cases in which the nurse is involved, under what circumstances do the courts view the role of the nurse as a limited one and rely heavily on the precedent of earlier years? In which cases does the court appear to depart from precedent and to define a new role in line with professional and social changes in our system?

The forces that converge to create the image of the reasonable practitioner of nursing are the demands of society, the nursing profession itself, scientific advances, and legal interpretation and enactment. It is conceivable that before the turn of the century, the accepted concept of the professional nurse will be one who is free of nonnursing activities, who is the clinical associate of the physician prepared to work directly with patients and to guide patient care given by other nurse members of the health team, to provide the kind and amount of nursing care when and where needed. If this occurs, it will be to this concept that the court will turn in applying, to the conduct of nurses, the standard of the reasonable professional man.

# NOTES

## (1) History of Negligence

The history and development of negligence are complex and fascinating. Professor John Wigmore, a renowned legal theorist and historian, described this process in a series of three articles in the *Harvard Law Review* in 1894.

The beginning point and the ending points of the analysis are indicated in the following passages from his work. The details are found in the articles themselves:

## Wigmore, J., *Responsibility for Tortious Acts: Its History,* 7 Harv. L. Rev. 42 (1894)*

> *Not infrequently do the records of the related laws serve as the sole resource, or the safest one, for a methodical explanation of dark and doubtful topics in the legal development of our own native system.*
>
> Brunner: *Deutsche Rechtsgeschichte*, i. 2.

"No conception can be understood except through its history," says the Positivist philosopher; and of no legal conception in Anglo-American law is this more true than of the notion of Responsibility for Tortious Acts. By this phrase is indicated that circumstance or group of circumstances attending the initiation and eventuation of an acknowledged harmful result, which induces us to make one person rather than another (or than no one at all) civilly amenable to the law as the source of the harmful result (and independently of whether this person can show some recognized justification for the harm); and it is this notion whose history we find it possible to trace back in a continuous development in our Germanic law, without a break, for at least two thousand years.

To get a starting-point, let us look back from present principles. The law to-day, so far as we are entitled to take it as standing on a rational basis, distinguishes classes of cases which may be roughly generalized for present purposes as follows: (1) Cases where the source of harm is pure misadventure, as where a customer is handling a supposed unloaded gun in a gun-store, and it goes off and injures the clerk; (2) Cases where no design to injure exists, but a culpable want of care is found; (3) Cases where no design to injure exists, and yet no inquiry into the actor's carefulness is allowed,—in other words, where he does the specific harm-initiating act "at his peril," as where he fires a gun in the street, or cuts grass or sells goods which prove to be those of another; (4) Cases where actual design to produce the harm exists. Now, the thing to be noted is that the primitive Germanic law knew nothing of these refinements; it made no inquiry into negligence, and it raised no issue as to the presence or absence of a design or intent; it did not even distinguish, in its earlier phases, between accidental and intentional injuries. The distinctions of to-day stand for an attempt (as yet more or less incomplete) as a rationalized adjustment of legal rules to considerations of fairness and social policy. But the indiscriminate liability of primitive times stands for an instinctive impulse, guided by superstition, to visit with vengeance the visible source, whatever it be,—human or animal, witting or unwitting,—of the evil result. Both these extremes are fairly clear; it is the transition from one notion to the other which forms the interesting and complex process.

## (2) Reasonable Man Concept as It Applies to Children

Although the reasonable man standard is acceptable where adults are concerned, it is clearly inappropriate if applied to children. The standard of conduct applied in such cases is, therefore, the conduct of a child with the experience and judgment to be expected of one of the age concerned. Such a standard may cause losses from an injury to fall upon a person harmed through childish activities, where the loss would have been shifted had the injury been caused by an adult.

The leading case discussing the standards applicable to children is *Charbonneau v. MacRury*, 84 N.H. 501, 153 Atl. 457 (1931). In that case, a seventeen-year-old boy had struck and killed an infant while driving his father's car. The jury was charged that the defendant's conduct "should be judged according to the average conduct of persons of his age and experience," and returned a verdict for the defendant. In approving the instruction, the court said:

It is error, however, to assume that the law requires reasonable care of adults and not of minors, or applies different measures to the primary and contributory faults of the latter. The law of negligence has for its foundation the rule of reasonable conduct. The general rule is more fully stated as reasonable care under all the circumstances of the particular case. . . . This is the true test or measure in all cases. In applying this rule to the conduct of adults recourse is had to a mythical person called the "standard man" with whose conduct that of the actor is to be compared, namely, the average prudent person placed in his position. . . . While this standard is external . . . it must necessarily be applied to the actor in the particular situation disclosed by the evidence. It is for the jury to say whether such standard person put in his place, possessed of the same knowledge and means of knowledge that he had of the surrounding circumstances would or might have done as he did. The knowledge which the actor had, or which he would have had if he had used his faculties, are facts in the light of which he is bound to act as the average prudent person would have acted in his situation. . . . The jury bring to bear their experience in the affairs of life and their knowledge of the motives that govern human action and of the conduct of reasonable prudent men. . . . In other words, possessed of a yardstick with which the law presumes them to be familiar, wholly external to the subject to be surveyed, the jury apply it to the conduct of the party in evidence and determine whether it measures up to the standard. . . . Such is the rule of reasonable conduct and the method of its application to the normal person whether he is charged with primary fault . . . or with contributory negligence. . . . How and why does the rule, or its application, differ if the actor is a minor? And is there anything in the basis for such difference that calls for any distinction between the minor's primary and his contributory fault?

We are told that "the personification of a standard person helps us realize that the actor's conduct is to be compared with that of a human being with all of the human failings." 41 Harv. L. Rev. 9. But such standard person is the average prudent adult. In striking this average the law takes into account the failings only of those who have come to maturity. A minor, in the absence of evidence to the contrary, is universally considered to be lacking in judgment. His normal condition is one of recognized incompetency. . . . He is a "human being" subject not only to the ordinary "human failings" but also to those normally incident to immaturity. It is a matter of common knowledge that the normal minor not only lacks the adult's knowledge of the probable consequences of his acts or omissions but is wanting in capacity to make effective use of such knowledge as he has. His age is a factor in so far as it is a mark of capacity. 37 Yale L.J. 618. But other qualities which are ordinarily the product of experience, using the term in its broader sense as inclusive of education and of the understanding that comes from practice and opportunity for observation, are important considerations in determining his ability both to appreciate the dangerous character of his conduct and to avoid its consequences. A danger may be concealed by the obscurity of intelligence due to immaturity as well as by its own inherent obscurity. . . .

It is for these reasons that the law recognizes that indulgence must be shown the minor in appraising the character of his conduct. This is accomplished however through no arbitrary exception to the general rule of reasonable care under all the circumstances. As we have said this is always the test. But what is reasonable when the actor is a minor? Manifestly the adult test of the standard man cannot be applied in disregard of the actor's youth and inexperience. Either a new standard denoting the average person of the minor's age and development must be taken as the yard-stick, or else allowance must be made for the minor's stage of development as one of the circumstances incident to the application of the general rule of reasonable care. As a practical matter it is not important which course is pursued.

Is this a reasonable result? Even if it could be shown that the majority of seventeen-year-olds were careless drivers, why should the court permit this factor to protect a seventeen-year-old defendant? Does the availability of insurance for minors bear upon the question?

## (3) Negligence Not a State of Mind

Negligence is sometimes said to consist of the "lack of due care." This implies that a person who meticulously and knowingly adopts a course of conduct would not be liable for injury caused by that conduct even though the conduct was patently stupid. This line of reasoning has been rejected by the advocates of an objective standard.

**Edgerton, H., *Negligence, Inadvertence and Indifference: The Relation of Mental States to Negligence*, 39 Harv. L. Rev. 849 (1926)** *

THE CONDUCT THEORY

. . . Negligence neither is nor involves ("presupposes") either indifference, or inadvertence, or any other mental characteristic, quality, state, or process. Negligence is unreasonably dangerous conduct—i.e., conduct abnormally likely to cause harm. Freedom from negligence (commonly called "due care") does not require care, or any other mental phenomenon, but requires only that one's conduct be reasonably safe—as little likely to cause harm as the conduct of a normal person would be. . . .

Is the question whether negligence is conduct or a state of mind a "matter of indifference"? Is "the practical result . . . the same"? It is, in the sense and to the extent that theories about negligence do not decide cases; that courts and juries really decide on the basis of an intuitive feeling that a defendant ought, or ought not, to be held. This is partly true, but it is not wholly true. If, as many courts and writers say, negligence involves or "presupposes" indifference or inadvertence, this means that "that anxious consideration of consequences which is called care" precludes negligence. If, as some eminent authors say, negligence *is* "a mental attitude of undue indifference," this means not only that anxious consideration precludes negligence, but also that indifference conclusively proves negligence. On the other hand, the proposition that negligence is conduct means that there is negligence if there are unreasonably dangerous motions, and not otherwise; consequently, that no particular mental shortcoming proves negligence or is necessary to negligence, and no particular mental attainment precludes negligence. Non-negligent conduct, and consequent freedom from liability, may coexist with a mental state that is dangerous, as involving inadvertence, lack of normal anxiety to avoid harm, or any other unsafe mental fact; negligent conduct, and consequent liability, may coexist with normal and proper advertence and anxiety. . . .

Probably no phrases about negligence are more ambiguous than the orthodox and apparently fundamental ones in which words like "care" occur. To take a current example of a formula with which every lawyer is familiar: "Negligence, generally speaking, means failure to exercise reasonable care. . . ." Whatever this means to the lawyer or judge, the meaning conveyed to a juryman must frequently be somewhat like the meaning given by the dictionaries. "Care" is defined by the Century Dictionary as "concern; solicitude; anxiety; . . . attention or heed, with a view to safety or protection." It follows that if one is "talking English, not law," the conventional definition of negligence as the antithesis of due care demands not reasonably safe conduct, but a reasonably attentive or anxious mind. Confronted with such a definition (unless it is effectively explained away), the intelligent juryman will gather either that negligence is, or that it necessarily involves, relative indifference or relative inattention; a failure to feel as anxious or to focus attention as closely as one should. He will accordingly refuse to find negligence unless he finds such a state of mind; and if he finds such a state of mind, he may, without more, find negligence. . . .

## (4) The Hasty and the Awkward Man

The renowned jurist Oliver Wendell Holmes, Jr., describes the reasonable man in this famous passage:

### Holmes, O. W., Jr., *The Common Law*, 108 (Boston: Little, Brown & Co., 1881)

The standards of the law are standards of general application. The law takes no account of the infinite varieties of temperament, intellect, and education which make the internal character of a given act so different in different men. It does not attempt to see men as God sees them, for more than one sufficient reason. In the first place, the impossibility of nicely measuring a man's powers and limitations is far clearer than that of ascertaining his knowledge of law, which has been thought to account for what is called the presumption that every man knows the law. But a more satisfactory explanation is, that, when men live in society, a certain average of conduct, a sacrifice of individual peculiarities going beyond a certain point, is necessary to the general welfare. If, for instance, a man is born hasty and awkward, is always having accidents and hurting himself or his neighbors, no doubt his congenital defects will be allowed for in the courts of Heaven, but his slips are no less troublesome to his neighbors than if they sprang from guilty neglect. His neighbors accordingly require him, at his proper peril, to come up to their standard, and the courts which they establish decline to take his personal equation into account.

The result of this view is that the "hasty and awkward" man is held to a standard that he is psychologically unable to meet. Research has shown that a relatively small percentage of the population is involved in a high proportion of accidents. See James, F. and Dickinson, J., *Accident Proneness and Accident Law*, 63 Harv. L. Rev. 769 (1950). Is it not just as artificial to hold such persons to a reasonable man standard as it is to hold children to such a standard? Should the law take such characteristics into account? If not, why not?

Is the nursing profession, or any other profession, under an obligation to exclude accident-prone persons, on the theory that they cannot possess the requisite skills to reach the level of practice prevalent in the community? What conflicting policies bear upon such a proposition?

## (5) Jury Instructions

In most situations the application of the reasonable man standard will be a matter in which different views could legitimately be taken. Therefore, in most litigated cases, the jury, rather than the judge, will decide whether the evidence presented to it shows that the reasonable man standard was met. The standard is, like other matters of law, described by the judge in his instructions. By the instructions, the jury is told what standard to apply, and thus the reasonable man standard reflects a choice and a compromise between a completely scientific standard and a completely arbitrary, *ad hoc*, one. This distinction is explained in the following article.

### Green, L., *The Negligence Issue*, 37 Yale L.J. 1029–33 (1928) *

Conceivably, a judge might follow one of two radically opposite methods. He might make use of very accurate and precise rules, expressed in terms of conduct and

* Reprinted by permission of the Yale Law Journal Company and Fred B. Rothman & Company from *The Yale Law Journal*, Vol. 37, p. 1033.

qualities of personality by which the jury might measure the particular conduct of the person in question. For instance, he might say: "Gentlemen, if you find that defendant was possessed of an intelligence quotient of more than 90, and average reaction time to visual and auditory stimuli of .22 sec. and .2 sec., respectively, and a score of over 70 in mechanical abilities, and a grade of not less than C in caution and self control, and that he failed to conduct himself in accordance with these standards in the case before you, then you will find for the plaintiff." Such instructions would be varied to suit the case. No doubt the judge would do some such thing if psychology could supply the law with dependable measurements and standards. On the other hand, the judge might merely say to the jury: "Gentlemen, this is your problem. You have heard the evidence. Give us your judgment." Either method might serve as well as the method which is now employed. But judges have employed neither; the one is clearly impossible, the other seems too dangerous. They have been more careful. Judges feel that laymen not only need assistance in handling these problems, but they must be kept within bounds. They cannot be permitted to roam at will nor to feel that they have an unlimited power in reaching judgment. Thus, judges have developed a technique of instructing juries as to the considerations (law) which shall guide them in their judgment. It is here, therefore, that there is a necessity for the ritualistic formula mentioned in the beginning. But in employing this ritual a judge is faced with two difficulties. In the first place, in order not to pass judgment himself on the very person and conduct involved in litigation, and thereby render the jury's function pointless, he must raise conduct to terms of the law's abstractions: "care," "prudence," "foreseeability," "reasonableness," and the like. But having converted the problem into such terms, he must then make these high abstractions intelligible to the jury. And to do this, judges attempt to objectify these abstractions. It was in this predicament that the "man of ordinary prudence" was conceived as a standard of conduct. He looks like a real fellow, the model of mankind. He is generally so considered. He is called the "objective" as opposed to the "subjective" standard. But all of this is due to vivid language. He is a mere figure of speech.

## (6a) Diagnosis as a Nursing Function

The ability for critical thinking and to make decisions, either deliberately or with great speed, has ever been a part of the standard of conduct of the practitioner of professional nursing. This function shifts in complexity with scientific advancement in health care, for to do critical thinking and take appropriate action the nurse must be able to draw from the biological and physical sciences that are continually feeding new knowledge into the field of medical science. The function has long been recognized as an indisputable part of nursing practice, but selection of the proper word to describe the function is a controversial issue.

Hammond and Kelly (Clinical Inference in Nursing, *Nurs. Res.*, 15:23, 1966), in their research on clinical inference in nursing, saw the inferential or diagnostic task as central to all of nursing practice. They noted that since the time of Florence Nightingale, emphasis had been placed not only on the need to observe but also on how to observe. As a part of this process, early recognition was given to the complexity of data available to the nurse to use in making judgments about the state or condition of the patient. For years the observational task of the nurse consisted of three activities, namely, observing, recording, and reporting. More recently, the observational function is now conceived to be a process that includes three specific operations: observation—recognition of signs and symptoms presented by the patient, inference—making the judgment about the state of the patient and/or nursing needs of the patient, and decision making—determining the action to be taken that will be of optimal benefit to the patient. Although all three tasks can best be described as cognitive functions, the second and third are clearly intellectual in character.

In reporting this research, the writers saw that a distinction must be made between the functions and responsibilities of the nurse as a diagnostician and the physician as a diagnostician. Just as the "keystone of modern medicine is etiological diagnosis and therapy, that is, the determination of the cause of the disease and its eradication through specifics," the keystone of modern nursing is the determination of a symptom and its alleviation. The actions taken by the nurse are not to be underestimated for they may have serious consequences for the patient; in fact, every inference made by a nurse involves a risk of error.

A further significant finding in their research was that one characteristic of the inferential task of the nurse is that the inference, decision, and action must, at times, take place in a span of a few minutes or less. Meltzer, co-director of the Coronary Care Unit of the Presbyterian Hospital in Philadelphia (*Mod. Hosp.*, 104:102, 1966), discusses this type of decision making of the nurse in caring for patients in the coronary units:

Because of the remarkably short time between the onset of the arrhythmias and death, it is absolutely essential that these abnormal rhythms be recognized and immediately planned action started, if lives are going to be saved. The death rate from arrhythmias will not be reduced appreciably if, with each alarm situation, the nurse can do no more than signal a physician, who will have to first ascertain the problem and then start treatment thereafter. . . . If a nurse is capable of ascertaining a potentially fatal arrhythmia, we believe this would be of only academic interest unless she is also able to terminate the arrhythmia, in the event that the physician has not arrived in the critical two minutes after the onset.

In summarizing the study Dr. Meltzer said: "The nurses have been completely able to fulfill the role we anticipated and have saved at least five lives by themselves, with the use of countershock or pacemakers."

Thus, Hammond and Kelly place the inferential or diagnostic task of the nurse well within the boundaries of nursing practice.

In line with the findings of research as reported above, the act of diagnosis, in general, is a mental process whereby one or more persons appraise a situation and make a decision based on their judgment, that may or may not lead to action. Viewed within this context, the acts of diagnosis may fall within a spectrum ranging from the simple to the complex. But does this mean that the act of diagnosis applies only to the practice of medicine? Clearly not; lawyers, engineers, and numerous other professional people diagnose just as do physicians and nurses. A skilled engineer is sent to examine a bridge in a flooded area. His trained powers of observation aid him in assessing the damage; his knowledge of engineering tells him the meaning of his observation, and then, based on his judgment, he makes a decision that the bridge may or may not be used with safety. Has he made a diagnosis?

In the medical field there would be many areas of diagnosis unique to nursing; others would clearly fall within the province of the physician. The role of the nurse as a diagnostician is not made clear by the simple statement of fact, however, for there is a real dichotomy in the use of this term in statutory law and in case law, as it applies to the practice of medicine and of nursing. A common exclusion clause in statutory law for the licensing of nurses is to prohibit the nurse from diagnosing or from the prescription of therapeutic or corrective measures, whereas in court decisions such as that of *Cooper v. National Motor Bearing Co., infra*, p. 109, the nurse was held negligent because she had failed to diagnose.

Rather than await settlement of this issue by the courts, the nursing and medical professions should recognize this debatable area of practice and move toward its clarification, in the best interest of the society being served.

## (6b) Legal View of Diagnosis as a Nursing Function

The Nursing Practice Act bars a nurse from making "acts of diagnosis," but the Act does not give any definition of the term "diagnosis," any guidelines as to its interpretation, or any qualification or limitations on the prohibition.

As we saw in the preceding Note it is exceedingly difficult to define the term in such a way that would exclude many everyday activities of nurses, particularly in areas of nursing care involving a high degree of training and specialization. Some of the problems that arise from the divergence between today's practice and the statutory definition are exposed and discussed in this Note. After studying the Note, the reader should consider whether she can accept or improve upon the definition approved by the authors of the Note, i.e., diagnosis is "the utilization of intelligence to interpret known facts, and acting upon the decision reached from this interpretation."

Among the questions that should be dealt with are whether the definition distinguishes medical and nursing practice, whether any such distinction is desirable, whether "known facts" and "intelligence" are the only factors which enter into a nursing judgment, and whether any additional factors should be introduced into the definition.

### Acts of Diagnosis by Nurses and the Colorado Professional Nursing Practice Act, 45 Denver L.J. 467 (1968)*

*The law hath not been dead, though it hath slept.*

William Shakespeare

INTRODUCTION

Patients returning from cardiac surgery in Denver's Saint Luke's Hospital are placed in a coronary intensive care unit. Also placed in the unit are patients with serious rhythm disturbances. Saint Luke's Hospital has claimed that the intensive care unit will reduce the mortality from heart failure threatening these patients by 50 percent. The success of the unit owes much to the skill of the specially trained nurses who monitor the heartbeat of each patient, often without a doctor's supervision. The unit will undoubtedly continue to be a valuable addition to Colorado's medical services, until a nurse in the unit is convicted of violating the Colorado Professional Nursing Practice Act. The charge would be that the nurse made an act of diagnosis.

The Nursing Practice Act states that the "practice of professional nursing . . . shall not be deemed to include acts of diagnosis or prescription of therapeutic or corrective measures." The question to be discussed in this Note is the meaning of "acts of diagnosis." To provide a factual focus, the authors interviewed and observed nurses in the city of Denver who have been given broad medical responsibility. In addition, documents were received from Saint Luke's Hospital outlining the duties of nurses in intensive care units.

The written standing orders of Saint Luke's intensive care unit will be used as a factual point of reference for the discussion of diagnosis. It is important to note that doctors have not been stationed in the unit on a full time basis. The unit is so designed that the nurse on duty will continuously monitor the heartbeat and general condition of the patient. If the nurse judges that the patient is having a cardiac arrest she will initiate resuscitative measures. If there is an arrest, the nurse is not to wait for a doctor's directions.

The nurses in the intensive care unit of Saint Luke's Hospital have the following standing orders:

*Emergency :* Respond promptly to alarm by going to bedside.

Check pulse (carotid or femoral) as well as cardioscope.

* Permission to reprint the following article written by Charles D. Burg, Thomas S. Brand, Mark C. Hinman, and G. G. Alan Vaughn has been obtained from the *Denver Law Journal,* University of Denver (Colorado Seminary), College of Law. This article appeared in Volume 45, Issue Number 3 of the *Denver Law Journal.* Copyright 1968 by the *Denver Law Journal,* University of Denver (Colorado Seminary), College of Law.

Be sure you aren't dealing with a false alarm.

Patient in true arrest (asystole or ventricular fibrillation) will be unconscious.

If true emergency:

    Call for help

    Start ventilating patient

    Start external cardiac compression

If *ventricular fibrillation* use defibrillator if no physician is present.

If *cardiac standstill* give 1cc 1:1000 Epinephrine intravenously (in the tube of the running I.V. solution) continuing external cardiac compression and ventilation.

Viewed in one light, the question of whether nurses in the intensive care unit may be violating the statutory prohibition of diagnosis is academic. None of the doctors or nurses interviewed were aware of any prosecution of a nurse for diagnosing. However, interviews did reveal an uncertainty about the meaning of the law. Uneasiness arose when a nursing procedure which appeared to be medically proper was analyzed in light of the statute. Several doctors complained that this uncertainty hobbled the planning of new medical programs designed to relieve overburdened doctors by giving more responsibility to nurses. Therefore, an inquiry into the meaning of diagnosis is far from academic if uncertainty about the diagnosis prohibition is retarding new medical programs for the citizens of Colorado.

## I. STATUTORY REGULATION OF WHAT A NURSE CAN DO

Colorado is not the only state which prohibits nurses from making acts of diagnosis; nineteen other states have similar provisions. Furthermore, the prohibition of diagnosis is not an archaic statutory provision; all of the states having the provision enacted them after 1947. The prohibition is usually added as a caveat to the statutory definition of the practice of professional nursing.

Most states have a definition of the practice of professional nursing similar to the Colorado provision, which reads:

The "practice of professional nursing" shall mean the performance for compensation of any act in the observation or care of the ill, injured, or infirm or in the maintenance of health or preservation of illness of others or in the supervision and teaching of other personnel or the administration of medicines and treatments as prescribed by a person licensed to practice medicine or dentistry in this state, requiring substantial specialized judgment and skill and based on knowledge and application of the principles of biological, physical and social sciences.

The Colorado statute then adds:

The foregoing shall not be deemed to include acts of diagnosis or prescription of therapeutic or corrective measures.

The question of whether the acts of nurses in the coronary intensive care units constitute acts of diagnosis could be answered if there were a judicial construction of the prohibition by the Colorado Supreme Court. However, the Colorado court has not been called upon to explain the statute's prohibition. The courts of the 19 other states prohibiting diagnosis are also silent.

## II. THE VARIED MEANINGS OF DIAGNOSIS

Attempts to understand the prohibition are not completely frustrated because the word "diagnosis" as it appears in other Colorado statutes has been defined both by statute and judicial construction. Colorado chiropodists are allowed to diagnose ailments of the human toe, foot, and leg and the statute allowing diagnosis says, "Diagnosis shall be held to mean ascertaining a disease or ailment by its symptoms."

In *Hurley* v. *People* the Colorado Supreme Court held that a man who was conducting a school for healing was not guilty of the unauthorized practice of medicine. Although he discussed disease in general terms, he made no examination of the ailments of any individual. The court said, "Clearly, as we conceive, the first and primary concern of the medical practitioner is to ascertain what afflicts his ailing patient—to make diagnosis; he then determines what will remedy the ills of the sufferer, which he proceeds to administer."

If the Colorado statutory and judicial definition of diagnosis is used—that it is the ascertaining of a disease or ailment by its symptoms—then a strong argument can be made that nurses in the intensive care unit are not diagnosing. Under the statute, diagnosis would be the determination of the disease based upon an evaluation of symptoms. Diagnosis would be the selection of one disease from a possibility of diseases suggested by the symptoms. On the other hand, diagnosis would not be a judgment of whether a symptom is present or a judgment of the seriousness of the symptom. When the nurse judges that the patient exhibits ventricular fibrillation she is merely observing a symptom, not diagnosing the disease suggested. In determining that the patient is suffering a true cardiac arrest she is exercising judgment as to the seriousness of the symptom, but she is not ascertaining the nature of the disease.

It also can be argued that the diagnosis of the patient has already been made when the doctor assigns the patient to the intensive care unit. The doctor has determined that the patient is suffering from a particular heart disease and that the medication called for in the nurse's standing order is always appropriate to ease the symptoms the patient is likely to exhibit. The nurse's responsibility is not to determine the particular disease nor is she called upon to decide what medication will ease the symptoms. Her responsibility is to judge the gravity of the symptom and to act under the direction of her standing orders.

However, this argument in favor of the legality of nursing duties in the intensive care unit seems to be rebutted by a 1963 letter from the Colorado Attorney General to the Colorado State Board of Nursing:

> In reply to your inquiry as to whether professional nurses may legally make a tentative diagnosis and then use a standing order signed by a doctor in the treatment of the particular condition involved, I wish to advise that acts of diagnosis are expressly excluded from the definition of the practice of professional nursing as set forth in C.R.S. '53 (1960 Perm. Supp.), 97-2-2(1). As we construe this section, a professional nurse is not authorized under the law, as part of the practice of professional nursing, to make a diagnosis.
>
> Diagnosis is recognition of a disease from its symptoms. [case cited from California] "Diagnosis means a summary of symptoms with the conclusions arrived at therefrom; determination of the distinctive nature of disease." [Minnesota case cited] A nurse is not permitted to make a diagnosis, tentative or otherwise.
>
> In answer to your second question as to whether a nurse following this procedure would be practicing medicine, C.R.S. 1953, 91-1-6(1)(a), includes "diagnosis" in the term

"practice of medicine." It would appear, therefore, that a nurse who made a tentative diagnosis of a certain condition would be practicing medicine.

Unfortunately, the letter provides no factual focus whereby one could distinguish between a nurse's judgment of symptoms and the act of making "a tentative diagnosis of a certain condition." The effect of the letter is not to clarify the distinction between proper nursing judgments and acts of diagnosis but to warn nurses that if they fail to make the right distinction they are subject to the charge of practicing medicine.

A review of decisions by other state courts reveals two different interpretations of the term diagnosis. Like the Colorado Supreme Court, other courts have had no difficulty in arriving at a definition of diagnosis. Almost all courts would agree that diagnosis is the determination of a disease from its symptoms. Confusion arises when the court applies the definition to the fact situation. According to the rationale of some courts, diagnosis only takes place when the nurse attempts to determine the particular disease. The nurse is properly allowed the responsibility of judging the gravity of symptoms without engaging in diagnosis. In opposition to this view are cases which hold that when a nurse evaluates a symptom and judges that no serious disease is indicated, she is making an act of diagnosis.

The rationale of the first case cited in the Attorney General's letter would seem to give the nurse wide discretion in judging symptoms. In *Maranville v. State Board of Equalization* the court commented that a lay technician who made x-ray pictures and analyzed their meaning in reports to doctors and dentists was not making acts of diagnosis. The court said, "He made no diagnoses from the radiographs. But he did advise the professional men of his conclusions of conditions of anatomies as they appeared to him in the pictures. He 'interpreted light shadows'." Although one would like to know more facts about the "conclusions of conditions of anatomies," the court in this case allowed the technician wide discretion in evaluating conditions without judging him guilty of diagnosing. It would seem that this court would allow a nurse similar discretion in evaluating symptoms as long as she does not attempt to determine the disease suggested by the symptoms.

Contrary to the reasoning of this case is *People v. Willis* in which an unlicensed chiropractor was convicted of treating the sick without being licensed by the state. The chiropractor defended on the ground that the chiropractic science does not recognize disease and hence no chiropractor could make a diagnosis. The California court rejected this argument by saying:

Indeed, it is difficult to conceive of any one trying to restore to a normal condition a person who is abnormal without a prior investigation and determination, in a general way at least, of the character of the abnormality. Manifestly, there are no fixed limits to a diagnosis. It may not amount to a scientific classification of the ailment, but it may go no further than an observation of the most obstrusive symptoms, and may be accurate or inaccurate, and yet be within the contemplation of the statute. It seems like an unjust aspersion on the character and intelligence of this respectable body of practitioners to intimate that they attempt to restore "the normal activity of the tissues" without any inquiry or investigation as to what tissues are affected and in what manner their activity may be abnormal.

This case indicates the problem of using the word "diagnose" in a variety of statutes designed to correct different abuses. Thus, courts may be tempted to adopt a broad definition of the word in a statute such as the Colorado statute which prohibits an unlicensed person to hold himself out "as being able to diagnose, treat, prescribe for, palliate or prevent any human disease. . . ." On the other hand, public policy may be better served by a strict definition of the word diagnosis in the Professional Nursing Practice Act.

Another example of a broad judicial definition of diagnosis is contained in *Cooper v. National Motor Bearing Co*. A nurse employed by the company treated a puncture wound in an employee's forehead caused by another employee who let a piece of metal slip from his hand. The nurse swabbed the wound with an antiseptic and put a bandage on it. The employee saw the nurse the next two days and she applied more medication but did not probe the wound.

The nurse worked under standing orders signed by a doctor who would accept patients injured beyond the scope of the nurse's practice. The employees had to see the nurse first and could only see the doctor upon the nurse's authorization. According to her testimony, it was her duty to refer any condition or injury she was not familiar with, or not sure about, to the doctor for diagnosis.

The employee's wound healed except for a small red mark. After two or three months the redness began to spread and started to become puffy. However, the nurse waited 10 months before referring the employee to the doctor. The injury was diagnosed as skin cancer and skin grafts were required to cure it.

The court affirmed a judgment that the nurse was negligent and said that evidence was sufficient to show that the nurse did not properly probe the wound for foreign matter, and that she unreasonably delayed in referring the employee to the doctor, despite indications that the wound was not properly healing.

The court then concluded that a nurse in evaluating the seriousness of a symptom is making an act of diagnosis:

> A nurse in order to administer first aid properly and effectively must make a sufficient diagnosis to enable her to apply the appropriate remedy. Usually she receives some history of the accident or illness from the patient, inspects a wound, and bases her choice of treatment on the deductions thus made. She has been trained, but to a lesser degree than a physician, in the recognition of the symptoms of diseases and injuries. She should be able to diagnose, according to appellant nurse's own testimony herein, sufficiently to know whether it is a condition within her authority to treat as a first aid case or whether it bears danger signs that should warn her to send the patient to a physician.

The reasoning of the *Cooper* case is persuasive because the nurse, in judging the gravity of symptoms, must base her judgment upon the seriousness of the possible diseases suggested by the symptoms. Her analysis of the patient's complaint duplicates in a less sophisticated degree the analysis of the doctor. Of course, the nurse's treatment of the patient differs from the doctor's in that she cannot prescribe the medicines that the doctor can. In looking at the facts of the *Cooper* case, one can ask whether the diagnosis dividing line can be drawn at the point where the nurse treats the patient. Did the nurse diagnose when she applied the antiseptic? The answer should be no, because the one important action by the nurse was her decision that no doctor was needed. Even if she had applied no medication, her decision that a doctor was not needed would be the factor that determined the patient's future medical care. Thus, a nurse may be guilty of making an act of diagnosis when she decides that no serious disease or symptom is indicated. Or, the nurse in the intensive care unit may be making a diagnosis when she determines that there is no false alarm and that the standing order should be executed. It is this decision that duplicates the decision a doctor would make in a similar situation.

The uncertainty surrounding diagnosis is recognized by professional nursing associations and authorities in this field of medical care. Their approach to the problem is keyed to the actual day-to-day practice of nursing, which recognizes the fact that nurses must observe symptoms and conditions and act on their observations. They define diagnosis as the utilization of intelligence to interpret known facts, and acting upon the decision reached from this interpretation. The differentiation of a "doctor's diagnosis" and a "nursing diagnosis" is based on the courses of action open to each profession after the decision from the observation is made. Nurses cannot prescribe therapeutic measures or positive treatment; this is the sole function of the doctor. However, the nurse can act to avoid further complication or aggravation of the patient's condition based on her observation of the symptoms present. It should be noted here that most of these authorities believe the emergency exception to the diagnosis prohibition allows the nurse to do all she deems necessary and proper, including that which is normally only action allowed a doctor.

The observation by the authors of nursing practices in Denver revealed that the above "professional" definition of diagnosis was the standard used between doctors and nurses. But, to reiterate, the actual practice of nursing under this definition does not correspond to the law of the State of Colorado.

Ironically, an admission that nurses make some type of diagnosis was also made in a paper entitled *Saint Luke's Hospital—Legal Aspects of Coronary Care*. The paper approvingly quoted a 1965 statement by the Cardiac Nurse Consultant of the Colorado Department of Public Health:

1. It would appear that defibrillation may fall in the same category as closed chest cardiac massage inasmuch as they both involve a potential diagnosis. However, in an emergency a nurse may be expected to make a diagnosis. Furthermore, if the medical staff of any institution gives written consent and it is accepted as part of the hospital routine, I would feel that the nurse is protected.
2. With the latest monitoring equipment and with proper teaching, a nurse can identify on the cardioscope the particular pattern which indicates ventricular fibrillation.
3. Experimentation being carried out today in specified intensive units for coronary care indicate that *immediate* application of emergency procedures, when necessary, has resulted in reversing the pattern of death from ventricular fibrillation.

The admission that the intensive care nurse will make a "potential diagnosis" is not the only point of interest in the statement; the defense of nursing conduct is hinged on the emergency exception. The major problem with this defense is that the statutory prohibition against the unlicensed practice of medicine limits the emergency exception to the "gratuitous rendering of services in cases of emergency." Since the intensive care ward nurse is a salaried employee of the hospital, the probability of convincing a court to apply the exception to her is almost nil. The inescapable conclusion is that this defense is not available in this situation.

Furthermore, the treatment of a patient in the intensive care unit is at best a planned emergency because the only unforeseen element is the time of the cardiac arrest. The person to be stricken by the emergency, the place of the emergency, and the nature of the emergency have all been anticipated and prepared for. The plan of the intensive care unit is that when the patient is stricken a nurse will initiate resuscitative measures. It is anticipated that no doctor will be in the unit to make the initial decisions.

The final question about the intensive care unit is the legality of standing orders. As the authors of *Nursing Practice and the Law* indicate in the following passage, the problem is based upon an interpretation of the meaning of diagnosis:

Great confusion prevails as to the validity of standing orders. In effect, standing orders presume to constitute medical direction for the execution of medical acts in the physician's absence. To the extent that they constitute instructions for cases *already diagnosed*, such orders are valid. Although no specific statute or judicial decision may be cited, it would appear that such standing orders should be signed by the attending physician.

To the extent that standing orders provide positive measures for cases to *be* diagnosed, such orders are invalid. A physician may not delegate the authority to diagnose, to treat or to prescribe. A standing order for treatment of a headache or a cold is illegal, since it presupposes a prescription based upon a diagnosis.

It appears that there are three uncertainties about the legality of intensive care units in Colorado: whether the nurse is making a diagnosis, whether the emergency exception applies, and whether standing orders are legal. The Colorado authorities and the judicial authorities of other states give no reassuring answer to ease these uncertainties.

### III. OBSERVATION OF DECISIONS MADE BY DENVER NURSES

One can hope that questions about the legality of intensive care units are academic. However, the observations by the authors of this Note revealed that the same charge of making acts of diagnosis could be leveled against the activities of other nurses in Denver.

Time was spent with two nurses from the Visiting Nurse Service of the City of Denver. Nurses in this organization visit families and individuals who have medical problems yet who cannot afford private physicians. One such visit illustrates the acts the nurse performs and the decisions she makes.

The Visiting Nurse called on a family that had recently migrated to Denver from a neighboring state. The mother and her three children were at home; the father was at work. The children were all under the age of six and the mother was expecting another child in two months. The mother complained about the poor heating in the house and said that the house temperature went rather low at night. Because of the cold, the family slept and played in the living room. The children had colds the week before but one was feeling much better. One child who had been sleeping on the couch woke up during the visit and complained of a sore throat. After some coaxing the nurse was able to get the child to open her mouth and let the nurse make an examination. The nurse said there was an inflammation but it did not look too serious. The nurse then counseled the mother on the need to keep shoes and clothes on the children and the need to take them to the neighborhood health center for inoculations. The nurse also said that the mother herself should be examined by a doctor. The mother admitted that it might be good for the children to get their shots, but she did not want to be lectured by a doctor. However, she said she would take the children to the health center even though she herself hated pregnancy examinations.

The nurse in this visit evaluated the health of the children and determined that none were seriously ill. Unfortunately, a doctor will not review her decision because the mother's fear of a doctor's lectures will probably overcome her good intentions. Later that day, the Visiting Nurse went ahead and made an appointment for the mother at the neighborhood health center. Observation of activities at this center revealed that some nurses who have received special instruction in pediatrics give children physical examinations. The nurse, free from the supervision of doctor, evaluates among other things the condition of the child's heartbeat, reflexes, eyes, ears and throat. A history of the health of the child is taken from the mother. Based on these indications the nurse evaluates the health of the child. She may judge that the child's health is satisfactory. She may judge that the child has a health problem but that the immediate attention of a doctor is not needed. Finally, she may judge that the child is seriously ill and that immediate medical attention is necessary.

Observations of the work of the Pediatric Nurse and the Visiting Nurse demonstrate that the nurse must contemplate the possible diseases indicated by the symptoms she observes. This is the basis of her decision that the child is in good or poor health. However, she does not attempt to ascertain a particular disease and hence her actions would not come within a strict interpretation of the wording of the Colorado statutory definition of diagnosis—ascertaining a disease or ailment by its symptoms.

The most important aspect of the nurse's activity is her evaluation of the person's condition. That conclusion temporarily determines whether there will or will not be future medical treatment. However, this activity does not distinguish the Pediatric or Visiting Nurse from other nurses with more traditional responsibilities. The nurse on the hospital floor who thinks that a patient's complaints do not merit a doctor's attention is making a similar evaluation or, perhaps, diagnosis. . . .

CONCLUSION

The City of Denver's nurses are involved in a number of programs which arguably violate the Attorney General's interpretation of the statute. The value of these programs is great, and the disservice done to the public if they were discontinued by a suit under the diagnostic prohibition would be greater. We live in a time of rapidly expanding health and medical services—both public and private. Many areas do not have enough physicians to handle the increased workload, so the burden is being shifted down to the next best trained group—the nurses. The Denver projects discussed in this Note are good examples of this expansion of nurse's responsibility to free the physicians for more important tasks.

The authors believe that the nurses involved with these projects do an excellent job and are an invaluable service to the people of the city and state. It would be a public disgrace to halt these projects under the diagnostic prohibition—an outmoded, although well intentioned law. The projects will continue as before without a change in the law, but the uncertainty it causes does not contribute to the effectiveness of the programs. We feel that the adoption of the changes in the law which were suggested in this Note would remove the uncertainty surrounding these projects and allow for expanding present programs or similar medical services conducted by qualified nurses.

## (7) Significance of Locality in the Establishment of a Standard of Care

What are the variables exemplified in the following article that tend to offset locality as a determining factor in the standard of care?

To what extent does this article offer an analogy to nursing care? Assuming that you agree with the writer in his position on locality as a factor in setting standards of medical care, what are some of the variables unique to nursing preparation and practice that cloud the application of Louisell's conclusions directly to nursing?

### Louisell, D., and Williams, H., *Trial of Medical Malpractice Cases*, 210 (Albany: Matthew Bender & Co., 1968)*

#### USUAL CASE: REASONABLE SKILL AND CARE—DIMINISHING SIGNIFICANCE OF LOCALITY

The geographic locality of a physician's practice historically has been a significant factor in judicial definition and application of the standard of reasonable skill and care. In the late nineteenth century the applicable standard was still that of the ordinary practitioner within the same community, but more recently there has been substantial authority that this is too restricted. A lucid opinion in *Small v. Howard* exemplifies the more sensible rule which is the current trend: a physician is bound to possess the ordinary skill, learning, and experience of his profession generally at the time, in similar localities with similar opportunities for experience.

Today the question of variation in medical standards according to area seldom arises except in the context of urban as contrasted with rural standards. Even that contrast is of diminishing significance; the truth seems to be that courts are becoming increasingly aware of the reality that medical standards are approaching uniformity nationwide. Indeed, so far as the malpractice standard of skill and care is concerned—as contrasted with standards of superior medical performance—it is arguable that the former is now nationally uniform. This is supported, for example, by the fact that the requirements for certification by all of the American specialty boards are nationally uniform.

In 1916 the Minnesota Supreme Court in *Viita v. Fleming* said:

We think it is plainly correct that the locality in which the physician or surgeon practices must be considered in determining whether he has the requisite skill and learning, but we do not think that he is bound to possess and exercise only that degree of skill and learning possessed by other practitioners in the same locality, if by that is meant, the same village or city. If the same general locality is meant, as, for instance, the Northwest, or the state, no fault could be found with such a rule. But in these days the physician or surgeon in a village like Cloquet is not hampered by lack of opportunity for advancement. Frequent meetings of medical societies, articles in the medical journals, books by acknowledged authorities, and extensive experience in hospital work put the country doctor on more equal terms with his city brother. He would probably resent an imputation that he possessed less skill than the average physician or surgeon in the large cities, and we are unwilling to hold that he is to be judged only by the qualifications that others in the same village or similar villages possess.

The progress since 1916 of medical science, public communications dissemination of medical knowledge, and transportation accentuate the current pertinency of these words. In *Geraty v. Kaufman* the Connecticut court analyzed the rule in terms of

---

* Reprinted with permission of Matthew Bender & Co., 235 E. 45th Street, New York.

a "medical neighborhood" which was deemed wide enough in that case to embrace both New London and New Haven. In *Cavallaro v. Sharp* the locality rule was interpreted broadly enough to allow a surgeon from Philadelphia to testify in a case in Providence, for of course the two cities are medically similar communities.

Whatever rational reasons there may have been for the locality rule in the past, are of diminishing validity today. If a physician practices in an area which lacks some of the skills and facilities regarded as standard elsewhere, he should be knowledgeable enough to advise his patients that superior medical talent and facilities are in existence. The responsibility thus to inform patients should be regarded as a part of the standard care required of physicians everywhere. In theory all licensed physicians meet the minimum standards of knowledge and skill required by their respective state licensing boards. Although this may prove to be a fiction in some cases, because of the fallibility of examining processes and the continuing effectiveness of a medical license once procured, society can hardly afford to indulge the assumption today that standards of knowledge and skill within the same state may still vary widely. Increasingly, realistic judges in this field as in others, will acknowledge that the legal rule ceases when the reasons for it cease.

## (8) Scope of Practice

This extract of the report of the Committee on Industrial Nursing in collaboration with the Legal Division of the American Medical Association is directed to the work of the industrial nurse. However, it equally well describes what is happening to nursing practice today and doubtless will happen in the future as well.

### The Legal Scope of Industrial Nursing Practice, *J.A.M.A.,* 169:1072 (1959)*

The purpose of this report is to discuss the legal scope of the practice of industrial nursing and the functions which a professional industrial nurse may legally perform. The intensification of the educational program of nursing, the increased dependence of the physician on the skills and discretion of the nurse, and the ability of the nurse to meet the challenge of an ever-rising standard of patient care have motivated the nursing profession to define and seek recognition for those professional functions which the nurse performs independently. This is especially true of the industrial nurse who often works without immediate medical supervision.

THE PRACTICE OF NURSING

Nursing and medical practice are interrelated and frequently indistinguishable from each other. The same act may be clearly the practice of medicine when performed by a physician and likewise a practice of nursing, depending on the circumstances, when performed by a nurse.

* Reprinted with permission of the *Journal of the American Medical Association.*

There are, of course, limitations on the functions which the nurse may perform, whether independently or under the supervision of a physician, and there are likewise limitations on the functions which may be legally assigned by a physician to a nurse. These will be discussed in this report.

The statutes of the various states which define professional nursing are too nebulous to provide a usable guide in determining the functions in which a nurse may legally engage. Essentially the statutes define professional nursing as involving the carrying out of treatment prescribed by a licensed physician and the application of nursing skills. Obviously, such definitions do not identify the particular functions in which a professional nurse may engage.

Probably the lawmakers should be commended for their foresight rather than criticized for ambiguity. A half-century ago when the first nursing practice acts were adopted the principal function of the nurse was to aid the physician by performing tasks under his direction. The functions of nursing are constantly expanding, and precisely drawn statutory definitions of the functions of nursing could not be kept up to date with changes in professional practices. However, the growing body of judicial decisions reflects the development of the profession of nursing and its expanding responsibilities in the wake of medical progress. The identification of particular functions as nursing functions and the standards of competence required of professional nurses in executing these functions have undergone a rapid and continuous process of evolution among those who are professionally responsible for the care of the sick and injured.

Courts have held that professional nurses have a legal duty to interpret evidence presented by the patient possibly indicating the need for medical attention, and to proceed in the light of that interpretation to do what is required for the patient, as for example the need to call a physician; to discontinue a treatment where there is evidence of its harmful effect, e.g., on an unconscious patient; or to determine the patient's need for special medication, e.g., sedatives. There can be little doubt that by custom and usage the relationship between doctor, patient, and nurse is one in which the parties recognize that the nurse as well as the physician has the function and responsibility to observe and interpret the patient's reactions.

The observation of symptoms and the making of a diagnosis imply the need for professional learning and mental acuteness. These functions are characteristic of the professional nature of nursing as well as medicine. The industrial nurse who observes the extent of illness or injury to an injured workman and determines whether she should render emergency treatment or wait until the physician arrives has made a vital diagnosis comparable in importance to many of those which physicians are called on to make. However, except for first-aid treatment and the employment of such measures as will prevent aggravation of the patient's injury or illness, the determination of therapy is within the exclusive domain of medical practice and beyond the limits of nursing practice. . . .

NURSING FUNCTIONS

It is axiomatic that the practice of medicine may not be delegated to non-physicians. Nevertheless there are numerous traditionally medical functions which are now also performed by nurses under the supervision or direction of a physician and recognized to be nursing functions. Accordingly, under the direction or supervision of a physician, a nurse may administer injections intravenously or intramuscularly or perform x-ray treatments.

Basal metabolism tests, anticoagulant therapy, and the administration of blood transfusions and oxygen are now routinely performed by nurses. The great progress in the science of medicine has led to the delegation of numerous medical procedures to nurses. The first-aid equipment used by the industrial nurse today could have been used only by a physician not too many years ago.

On the other hand the order of a physician purporting to delegate to a nurse the authority to perform an abdominal operation, or an amputation, or to set a fracture or to perform any similar procedure would undoubtedly be considered invalid by the medical and nursing professions as well as the courts. In realistic terms, professional nursing practice includes not only emergency diagnosis and treatment but those medical acts and techniques which are commonly performed by qualified nurses under physicians' orders. Fundamentally, the scope of nursing practice is determined by medical custom. None of the statutes relating to nursing practice attempts to set forth the specific functions of nursing. This statutory flexibility has allowed for the rapid growth of nursing. Consequently the courts have been guided in identifying nursing functions by customs and practices of the medical profession, since physicians can best recognize the proficiency and attainments of nurses. . . .

SUMMARY

The profession of nursing is a dynamic discipline which embraces an ever-increasing number of functions. Nurses, particularly those employed in industry, should be careful to limit their diagnostic and therapeutic activities to emergencies and to avoid continued treatment of a patient unless such treatment involves the carrying out of the specific orders of a physician who is in charge of the case.

Under the direction or supervision of physicians, nurses are performing as nursing practice numerous procedures which were formerly performed exclusively by physicians. The limitations on the procedures which a nurse may properly perform are governed by (a) the nature of the relationship between the medical and nursing professions in the community, (b) the scope of training offered in recognized nurses' training schools, and (c) the training, experience, and proficiency of the individual nurse.

In emergency cases, industrial nurses have a duty to determine the need for prompt medical attention, to make a tentative diagnosis of the patient's condition, and to employ necessary resuscitative and first-aid measures.

# CASES

The cases that follow are those in which the practitioner of nursing was involved. In the Appendix, it is pointed out that for the nurse, the analysis of a case falls into two parts, the fact pattern and the judicial decision. In the study of these particular cases the student is called upon to equate the behavior of the nurse or nurses in question with that of a reasonable standard for a professional practitioner in her field. A basic assumption is proposed: no harm would have occurred to the patient if the quality of nursing care had not broken down. In your study of the facts of the case, seek the point at which, if the nurse had taken appropriate action, litigation might have been avoided. Identify the legal issues in each case which grew out of the mismanaged nursing care.

### *Valentin v. La Societe Francaise,* 76 Cal. App. 2d 1, 172 P. 2d 359 (1946)

Moore, Presiding Justice.

Plaintiff's son, August, underwent a successful operation for hernia August 19, 1940, in defendant's privately owned hospital in Los Angeles. His condition remained normal for eight days, after which for three days he exhibited distressing symptoms of a disease which turned out to be tetanus. After a definite diagnosis he was moved to the county hospital September 1, at 12:15 a.m. for antitetanic treatments and expired at 9:10 p.m.

Basing his action upon the wrongful death of his son, appellant demanded damages. At the conclusion of the trial defendant's motion for an instructed verdict was denied. After a verdict had been returned in appellant's favor for ten thousand dollars, defendant's motion for judgment notwithstanding the verdict was granted on the ground that there was no evidence proving or tending to prove negligence proximately causing the death. Following a denial of his motion for a new trial plaintiff appealed. The question for decision is whether the court committed prejudicial error in granting defendant's motion.

#### THE COURT EXCEEDED ITS POWER

The trial court's power to grant a judgment notwithstanding a verdict has been repeatedly defined. It is only after it has disregarded contrary evidence, accorded to the prevailing evidence and all of its legitimate implications the full value to which they are entitled and has found no substantial evidence in support of the verdict that the court should enter a contrary judgment. If at the time the case was submitted to the jury there was any substantial evidence in the record to prove that defendant was negligent in its treatment or in its care of decedent and that such negligence was the proximate cause of the death, the court erroneously granted the motion.

#### SUBSTANTIAL EVIDENCE

Defendant was bound by express contract to furnish decedent with the services of competent, learned, skillful physicians and surgeons and with the care of trained nurses. It is the duty of any hospital that undertakes the treatment of an ill or wounded person to use reasonable care and diligence not only in operating upon and treating but also in safeguarding him, and such care and diligence is measured by the capacity of the patient to care for himself. It has been held negligence (1) for a surgeon to fail to discover a hemorrhage which he had caused or for him to refuse to suture the operative wound; (2) for nurses to allow a patient to be burned by an electric heating pad; (3) for the management of a hospital to allow the continued use of a lamp after the insulation on its key used for turning on the light had broken off, exposing the metal; (4) for a sanitarium in caring for alcoholics to leave a window unguarded through which a delirious patient might plunge. Whether the hospital or its nurse should have foreseen the casualty and have protected the patient by timely warning of a known danger are questions ordinarily for the jury.

If a hospital is obliged to maintain its premises and its instrumentalities for the comfort of its patients with such care and diligence as will reasonably assure their safety, it should be equally bound to observe the progress of a patient in his recovery from a major operation with such care and diligence as his condition reasonably requires for his comfort and safety and promptly to employ such agencies as may reasonably appear necessary for the patient's safety. Whether a hospital has exercised such reasonable care under the circumstances of a case is for the determination of the jury. It follows that if the record shows substantial evidence of defendant's negligence and that such negligence was the proximate cause of decedent's death the judgment must be reversed.

Malpractice is the neglect of a physician or a nurse to apply that degree of skill and learning in treating a patient which is customarily applied in treating and caring for the sick or wounded similarly suffering in the same community. See Webster's International, Oxford and Bouvier's Dictionaries; C. J., Am.Juris. While proof of it is customarily made by the testimony of experts, and while the law makes allowances for human weakness in the application of skill and learning, the facts of each case must be judged according to their own merits. If the alleged neglect relates to matters or conduct which are reasonably within the ken of the average layman the jury may determine the culpability of the person charged therewith without the aid of experts. If it relates solely to the exercise of judgment in the application of skill and learning then proof of the negligence must be made by experts. Viewing the facts of this case from either angle it is inescapable that in the treatment and nursing of decedent by defendant there is substantial evidence that the servants of defendant were negligent in failing to exercise ordinary care in two respects, namely: (1) In the application of the skill, learning and diligence reasonably required in a private hospital in Los Angeles in 1940, and (2) in refusing to take steps for the protection of decedent or to act when evidence of the presence of a pathological condition and of a progressive deterioration was brought to their attention. A private hospital is required to give its patients the character of treatment customarily administered for the same disease or symptoms by similar hospitals in the same locality and at the time in question. It must exercise such reasonable care in treating a patient as his known condition may require.


PLAINTIFF'S EVIDENCE WAS SUBSTANTIAL

The complaint alleged (1) that the tetanus infection resulted from negligence in the operation or from the subsequent negligent care of the patient, or (2) in failing to discover its presence or to prevent its development following a definite diagnosis. Inasmuch as the record discloses positive evidential support of the second allegation, a discussion of the claim of negligence in the operation will be omitted.

On entering the hospital August Valentin was 20 years of age. He was in good health except for the hernia. Following the operation on August 19 his condition was normal until August 27, when his temperature of 101 degrees and a pleuritic pain in his right side were diagnosed as broncho-pneumonia. On the 28th and 29th his fever registered 102.6 degrees and he was flushed and dyspnoeic. On the 30th at 5 p.m. Mrs. Broguiere, whose son occupied the same room where she had called frequently, observed that August was not reading and was less talkative than usual. Although his temperature showed a decline on Saturday the 31st, he complained of soreness in his chest and of his inability to chew. At noon, on request of the bedside nurse that he be examined, Doctor Hawkins, the resident physician, found him suffering a tight feeling in his throat and pain on attempting to open his mouth. Doctor Hawkins reported to the supervisor of nurses that it looked to him "like this might be a case of tetanus" and instructed her to call the attending physician. He then left for the day. As to the operating surgeons, Doctor Lopizich was on vacation; Doctor Hull did not arrive before 11 p.m., after a diagnosis of tetanus had been made definite by Doctor Bennett and the boy faced eternal sleep.

The nurse's chart for that Saturday afternoon showed a progressive deterioration; pain and stiffness in the neck, tightness in the chest, difficulty in opening the mouth and in swallowing; poor appetite, much expectoration, drowsy. At 7:30 p.m. Mrs. Valentin arrived and was alarmed to find the marked change in her son for the worse. She reported her observations to the head nurse, expressed her extreme anxiety and demanded that some physician be called at once. During more than three hours she continued her remonstrances in vain. She reminded the night supervisor of nurses that there were many doctors and insisted that one be called. Just after her departure at 10:30 p.m. Doctor Bennett, on leaving a patient upon whom he had called, at the request of the night supervisor examined young Valentin, announced him to be suffering from tetanus and advised that he be at once transferred to the county hospital. After his arrival there at 1:50 o'clock Sunday morning antitetanic treatments were vainly administered throughout the day.

In the light of the foregoing rules governing the proof of malpractice and the responsibilities of private hospitals the proof of defendant's negligence and that it was the proximate cause of the death of August Valentin is substantial. It is established by evidence of the inaction of the nurses in the presence of signals of danger which would have moved a reasonably intelligent attendant promptly to import a competent physician for the purpose of taking necessary precautions to prevent the development of the disease. For a supervisory nurse to permit a patient recovering from a major operation to suffer symptoms indicating a growing pathology for three days without medical care merely because the attending physicians were not available is a type of conduct that is negligence.

In addition to the appeal to the lay mind by the occurrences detailed by the witnesses, the testimony of Doctor Webb fills all of the essential requirements for an expert to prove malpractice of the hospital. Doctor Webb had been chief autopsy surgeon of Los Angeles County for many years, and served for fourteen years as assistant to his predecessor. Following his graduation from Columbia College of Physicians and Surgeons in 1902 he served in a government hospital in the District of Columbia and in New York City in the treatment of pathological diseases until 1912. He then served a Canadian railroad in the treatment of personal injuries, which required a knowledge of tetanus, of its symptoms and mode of treatment. After locating in Los Angeles in 1915 he taught in a local university until 1923. During the latter five years of that period he was instructor in histology and pathology, which "pertained directly to tetanus," its diagnosis, prevention and treatment. Having been licensed to practice while teaching he became an assistant autopsy surgeon in 1923 and took the post of autopsy surgeon in 1937. He had read many clinical reports on tetanus cases with special attention to the advantage gained over the disease by early treatment. He had kept informed as to the methods of treating tetanus patients by conferring with attending physicians and hospital authorities prior to August, 1940, and was thereby made familiar with the methods in vogue in Los Angeles in August, 1940, having performed post mortem examinations in many cases which had come from prominent, private, well-managed hospitals of Los Angeles. Also, he was familiar with the literature on the care of tetanus and with hospital histories of cases and had learned of the procedure and usage of such hospitals from such histories. Furthermore, he was familiar with the reports of the county hospital on 100 cases of tetanus treated in that institution and knew that the antitetanic serum is "the only recognized remedy for cure."

Upon his qualifications as shown by this testimony the court below allowed the doctor to testify that tetanus is curable; that medical science has a specific cure which when promptly applied is effective in the great majority of cases; that such remedy was commonly known and available and was usually applied by physicians and surgeons in the practice of their profession in and around Los Angeles in the summer of 1940; that it is imperative that such antitetanic treatment be administered promptly upon the appearance of the symptoms of tetanus and that if so applied 80 per cent of those afflicted will probably recover. His testimony was supported by the record kept by the Los Angeles county hospital during 1940 and 1941 of 100 consecutive cases of tetanus treated there. Such record concludes with the declaration that the application of the same cure in an identical manner resulted in the reduction of the gross mortality rate of 56.5 per cent in past years to a current rate of 29 per cent, and that if the patients who had succumbed during the first 24 hours of hospitalization be excluded from the calculation the series presents a net mortality rate of but 19.3 per cent among 88 patients.

Upon such proof the jury were warranted in finding that with a specific and efficacious cure available its merits were necessarily known to the resident physician and to the supervising nurses of defendant, and that they were negligent (1) in not making it available promptly to decedent when Doctor Hawkins declared that the disease might be tetanus, (2) in not employing other physicians as soon as decedent's symptoms indicated a constant deterioration, and (3) in not proceeding as diligently with the care of him as the prevailing usage, procedure and practice of well-ordered hospitals in Los Angeles in 1940 required under such circumstances. On the occurrence of such changes ordinary care would have impelled the nurse in charge to call another physician if the attending physicians were not available. While the symptoms manifested by decedent were in themselves sufficient to stimulate a nurse of ordinary prudence to energetic action, those in attendance had the additional alarms sounded by Mrs. Broguiere on Friday and by Mrs. Valentin on Saturday evening that August was desperately ill. But not an effort was made to procure another physician until 10:40 p.m. Saturday, when by chance the diagnosis of Doctor Bennett was announced. Whether such behavior of nurses who had knowledge of the progressive deterioration of decedent constituted negligence was properly a question for the jury.

Objections were made to much of the evidence prior to its admission but none of it was ever stricken. It accompanied the jury to their deliberations and upon it the verdict in favor of plaintiff was returned. From it they could and evidently did find that had defendant caused an examination by a physician on Friday at 5 p.m. when decedent displayed the first symptoms of tetanus the virus would then have been found and the patient might have had 49 hours of antitetanic treatments before 9 p.m. on Sunday instead of only 12. They could and evidently did find that had defendant effected an intelligent examination of decedent at noon on Saturday, when it appeared to Doctor Hawkins like a case of tetanus, the boy would then have had 31 hours of expert care and antitetanic treatments instead of only 19 hours before 9 p.m. Sunday. Finally, the jury could find, as indeed they must have found from the records of the county hospital that decedent was in a dying condition during his 19 hours there.

It follows that the jury had substantial evidence from which it could determine that the delay in causing the appropriate medical treatment to be given decedent was the proximate cause of his death.

The order granting the judgment notwithstanding the verdict is reversed and the court below is instructed to enter a judgment in favor of plaintiff in accordance with the verdict.


ANALYSIS

1. What was the pattern of facts upon which the parents of August Valentin based their complaint?

2. Did the issue of locality have a significant bearing on the evaluation of the conduct of the nurse? Would the answer have been the same if the court had held that the nurse should possess the ordinary skill, learning, and experience of a member of her profession in any locality? As a nurse would view it, why is locality a debatable issue in appraising conduct?

3. What procedure was followed at the trial in qualifying Dr. Webb as an expert witness? In his testimony, at what point did he draw upon his scientific background and when did he draw upon his experience?

4. Not to replace the medical expert witness but to bring into evidence the contribution of the nurse as an expert witness, hypothesize on the qualifications of a nurse clinician who might have been called to testify on her evaluation of nursing care. What education and experience might she have had that would have permitted her to make a unique contribution? What testimony might she have given about the scientific knowledge the nurses should have demonstrated in this situation? Having established what the nurses should have known, what then might have been her assessment of the quality of nursing care, in terms of observation, critical thinking, and nursing judgment that would have been reasonable to expect?

5. Upon what evidence did the court base its conclusion that the supervisory nurse was negligent?

**Cooper v. National Motor Bearing Co., 136 Cal. App. 2d 229, 288 P. 2d 581 (1955)**

Kaufman, Justice.

This is an appeal from a judgment in favor of plaintiff after jury verdict in a malpractice action brought by respondent Bernard Cooper against Lillian Elson, a trained nurse employed by appellant, The National Motor Bearing Company, Inc., and against said company. Respondent Cooper was also an employee of the aforesaid company. A verdict in the sum of $25,000 in favor of respondent was returned by the jury. A motion for new trial was denied on condition that respondent would consent to a reduction of the judgment to the sum of $15,000. Such consent was thereafter filed.

In May, 1951, Bernard Cooper, while engaged in the course of his employment for appellant company received a puncture wound on the left side of his forehead when another employee let a piece of metal slip from his hand. He went directly to the First Aid Room of the plant and received treatment from the nurse, Mrs. Lillian Elson. She swabbed the wound with mercurochrome or some other antiseptic and put a bandage on it. No one else was in the room. She did not ask him to sit down, but treated it while he was standing. According to respondent's testimony she did not examine or probe the wound, but just swabbed and bandaged it. He was told to return the next day which he did. Mrs. Elson again applied antiseptic but did not probe it. On the next day he also went to the dispensary, but on that occasion the nurse just looked at the wound.

The wound appeared to close up but left a little red mark about the shape of the cut. The redness did not go away until the operation. After about 2 or 3 months the redness began to spread, and the area became puffy and raised in about 3 or 4 months after the original injury. Respondent on visits to the dispensary in this period would point out to Mrs. Elson that the wound didn't seem to be healing properly and she would say if it didn't she would have to do something. Some months later a little scab started to appear in the center.

In March 1952, respondent visited the dispensary for a check of a chest injury and asked Mrs. Elson if she would send him to a doctor to examine his forehead. She referred him to Dr. Arden Hedge who excised a piece of tissue for laboratory examination. Dr. Lindsay, a pathologist, examined the specimen and reported that it contained a basal-cell carcinoma, and the carcinoma had not been fully removed by the excision. On March 23, 1952, respondent was operated on, and a large area was excised. Skin was removed from his right forearm and grafted to the forehead. He was hospitalized for four days. The entire basal-cell carcinoma was removed in the second operation.

Respondent testified that he was absent from work for 35 days on account of the operation. He had headaches that continued from the time of the operation up to and including the time of trial. There was a feeling of tightness in his forehead, and when he combed his hair he experienced a prickling sensation. There was some limitation of motion in his arm for some months after the skin was removed for the graft. He experienced considerable embarrassment because of the livid scar on his forehead the size of a half dollar. There was testimony by Dr. Jessie Carr that respondent has the type of skin subject to this type of cancer, and that he will probably get more cancer in the area where the excision has been done. . . .

It is next contended that the evidence is insufficient to support the verdict. Respondent's complaint alleged that he received an injury in the scope of his employment on May 11, 1951, consisting of a laceration of his forehead, for which he was treated by defendant Lillian Elson, that he was continuously treated therefor until March, 1952, when he was instructed by defendants to secure further treatment from a licensed physician and surgeon. He then learned for the first time, it is alleged "that the lacerated injury to the forehead had become infected and that a malignant condition had developed in the aforesaid infected area," that respondent underwent two surgical operations for the treatment of the malignant condition, and that the malignant condition is permanent. . . .

The appellant nurse admitted that it was her duty to refer any condition or injury she was not familiar with, or not sure about, to a doctor for diagnosis. The standard of good nursing care in the community required the nurse to examine the wound for foreign bodies. If splinters were too deeply imbedded, the nurse was to send the workman to the doctor. Respondent's type of wound should normally have healed in a week or so. If a wound persisted and did not heal, proper nursing care would require that the workman be sent to the doctor, for such a condition would indicate to a nurse that something was wrong. Appellant nurse admitted that she was familiar with the seven danger signals of cancer, one of which is "any sore that does not heal." Nevertheless, she continued to treat the wound for ten months before sending respondent to the doctor. . . .

Respondent herein had never had any prior skin trouble, had had no prior injury to his forehead, and had no personal history or family history of cancer. The area from which the cancer was later removed was in the very area where he had received the injury ten months earlier. It is true that there was testimony that respondent has a type of skin which is more subject to cancer than are other types. But respondent's testimony shows that prior to this injury he was not afflicted with that disease. In Austin v. Red Wing Sewer Pipe Co., 163 Minn. 397, 204 N.W. 323, 324, a case wherein an employee had developed a cancer on his cheek in the area where he had been injured, it was said that that circumstance was pretty strong evidence that the injury was the proximate cause of the result, and that if the medical profession did not know the cause of cancer, "the connecting events between the cause and effect . . . might be sufficient to justify the conclusion that the injury was the legal cause, and that the result should be compensable."

It was said in Fireman's Fund Indemnity Co. v. Industrial Accident Comm., 93 Cal. App.2d 244, 246, 208 P.2d 1033, 1034, that "expert evidence of a medical possibility taken with other evidence of a non-expert character may be sufficient to support an inference of medical probability." The jury may have concluded from the evidence herein that the nurse did not carefully probe the wound for foreign matter, that this caused the cancer in respondent's skin which was a type of skin subject to cancer. They may well have concluded that the delay in sending respondent to the doctor made necessary the excision of a much larger area, and hence a greater disfigurement than he would have suffered, if he had been referred when the wound had failed to heal within the normal period. The public has been educated to the importance of the early detection of cancer so that the average layman knows that if detected early, surgery will affect a much smaller area than if detected in later stages. . . .

Appellants, in violation of proper procedure on appeal, raise an entirely new claim of error for the first time in their Reply Brief. It is contended that error was committed in giving the following instruction:

"A patient is entitled to an ordinarily careful physical examination, such as the circumstances, the condition of the patient, and the nurse's opportunities for examination will permit. If there is a reasonable opportunity for examination, and the nature of the injury or ailment can be discovered by the exercise of ordinary care and treatment, then the nurse is answerable for failure to make such discovery.

"The same degree of responsibility and the same duty of care is imposed upon a nurse in the making of a diagnosis as is imposed upon her in the prescribing and administering of treatment."

It is argued that these instructions are taken from cases concerned solely with malpractice of physicians or surgeons, and not those where nurses are involved. The effect was, they say to install the nurse in a position of equal responsibility with a physician for diagnosis, prescription and treatment, and to impose on her a duty to practice medicine from which she is prohibited by law, and that this instruction must have led to confusion in the minds of the jury. Appellants center their attack chiefly on the use of the word "diagnosis" and contend that the jury might be led to believe that the nurse was held responsible for diagnosing the malignant condition, when such diagnosis can be made with certainty only by a pathologist. In the present case, Dr. Hedge did not diagnose the case as a malignant growth until he had received reports from the pathologist.

However, we believe the jury properly understood the instruction to mean that a nurse's diagnosis of a condition must meet the standard of learning, skill and care, to which nurses practicing that profession in the community are held. A nurse in order to administer first aid properly and effectively must make a sufficient diagnosis to enable her to apply the appropriate remedy. Usually she receives some history of the accident or illness from the patient, inspects a wound, and bases her choice of treatment on the deductions thus made. She has been trained, but to a lesser degree than a physician, in the recognition of the symptoms of diseases and injuries. She should be able to diagnose, according to appellant nurse's own testimony herein, sufficiently to know whether it is a condition within her authority to treat as a first aid case or whether it bears danger signs that should warn her to send the patient to a physician.

Since no doctor was involved as a defendant in this case, it is not probable that the jury confused the standards of diagnosis demanded from a nurse with those of a doctor. The jury was in fact instructed that "a nurse by law is not authorized to practice medicine or surgery or to undertake the prevention, treatment or cure of disease, pain, injury, deformity, or mental or physical condition in violation of any provisions of law." . . .

Judgment affirmed.

## ANALYSIS

1. What does the court say the nurse was required to do that she did not do? Why does the court say she was required to do that which she did not do?

2. What were the expectations of the company in assigning nurses to the clinic? What were the expectations of the patient when he went to the nurse? Was the nurse

occupying a role different from that of a doctor, had he been present and in charge of the dispensary (a) from the point of view of the patient? (b) from the point of view of the nurse's employer? (c) from the point of view of the nurse? If so, what, in each case? Should these expectations play a part in the court's decision?

3. To what standard did the court hold the nurse in this case? What had she done that was not in accordance with this standard?

4. How might this opinion affect nursing practice for the future? Are the effects desirable or undesirable? Does this opinion identify a new role for the nurse, with expanded duties, or was the nurse in a situation that is routine for the occupational health nurse working under medical supervision subject to call?

### *Ault v. Hall,* 119 Ohio 422, 164 N.E. 518, 60 A.L.R. 128 (1928)

Marshall, C. J. This action originated in the court of common pleas of Cuyahoga County as a suit for damages for malpractice. Mrs. Ault, a woman of about 74 years, consulted Dr. Hall, and her ailment was diagnosed by him as requiring the surgical removal of her gall bladder. She accordingly contracted with him for such operation, and the surgeon selected St. John's Hospital in Cleveland as the place of operating, he being a member of the staff in that institution. Mrs. Ault had no choice in the selection of the institution or the surgeon's assistants, but made no objection thereto. The operation took place May 25, 1925. It being an abdominal operation, numerous surgical sponges were employed for wiping and walling off the abdominal cavity from possible infections, and for packing off intestines and arresting hemorrhages. At the conclusion of the operation the incision was closed, and one of the sponges was permitted to remain in the abdomen. The incision did not heal, and the suppuration became more pronounced, and the incision was repeatedly cauterized, until nearly eight weeks later it was discovered that the trouble was due to a sponge. On removal of the sponge it was found that it had rotted a hole in the stomach, so that when the sponge was removed food taken into the stomach seeped out through the hole in the stomach through the open wound. Further treatment followed during which the patient was kept alive by rectal injections of food and subcutaneous injections of moisture until the hole in the stomach sufficiently healed to retain food. As a result the patient has endured great suffering and it is claimed that her health has been permanently impaired.

The testimony adduced in the course of the trial shows that the surgeon had a first and second assistant surgeon and three nurses, each of whom was subject to his orders and control; that in the course of every such operation it is necessary to use surgical sponges consisting of long strips of gauze; that it is the approved practice to require a pair of forceps, called a hemostat, to be attached to every sponge left in the abdomen during the operation; that wiping sponges do not under the approved practice require a hemostat to be attached, because they are removed from the abdomen as soon as they are used; that during the operation a wiping sponge was in fact placed within plaintiff's abdomen and allowed to remain there without a hemostat attached.

Dr. Hall in his answer admitted performing the operation but claimed that he had at all times exercised due and proper care. As further defensive matter he alleged that it is the custom and practice generally among surgeons, where an abdominal or major operation is to be performed, to have present a house surgeon, a first assistant surgeon, an anesthetist, a table nurse, a sponge nurse, and an instrument nurse, and that this custom and practice prevails generally in the locality of Cleveland and was the practice and custom in St. John's Hospital. He further alleged that all said employees were present in the operating room and assisted in the operation. He further alleged that it is the duty of the "sponge nurse" to correctly count the number of operative sponges used, and that it is the custom of surgeons generally in Cleveland, Ohio, and particularly in St. John's Hospital, to rely upon the sponge count so reported by the sponge nurse, and that he did in fact rely upon her count and thereby followed the general practice of surgeons, and thereupon closed the incision. He further alleged that neither the anesthetist, the assistant surgeons, nor any of the nurses, were employed by or selected by him.

There was very little if any contradiction in the testimony, and for the purposes of this discussion we will assume that all the foregoing matters were definitely established. All witnesses agreed that a large sponge used for packing or walling off or stanching blood or pus should have a hemostat attached, which would be left hanging over the outside of the body, and that such precaution would be absolute insurance against a sponge being left in the body. They likewise agreed that a wiping sponge need not have such attachment, because such a sponge is never left in the abdomen beyond the period of its immediate use. This particular sponge was of gauze material several inches wide and two or three feet long, and was large enough to have been employed either as a wiping sponge or for packing.

It is self-evident that someone was guilty of negligence. If the sponge was used for packing purposes the usual precaution of attaching a hemostat was omitted. If it was used for wiping purposes the surgeon or assistant surgeon who used it did not immediately remove it. The trial did not establish who was the negligent party, but it must have been Dr. Hall, or one or the other of his two assistants, and the only testimony on the point was that of Dr. Hall, who testified as follows:

"Now I could not know whether it was put in through one of my assistants under an emergency or not. I am unable to say. I remember that we had quite a little difficulty in controlling hemorrhage and in the stress of that moment my assistants might have done it. I might have done it." . . .

The situation created by the frank admission of Dr. Hall that the unattached sponge may have been placed in the cavity by himself, and that in any event it was so placed either by himself or one of his assistants, is sought to be obviated by the proof of the practice or custom of relying upon the sponge nurse. In the state of this record, as presented to us, this alleged custom is the final inquiry concerning the legal responsibility of Dr. Hall. . . . It is evidently the insistence of counsel for Dr. Hall that this portion of the performance of an abdominal operation is by general custom delegated to a nurse, and that the surgeon by reason of that custom is permitted to rely upon the accuracy of her count and the care with which she discharges that service, and that no further responsibility attaches to the surgeon for unattached sponges permitted to be left in the abdominal cavity.

Even though it is admitted that the sponge was left in the cavity, and that Dr. Hall himself might have done it, counsel presents for our determination the question whether such a practice or custom if followed will relieve a surgeon from legal responsibility. More definitely stated, the question is whether such a practice or custom is competent to be shown as a complete defense to the action, and not merely as competent to be shown as bearing upon the question of due care. . . .

The evidence is uncontroverted that surgeons practicing in the vicinity of Cleveland, Ohio, are accustomed to rely upon the count of the sponge nurse, and this special instruction given before argument afforded counsel for the defendant the opportunity to impress upon the jury that there was no alternative except to render a verdict in defendant's favor.

No one will for a moment question the wisdom of a system of committing to a nurse the duty of preparing in advance a supply of sponges, carefully counted, and to continue to have the custody of the sponges, and to hand them to the operating surgeon as required, and to receive them back from the surgeon after they have served their purpose, and again to carefully count them to be sure that they have all been returned. If this system is followed and no sponges are used other than those issued by the sponge nurse, and the number issued by her tallies with the number returned to her by the surgeon, it is impossible that any sponges could be left in the body of the patient. The system itself must therefore be held to be reasonable in furtherance of the great care and caution necessary on such occasions. The cold fact remains, however, that after all such precautions have been exercised, sponges are occasionally left in the wound after being closed. It would seem therefore that nothing further need be stated to show that the system is not an absolute guaranty against mistakes. These mistakes frequently result in permanent impairment of health, and even death. That the system itself is a reasonable one is self-evident. That it is usually employed by physicians and surgeons in abdominal operations generally, and particularly in the vicinity of Cleveland, is fully established by this record, and is uncontradicted. Whether or not Dr. Hall had a right to rely upon the accuracy of the nurse is another and different question.

The service of the sponge nurse reduced the hazards of the operating room and was one of the facilities provided by the operating surgeon for guarding against accidents, for which he was entitled to credit, and the trial court properly permitted the system to be shown as reflecting upon the care and caution of the surgeon, but that system cannot be accepted as the only security upon which the patient had a right to rely and as displacing the personal care and caution which she had a right to expect from Dr. Hall himself. A duty still rested upon the surgeon to employ his own skill and observation to assure himself that no sponges had been allowed to remain within the wound at the time it was closed. The plaintiff was unconscious, and there is nothing to show that she understood the system whereby sponges were to be accounted for, and there is nothing to show that she was consenting that the surgeon should be relieved of all responsibility by employing a system which was entirely reasonable within itself. We have already observed that the removal of surgical sponges is a part of the operation itself. The surgeon being charged with the duty of removing them, ordinary care and caution forbids that he should have the right to delegate that responsibility in an unqualified manner to any system, however efficient. We have also observed that the surgeon is not an insurer of a successful operation, and we do not now go to the extent of saying that the surgeon insures that all sponges will be removed. He is only charged with that degree of care and caution commensurate with the importance of the task he has undertaken. Under our system of jurisprudence it is the province of the jury to determine whether all was done that reasonable care and skill required. This inquiry was not submitted to the jury for their determination in the instant case, but they were only required to ascertain whether the system of employing a sponge nurse prevailed in the vicinity of Cleveland, and whether it was in fact employed by Dr. Hall, and the determination of that question in the affirmative required a verdict in favor of the defendant. There is nothing in this record to indicate that the sponge which was the cause of the injury might not readily have been discovered by the surgeon if he had made a search for it before the wound was closed. . . .

. . . The overwhelming weight of authority supports the general rule that customary methods or conduct do not furnish a test which is conclusive, or fix a standard. It is obviously a dangerous practice to permit any business, trade, or profession to fix its own standards. It is equally obvious that any court which determines the proper standard has usurped the functions of a jury. These authorities are so numerous and so uniform that we shall not undertake to cite or discuss them. The subject of custom, in the technical sense of usage which has attained the force of law, is not involved in this proceeding. We have before us nothing more than an attempt to show the usual method or system of doing a practical thing which must necessarily be done in some way, and may be done in a variety of ways. Surgical science should be commended for the practice of having a nurse whose special task is to account for sponges, but it ought to be severely condemned if it places sole reliance upon that practice. The duty of a surgeon to exercise care cannot be delegated to another, without recourse. Custom will not justify a negligent act or exonerate from a charge of negligence. Long-continued careless performance of a duty by any trade, business or profession will not transform negligence into due care. Usage cannot avail to establish as safe in law that which is dangerous in fact. We therefore hold both upon reason and authority that the test of the usage or practice of having a sponge nurse to count the sponges is competent as reflecting upon the care and diligence of the surgeon, but that reliance upon such custom alone is not a complete defense to the charge of negligence. . . .

The judgments of the lower courts must be reversed and the cause remanded to the court of common pleas for new trial in accordance with this opinion.

Judgment reversed.

ANALYSIS

1. What arguments did the court use to support its holding that the conduct of the surgeon was open to scrutiny? Could it be said that he exercised due care when he accepted the sponge count as made by the nurse? What might the surgeon have done that he did not do?

2. What were the arguments for and against allowing custom and usage to serve as complete defense? What arguments might you set forth to abolish the defense of locality?

3. In reviewing the facts of this case, does it appear to you that the case turned on the most critical issue? If not, what might have been the focus?

## CASES FOR FURTHER ANALYSIS

### *Honeywell v. Rogers*, 251 F. Supp. 841 (W.D. Penn. 1966)

An action was brought against physician and hospital for alleged negligence of nurse in administration of intramuscular hypodermic by parents of a minor plaintiff, eleven months of age, who was admitted to the Conemaugh Valley Memorial Hospital and under the care of Dr. Rogers for an acute attack of bronchitis and anemia. The child was in the hospital for ten days and during that time received approximately eighteen intramuscular injections of various drugs including penicillin and iron dextran. Graduate and student nurses, as employees of the hospital, gave the injections. Just prior to dismissal, the physician ordered one more dose of the iron preparation. A student nurse, under the supervision of a graduate nurse, gave the intramuscular injection in which the site, according to the mother, was more nearly toward the center of the buttock and not in the upper outer quadrant as had been previously used. The child on her return home favored the leg, which was cold to the touch and painful. Symptoms of sciatic and peroneal nerve involvement appeared followed by paralysis of the lower left leg and foot.

There was no evidence of personal negligence on the part of the doctor; the jury exonerated him. A major issue centered on the standard medical and nursing procedure for the selection of a site for an intramuscular injection of this type. Evidence was presented concerning the training and supervision of students with reference to this particular technique. It was fully established by the plaintiff that proper medical and nursing technique did not permit an injection in the buttock in the area of the sciatic nerve.

The issue of standard of care was properly submitted to the jury and the evidence was sufficient to support that the nurse was negligent in the administration of the injection.

### *Jones v. Hawkes Hosp.*, 175 Ohio 503, 196 N.E. 2d 592 (1964)

This was an action against a hospital for injuries sustained by a patient who fell from a bed in the obstetrical department labor room. The essentially undisputed facts were that the patient, a primipara, was in the labor room. She was drowsy, lethargic, restless, and had made several attempts to get out of bed. One of the nurses raised the guard rails to their highest level. Two of the four nurses assigned to this area were in the delivery room. The head nurse was observing the progress of another patient, which left one nurse to observe the room of the appellant. A physician, not connected with the appellant in any way, appeared and requested the nurse to accompany him to see another patient. Because it was a rule of the hospital that no physician could attend a woman in labor except in the presence of a nurse, she accompanied him. She was not gone more than five minutes, but during this time the patient crawled over the side rail, fell on the floor, and sustained a deep cut over the cheek bone and a contused left eye. On these facts the court held that there was substantial evidence for the consideration of the jury that the nurse had been negligent in leaving the room.

One issue was on the method of establishing, by evidence at the trial, a standard of care exercised by hospitals in their labor rooms. Ordinarily this standard would be established by expert opinion. The court stated that when questions of science or art involving professional or mechanical skill were involved the jury would not be competent to judge, for such matters would not fall within common knowledge. However, if a matter can be decided from ordinary experience and knowledge the jury should be allowed to do so.

The court held that expert testimony was not necessary under these facts and upheld the verdict for the plaintiff.

### *Stone v. Proctor*, 159 N.C. 633, 131 S.E. 2d 297, 99 A.L.R. 2d 593 (1963)

This was an action by a patient against a psychiatrist for alleged malpractice in connection with electroshock therapy. The plaintiff, a patient in a hospital for the mentally ill, was given a series of electroshock treatments on the order of the defendant physician. Following the first treatment, the plaintiff immediately suffered and complained of severe pain in the lower back. He was given heat treatments and injections for the pain, but at no time was an x-ray examination made of his back. Following discharge from the hospital and while he was still suffering from the back condition, plaintiff consulted a radiologist who upon examination discovered that the patient had a compressed fracture of the ninth thoracic vertebra.

In its opinion the court called attention to the threefold obligation of a physician or surgeon in rendering a service [make an analogy to nursing]: he must possess the degree of learning and skill that others similarly situated possess, he must exercise reasonable care and diligence in the application of this knowledge and skill, and he must use judgment in the treatment and care of the patient. In this instance, the court acknowledged professional learning and skill requisite to diagnose and treat the patient; however, in the area of judgment the physician's performance was questioned. The defendant was a Fellow in the American Psychiatric Association, which promulgated "Standards of Electroshock Treatment" prepared by the Committee on Therapy and approved by the Council of the Association. The defendant admitted he was familiar with the standards and that they were applicable to the Winston-Salem area where he practiced. In lieu of expert testimony, the court used the standards of the American Psychiatric Association to establish a standard of care. Among the standards was one requiring examination and x-rays if a patient complained of pain or impairment of function after electroshock therapy. The defendant having failed to abide by this standard, negligence was inferrable. What comparable pronouncements of the standard of care concerning nursing are available to guide court action in litigation concerning nursing?

The decision of the lower court in favor of the physician was reversed.


### *Burns v. Bakelite Corp.*, 17 N.J. Super. 441, 86 A. 2d 289 (1952)

This was an action for the death of the plaintiff's husband as the alleged result of negligence of a registered nurse in charge of the decedent's employer's first-aid station.

Mrs. Brodie, registered nurse in the first-aid station of the Bakelite Corporation, saw the decedent when he came to the dispensary, pale, perspiring, and complaining of severe chest pain. He said he thought he had indigestion. His temperature and pulse were normal. The nurse tried unsuccessfully to reach the doctor of his choice. Burns then at his request was sent home in a chauffeur-driven company car where he was met by his wife, who was a trained nurse. The distance from the car to the house involved climbing several steps, and Brodie refused the help of the driver. The patient was taken to the hospital later in the day and in six days he died of a coronary occlusion.

The case turned on the issue of whether or not the nurse should have recognized the symptoms as typical of the onset of a heart attack and having done so have given him more supportive care. The court reasoned that Mrs. Brodie was not a physician, she did not realize the seriousness of his condition, and even if she had diagnosed his condition, she was in no position to have given the morphine that was indicated.

In the decision for the defendant, the nurse was not held to the standards of diagnosis required of a physician. Nevertheless, members of the nursing profession might well feel that the professional nurse is capable of a higher standard of performance than was demanded by the court in this case. Is there a difference in the image the court held of the nurse in this case as compared with that of the nurse in the case of *Cooper v. National Motor Bearing Co.* (*supra*, p. 109)?

# Recommended Source Material

TEXTS

Gregory, C., and Kalven, H., Jr., *Cases and Materials on Torts*, 89–160 (Boston: Little, Brown & Co., 1959).

Harper, F., and James, F., *The Law of Torts*, Vol. 2, 729–1014 (Boston: Little, Brown & Co., 1956).

Louisell, D., and Williams, H., *Trial of Medical Malpractice Cases*, 1–10, 187–201 (New York: Matthew Bender & Co., Inc., 1966).

Prosser, W., *Handbook of the Law of Torts*, 142–205 (St. Paul: West Pub. Co., 3rd ed., 1964).

Shartel, B., and Plant, M., *The Law of Medical Practice*, 114–45 (Springfield: Charles C Thomas, Publisher, 1959).


PERIODICALS

Challener, W., Jr., *The Rights, Liabilities and Duties of a Professional Nurse*, 54 Dick. L. Rev. 280 (1950).

Jenkins, R., *Medical Malpractice*, 26 Tenn. L. Rev. 514 (1959).

Pratt, M., The Doctor's View of the Changing Nurse-Physician Relationship, *J.Med. Educ.*, **40**:767, 1965.

Sadusk, J., Hazardous Fields of Medicine in Relation to Professional Liability, *J.A.M.A.*, **163**:953, 1956.

Sandor, T., History of Professional Liability Suits in the United States, *J.A.M.A.*, **163**:459, 1957.

Schlotfeld, R., The Nurse's View of the Changing Nurse-Physician Relationship, *J. Med. Educ.*, **40**:772, 1965.

# Chapter Four

# Legal Duty

We have discussed at some length the idea of standard of care as it applies to both ordinary life and professional conduct. Day-to-day conduct is measured against that of the reasonably prudent man; professional conduct is measured against that of a specialist practicing in the same area. In this section, another definition of standard of behavior is presented in terms of duty owed to others.

A passenger entered a New York railway station carrying under his arm a small package wrapped in newspaper. His train had begun to move and he dashed forward to catch it. A railroad porter attempted to assist him aboard and did so in such a negligent and careless manner that the passenger's package was dislodged and knocked to the rails. The package contained fireworks, and a violent explosion followed. As a result of the explosion, a scales a considerable distance away fell and struck Mrs. Palsgraf, who was waiting for a train. Mrs. Palsgraf sued the railroad, claiming that her injuries were due to the negligence of the porter, and at the trial the jury found in her favor. On appeal, the highest court in the State of New York reversed the verdict. The court said it was not within the range of foreseeability that the porter's negligent act of knocking a seemingly harmless package from a passenger's arms would result in the injury that befell the plaintiff, and consequently, Mrs. Palsgraf's injuries remained uncompensated. [*Palsgraf v. Long Island Ry.*, 248 N.Y. 339, 162 N.E. 99, 59 A.L.R. 1253 (1928).]

## Concept of Legal Duty

A significant part of our law is concerned with the establishment and enforcement of legal duty. We have legal duties to others by virtue of the contracts we may enter with them, duties not to violate the state criminal

120

statutes, or we may owe to another the duty of support, as husband to wife and children, or duties to obey the orders of duly constituted courts. These legal duties are declared by statute or by the common law. The breach of any such duty may lead to sanctions: financial penalties, imprisonment, even death. The law does not impose upon us any duties to make life more pleasant, such as duty of politeness or courtesy, or moral and ethical duties that may be established by a religious system. Such duties, so long as they do not transgress our notions of legal duties, are not recognized in our courts and their breach invokes none of the penalties our law provides.

The fundamental duty imposed on each of us by the law of torts is the duty to behave ourselves reasonably in all our conduct and in such a way that harm to others is avoided. *When a person breaches this duty, and injury results, he may be required to pay for the injury he has caused.* An English court many years ago gave this description of duty [*Heaven v. Pender*, 11 Q.B.D. 503, 509 (1883)]:

> Whenever one person is placed by circumstances in such a position in regard to another that everyone of ordinary sense who did think would at once recognize that if he did not use ordinary care and skill in his own conduct with regard to those circumstances, he would cause danger of injury to the person or property of the other, a duty arises to use ordinary care and skill to avoid such danger.

If one engages in unreasonable conduct leading to foreseeable harm, the law will consider that a breach of duty has occurred. But, although the law imposes duties, a breach of duty alone does not make the actor liable; rather, it is only a step in the chain of circumstances which can result in liability. It is a necessary, but not a sufficient, condition. A breach of duty will not be followed by liability unless the breach of duty results in an injury, and unless the breach of duty is the cause of an injury which does in fact occur. Hospitals may breach a duty by negligently blocking a fire exit, but if a fire does not occur, no tort liability would arise from such breach. The surgical nurse breaches a duty when she leaves the operating room when a sponge count is due. But if no sponge is left in the abdomen, no liability could be predicated on the breach.

If we define duty as the obligation to refrain from unreasonable conduct, we must then deal with the additional problem presented in *Palsgraf*, which is whether conduct which is clearly unreasonable to one person is also unreasonable to everyone else. There, the porter's conduct was unreasonable insofar as the passenger with the package was concerned, but was it also unreasonable as to everyone else on the platform, including Mrs. Palsgraf? The court in *Palsgraf* decided that the conduct of the porter was not unreasonable as to her, and most modern courts would probably reach the same result. The law, following Judge Cardoza in *Palsgraf*, qualifies its definition of duty by a significant limitation. The definition, so qualified, measures a person's duty to others by *the risk of harm that can reasonably be foreseen as a consequence of that person's conduct.*

Under this definition, a plaintiff seeking to recover for another's breach of duty must demonstrate that injury or harm was foreseeable as a result of the defendant's actions. A plaintiff need not show that the defendant had him specifically in mind. What he must prove is that he, the injured person, was within the class of persons to whom injury was foreseeable and therefore was within the class of persons to whom the defendant owed a duty. When a drunken driver takes to the road and drives at a high rate of speed, no particular injury to a particular person is necessarily foreseeable, but the class of persons using the highway is endangered. Any member of that group unfortunate enough to be in the path of the car would be able to claim that a duty to him had been breached by the drunken driver.

There are no physical or geographical boundaries placed on the idea of foreseeability, nor is it necessarily limited in time. Stated in another way, an injury occurring remote in distance and time from the site of the negligent conduct is no less foreseeable merely because of the geographic or time factors. The negligent firing of a high-powered rifle can obviously result in injury to one a considerable distance away; the injury can reasonably be foreseen in spite of this distance from the scene of negligence. Negligent manufacture or installation of an airplane part may cause a major tragedy on the far side of the globe. Similarly, unreasonably leaving explosives lying about may foreseeably result in harm a considerable time after the actual act.

Included in the foreseeability concept is the notion that the injury actually suffered must bear a relationship to the injury that could have been foreseen. When the drunken driver collides with another car and breaks the leg of the driver, one experiences no difficulty in concluding that the likelihood of the injury actually suffered was in fact that which made his conduct negligent in the first place; that is, drunken driving was a breach of duty to road users because injury from collisions was readily foreseeable. However, as an illustration of a situation where the question arises about the foreseeability of the particular type of injury, consider the obvious negligence of permitting a loaded revolver to be handled in a crowded room by a lively ten-year-old boy interested in cowboys. Clearly, the danger that he will shoot someone is unreasonably great, and most of us would find little difficulty in ascribing unreasonable conduct to the person furnishing the boy with the firearm. But if, rather than shooting someone, the boy drops it on his neighbor's foot, the broken bone in the foot is not the injury so readily foreseeable (i.e., the gunshot wound) as the probable consequence of the original act of giving the boy the gun. In this situation, the question would be whether harm was foreseeable from supplying the boy with an object the size and weight of the gun, rather than from giving him the control of a deadly weapon. One could conclude that the conduct was not unreasonable because placing another object of like weight to the gun in the hands of a ten-year-old boy would not have been so perilous as to render an injury foreseeable.

Foreseeability is analyzed in terms of likelihood under all the existing facts and circumstances; it includes consequences that closely or predictably— "proximately" is a word frequently used in law—follow from a course of conduct, but it excludes remote or coincidental results, however serious those results are to the injured party.

The duty rules apply to professional as well as nonprofessional conduct. When one is acting in his professional capacity, his duty is measured by a professional yardstick. The duty to use ordinary care and skill is replaced by the duty to use expert care and skill. In the case of a medical practitioner, the duty may be to act with a certain level of skill not possessed by the ordinary layman, but possessed by others engaged in medical practice in a particular geographic locality. The duty to perform as a professional person is as inherent in professional life as is the duty of all of us as citizens to behave reasonably when we drive an automobile or walk the streets or shoot a gun. In each case, the likelihood of harm can readily be recognized in the event of actions that exhibit a want of skill.

The duty to exercise professional skill is based upon the same foreseeability definition as for the layman. The measure of professional duty is based upon foreseeability of harm. By virtue of his skill, training, and knowledge the professional practitioner can perceive risks and problems not apparent to the average citizen.

The legal notion of duty and the legal notion of the reasonable man are closely related. The problem of whether one has behaved as a reasonable man behaves, which arises in many negligence cases, and the problem of whether one has behaved in such a way as to fulfill his duties toward his fellow man, which arises under the foreseeability test, are governed by much the same considerations. In each case, the question is whether the conduct could foreseeably result in injury to others. If so, it is at once negligent and a breach of duty.

Whether a particular harmful consequence could reasonably have been foreseen is basically a question that will be decided in the individual case by the jury, and, like most such questions, will be subject to a difference of opinion. For example, if a nurse were to leave unattended a delirious patient in a bed near an open window she would be neglecting her legal duty because of the readily foreseeable harm that might befall the patient.

Suppose, however, the delirious patient left his bed, ran into the hall and rang the general fire alarm. In the ensuing rush to the fire escape, a patient in another ward was injured and claimed damages. The jury might conclude that the nurse had not breached a duty to the injured patient, in that she was not required to foresee the injurious consequences to patients in other wards in her act of leaving the delirious patient.

## Duty: A Component of Patient Care

Nurses are familiar with the term "duty," which frequently carries with it a sense of moral obligation, rather than a legal connotation, and is often expressed in terms of duty to one's patient, family, or community. Legal duty and moral duty co-mingle in professional practice, but when the nurse is charged with a breach of duty, it is the idea of legal duty that is brought to bear on the analysis of her conduct. It has been stated that the measure of a person's duty is to foresee the consequences of one's conduct, in relation to harm to another that might result from that conduct. These principles are readily translated into the context of nursing practice. In fact, the degree to which the nurse can or should foresee possible harm to her patient becomes a measure of her duty and a duty to which she will be held.

The level of preparation of the nurse practitioner would have immediate bearing on her range and depth of foreseeability as exercised in giving patient care. For example, the depth of knowledge of physical, biological, and social sciences and the ability to apply this knowledge would differ for the professional and the technical nurse and would be one measure by which each would be judged in the exercise of her duty of care. Both practitioners, for example, would be able to take a blood pressure accurately, but the professional nurse would be expected, from the reading, to foresee danger signals and to discharge her duty to protect her patient by taking appropriate action. A knowledge of physical science and the physiology of the circulation of the blood is essential for the professional nurse if she is to foresee the possible dangers in the administration of intravenous fluids.

Defining a duty to foresee harm is one way of looking at the standard of conduct of the nurse, and an integral part of all of nursing practice. Examples are numerous, but to illustrate in a single area of nursing practice, let us consider administration of medications and treatments. Here the nurse is called upon to make numerous decisions and to move with certainty, at all times aware of the importance of foreseeing the consequences of her acts. Medication accidents can be catastrophic in the damages that may result; the medication can be wrong, or it may be given at the wrong time or to the wrong patient or by the wrong mode of administration. Over and beyond these errors, the nurse may fail to exercise her duty in numerous ways throughout the total procedure. The act of administration of a medication or treatment is composed of two separate nursing functions each requiring different competencies and each carrying a duty to foresee the risk of harm through derelict conduct on the part of the nurse. The first function is the reading and interpretation of the order, which requires that she have a knowledge of the drug, the purpose for which it is given, the range in dosage, and the possible untoward effects. If she does not have this information it is her duty to seek it as a part of her understanding of the order. The second function is the administration of the drug, which requires, first, the ability to evaluate the condition of the patient as it relates to the drug to be given, and, second, that evaluation having been properly made, she must then have the necessary skill to carry out the particular mode of administration as ordered. Harm may be foreseen at any point in this process, and the nurse may defer the dose until she seeks medical reconsideration, or she may decide, from her evaluation, to give the drug and observe the patient closely during administration and afterward for any reaction.

When a nurse encounters an illegible or incomplete order, her duty is obvious; she must contact the physician who wrote the order and find out what was intended, for such an order does not constitute precise instructions and therefore is not an order at all. If the nurse were to give what she thought the doctor intended and the patient suffered harm because the wrong drug or dosage was given, she would bear full legal responsibility.

Another source of danger is when the nurse is given what appears to be an erroneous order. It would indeed be a misconception for a nurse to lull herself into a false sense of security and to believe that to follow a doctor's order would obviate all legal responsibility for her part of the act. She is a person of substantial preparation in the use of medications and has a responsibility to use that knowledge. To request confirmation of a doctor's order is simply a part of intelligent nursing practice. It is not only accepted, but it is encouraged by the medical practitioner who is aware of the dual responsibility of the doctor and the nurse. Indeed, in circumstances where injury is foreseeable, the nurse has not merely the privilege but the obligation to question the order, for by failing to do so she compounds the negligent giving of an erroneous order, and implicates herself in the resulting harm to the patient, should it occur.

When a nurse is given an order to administer a drug and she does not know the nature of the drug or the effects to be anticipated, she is not in a position to foresee the consequences of the act of administering the drug. For example, reactions to drugs employed as diagnostic or therapeutic measures are not uncommon. Here both the doctor and the nurse must be alert to recognize untoward reactions or complications and must know the steps to take when they occur.

Another area in which the legal duty of the nurse is clear is when she is confronted with an order for a mode of administration that she does not feel competent to carry out. Her duty to her patient, derived from her ability to foresee the harm she might do if the procedure were not carried out with safety, would lead her to withhold administration and report to her supervisor, if she were in a hospital setting. If she were working alone, in a public health or industrial area, she should advise the doctor. At times, to withhold action or refuse to act, if it is done in the best interest of the patient, is in itself a good legal defense.

DUTY OF AFFIRMATIVE ACTION

One of the flagrant breaches of moral duty in our literature is found in the biblical recital of the priest and the Levite passing by the unfortunate man by the side of the road. Ultimately, in that case, no harm was done because the Good Samaritan followed the priest and the Levite and fulfilled his moral duty. However, whatever strong moral sanctions might be visited upon the priest and the Levite, so far as our law is concerned, they would find themselves in no difficulty. In such a society as ours with its emphasis on individual rights, it is firmly established that there is no legal duty upon any person to take any steps or to expend the slightest effort to assist or aid another in avoiding injury, regardless of how simple or easy it would be to take the necessary action, provided only that the injury is not threatened as a result of the wrongful conduct of the observer. The law in its wisdom permits an expert swimmer to watch a child drown in a shallow pool without thereby having breached any duty. Sins of omission, where no duty is owed, as opposed to sins of commission, are thought not to be within the sphere of the law. The law tells no one how to be good or moral or just. It says only that when one acts, one must act in such a manner as to avoid injury to his fellow man.

Although, as an abstract principle, no duty of affirmative action exists toward fellow men in general, the question rarely arises in court. Far more common is the situation arising where a person gratuitously undertakes to render aid or assistance to another and where, for one reason or another, he bungles the job. Any affirmative action must be undertaken with due regard for the foreseeable consequences, that is, in full compliance with the reasonable man standard and the mandates of a legal duty. The utmost in good faith, or the purest of motives, does not ever justify unreasonable conduct. The law thus shields the callous and indifferent from liability, no matter how simple it might be for them to aid others. At the same time, it tends to expose to liability those who in all good faith and from proper motives intervene to assist those in difficulty.

The problem of liability for inept though voluntary care arises most frequently from real or imagined emergencies, which catch the interest and sympathy of onlookers. Here, as in other circumstances, the actions taken must be reasonable under the circumstances. Anyone who acts does so under the obligations the law imposes. Of course, the cleanliness of the hospital is not required of emergency treatment at the roadside. But the nurse or other medical practitioner who steps into an emergency scene is clothed with the same duty as he is in his routine professional life: the duty to conduct himself in accordance with professional, not lay, standards.

This privilege of nonrescue or nonassistance, although well established insofar as strangers to one another are concerned, has no application in cases where particular relationships exist that justify or require the imposition of a duty to aid and assist. Thus, it is clear that a nurse owes a duty to her patient to take whatever steps are required to provide proper care. The patient is in the hospital or other health care facility expecting that very treatment and the nurse has knowingly accepted the responsibility of providing such treatment within the limits of her skill and knowledge. Once this special relationship comes into being, no defense of lack of duty of affirmative action will ever be allowed by the courts.

Although the relationship to the patient of the physician and the nurse is in many ways properly viewed as a joint one in which there is coordination of effort and responsibility, it is always the duty of the nurse to take positive and even forceful steps, if she sees the patient's condition deteriorating. First, she should bring the problem to the attention of the attending physician, or, if he is not available, she should secure the judgment of another physician. This responsibility for action is also shared by those administratively responsible for nursing service, and if the risk to the patient is great and medical judgment cannot be secured, appropriate action must be taken by the nurses until the time that medical assistance arrives.

In *Goff v. Doctors General Hosp.*, 166 Cal. App.2d 314, 333 P.2d 29 (1958), suit was brought against the hospital, the nurses, and the attending physician for wrongful death. The wife of the plaintiff was admitted to the obstetrical unit of the hospital, where prior to the birth of the child the physician made an incision to the left of the twelve o'clock position in the cervix to relieve a constrictive band of tissue. The incision was not sutured; instead, pelvic packs were inserted to control bleeding. During the two-hour interval following delivery, the nurse testified that on three different occasions she advised the physician that, in her opinion, the patient was bleeding too much and his response was that it was normal. Later, when the hemorrhage continued, the nurse did not check vital signs nor did she call the supervisor. According to the testimony of the nurse, her reason for not calling the physician was that "in her opinion he would not have come anyhow." About four hours after delivery, the patient went into shock and, in spite of limited emergency measures, she died of hemorrhage. The court found the hospital liable for the conduct of the nurses in their failure to exercise a proper duty of care. The nurses knew of the peril of the mother, knew the cause and origin of the danger, and their inaction was sufficient to show negligent conduct in professional practice, even though in his own right, the physician was also negligent in numerous respects.

Likewise, in *Norton v. Argonaut Ins. Co.* (*infra*, p. 189) the nurse was found guilty of failure to exercise the proper duty of care when she administered, as ordered, a drug with whose mode of administration she was unfamiliar. It was shown that she had a positive duty to confirm the dosage and the route of administration, intravenous or oral, prior to administration thereof, if she was in any doubt.

## Duty to Protect Special Interests

To this point, it has been shown that, in general, the legal right to protection from negligent injury has been extended for every person in almost all areas of personal security. The law through years of case law decisions has shown its recognition of these individual rights and at the same time it has consistently excluded certain rights from this protection. A characteristic and strength of the common law is that it may be both fixed and fluid—fixed when its decisions are consistent in following recurring facts and situations, fluid when it takes into consideration social change and advancement in a world of expanding science and technology. Illustrative of the latter characteristic are two interests that the courts have not in the past chosen to protect, but that are being recognized in light of social changes due, in a large part, to advances in medical science.

### UNBORN CHILD AS PLAINTIFF

The first interest is the duty owed to the unborn child. For many years, the law has regarded the unborn child as outside the scope of its protection and would not allow a child compensation for injuries suffered before birth. Some reasons given were that the child was not a "person" who had standing in the court of law, and that the unborn child was part of the mother at the time of the injury and that damage to it was recoverable by her. At the same time, however, inconsistencies in legal reasoning existed, in that the unborn child was recognized for the purpose of protecting property rights.

The change that has taken place in tort law is illustrated in the following contrasting decisions. *Stemmer v. Kline*, 128 N.J.L. 455, 26 A.2d 489 (1942), was an action for the negligence of the doctor in incorrectly diagnosing a pregnancy as a tumor, which led to x-ray treatments three times in the later stages of the pregnancy. A child was born who was incapable of speech or action and was without hearing. Medical science had established, at the time of this decision, that x-ray during pregnancy, to which the fetus was exposed, could be expected to cause serious damage to the central nervous system. In this instance, the law had not moved with medical science, and the court ruled that the child had no right to recover for the negligently caused injuries before birth.

In 1949, came a decision that was influential in reversing the pre-existing pattern; *Williams v. Marion Rapid Transit, Inc.*, 152 Ohio St. 114, 87 N.E.2d 334 (1949), held that, in the absence of a statute, a child who survives birth can bring action for prenatal injuries. The plaintiff was a child suing for injuries incurred while the mother was pregnant with her. It was alleged that because of the negligence of a bus driver, the mother fell when alighting from the bus. At the time of the accident the child was viable; the child was prematurely born. Subsequent heart trouble, jacksonian epilepsy, and inability to walk were claimed to be due to the injuries in utero. The court stated that "injuries to an unborn child capable of existing independent of the mother were injuries done him in person," and that following birth he could maintain an action to recover damages for injuries so inflicted.

In later decisions, the requirement of viability was challenged and the trend now is to recognize the child as a person from the time of conception, and to permit compensation for negligently caused injuries. It still appears to be the law, however, that a child born dead or a fetus killed by a tort has no right of recovery.

Although there seems to be a more flexible approach to the extension of the rights of the unborn baby tortiously injured, there is need to continue this type of critical legal reasoning, aided by advancements in medical science. It is likely that in the next several decades this area of common law will expand as claims arise from automobile accidents, excessive use of drugs, and numerous other medically recognized sources of trauma to the unborn.

MENTAL TRAUMA

The second interest the law has been slow to protect is mental trauma not associated with a physical injury, although as early as 1890, in the case of *Hill v. Kimball*, 76 Tex. 210, 13 S.W. 59 (1890), the court stated "that a physical personal injury may be produced by a strong emotion of the mind, there can be no doubt." This was a farseeing idea for that time, but several forces deterred the courts in expanding the idea. Medical science did not have actual knowledge of the power of the emotions on the human body in the precipitation of physical disorders of an organic or functional nature; the problems of proof were difficult and it was feared that to allow recovery for emotional trauma, not associated with physical impact or injury, would lead to increased litigation in which there might be many fictitious claims.

This reluctance on the part of the courts to recognize a causal connection between physical manifestations and emotional trauma is showing signs of weakening, on the grounds that no sound principles for denying a remedy could be advanced where disabling injuries are real and tangible and, further, because there is increasing judicial recognition that what the courts may have decided as a point of law could more properly have been established by medical science as a question of fact in each case. In *Falzone v. Busch*, 45 N.J. 559, 214 A.2d 12 (1965), the decision of the Supreme Court of New Jersey reflected the reconsideration of the legal principles underlying the previous decisions and held that the plaintiff could recover for any substantial bodily injury or sickness proximately resulting from the defendant's negligence in operating an automobile so close to the plaintiff as to put her in fear of her safety, despite the lack of physical impact.

Although the courts have been slow to change their position regarding emotional trauma without impact, they have for some time viewed more favorably those claims in which emotional trauma has been accompanied by demonstrable physical injuries. Because the courts have perceived that actual injuries can arise from emotional trauma, they have freely sought to permit recovery in such cases and have often resorted to very technical and imaginary holdings of what constituted physical injury. Some courts have indulged themselves in the fiction of holding that whenever there is the slightest impact upon the plaintiff, a sufficient physical invasion has occurred to carry with it all emotional difficulties, however extensive. In *Hess v. Philadelphia Transp. Co.*, 358 Pa. 144, 56 A.2d 89 (1948), plaintiff's car was stopped for a traffic light when a trolley wire came loose as a result of the defendant's negligence and came in contact with the car. Plaintiff testified as to blue flames surrounding his car and as to shock he received. He suffered no physical injuries but developed an "intense psychoneurosis" virtually disabling him, which psychiatric testimony linked to the fright plaintiff received. The court noted that in Pennsylvania there could be no recovery for fright alone, but held the electric shock to constitute a physical injury. In affirming a verdict for plaintiff, the court held that damages for fright could be recovered where fright was associated with physical injury.

Although the approach of approving substantial recoveries for emotional stress where physical injuries are minimal is somewhat of a fiction, it has served to protect honest and just claims of emotional harm arising from a defendant's negligence.

The concept of foreseeability is significant in this area in that emotional harm which is not readily foreseeable will not support recovery. Thus, for example, a person who observes a mutilation caused by the defendant and who injures himself falling in a faint would, under the present law, be said to be outside the zone of foreseeability and therefore not entitled to recovery from the defendant regardless of how negligent his conduct was in causing the accident. The contrary result might prevail if fainting occurred when the spectator witnessed the mutilation of a member of his family.

## NOTES

### (1) Duty of Disclosure

The duty to disclose to the patient the nature of the treatment being undertaken and the possibility of adverse results rests squarely upon the physician. It is a duty that cannot be delegated except to another physician; it may not be delegated to the nurse. However, the nurse may play an important but informal role in disclosure as it affects good patient care and her colleague relationship with the physician. Through an awareness on her part of the legal implications of disclosure, she can many times safeguard the interests of the patient and the physician. For example, in her close contact with the patient the nurse may be alerted to the fact that the patient is anxious about approaching surgery because he feels that information is being withheld and that the operation may be more serious than is being admitted to him; this reaction can be passed on to the surgeon in time for him to allay anxiety if possible. Emotional tension and apprehension of the patient may cloud comprehension, and even though the surgeon feels that the contemplated surgery or treatment has been fully discussed, a word from the nurse may lead the doctor to review his plans again. Many times the patient is not satisfied with information concerning proposed medical care but hesitates to ask the physician for fear the physician will think he distrusts him and his ability, or the patient may also feel that the physician is so hurried that he does not have time to answer questions. These and numerous other instances are clues to the nurse that she has a responsibility to discharge to both physician and patient.

The courts have frequently said that the relationship between the physician and his patient is one of trust and confidence, and that the physician has a duty to make a full and frank disclosure of all the facts relative to treatment being advised. The support for this legal position comes from the oft-repeated principle that every human being of adult years and sound mind has an absolute right to determine what shall be done with his own body. He might not choose to live were he to be handicapped or if a long illness would lie ahead with little hope of recovery and he knew that such an illness would place a heavy financial and emotional burden upon his family. The decision whether to risk a cure when faced with possible adverse effects is the patient's alone to make, based on his personal evaluation of the relative disadvantages in light of the physician's evaluation of the probabilities of success or failure.

The extent to which the physician is under a duty to warn a patient of the possibility of an unfavorable result of a proposed treatment depends upon the circumstances of the particular case, and, in some jurisdictions, on the practice followed by the medical profession in the community with respect to such cases. Thus, the "standard of the community" test was applied in upholding a verdict in favor of the defendant surgeon in *Di Filippo v. Preston*, 53 Del. 539, 173 A.2d 333 (1961), where medical experts had testified that it was not the practice in the community to warn patients of the possibility of resulting injury to the recurrent laryngeal nerves following a thyroidectomy.

At times, the particular religious belief of the patient could lead him to refuse treatment. Whatever reasons the patient has, his right to make his own election should be recognized, provided that he is fully aware of the consequences of his action and is capable of making a decision.

In *Erikson v. Dilgard*, 252 N.Y.S. 2d 705 (Sup. Ct. 1962), the patient was suffering from gastrointestinal bleeding and had refused to submit to a blood transfusion prior to surgery. This, in the opinion of the attending physician, made it a virtual certainty that the patient would not survive the operation and therefore, from a medical point of view, constituted suicide. The hospital sought a court order to direct the patient to submit to the transfusion. The court, upon finding that the patient was competent and able to make his own decision, refused to issue a compulsive order and held that the man had a right to make his own decision, unreasonable though it might seem to the medical experts.

A case directly contrary to *Erickson* in result is *Application of President and Directors of Georgetown College, Inc.*, 331 F.2d 1000 (D.C. Cir. 1963). There a woman member of the Jehovah's Witness religious group, and the mother of a seven-month-old child, refused a blood transfusion even though it appeared vital to save her life. Upon her refusal, her doctor sought a court order permitting the transfusion. Such an order was granted, upon the ground, among others, that the mother would be guilty of abandoning her child by dying, if the transfusion were not administered, and that the state could not sanction child abandonment. The *Georgetown* case, and a similar case in Illinois, is discussed in a *Note*, 18 *Univ. Fla. L. Rev.* 595 (1966).

Although the law directs that full information should be made available to the patient and he be allowed to make a decision knowing the consequences of his act, it also recognizes that this course of action does not offer an easy solution for the members of the medical profession, and that the absolute duty of disclosure may be tempered in some situations. Each doctor must endeavor to do what his professional opinion dictates should be done for the welfare of the patient, and in particular, he is also legally obligated to refrain from undertaking a course of action, including disclosure, which may result in undue emotional harm.

However, to minimize the risk or to deny the risk to secure the patient's cooperation has been found by the courts to amount to a lack of disclosure. In *Woods v. Brumlop*, 71 N.M. 221, 377 P.2d 520 (1962), a patient under the care of a psychiatrist followed his advice and submitted to electroshock treatments in a mental institution; the treatments resulted, according to the plaintiff, in a compression fracture of the spine and loss of hearing. The basis of her complaint was that her physician had failed to advise her of the inherent danger of electroshock treatment and, further, that upon direct inquiry, he had told her that no harmful results could occur. Counsel for the defendant psychiatrist argued that an exception to the rule of full disclosure should be made, because the patient was emotionally upset and that a discussion of the dangers of the treatment would have tended to increase the emotional unbalance. The court in its decision recognized this as a possible defense, but went on to say:

A physician who misleads a patient by not only failing to give a warning of reasonable and recognized risks inherent in a treatment after which the patient would have refused the treatment, but by affirmatively assuring her that there are no risks, knowing such statement to be untrue, is liable for the harmful consequences of the treatment. Such a failure to disclose, or the giving of an untrue answer as to the probable consequences of a treatment constitutes malpractice; and a doctor who fails to so advise his client, or gives an untrue answer as to such consequences, is liable for malpractice unless his failure to do so comes within one of the exceptions to the rule requiring candor and disclosure. Under the circumstances of this case, a fact issue was presented for determination by the jury upon which there was no necessity for expert medical testimony.

In brief then, the physician must balance the patient's possible psychophysical response to apprehension, which could well heighten the risk of the diagnostic measure or treatment, against full disclosure to enable the patient to make an informed decision. The medicolegal position regarding duty of disclosure is well summed up in *Slago v. Leland Stanford Jr. Univ. Board of Trustees*, 154 Cal. App.2d 560, 317 P.2d 170 (1957):

A physician violates his duty to his patient and subjects himself to liability if he withholds any facts which are necessary to form the basis of an intelligent consent by the patient to the proposed treatment. Likewise the physician may not minimize the known dangers of a procedure or operation in order to induce his patient's consent. At the same time, the physician must place the welfare of his patient above all else and this very fact places him in a position in which he sometimes must choose between two alternative courses of action. One is to explain to the patient every risk attendant upon any surgical procedure or operation, no matter how remote; this may well result in alarming a patient who is already unduly apprehensive and who may as a result refuse to undertake surgery in which there is in fact minimal risk; it may also result in actually increasing the risks by reason of the physiological results of the apprehension itself. The other is to recognize that each patient presents a separate problem, that the patient's mental and emotional condition is important and in certain cases may be crucial, and that in discussing the element of risk a certain amount of discretion must be employed consistent with the full disclosure of facts necessary to an informed consent.

## (2) Good Samaritan Acts—Moral or Legal Obligation

A trespasser in the railroad yard was struck by a freight car, solely because of his own negligence. The employees of the railroad did not assume charge of the injured man but did call an ambulance when the train reached a place where it could be safely stopped and not block the track. To the charge that the railroad employees failed to exercise a duty the court, in *Union Pac. Ry. v. Cappier*, 66 Kan. 649, 72 Pac. 281 (1903), replied:

With the humane side of the question courts are not concerned. . . . For withholding relief from the suffering, for failure to respond to the calls of worthy charity, or for faltering in the bestowment of brotherly love on the unfortunate, penalties are found not in the law of men, but in the higher law, the violation of which is condemned by the voice of conscience.

Although the nurse can maintain the aloofness which characterized the railroad men, she, because of her professional commitment to mitigate human suffering, is faced with a difficult moral question when she is confronted with a situation outside her professional relationships in which another person is in peril and in need of her professional service. As we have seen, any bystander— including a nurse—who does attempt to render assistance must do so in a reasonable fashion in light of existing circumstances; we have also seen that the duty upon a nurse is to act as a reasonable practitioner of nursing if she chooses to act. Although the nurse, like everyone else, is legally free not to act, she knows that the ethical obligations of her profession require devotion to the interest of others and that the knowing failure to come to the aid of an injured person would severely clash with her professional obligations. Yet she is reluctant to intervene on her own because of the possibility that her actions will later be called into question and that she will be sued.

Because the public interest seems to require that persons with skill and training be encouraged to use their abilities to aid others in emergencies, the legislatures of many states have relaxed the standards of legal liability applicable to members of the medical professions by so-called Good Samaritan Acts. These statutes are designed to protect medical practitioners from litigation, in that specified medical practitioners are absolved from liability except for gross negligence in the manner in which they undertake to render care. (Gross negligence is generally considered to be the willful or wanton disregard of the rights of others.)

The extent to which such statutes offer protection to any person or class of person depends on the language of the particular statute and may vary considerably in scope from state to state. For example, some such statutes apply only to physicians, some include nurses as well, and some apply to anyone attempting to provide assistance. For full discussion of these statutes, see Flowers and Kennedy, *Good Samaritan Legislation*, 39 Temple L.Q. 481 (1965). In Ratcliffe, R., *The Good Samaritan and the Law* (New York: Doubleday and Company, Inc., 1966) there is an excellent compilation of essays and articles on all aspects of the problem.

In a note in the *Columbia Law Review* concerning Good Samaritan Acts, the author considers the problems giving rise to legislation, the effect of the statutes, and possible alternative solutions. His conclusion is that a better solution to the problem caused by medical emergencies would be legislation *requiring* doctors to provide emergency treatment. Do you agree? Should such a law apply to nurses as well? The following is an excerpt from the note.

## Good Samaritans and Liability for Medical Malpractice, 64 Colum. L. Rev. 1301 (1964)*

A skier who had fallen in pain upon a slope in the Sierra Madre mountains was refused attention by several physicians in the vicinity. On the Bronx Whitestone Bridge, a motorist lay in need of urgent medical attention as a physician drove past and deliberately declined to stop. In each instance the doctors were deterred by the awareness that, in the rendering of assistance, any allegable failure to perform the task with reasonable care would expose them to possible suit for malpractice. The physicians realized that, on the other hand, they could ignore the injured person with complete immunity. For at common law it is the "Good Samaritan" who "may find himself liable where those who passed by on the other side will not."

GOOD SAMARITAN STATUTES

Viewed against a background of increasing liability for doctors, the various Good Samaritan statutes represent attempts to induce the physician to render

* Reprinted with permission of the *Columbia Law Review*.

volunteer assistance in rescue operations by granting immunity from actions for malpractice. The primary question is whether the statutes achieve their avowed objective by providing adequate assurances of protection from suit.

A. Statutory Interpretation

In Good Samaritan statutes the scope of immunity is invariably qualified, often by the condition that the doctor invoking statutory protection must have acted in "good faith." This particular condition, however, is susceptible to two conflicting interpretations: it can either refer exclusively to a subjective state of mind and honesty of purpose notwithstanding facts indicating misconduct, or it can require objective standards of behavior to avoid granting a "carte blanche to recklessness or to wholly unnecessary disregard of life, limb and property." The Good Samaritan statutes generally fail to choose between these two possible constructions of good faith. Even Pennsylvania, the only state that attempted to define the statutory term, failed to distinguish clearly between subjective and objective standards. Although in that instance confusion may have been significantly lessened by imposition of a second qualification—that the physician must have acted without gross negligence or intent to cause harm—for statutes that require merely good faith for immunity from suit, the ambiguity remains unresolved. Confusion is further compounded in California where, under two Good Samaritan statutes enacted four years apart, physicians are held to a standard of good faith alone, while nurses must in addition not have been guilty of gross negligence.

The scope of immunity conferred upon the Good Samaritan doctor may be limited by other statutory conditions that are similarly subject to conflicting interpretation under the traditional definitions of tort law. The physician may be required to have acted with "due care," without "gross negligence" or without "willful or wanton" misconduct. The statutory term "due care," however, may signify the absence either of negligence or of something approximating gross negligence. Gross negligence is usually described as the failure to use slight care, but at best differs from negligence only in degree. And the contradictory term "willful and wanton" negligence, vaguely denotes quasi-intentional conduct that is qualitatively different from negligence. These statutory terms—of uncertain content and vague definition—severely condition the doctor's immunity from suit; in large measure they still leave his liability for malpractice in rescue operations to the determination of the jury.

Under most of the statutes immunity will be granted only in an "emergency" situation or for the rendering of "emergency care." The concept of emergency has been employed in the field of tort law to refer to an unforeseen combination of circumstances calling for spontaneous action to avoid an imminent danger. The application of this accepted definition to the Good Samaritan statutes immediately raises a number of important questions. Will the physician who has been called to the aid of a seriously injured person but has had time to consider what steps he must take, be denied immunity because his conduct did not constitute spontaneous action? The statutes do not indicate when an emergency will be considered as terminated. Will the doctor who continues to treat an injured person after he has reached the hospital fall within the scope of legislative protection? Most of the provisions do not limit the physical locus of the emergency. Does this mean that an emergency can occur even during hospital or office treatment, or that in the course of an operation a surgeon can declare an emergency upon discovery of an unforeseen difficulty? Furthermore, in analogous contexts several courts have introduced the additional requirement that the threatened danger appear to be one of death or serious injury. When the physician arrives at a motor accident where tragedy appears to be imminent, but finds instead that the driver has suffered only minor injuries, will statutory immunity be denied for lack of severe injury?

A number of provisions impose the additional requirement that aid be rendered at the scene of an "accident," thus raising further complications. An accident is generally defined as an event proceeding from an unknown cause and occurring without the will or fault of the person involved. Will the physician then be protected in any rescue situation, or must he have a reasonable belief that the injured person was not at fault? Will the doctor be held liable if in fact the injured person was not completely free from negligence?

Two other problems involving remedies and conflict of laws arise in the interpretation of Good Samaritan statutes. Many of the provisions state that immunity will not be granted when assistance is rendered "for remuneration or with the expectation of remuneration." Under established practice, doctors may recover in quasi-contract for services rendered in rescue operations. The statutes, however, apparently require that the remedy be surrendered as a prerequisite to protection. Thus the physician who desires to collect for rescue services performed may have to wait to see how fully the patient recovers before requesting his fee. Moreover, in view of the indefiniteness of the "emergency" concept, the physician wishing to claim possible immunity in ambiguous rescue situations must necessarily limit his demands for compensation to those services unquestionably not connected with the emergency. . . .

## B. Conclusion

In encouraging volunteer medical assistance in rescue operations, the Good Samaritan statutes may prove to be just as ineffective as the immunity they purport to confer is uncertain. The statutory conditions placed upon the grant of immunity are vague and ill-defined; they leave a great many factual questions to be decided by a jury, thereby encouraging the emergency patients to bring actions for malpractice. It is, therefore, overly optimistic to anticipate that substantially more doctors will stop at automobile accidents or aid injured strangers. The fear of malpractice suits persists less from the threat of an adverse judgment than from a concern that the commencement of any action will damage the doctor's reputation. By failing both to provide a secure immunity from suit and to discourage malpractice actions, the Good Samaritan statutes may in effect have perpetuated the physician's identification of emergency assistance with very possible malpractice liability. . . .

## C. Statutory Affirmative Duties for Physicians

Statutes imposing affirmative obligations upon physicians as a class could constitutionally be enacted by the various state legislatures. The power of the state over the medical profession and the practice of medicine has been recognized as complete. With respect to requiring positive action, in the past the legislatures have created new liabilities and imposed new duties in the interest of public health and welfare. For example, a number of statutes direct an automobile driver to render assistance to any person he has injured even though the original accident was not the driver's fault. Under a federal statute, the master of a vessel—where there is no "serious danger" to his own ship, crew or passengers—must render assistance to "every person who is found at sea in danger of being lost." Most important, doctors in many states are subject to the affirmative obligation to report all cases in which a child has been treated for injuries that may have been caused by parental mistreatment or neglect.

The potential value in imposing affirmative duties has been obscured by the traditional and largely unchallenged fears that obligating persons to render aid will enslave them and create an "exalted form of socialism," that it will tend to destroy individualism and make each man his brother's keeper, and that it cannot command general compliance or be effectively enforced in individual cases. It should be noted, however, that in many European countries statutes creating these duties have been enforced and in this country affirmative obligations have been imposed in several areas without subverting the rights of the individual. Finally, since the statute reinforces an already established ethical standard of the medical profession, widespread noncompliance seems unlikely. While a few individual doctors may deliberately pass by the scene of an accident without being detected, the legislative purpose may nevertheless be achieved—to induce the desired conduct on the part of the general profession rather than to coerce or police individual physicians.

The traditional arguments should not remain unquestioned. The needs of the public in a changing order continuously demand a new balancing of values, a new evaluation of what the law ought to be. The strongest considerations favoring the imposition of affirmative duties upon physicians can be found in the public interest in insuring available medical assistance in emergency situations and in the role of the medical profession in society. It would seem that an analogy could properly be drawn between the doctor and the lawyer—an analogy directed particularly to the attorney's affirmative duty to defend indigents in criminal actions. The profession of medicine, like that of law, is affected with a public interest. Surely the question must arise, "why, in extreme cases, should not the nearby physician be placed under the same obligation?"

Once the alternative of affirmative duties has been accepted, any legislative attempt to require medical assistance in rescue situations must adequately resolve numerous problems of definition and limitation. The statute must clearly identify those who are under a duty to act, for the benefit of whom, and under what circumstances the duty will arise. Is liability to depend upon a mere failure to render assistance or is it to be predicated on and proportioned to the injurious effects suffered as a result of the failure? The legislature must also decide whether to obligate only physicians directly confronted with the rescue situation or, in addition, those doctors summoned to render assistance by a third party. Will criminal sanctions be employed? If civil enforcement is considered desirable, will the injured individual be given a cause of action or will the physician be subject to administrative suspension of license? Certain affirmative defenses must be considered: specifically both the excuse that to have rendered aid would have created a risk of equal danger, and that the physician honestly or reasonably believed that the particular situation did not require his assistance. If duties are to arise from a summons by a third person, will the doctor be permitted to fulfill his obligation by requesting aid from another physician more readily accessible to the injured person? Finally, the statute will have to consider the legitimate interests of the physician who fulfills the affirmative obligations imposed. Should it preserve the doctor's right to recover in quasi-contract for his services? Should liability for malpractice in rescue operations be limited, or—if not precluded by constitutional restrictions—completely abolished?

CONCLUSION

Underlying the recently enacted Good Samaritan statutes is the legislative determination that the failure of doctors voluntarily to render medical aid in rescue situations requires statutory correction. Not only are these statutes contrary to the trend of increased liability for doctors, but unfortunately the attempt to encourage assistance by limiting remedies for malpractice seems doomed to failure both by the inherent ambiguities in the statutory provisions and by the exaggerated fear of malpractice suits. If this prophecy is fulfilled in practice, the various state legislatures will be confronted with the difficult choice between the complete abrogation of liability for malpractice in emergency situations and the impositions of an affirmative duty to render medical assistance. Total immunity for doctors might be struck down as unconstitutional, particularly in states with a right to a remedy provision; moreover, even if sustained, immunization could very well fail to secure the desired objective. Legislatures, therefore, might seriously consider taking the less circuitous course of requiring physicians to render assistance in emergency situations.

The imposition of affirmative obligations on any group of persons is neither historically unjustifiable nor repugnant to the moral sensibilities of society. In a sense, development within the law may be seen as a widening circle continuously encompassing a greater range of moral obligations. In situations where the exhortation of morality or professional ethics is obscured by anxiety over individual well-being, it is arguable that in the interest of the general welfare the state should reinforce a felt obligation to society by an affirmative command.

## (3) Hospital Liability for Patient Care—An Expanded Responsibility for the Nurse

A recent decision of the Illinois Supreme Court, [*Darling v. Charleston Community Memorial Hospital*, 33 Ill. 2d 326, 211 N.E. 2d 253 (1966)] redefines and expands both the corporate duties of a hospital and the duties of the nurses working as hospital employees. The facts of the case are reported in detail in 50 Ill. App.2d 253, 200 N.E.2d 149 (1964). In that case, Dorrence Darling, the son of the plaintiff, was admitted to the emergency room of the Charleston Community Hospital for the treatment of an injury to his leg incurred during football practice. The hospital, a 45-bed institution, was a member of the American Hospital Association, and accredited by the Joint Commission on Accreditation of Hospitals, and licensed by the State of Illinois. The hospital maintained an active and a consultative medical staff, which did not include an orthopedic surgeon on active status. However, two well-qualified practitioners in orthopedics from a nearby town had been appointed to the consultant staff. The nursing service consisted of registered nurses, students of nursing, and practical nurses as well as nurse's aides. Laboratory and x-ray facilities, appropriately staffed, were available to augment patient care, and a registered pathologist was on call.

Medical service for the emergency room was on a rotating basis, and on the day of Dorrence Darling's injury, a surgeon who had long been on the staff was called. On arrival, he ordered an x-ray of the boy's leg, which showed a comminuted fracture of the right tibia and fibula. The surgeon brought the bones into proper alignment and applied a cast directly to the leg, using no stockinette or padding under the plaster cast. The boy was then sent to a room in the hospital, where over a two-week period the condition of the leg steadily deteriorated. Then, his parents moved him to another hospital, where, under the care of a skilled orthopedic surgeon and in spite of every effort to save the leg, amputation below the knee was necessary.

Suit was brought against the hospital and the treating physician. The hospital records, including the nurses' notes, were admitted into evidence at the trial. They indicated the events that had led to the charges of negligence made against the doctor and against the hospital. Frequent notations were made by the nurses of the condition of the toes, which were not covered by the cast. Early notations reported the degree of swelling and that the color was good and the toes were warm. Over a three-day period, the notes reflected observation of edematous toes, dark in color and insensitive to touch. Repeated notations were made in the nurses' notes of pain and of the ineffectiveness of the drugs given in an attempt to relieve this pain. The surgeon visited the patient frequently but did not call an orthopedic consultant, for in his opinion, the situation was satisfactory. Two days after the cast was applied, the surgeon "notched" it to free the toes, and one day later a lengthwise strip was cut from the cast. When this was done, the leg was cut on both sides through the misuse of the Stryker saw, which was later followed by seepage of blood and a strong odor.

Prior to trial, the doctor settled the claim against him for $40,000, and the case proceeded against the hospital. At the trial, the jury found the hospital liable and damages against it were ultimately awarded in the amount of $110,000. The hospital appealed, contending that the care that had been provided by it was in accordance with standard practice obtaining in similar hospitals, and that it was powerless to forbid or command any act of the physicians or surgeons in the practice of their profession. It also contended that it was not liable for the nurses' conduct since they were acting under the orders of the physician.

The court held that the hospital could be found liable either for breach of its own duty or for breaches of duty by its nurses. In so holding, the court set forth a legal doctrine concerning hospitals that appears to create new legal obligations for both the hospital and the nurse.

### DIFFERENT APPROACH TO DETERMINING A STANDARD OF CARE

Instead of the usual means of establishing the standard of care on the basis of current practice in the community, the plaintiff introduced into evidence hospital bylaws, regulations based on state statutes governing the licensure of hospitals, and the criteria for accreditation of the Joint Commission on Accreditation of Hospitals. These documents, the Illinois court reasoned, constituted a commitment to a standard of conduct that had not been fulfilled. The regulations provided, among other things:

2. The medical staff shall be organized in accordance with written by-laws, rules and regulations, approved by the governing board. The by-laws, rules and regulations shall specifically provide:

h. For consultation between medical staff members in complicated cases.

The Standards for Hospital Accreditation promulgated by the Joint Commission on Accreditation of Hospitals, provided among other things:

6. ... It is the duty of the hospital staff to its Chief of Service and Executive Committee to see that members of the staff do not fail in the matter of calling consultants as needed.

Similarly, the hospitals' own bylaws provided that:

The purpose of this organization shall be:
1. To insure that all patients admitted to the hospital or treated in the out-patient department receive the best possible care.

The bylaws also provided:

11. Consultations.
Except in an emergency, consultation with a member of the Medical Staff will be required in all major cases in which the patient is not a good risk or should the diagnosis appear to be obscure ...

The court said that these matters were appropriate for the jury to consider as the measure of defendant's legal duty, and that even though it was not the current practice in the community to oversee the doctor's treatment, the evidence of the bylaws, standards, and regulations aided the jury in deciding what was feasible for the hospital to undertake, and what it knew or should have known in the course of providing care for the patient.

The court, in holding that the materials were appropriate to consider, said:

The Standards for Hospital Accreditation, the state licensing regulations and the defendant's by-laws demonstrate that the medical profession and other responsible authorities regard it as both desirable and feasible that a hospital assume certain responsibilities for the care of the patient.

Additional comments were that the hospital had failed to perform its duties to review the work of the physician or to require consultation when the patient's condition clearly indicated the necessity therefor.

A NEW DUTY OF CARE FOR THE NURSE

We have already seen cases in which the courts have found nurses derelict in their duty in failing to bring to the attention of the physician the deteriorating condition of the patient. However, the court in *Darling* went further. It defined a new duty for the nurse, that of informing the hospital administration of any deviation in proper medical care that poses a threat to the well-being of the patient. After holding that the hospital was required to have a sufficient number of trained nurses capable of recognizing the progressive gangrenous condition of the plaintiff's right leg and of bringing the same to the attention of the hospital administration, the court went on to say:

. . . the jury could reasonably have concluded that the nurses did not test for circulation in the leg as frequently as necessary, that skilled nurses would have promptly recognized the conditions that signalled a dangerous impairment of circulation in the plaintiff's leg, and would have known that the condition would become irreversible in a matter of hours. At that point, it became the nurses' duty to inform the attending physician, and if he failed to act, to advise the hospital authorities so that appropriate action might be taken [211 N.E. 2d at 258].

NURSING ADMINISTRATION UNDER THE DARLING RULE

The job of the courts is to define legal duties, not to define their scope in particular situations or direct how they shall be discharged. The *Darling* court followed this pattern, where it defined expanded duties for both the hospital and the nurse, but gave no hint as to how those duties should be carried out. Questions therefore immediately arise concerning the effect of this decision on the future practice of nursing, both in the sense of discharging the nurse's own newly expanded duty and also her role as a hospital employee in implementing the responsibility of the hospital to supervise medical care. The nurse is a key figure in each of these new duties. Her first responsibility when concerned over the progress of a patient has always been to bring it to the attention of the attending physician. Under rare circumstances when satisfaction is not obtained, under the *Darling* rule, the role of the nurse may then be to follow appropriate administrative channels in which she has a definite obligation to her employer to *initiate an inquiry* into the condition of a patient. It would then fall upon the hospital administration to carry the inquiry forward with the medical staff. To protect the nurse and the hospital, there should be clear-cut administrative policies that would show that the obligation of inquiry is assumed by nursing service and spell out the channels to be followed.

The formulation of policies dealing with the conduct of the nurse in this particular area should first be developed within the nursing service organization and then be processed for approval by hospital administration and the medical staff organization. Some hypothetical questions for nursing service staff discussion to stimulate thinking regarding policy level considerations are:

Assuming that in the same factual situation as arose in *Darling*, the staff nurse reports to the director of nursing service that the cast appears to be too tight, and the director states that she will deal with the situation and nothing is done. What should the staff nurse do?

In the same factual situation, assume that the staff nurse reports to the director of nursing service, and she goes immediately to the hospital administrator, who takes the attitude that to make any move would put the hospital in the position of practicing medicine and might lead to serious problems with the medical staff. Do the members of the nursing staff have any further responsibility?

Although it is the responsibility of the patient's physician to request consultation when indicated, under the *Darling* decision, it is the responsibility of the medical staff, through its chiefs of service and executive committee, to make certain that members of the staff do not fail in the matter of calling consultants as needed. As the director of nursing service, you are aware of the critical need for medical attention in a situation similar to that of the Darling boy. Will you bring this situation to the attention of the chief of staff and try to deal with the problem on this level before going to the hospital administrator? Will you report to both? Or will you rely solely on the hospital administrator to work it out on that administrative level?

The *Darling* case has received much legal comment. See Note, *Hospital Liability—A New Duty of Care*, 14 Maine L. Rev., 102 (1967); Chayt, A., Hospital Responsibility for Medical Care, *New Eng. J. Med.*, 274:507 (1967). These articles should be examined for various analyses of the *Darling* decision.

## (4) Prevention of Professional Liability of the Nurse

In the article which follows, the physician in relation to his professional liability is discussed. Substitute the term "professional nurse" for "physician" and then consider the three basic causes of liability as defined by this writer. What application can you make to the conduct of the nurse that would aid her in preventing litigation? Is there a direct analogy between the legal pitfalls for the physician and those for the nurse? Are there deviations in nurse–patient relationships compared with those of the physician; if so, would these deviations render the nurse any less liable to suit?

### Hassard, H., Professional Liability Claims Prevention, *J.A.M.A.*, 163: 1267 (1957)*

Analysed in retrospect to trace causes, nearly all professional liability claims are found to have been preventable. But when we compare these real causes of claims and suits with the kinds of professional liability claims prevention we often hear recommended, the treatment appears to be directed at symptoms rather than at the disease.

Professional liability claims will be neither prevented nor reduced in size or frequency by "educating" attorneys, by reducing the amount of insurance physicians carry, by attempts to cover up in cases in which the doctor is legally liable for injuries suffered by the patient, by seeking special legislation that would in effect place the physician above the law, by circularizing lists of patients who have sued doctors, or by any other action that does not strike at the real causes of claims and suits. Any program that is unrealistic, that is unobjective in its approach or that is retaliatory against the public or any of its segments might just as well not be undertaken; it simply will not work. Worse, it will probably backfire and aggravate the problem.

The real causes of professional liability claims are (1) misunderstanding by the physician of his legal duties to the patient; (2) actual malpractice; and (3) human relations problems. Claims prevention, to be successful, must center upon the treatment of these causes.

### DEFINITIONS

The first point to consider is the word "prevention." Actually, medical malpractice cannot be completely prevented, at least until the human being incapable of making a mistake is invented. Since medical malpractice is the law of negligence applied to professional services, 100% prevention of professional liability claims would necessitate a profession that never ever is negligent either by omission or commission. Of course, at this writing such prevention is not possible, in physicians or anyone else.

* Reprinted with permission of the *Journal of the American Medical Association* and Howard Hassard.

What is really meant by the term "claims prevention" is a safety program, an understanding of the methods of conducting a medical practice that, first, will minimize professional error, and, second, will reduce the likelihood of an angry patient if the results of treatment are less than could be desired by the patient or are due to error. Industrial accidents have not been eliminated, but a diligent industrial safety program has reduced their frequency. Fires have not been prevented, but a diligent safety program has reduced the incidence of destructive fires.

"Malpractice" is just another way of saying failure of a physician to use average skill, care, and precaution in rendering his professional services to a patient. The law of malpractice is a part of the over-all law governing human relations, which requires that all of us use reasonable care to avoid injuring others. It is a special part of the general law of negligence, applicable to those who undertake to treat the sick and injured.

"Malpractice" is an unfortunate word, because it so commonly implies that its victim is a bad doctor. This is not so. The best trained and most conscientious physician may err in a particular case, or his legal agent (nurse, technician, assistant) may err, and the law may consider such error to be his negligence as to that particular case. Legally, no generalization is implied or warranted. Further, "malpractice" as a rule of law is not limited to physicians; it applies to all professional services furnished on a contract basis. It is applicable to attorneys, dentists, engineers, construction contractors, architects, and barbers, to name a few. Under a different label, that of "products liability," it applies to manufacturers.

A more accurate term for physicians' legal responsibility would be "professional tort liability." However, "malpractice" is imbedded in both legal and medical literature and habit of thought, so its use no doubt will continue.

The law requires physicians (*a*) to possess at least the average skill and knowledge possessed by other physicians in the same community and in the same field of practice and (*b*) to apply their skill and knowledge carefully and prudently.

These requirements are imposed by law at the very instant the physician-patient relationship is created, and these legal duties are independent of any other factor, including compensation.

## THE CAUSES OF CLAIMS

The first step in a safety or prevention program is a realistic appraisal of the reasons why some patients resort to law for redress of grievances, actual or fancied. To determine these causes, inquiry must be made into all facets of malpractice claims; an objective and systematic study is necessary.

Efforts along this line have been undertaken in New York and California; the results are not necessarily conclusive, but I mention them as illustrative of the type of inquiry that must be undertaken to get at causes. Most cases, both warranted and unwarranted, are found to stem from human relations problems. There is a lack of frankness or human understanding by the physician; people are not inanimate objects, nor can they be assumed to be stupid. The physician must be kind, courteous, sympathetic, and frank if he is to avoid sowing the seeds of doubt, resentment, distrust, and anger. Many claims originate from malicious or thoughtless and uninformed criticisms by a physician to a patient regarding the care received from another doctor. Another substantial cause is hasty sending of a bill or resort by physicians to collection agencies, particularly without adequate prior sympathetic effort to ascertain the patient's state of mind with respect to the services furnished and the results obtained. Frequently, friends or relatives who are physicians, nurses, pharmacists, or lawyers stimulate dissatisfaction and urge the dissatisfied patient to sue.

Another group of professional cases results from the physician's lack of understanding of his legal duties to the patient. In this general category are failures to obtain proper consents, failure to put the uncooperative patient on notice that his refusal to follow advice will result in harm to him, and failure to arrange for a substitute when unable to attend in person.

A final group of claims and suits results from actual medical malpractice. This group is relatively small. In northern California in the past 10 years approximately 10% of all closed malpractice claims have involved out of court settlements or court-awarded damages. This means that 90% of all claims were not sufficiently meritorious to warrant compensation to the patient. Granted that some were borderline, with honest differences of opinion that could be settled only by litigation, nevertheless a large proportion could have been eliminated if a proper understanding between physician and patient had existed. But actual malpractice does occur.

## PREVENTION

What, then, may be done to reduce the frequency of claims?

The most important element in a prevention program is the intensive education of each and every physician with respect to (a) his legal duties (i.e., what is medical malpractice), (b) his responsibilities to the public, (c) the real underlying causes for patient dissatisfaction, (d) the do's and dont's to avoid being sued, and (e) the inter-relation of his responsibilities with those of others (i.e., nurse, hospital, consultant, laboratory, etc.).

It is essential that practising physicians be at least reasonably well informed on the basic legal rules that govern their activities. To too many physicians the law is a mystery, paralleled only by the mystery of medicine to lawyers. Two serious consequences, malpracticewise, of inadequate legal knowledge by physicians are: (a) Nonrecognition by a physician of the fact that a particular course of action is contrary to law until it is too late; and (b) Erroneous judgment of the acts of another physician because of application of a nonlegal standard to the other doctor's acts (this frequently triggers a malpractice claim or suit).

An explanation of the basic rules of medical malpractice and their everyday application must be available to every practicing physician, and if necessary must be emphasized over and over again until the lesson is learned. An elementary exposition of the law of malpractice in plain English is an integral part of any worthwhile educational program. It should start in the medical schools. There should be a brief course taught in a realistic and elementary fashion in every medical school. The subject should be repeated to hospital residents by means of short lectures during the period of residency; the subject should again be repeated to all applicants for admission to county medical society membership. Sufficient time for at least an elementary discussion of malpractice should be allotted in each of these forums. In addition, seminars on medical malpractice should be conducted periodically by each county medical society.

Written material such as textbooks and pamphlets have their place, but they cannot and do not convey a basic understanding; old-fashioned classroom teaching has no substitute.

Basic instruction in "malpractice prevention" should stress, at the very least, these major points:

1. Do not undertake any procedure unless you are fully qualified.
2. When in doubt—consult.
3. Shun experimentation or the use of drugs or procedures with which you are not fully familiar—if the patient's welfare requires a calculated risk, explain it in advance.
4. If an accident happens (e.g., foreign body lost during surgery, wrong bottle taken from shelf, etc.), explain fully and carefully what occurred—do not conceal, do not say "I made a mistake," do not blame someone else (nurse, etc.)—but, do explain the facts.
5. At all times maintain current, accurate and legible records—never alter, or destroy, a record after a complaint is registered.
6. Don't take on more work than you can reasonably handle—remember, fatigue causes accidents everywhere, not just on highways.
7. If you and a patient are not compatible, sever relations and help the patient to another physician—you will both be happier.
8. Discuss your fees frankly and in advance. Realize that people have many obligations other than the cost of medical care.
9. Keep abreast of medicine. Physicians and lawyers alike never complete their schooling. Remember, we asked for it.


## (5) Shifting Legal Viewpoint on Prenatal Injuries

Prenatal injuries were long denied recognition by the courts, but because of advances in medical sciences, legal decisions came to recognize a right of action for congenital malformations and other defects resulting from environmental causes. The following note suggests the impact of advances in medical science on the law, and how scientific knowledge can alter long-standing legal principles.

Over the years, one reason given for failing to give legal recognition to prenatal injuries as a cause of action was that it would open the doors of the courts to many fictitious claims. From your study of the medical basis for prenatal injuries, do you see this as a possible danger or is medical science becoming sufficiently conclusive in this area that proof of a causal relationship can be established? What supporting evidence can you add to those illustrations given in this article?

### The Impact of Medical Knowledge on the Law Relating to Prenatal Injuries, 110 U. Penn. L. Rev. 554 (1962)*

Until recently, teratology, the study of congenital malformations—here defined as gross structural defects—has been a somewhat neglected field of medicine. The apathetic state of medical research in this area was the natural result of the now discredited belief that all congenital anomalies are of hereditary origin. It was thought that the fetus, protected from environmental influences by maternal inclosure, develops in a state of uterine bliss. It followed from this belief that teratological research was thought to have little besides eugenic significance. The fundamental error of this position has now been dramatically exposed. In the 1940's, three catalytic developments—a German measles epidemic in Australia, research on the inheritance of the Rh factor in fetal blood, and the bombing of Hiroshima and Nagasaki—implicated environment as a cause of congenital malformation and spurred research in this field. This history helps to explain the great strides taken by the science of teratology in the last few years and the resulting rapid emergence of a new field of medicine, here termed antenatal pediatrics. It also casts light on some recent developments in the law of torts dealing with prenatal injuries and calls for increasing awareness by lawyers and law scholars of what medicine now knows and does not know about why some children are born with imperfect bodies or minds.

It is now known that congenital defects can result from heredity, from environmental factors—any causative agent other than those present as the sole result of inheritance from the parents—, or from a complex interaction between the two. The fetus can be adversely affected by environment either directly, through gross mechanical injury—usually a strong blow inflicted upon the mother's abdomen—, or indirectly, through the mother. The latter process can result from a causative agent initially within the mother or from the mother's exposure to some external factor, the effects of which are transmitted through her to the fetus. In most cases this transmission operates through the placenta—the bridge between the fetal and maternal circulatory systems which serves to transport nutriment and respiratory gases to the fetus. Imbalances in the mother's circulation can have an effect on the fetus; the resulting change in intrauterine environment can cause difficulties ranging from prenatal death to minor congenital defects. Beyond these general propositions, however, much remains unknown; in most cases it is impossible to isolate the exact cause of a particular defect.

Contemporaneous with the rapid expansion of knowledge about congenital malformations has been a complementary legal development of major significance. Beginning in 1946 with *Bonbrest v. Kotz*, many courts, overturning a long line of decisions stemming from the famous opinion of Mr. Justice Holmes in *Dietrich v. Northampton*, have recognized a cause of action for negligently inflicted prenatal injuries. In most states that have recently considered the question, this right of action has been upheld, at least if the injuries were suffered by the fetus after it reached viability, the final period of intrauterine development, from approximately the twenty-sixth week of pregnancy, during which a fetus is capable of independent existence if prematurely separated from the mother. Some courts have allowed actions for the similarly caused death of a fetus or child. On the whole, the courts have not treated these two causes of action differently. Although a death action is

* Reprinted with permission of *University of Pennsylvania Law Review*.

technically a new cause of action brought on behalf of the decedent's relatives or estate—unlike a survival action where any cause of action the decedent had before his death "survives" to his estate—the courts have tended to construe as "derivative" those death statutes that are not explicit on this point to the extent no cause of action lies in favor of the estate unless the infant had a cause of action at the time of his death. Thus, the fundamental question in suits of either type is the same: whether the infant has, or had before his death, a cause of action for prenatal injuries negligently inflicted.

## (6) Traumatic Neurosis

The problems attendant to legal recognition of emotional damage present difficulties for both law and medicine. Some of these problems are discussed in the following comment.

### *Traumatic Neurosis*, 41 Marq. L. Rev. 431 (1958)*

I. INTRODUCTION

Every personal injury affects in some measure both the mind and the body. The legal compensability of the mental aspect of such injury was, for centuries, so limited as to be practically nonexistent. An emerging body of modern medical and scientific theory respecting the nature and degree of mental harm has been reflected in recent tendencies to re-examine the traditional legal attitude.

Insofar as mental injury disables the victim of tort to an extent no greater than a coinciding physical injury, no substantial problem of compensation is likely to arise. The legal approach to such cases is simply to merge the mental injury, most commonly under the label of pain and suffering, in the physical, permitting the latter to control the value of the case. Mental injury may, however, be substantially more disabling, or it may persist far longer than the physical injury. Or, there may be evidence of mental harm where no physical injury in fact resulted from the tort. In these instances, the mental harm may be considered to be excessive, or unrelated to the physical injury. Whenever disproportionate mental harm is encountered as one of the consequences of a tortious act, traumatic neurosis may constitute an element of the injury.

It is the purpose of this article to indicate the present state of medical and scientific progress in the field of traumatic neurosis. It will be the further purpose to summarize the present legal status of mental harm as a basis of civil liability in general and to consider the rationale underlying liability and compensation for mental harm, particularly with respect to traumatic neurosis. . . .

II. MENTAL HARM AS A BASIS OF TORT LIABILITY

A. Present Status

When dealing with traumatic neurosis as an element of damages, it must first be inquired whether mental harm in general may be compensable under the facts of the given case. The basic problems which accounted for the traditional reluctance

* Reprinted with permission of the *Marquette Law Review*.

to accord legal recognition to mental harm must be met by the courts today in a re-examination of the question of the compensability of injury to the mind. Essentially, this reluctance arises from the intangible and subjective nature of the harm. Because such harm is not susceptible of objective determination, doubt as to its reality and extent led, in the past, to the formulation of rules to the effect that mental harm, independently, could not support a cause of action. The rationale of these rules varied with the nature of the action in which compensation for mental harm was sought, as well as with the particular views of the various jurisdictions. Thus, it has been held that mental harm was speculative, that its compensation would lead to vexatious and fictitious claims, and that there was no reliable standard of measurement. In negligence actions it was decided that no duty could be owed to any person to refrain from inflicting mental harm upon him; that such harm could not reasonably be foreseen; that such harm was not proximately caused; that it was too remote; or simply, that such harm did not warrant legal redress as a matter of public policy.

Notwithstanding the traditional views, decisions today reveal a trend toward greater liberality in the compensation of mental harm. Earlier objections have been overcome in part by the recognition of scientific advances and by changing social and judicial attitudes. Nevertheless, the older problems, as well as new questions incident to the application of medical facts to legal doctrines have not been fully resolved. As yet there are no clearly defined rules of general applicability governing the status of mental harm as a basis of tort liability. . . .


IV. CONCLUSION

Compensation for mental disturbance such as traumatic neurosis is being demanded and granted with increasing frequency. This may be due to a number of causes, such as the relatively high incidence of the neuroses in the general population; the numerous anxiety producing factors inherent in the daily life of our complex, charged-with-tension society; the identification by medicine of the distinct entity of these mental disorders, their etiology, symptomatology, prognosis and therapy; and changing judicial attitudes toward the compensability of mental harm in general.

Notwithstanding the general rule that the interest in peace of mind is not protected against invasion by negligent conduct, recent cases involving the compensation of harm following psychic impact indicate a trend which may lead to the independent recognition of this interest in negligence, as it has been recognized in intentional tort. In effect, this accords protection to the personality as a whole and reflects philosophical as well as scientific concepts of the nature of man.

In view of the transitional state of the law, legal concepts as to the nature of trauma, pain and suffering, physical injury and mental injury require clarification to avoid ambiguity and inconsistency with scientific fact. That mental states have both objective and subjective aspects is particularly significant in instances of traumatic neurosis. Either aspect may result in severe anguish, impairment and incapacity.

Whenever an alleged mental or physical disturbance seems to be unusual, out of proportion to the impact of the tortious conduct, or unrelated to the expected physical injury, the presence of traumatic neurosis should be suspected and every effort be made to confirm or rule out such a diagnosis by submitting the problem to a qualified psychiatrist. To the plaintiff the importance of such a diagnosis lies in establishing the presence of a "recognizable mental disorder," known to afflict a "substantial minority" of people, thereby ruling out esoteric responses and malingering. The defendant may further his cause by demonstrating the unusual susceptibility to harm, the aggravation of an existing impairment, and the many factors, of which trauma is only one, operative in the production of a neurosis.

When confronted with traumatic neurosis as an element of the harm sustained, the lawyer is faced with special problems. He must sufficiently understand the technical concepts and language involved. He must be able to translate these terms into language meaningful to the trier of facts and yet preserve their accuracy. He must further be prepared to face honest differences of opinion among the experts. In the interpretation of predominately subjective phenomena, each specialist is conditioned by the views of the school in which he was trained, as well as by his personal attitudes and experience. It will be found, however, that there is general agreement as to the psychogenic origin of the neuroses, and as to the involuntariness of their symptoms, difficult as an acceptance of such concepts may be for the lay public. The question of malingering may be particularly troublesome. Here, too, the experts may differ in good faith due to influences in their background and experience.

One objection to the legal recognition of subjective, intangible harm raised today, is the possibility of "vexatious and fictitious" claims. This objection may be met to some degree by a requirement of competent proof of the alleged harm. Here it is hoped that further progress in medicine and particularly in psychology and psychiatry will furnish a greater degree of certainty by demonstrating tangible physiological and anatomical changes incident to the psychological process involved in emotional states. As competent proof is forthcoming to support claims of mental harm resulting from impact tortiously caused, there is correspondingly less justification to deny compensation for the disability of mental harm while allowing it for physical injury occurring under similar circumstances.

Possible limitations on liability and on the amount of damages recoverable for mental harm such as traumatic neurosis deserve consideration. In intentional tort, liability for invasion of mental tranquillity is conditioned on the character of the defendant's conduct. In negligence, the primary condition imposed on recovery is an objective manifestation of the state of mind or a consequential physical injury. Predicating liability on the objective nature of the harm sustained may lead to what an older view rejected as creating a cause of action in favor of the specially predisposed claimant while denying it to the normally constituted, equally situated person. This result may be avoided to some degree by giving greater weight in the initial determination of liability to the total occurrence constituting the tort, that is, to the circumstances occasioning the mental harm, such as the imminence of personal danger creating the psychic trauma for which compensation is sought. Weight to be accorded to the various factors spelling liability is within the realm of judicial policy in determining standards of conduct. Policy may further consider the economic and social consequences of the burden of potential liability on every actor resulting from an extension of compensability of mental harm in personal injuries.

# CASES

Following are cases for analysis, in which the concept of duty has entered into the judicial decision. To carry forward the inquiry first posed in connection with cases in the standard of care section, if the nurse had foreseen the consequences of her conduct, might she in the exercise of her duty have prevented the harm that did occur? At what point in nursing care did dereliction in duty become evident? In these decisions, do you agree with the position taken by the court in the duty it found for the nurse?

## *Wilmington General Hosp. v. Manlove,* 54 Del. 15, 174 A.2d 135 (1961)

Southerland, Chief Justice.

This case concerns the liability of a private hospital for the death of an infant who was refused treatment at the emergency ward of the hospital. The facts are these:

On January 4, 1959, Darien E. Manlove, the deceased infant, then four months old, developed diarrhea. The next morning his parents consulted Dr. Hershon. They asked whether the medicine they had for him was all right and the doctor said that it was. In the evening of the same day Mrs. Manlove took the baby's temperature. It was higher than normal. They called Dr. Hershon, and he prescribed additional medication (streptomycin), which he ordered delivered by a pharmacy.

Mrs. Manlove stayed up with the child that night. He did not sleep. On the morning of January 6th the parents took the infant to Dr. Hershon's office. Dr. Thomas examined the child and treated him for sore throat and diarrhea. He prescribed a liquid diet and some medicine.

When Mr. Manlove returned home that night, the baby's condition appeared to be the same. His temperature was still above normal, and again he did not sleep during the night.

On the morning of January 7th (a Wednesday) his temperature was still above normal—102. Mr. and Mrs. Manlove determined to seek additional medical assistance. They knew that Dr. Hershon and Dr. Thomas were not in their offices on Wednesdays, and they took their infant to the emergency ward of the Wilmington General Hospital.

There is no real conflict of fact as to what occurred at the hospital. The parents took the infant into the reception room of the Emergency Ward. A nurse was on duty. They explained to the nurse what was wrong with the child, that is, that he had not slept for two nights, had a continuously high temperature, and that he had diarrhea. Mr. Manlove told the nurse that the child was under the care of Dr. Hershon and Dr. Thomas, and showed the nurse the medicines prescribed. The nurse explained to the parents that the hospital could not give treatment because the child was under the care of a physician and there would be danger that the medication of the hospital might conflict with that of the attending physician. The nurse did not examine the child, take his temperature, feel his forehead, or look down his throat. The child was not in convulsions, and was not coughing or crying. There was no particular area of body tenderness.

The nurse tried to get in touch with Dr. Hershon or Dr. Thomas in the hospital and at their offices, but was unable to do so. She suggested that the parents bring the baby Thursday morning to the pediatric clinic.

Mr. and Mrs. Manlove returned home. Mrs. Manlove made an appointment by telephone to see Dr. Hershon or Dr. Thomas that night at eight o'clock.

At eight minutes past three o'clock in the afternoon the baby died of bronchial pneumonia.

The foregoing facts are taken mainly from the deposition of the plaintiff.

Plaintiff, as administrator, brought suit against the hospital to recover damages for wrongful death. The complaint charged negligence in failing to render emergency assistance, in failing to examine the baby, in refusing to advise the interne about the child or permit the parents to consult him, and in failing to follow reasonable and humane hospital procedure for the treatment of emergency cases. Defendant answered denying negligence and averring that, pursuant to its established rules and community practice, plaintiff was advised by its employee that it was unable to accept the infant for care.

Discovery proceedings were taken by both parties, eliciting the facts set forth above. Defendant then moved for summary judgment, and attached an affidavit from the nurse on duty when the infant was brought to the hospital. Her statement concerning the refusal of treatment is:

I then told Mr. and Mrs. Manlove that the rules of the hospital provided that in such cases, where a person is under attendance and medication by a private doctor, *and there is no frank indication of emergency*, no treatment or medication may be given by doctors employed by the hospital until the attending doctor has been consulted. [Emphasis supplied.]

The issues made by the parties below were in effect two:

1. Whether the hospital was under any duty to furnish medical treatment to any applicant for it, even in an emergency;

2. Whether the existence of an apparent emergency was a material fact in dispute.

The holding of the court below may be summarized as follows: . . .

2. There was some evidence of an apparent emergency because (1) of death following in a few hours, and (2) of the child's symptoms as recited by the nurse.

Hence the court denied the motion. The hospital appeals.

We take a somewhat different view of these questions from that of the learned judge below. . . .

The above authorities announce a general rule governing the question of admissions to a private hospital. Does that rule apply to the fullest extent to patients applying for treatment at an emergency ward?

Defendant stresses the rule or practice of the hospital to decline to give medical aid to persons already under the care of a physician. This is no doubt entirely reasonable, but we do not think the rule controlling in this case. We are not furnished with a copy of the rule, or with an affidavit explaining it, but it would seem to be applicable to all admissions—not especially to admissions to the emergency ward. Its significance here appears to lie in the fact that it impliedly recognizes that in case of "frank"—i.e., unmistakable—emergency there is some duty on the part of the hospital to give help.

We return, then, to the important question: Is there any duty on the part of the hospital to give treatment in an emergency case, i.e., one obviously demanding immediate attention?

It may be conceded that a private hospital is under no legal obligation to the public to maintain an emergency ward, or, for that matter, a public clinic.

But the maintenance of such a ward to render first-aid to injured persons has become a well-established adjunct to the main business of a hospital. If a person, seriously hurt, applies for such aid at an emergency ward, relying on the established custom to render it, is it still the right of the hospital to turn him away without any reason? In such a case, it seems to us, such a refusal might well result in worsening the condition of the injured person, because of the time lost in a useless attempt to obtain medical aid.

Such a set of circumstances is analogous to the case of the negligent termination of gratuitous services, which creates a tort liability.

It must be admitted that there is a dearth of helpful legal precedent. There are very few cases dealing with the liability of a hospital for negligence in connection with the care and treatment of a patient brought to an emergency ward. See annotation at 72 A.L.R.2d 396. Nearly all the decisions that have been found deal with charges of negligence in the treatment of a patient who has been accepted for treatment. See Bourgeois v. Dade County, Fla., 99 So.2d 575, 72 A.L.R.2d 391 (interne charged with negligent examination of patient); Leavy v. Yates, Sup., 142 N.Y.S.2d 874 (doctor charged with negligent diagnosis of injured patient); Wade v. Ravenswood Hospital Association, 3 Ill.App.2d 102, 120 N.E.2d 345 (charge of lack of competent medical care).

But this is not a case in which the hospital assumed to treat the patient. The claim is that it should have treated him, and that the nurse was negligent in failing to have the infant examined by the interne on duty, because an apparent emergency existed.

This leads to the inquiry: What is the duty of a nurse to one applying for admission as an emergency case? Obviously, if an emergency is claimed, some one on behalf of the hospital must make a *prima facie* decision whether it exists. The hospital cannot reasonably be expected to station an interne at all times in the receiving room. It therefore keeps a nurse on duty. If the nurse makes an honest decision that there is no unmistakable indication of an emergency, and that decision is not clearly unreasonable in the light of the nurse's training, how can there be any liability on the part of the hospital?

The only case cited to us involving refusal of treatment at an emergency ward is that of O'Neill v. Montefiore Hospital, 11 A.D.2d 132, 202 N.Y.S.2d 436. In that case Mr. and Mrs. John J. O'Neill came early one morning to the hospital emergency ward. O'Neill complained of symptoms of a heart ailment or attack. He was refused admission because he was a member of a Hospital Insurance Plan and the hospital did not take such cases. The nurse called an H.I.P. doctor, and Mr. O'Neill took the telephone and described his symptoms. The nurse then arranged for O'Neill to see that doctor a few hours later. Mrs. O'Neill asked to have a doctor examine him because it was an emergency, but this was not done. The O'Neill's returned home, and O'Neill died in a very short time.

In a suit against the doctor and the hospital the trial court found for the defendants. The Appellate Division unanimously reversed as to the doctor. As to the hospital, three judges held there was a question of fact for the jury to decide, that is, whether the nurse's conduct was a personal favor to deceased, or whether her conduct was that of an attaché discharging her duty, and if the latter, whether what she did was adequate. Two judges dissented, pointing out that the doctor called by the nurse did not, after talking to the patient, indicate that any emergency treatment was required, or request that the patient be admitted to the hospital. In these circumstances they found no liability.

The difference of opinion in that case seems to turn on the question whether, by calling a physician for the applicant, the nurse assumed to give him hospital service. The case does not discuss the questions of what constitutes an emergency, and what is the duty of the nurse in such cases.

As to the majority holding that the nurse's telephone call gave rise to liability, we respectfully dissent. We think the minority opinion is the better view.

As above indicated, we are of opinion that liability on the part of a hospital may be predicated on the refusal of service to a patient in case of an unmistakable emergency, if the patient has relied upon a well-established custom of the hospital to render aid in such a case. The hospital rule with respect to applicants already under the care of a physician may be said to be an implied recognition of this duty.

Applying this rule here, we inquire, was there an unmistakable emergency? Certainly the record does not support the view that the infant's condition was so desperate that a layman could reasonably say that he was in immediate danger. The learned judge indicated that the fact that death followed in a few hours showed an emergency; but with this we cannot agree. It is hindsight. And it is to be noted that the attending physician, after prescribing for the child on morning before, did not think another examination that night or the next morning was required. If this case had gone to the jury on the record here made, we would have been required to hold that it was insufficient to establish liability. We cannot agree that the mere recitation of the infant's symptoms was, in itself, evidence of an emergency sufficient to present a question for the jury. Before such an issue could arise there would have to be evidence that an experienced nurse should have known that such symptoms constituted unmistakable evidence of an emergency.

We must keep in mind the fact that this is not the ordinary accident case in which the services of the hospital emergency ward are sought because of a showing of serious physical injury, or of a danger of such injury. It is a case of disease. This is not to say that an emergency could not arise out of a diseased condition; it is only to say that some degree of experience and knowledge is required to make a *prima facie* determination of the existence of such an emergency.

We do not think that the record made below satisfactorily developed the pertinent facts. What is standard hospital practice when an applicant for aid seeks medical aid for sickness at the emergency ward? Is it the practice for the nurse to determine whether or not an emergency exists, or is it her duty to call the interne in every case? Assuming (as seems probable) that it is her duty to make such a determination, was her determination in this case within the reasonable limits of judgment of a graduate nurse, even though mistaken, or was she derelict in her duty, as a graduate nurse, in not recognizing an emergency from the symptoms related to her? To resolve these questions additional evidence, probably expert opinion, would seem to be required.

It may be said that it was the duty of the plaintiff below, when confronted with the motion for summary judgment, to offer additional proof by affidavit or otherwise. This is perhaps so, but the defendant also could have submitted evidence on the questions we have referred to. As it was, the defendant pitched its case on the theory that under no circumstances could it be liable. The possibility that the case might turn on additional evidence respecting the matters we have touched upon was not considered either by the court or counsel.

In the circumstances we think the case should go back for further proceedings. We should add, however, that if plaintiff cannot adduce evidence showing some incompetency of the nurse, or some breach of duty or some negligence, his case must fail. Like the learned judge below, we sympathize with the parents in their loss of a child; but this natural feeling does not permit us to find liability in the absence of satisfactory evidence.

For the reasons above set forth the order denying summary judgment is affirmed, without approving the reasons therefor set forth in the court's opinion.

## ANALYSIS

1. What is the basis for the claimed liability of the hospital? Could the nurse be individually liable?

2. What reasons can be given to support the court's conclusion concerning the authority of a private hospital to establish its admission policies? Does the same rationale hold for the admission to emergency wards? What distinguished one from the other? Is the foreseeability concept involved?

3. What evidence could be adduced at the trial by the nurse to justify her conduct? By the plaintiff to show her conduct to be wrongful?

4. You are assigned as a head nurse in the emergency unit. Hospital policy states that if a person has a private physician, you are to accept him only if there is "unmistakable evidence of any emergency." What sources and methods would you use on which to base your evaluation of what constitutes an emergency? How would you prepare yourself and your staff to make the decision at the time?

5. Has not the court placed the nurse under a duty to observe and evaluate the symptoms of the patient? In exploring the conduct of the nurse, did the court overlook the statutory definition of nursing practice? Did the nurse behave as a nurse should have behaved in line with this definition?

6. What do you believe to be the significant difference in the fact pattern of the behavior of the nurse in *O'Neill v. Montefiore*, cited in the *Manlove* case, as compared to the *Manlove* case? In each instance, was the nurse equally vulnerable to suit?

7. The court asked, rhetorically, "How can there be any liability on the part of the hospital" if the nurse made an "honest decision . . . not clearly unreasonable in the light of the nurse's training?" Can you give any reason why the hospital should be held liable under the circumstances? Can you justify such liability in terms of foreseeable harm?

## Spivey v. St. Thomas Hosp., 31 Tenn. App. 12, 211 S.W.2d 450 (1947)

Felts, Judge.

Mrs. Spivey sued St. Thomas Hospital for alleged negligence causing the death of her husband, Jesse James Spivey. He was suffering with pneumonia and a high temperature. He was brought to the hospital, accepted as a paying patient, and put on a bed near a window on the third floor. A few hours later, while delirious with fever and knowing not what he was doing, he got out this window, fell about 14 feet, struck a concrete porch, and his death ensued next day.

The negligence alleged was that through its interns and nurses—its employees and agents—defendant knew he was delirious and irrational and, if left unattended, would likely get out of bed and harm himself; that with this knowledge it undertook to keep him in bed and give him proper care by its interns and nurses; and that it failed to give him proper care, but left him unattended near this unguarded window, let him in his delirium fall or jump out, and thereby caused his death.

It was further alleged that defendant failed to have enough nurses in attendance, failed to keep someone in the room with him, failed to install some device at this window to prevent him from falling through it, failed to use restraints to keep him in bed, or at least did not use them in a proper or sufficient manner, and did not secure the fastenings or other means to prevent him from leaving his bed. Defendant pleaded not guilty.

The case was tried before the judge and a jury. At the close of plaintiff's evidence defendant moved for a directed verdict, which motion was overruled. Defendant did not stand on its motion, but put in evidence by its witnesses to negative negligence and show the death was an unavoidable accident. At the close of all the evidence defendant moved for a directed verdict, which motion was likewise overruled. The jury rendered a verdict for plaintiff for $20,000. The judge approved the verdict and entered judgment upon it.

Defendant appealed in error and has assigned a number of errors. Its first insistence is that there was no evidence to support a verdict for plaintiff, that its evidence established beyond dispute that it was guilty of no negligence and the event was altogether unforseeable and unavoidable, and that a verdict should have been directed for it at the close of all the evidence.

Learned counsel sharply differ in their views of the evidence. It is not for us, however, to settle such differences. That was for the jury. They rendered a general verdict for plaintiff, and we must take it as settling most of such differences in her favor. We have to decide only whether the circumstances of the case for plaintiff were sufficient, in point of law and reason, to permit the jury to find a verdict for her. . . .

Upon such a view of the evidence, we summarize the circumstances tending to support the case for plaintiff. Defendant is an eleemosynary corporation operating a general hospital in Nashville for the care of the sick. For this purpose it employs a resident physician, several interns, and a large number of nurses and student nurses. It accepts both charity patients and paying patients. Jesse James Spivey was 26 years of age, a veteran of World War II, and had a wife and a three-months-old child.

He and his wife and child lived on a farm near Gainesboro. About February 1, 1946, he became ill with pneumonia. His condition grew worse and at times his temperature was so high that he would be delirious, not know what he was doing, and try to get out of bed. That he might have better care, he was brought in an ambulance to St. Thomas Hospital. His brother, Clayton Spivey, and his brother-in-law, Luther Trisdale, rode in the back part of the ambulance with him. During most of this journey he was irrational.

They arrived at the hospital about 6:00 p.m. February 4. His brother went to defendant's office, arranged for his admission, and paid defendant's charges for a week in advance. He was taken from the ambulance to Room 309, on the third floor, and put on the bed nearest the window. There was another bed in the room but no patient in it.

Some of the defendant's employees telephoned Dr. J. D. Lester, a prominent Nashville physician, to whom one of Spivey's local doctors had referred him, and who usually had a large number of patients in the hospital. Dr. Lester said he would see Spivey later that evening along with his other patients there, and he told the resident physician to begin giving Spivey the routine treatment for pneumonia cases. Defendant's interns and nurses did this.

Spivey's temperature when he was admitted was 106, which is "a very high fever." Its effect was to make him delirious, not know what he was doing, and try to get out of bed and leave. There was conflict in the evidence as to his condition during his first few hours in the hospital. Defendant's nurses said he was perfectly rational, but his brother and his brother-in-law said he was not, and we must assume the jury accredited the latter.

The window was about two or three feet from his bed. The bottom of it was about the same height as the bed. Its lower sash was movable, unfastened, and unprotected. It is true there was sharp conflict in the evidence as to whether there was a screen outside this window. Defendant's nurses said there was a screen, and those on duty at the time of the accident said the screen was latched. But Clayton Spivey testified quite positively to the contrary. He said he noticed the window that night and looked at it again next day, and there was no screen.

He and Trisdale stayed that night in the room with the patient until about 8:30 or 9:00. During part of this time he was delirious, "not at himself," and he tried to get up, sat up in bed, and his brother "got hold of him and got him to lay back down." About 8:30 the nurse in charge turned out the hall light, came into Spivey's room, and told his brother and brother-in-law visiting hours were over and they would have to leave. His brother insisted on staying with him, and told the nurse he had tried to get out of bed and "he would get out of bed and leave if somebody didn't stay in there with him."

Here again there was conflict in the evidence. The nurse said she told them visiting hours were over, and when they insisted on staying, she told them she would get permission for one to say, but the other would have to leave. Clayton Spivey, however, testified that she said both would have to go.

Trisdale did go down and wait on the first floor, but Clayton still stayed in the room. About 9:20 or 9:30, he said, the nurse came back and told him under the rule of the hospital he would have to leave. He wanted to stay till Dr. Lester came and talk to the doctor about getting a special nurse. But the nurse said he could stay no longer. He again told her his brother "would get out of bed if somebody didn't watch him." She said: "I will tie him in bed if he tries to get up; I will keep him in bed some way." Then the brother and brother-in-law left the hospital.

The only evidence as to the rest of the circumstances comes from defendant's witnesses. Dr. Lester came about 10:00 or 10:30. He made a cursory examination, he said, and found Spivey rational, his fever down to 102, and his condition very good. The night supervisor of nurses said the doctor told her that the patient was doing well and would be all right till morning.

This supervisor and the nurses were relieved about 11:00 by another supervisor, Mrs. Short, and two student nurses, Miss Mitchell and Miss Wiggins. Each of these student nurses had charge of a section of the third floor, with about fifteen patients each. In each section there was a nurse's station where the charts of the patients were kept and where there was a signal showing when any patient called for the nurse. Each nurse stayed at her station, keeping the charts and watching for the signals, when not going on her rounds answering calls or checking on patients.

These two nurses alternated in checking on Spivey. They checked on him about every ten minutes while he was being given an intravenous solution of glucose. This was stopped about 12:15, and Miss Mitchell, the student nurse in charge of his section, said she "fixed him comfortable for the night." About 1:00 she checked on him again and he was restless and tossing. These two nurses put up sideboards to his bed to keep him from falling out. The supervisor, Mrs. Short, got an order from an intern permitting the nurses to give Spivey a hypodermic dose of sodium luminal to make him sleep.

In addition to the sodium luminal they also gave him aspirin and an alcohol bath. But by 2:30 he was more restless, his fever was 105.8, and the nurses saw he "wasn't rational," "didn't know what he was doing." The supervisor told them to put him in restraints to keep him from getting out of bed. The restraints were two leather straps buckled around his ankles and buckled to the foot of the bed, and two canvas straps tied around his wrists and tied under the bed.

The use of such restraints appears to be a common practice in hospitals when patients are in danger from delirium and such restraints are necessary to protect them from getting out of bed and harming themselves. This had been part of the training of these two young nurses. But when they undertook to put the restraints on Spivey, he was so irrational and violent that they had to call two orderlies, two strong Negro men, to help Miss Wiggins hold him while Miss Mitchell put on the restraints. It took all of them from about 2:30 to about 3:00 to do this. They also tied a canopy sheet over his bed.

These two nurses said they alternately checked on him about every five or ten minutes. That is, they would go to his door and peep in. They said the restraints were in order and the patient seemed to be quiet. Mrs. Short, the supervisor, said she saw him at 3:20, and he was in full restraint and apparently sleeping.

About 3:45, Miss Wiggins said, while coming from the kitchen down the hall by Spivey's room, she saw him "out of bed, with his arms out of restraints but his feet were still in restraints." She said he was not "fumbling with the buckles or trying to get them loose"; "he was just sitting there looking out in the hall." She called to Miss Mitchell that he was out of bed, and she ran down the hall for an orderly. One of the orderlies was on the fourth floor and the other was operating the elevator.

At the moment of this call Miss Mitchell was standing in front of her chart room door, only about 25 feet from the door to Spivey's room. She said she ran to his door, saw him "standing by the bed." She ran back to the telephone and called

Mrs. Short, who was operating the switchboard, to send help. She said she ran back to Spivey's door "to help them keep him from coming out in the hall because he had made the statement he would kill us if he ever got his hands on us." Just as she got to the door, she said, she saw "him going out the window"—"saw his feet."

As stated, the lower sash of the window was movable, unfastened, and unprotected. It had a latch or lock to fasten it down, but "the window wasn't locked." After the accident the window was not broken; its bottom sash was up. One end of each of the leather ankle straps was still buckled to the foot of the bed; but none of defendant's witnesses was able to state whether the other end of these straps had been unbuckled or was still buckled. As for the canvas straps, which these young nurses said were tied underneath the bed so he couldn't reach down to untie them —both of these "had come loose from the bed." The other end of one of these straps was still tied around Spivey's arm, while the other strap was found on the ground beneath the concrete porch upon which Spivey fell.

He fell about 14 feet, and his head and other parts of his body struck the concrete porch. As soon as his body was found, he was taken to the emergency room, and Dr. Lester was called. But nothing could be done for him. He was suffering from a brain trauma and a cerebral hemorrhage; he was unconscious and in a deep coma. He never regained consciousness, but died next day—about 2:00 a.m. February 6.

These circumstances, we think, were sufficient to raise a duty upon defendant to take care to protect its patient Spivey against the risk of his getting out of bed and harming himself. . . .

Here Spivey's condition was fully known by defendant's nurses and interns. He was suffering from pneumonia and a very high fever, was so irrational as to be violent, and wanted to get out of bed and leave. They had refused to let his brother stay with him and watch him, or stay to see the doctor about getting a special nurse for him. They realized he was in danger from his delirium, said they would tie him if he tried to get up, and by restraints undertook to keep him from getting out of bed and harming himself.

Despite this danger they failed to keep someone in his room to watch him, but left him in his delirium but a step from this unfastened and unguarded window, and failed to fasten the restraints securely or at least to see that the restraints did not come loose. And after they saw him free of the restraints and out of bed, they did nothing effectual to get him back in bed or protect him in his helplessness from falling or jumping out the window.

It is urged for defendant, however, that they said they securely fastened the restraints and continually watched to keep them fastened, and that their testimony must be taken as true. But the admitted fact is that the restraints did come loose, which could hardly have happened if they had been properly fastened and if these witnesses had continually watched to keep them fastened. We think their credibility was a matter for the jury.

We think the jury could have reasonably found that defendant failed to exercise ordinary care and was negligent in several of the particulars alleged: in failing to keep someone in his room to watch him, in view of its actual knowledge of his danger from his condition; in leaving him unattended in such condition only two or three feet from the unfastened and unguarded window; and in failing to fasten the restraints securely or at least to see that they did not come loose so as to permit him to get up and get out of this window.

To say the least, there was room for reasonable minds to differ as to whether defendant was negligent in these particulars. This being so, the questions were for the jury. "When a given state of facts is such as reasonable men may fairly differ upon the question as to whether there was negligence or not, the determination of the matter is for the jury. It is only where the facts are such that all reasonable men must draw the same conclusions from them that the question of negligence is ever considered one of law for the court."

Learned counsel for defendant, however, contend that the patient's act of jumping out the window was so unusual and extraordinary that it was altogether unforeseeable, that it was only a possibility and not a probability, and that defendant cannot be charged with negligence for not foreseeing and guarding against such an act.

Some cases do say foreseeableness is not only the measure of duty—the test of negligence—but also the measure of liability for damage caused by the breach of duty. But they rarely in practice apply this double test of foreseeableness. If they did, few, if any, defendants would ever be held for ordinary negligence, because accidents almost invariably are surprises, in the sense that the precise manner of their occurrence can not be foreseen.

The majority of the well-considered cases, we think, apply foreseeableness only as a test of negligence: whether defendant's conduct created an unreasonable risk of harm to plaintiff. If it did, such cases hold defendant liable for all the injuries within the reasonable range of such risk, whether they could have been foreseen or not.

It is often said that a negligent defendant is liable for all the natural and probable consequences of his wrong, irrespective of whether he could have foreseen them or not. But here the word "probable," if used in its usual sense, is misleading. That is, if used in the sense that the chances in favor of the occurrence outnumber the chances against it. In this connection Professor Prosser, after stating generally that no one can be expected to guard against events which are not reasonably to be anticipated, or are so unlikely that the risk would be commonly disregarded, says this:

"On the other hand, if the risk is an appreciable one, and the possible consequences are serious, the question is not one of mathematical probability alone. The odds may be a thousand to one that no train will arrive at the very moment that an automobile is crossing a railway track, but the risk of death is nevertheless sufficiently serious to require the driver to look for the train. As the gravity of the possible harm increases, the apparent likelihood of its occurrence need be correspondingly less." Prosser on Torts, 221–2. . . .

So the particular harm which actually befell Spivey need not have been foreseeable. It is enough that some such harm of a like general character was reasonably foreseeable as a likely result of defendant's failure to use due care to keep him in bed and to protect him against getting out of the window in his delirium.

But quite apart from this view of the case, we think the jury could well have found that his act was not so unusual or extraordinary as to be beyond the range of reasonable expectation; but that it was a thing which might reasonably have been expected to occur in view of his condition. Common experience shows that patients in such condition often jump or fall out of upper-story windows of hospitals. Such cases are numerous in the reported decisions.

A leading case is that of Wetzel v. Omaha Maternity and General Hospital Association, 96 Neb. 636, 148 N.W. 582, 583, Ann. Cas. 1915B, 1224. There a patient was delirious with typhoid fever. In the absence of the nurse, and under circumstances quite similar to those in the case before us, he jumped out a third-story window, struck the pavement, and his death resulted. The court said under the circumstances his act "may well have been foreseen." . . .

For defendant it is objected that there was no evidence to show Spivey might not have died of pneumonia, even if he had had no accident. There is no merit in such an objection. There was ample evidence to support the jury's finding that Spivey's death was caused by the injuries he sustained in the accident. The fact that he was ill, even if it could be said he might later have died of such illness, did not prevent defendant's negligence from being the legal or proximate cause of his death.

So we think the trial judge rightly submitted the case to the jury, and there is ample evidence to support the verdict. . . .

All of the assignments of error are overruled. The judgment of the circuit court will be modified as above indicated and as modified will be affirmed. The costs are adjudged against defendant and the surety on its appeal bond.

## ANALYSIS

1. What are the facts that support the proposition that the defendant was under a duty to avoid the injury to the plaintiff? Hospital policy apparently ran counter to the best interest of the patient; what principles of administration were not considered in the implementation of the policy?

2. From the facts, what nursing measures were taken that indicated that the nursing staff did foresee probable or possible harm? At what point did the nurses responsible fail to properly assess the situation? What knowledge of medical science might have guided the nurses and interns in foreseeing the consequences?

3. Apply to this and other nursing situations the duty theory that as the possibility of serious harm increases, its apparent likelihood of occurrence need be correspondingly less.

4. What was the holding in the case? Had you been the judge, would you have decided the same way? How would you explain your reasoning?

## Mundt v. Alta Bates Hosp., 35 Cal. Rptr. 848 (1963)

Shoemaker, Presiding Justice.

Plaintiff Mildred Mundt brought this action to recover damages for personal injuries allegedly caused by the malpractice of defendants Dr. Sheldon Margen, Dr. Rubin Lewis, Dr. Paul Schneider, and Alta Bates Hospital. The complaint, as modified by the pretrial conference order, alleged that plaintiff, while a patient at Alta Bates Hospital on April 3, 1959, underwent certain operative procedures; that each of the defendants, with the exception of defendant Schneider, thereafter negligently

injured plaintiff by allowing a solution of dextrose and potassium chloride to infil-
trate into the tissue of her leg; that defendant Schneider thereafter aggravated
plaintiff's injury by his negligence in performing plastic surgery upon her.

The case was tried before a jury. All defendants moved for a nonsuit, and the
motions of defendants Schneider and Lewis were granted. Upon the conclusion of
the trial, the jury returned a verdict in favor of the two remaining defendants, and
judgment was accordingly entered.

Plaintiff thereafter moved for a new trial against defendants Lewis, Margen, and
Alta Bates Hospital. The court set aside the judgment of nonsuit in favor of Lewis
and granted plaintiff a new trial against this defendant on the ground that the
granting of the nonsuit was the result of error of law. The court also granted plaintiff
a new trial against Margen and Alta Bates Hospital on the ground of the insuf-
ficiency of the evidence to justify the verdict. Defendants appeal from the order
granting plaintiff a new trial. . . .

The second and final contention raised by each of the three appellants is that
the evidence was insufficient as a matter of law to support a judgment against them
and that the order granting a new trial must therefore be reversed.

The record shows that respondent, a woman 39 years of age, had suffered for
many years from a progressive and incurable disease of unknown cause, characterized by an inflammatory reaction occurring in the tissue and vascular systems of the
body. In 1954, Margen, a specialist in internal medicine, assumed charge of
respondent's care and treatment. Part of the treatment which he administered to her
during flareups of the disease consisted of intravenous or intramuscular injections
of ACTH.

In March 1959, respondent suffered a particularly severe flareup. When she
failed to respond to subcutaneous and intramuscular injections of ACTH, Margen
concluded that it would be necessary to hospitalize her in order that he could
undertake an intravenous infusion of ACTH over a continuous 48-hour period. On
April 3, 1959, respondent was admitted to the Alta Bates Hospital and intravenous
infusion was unsuccessfully attempted by him.

By the following day, April 4, 1959, Margen had determined that it would be
necessary to perform a "cut-down," an operative procedure whereby an incision
is made over a vein and a tube or catheter is then inserted directly into the vein.
Margen called in Lewis, a specialist in surgery, to perform the "cut-down," which
was commenced at 7:30 p.m. on the same day. Lewis determined that the most
suitable site for the operation was the inner side of respondent's lower right leg,
just above the ankle, and Lewis made an incision at this site, introduced the
catheter into the vein, and gently pushed the catheter up the vein some 10 or 12
inches. When the intravenous fluid began to flow into the catheter, respondent
complained of pain and Margen and Lewis observed a slight bulging at the point
where they judged the tip of the catheter to be. Upon concluding that the catheter
had penetrated the vein wall and that intravenous fluid was escaping into the
surrounding tissue, Lewis withdrew the catheter approximately an inch and a half
to two inches and applied pressure to the area over the vein. The intravenous fluid
then began to flow normally into the vein. They continued to observe the site for
an additional 20 or 30 minutes. When there was no increase in swelling and the
intravenous fluid continued to flow freely, Lewis concluded that the infusion had
been successfully accomplished.

Since respondent did not call an independent expert witness, the medical testimony bearing upon the propriety of the procedure thus far described consisted solely of that elicited from Lewis and Margen under Code of Civil Procedure, section 2055. Lewis testified that he had inserted the catheter into the vein in a manner entirely consistent with good medical technique, applying a minimal amount of pressure. He stated that it was extremely unusual for a vein to be punctured by a catheter and that he could offer no explanation for this occurrence. Once having realized that the vein had been penetrated, however, he was confronted with the choice of removing the catheter and undertaking a second "cut-down" on another area of respondent's body, or allowing the catheter to remain in place despite the fact that a certain degree of infiltration was taking place. Upon partially withdrawing the catheter and observing that the intravenous fluid was flowing normally and that there was no increase in swelling, he concluded that the best and safest course would be to leave the catheter in place. In arriving at this decision, he had in mind that there was virtually no other site where a second "cut-down" could be performed, that the intravenous fluid to be administered was noncorrosive and could safely be injected under the skin, and that the hole in the vein appeared to be a small one which had closed itself after the catheter was partially withdrawn.

Margen testified that infiltration around veins was an extremely common occurrence in connection with intravenous infusions and that there was no danger to the patient unless a large amount of fluid escaped from the vein. He stated that it was not uncommon for a catheter to be pushed through the vein wall during an intravenous infusion and that good medical practice did not require that the catheter then be removed to another site. He also confirmed the fact that the fluid to be given respondent was a noncorrosive substance which could safely be introduced beneath the skin. He stated that there was almost invariably some infiltration around a "cut-down" and that a small infiltration was not dangerous to the patient because the fluid would merely be absorbed by the surrounding tissues.

Following the completion of the "cut-down" procedure, Lewis' connection with the case terminated, and respondent was left under the care of Margen and the nurses employed by appellant Alta Bates Hospital. Margen ordered the nurses to administer to respondent a solution consisting of glucose, water, potassium chloride, and ACTH, at the rate of 1,000 c.c.'s per 12 hours. In addition to regulating the rate of flow into the catheter, it was also the duty of the nurses to observe the area of the "cut-down" for swelling, redness, or other signs that the intravenous infusion was not running properly.

The nurses attending respondent during the period following the "cut-down" noted nothing unusual, and by 6:40 a.m. on April 5, the first 1,000 c.c.'s of intravenous solution had been fully absorbed and a new bottle of solution was started.

Nurse Griffin came on duty at 7 a.m. on April 5. At 8:20 a.m. she observed the area of the "cut-down" and concluded that the solution was not running properly and that infiltration was occurring. She wrote "Calf edematous and firm" on respondent's chart. At 10:30 a.m. Margen visited respondent and examined the "cut-down" area. Although he read nurse Griffin's chart notation, his own observation of respondent's leg indicated no more infiltration than could be expected from a normal "cut-down" reaction. He gave no order that the intravenous infusions be discontinued. By 3 p.m. nurse Griffin observed that the intravenous solution was running extremely slowly and asked the charge nurse, Miss Terazawa, to observe respondent's leg. A call was then made to Margen and nurse Griffin informed him of her observations. Margen inquired whether there was any great change in the leg since morning, and she replied that there was not. He then instructed her to continue the intravenous infusions. At this time, the change of nurses took place and nurse Jones again came on duty. By 4:30 p.m. she concluded that the infusion was not going properly and noted on respondent's chart "leg firm and edematous." At 10 p.m. she charted "Right leg edematous and slightly red on inner calf." She also reported this observation to the charge nurse, but appellant Margen was not called.

At 11 p.m. on April 5, nurse Mello came on duty and was informed that respondent was suffering from edema of the leg, but that Margen had ordered the infusions to continue nevertheless. At 11:30 or 12 o'clock, nurse Mello noted on respondent's chart "Right leg on pillows—appears edematous." She testified that at the time of this notation, respondent's right leg was noticeably larger than her left. The condition of respondent's right leg became worse toward morning and at 5:40 a.m. on April 6, nurse Mello charted "leg appears more edematous." At 6:20 a.m. she asked the charge nurse to observe the leg, and at 6:55 a.m. was instructed to call Margen. The testimony relative to this conversation was conflicting in that nurse Mello stated that she informed him that there was "increasing edema," whereas he testified that he was told only that respondent's leg was "still edematous." In any event, Margen instructed nurse Mello to continue the intravenous infusions.

At 7 a.m., charge nurse Terazawa came on duty, and, upon examining respondent's leg concluded that it had undergone a marked change for the worse since she had last examined it at 3 p.m. on April 5. By 8:30 a.m. the swelling in respondent's leg had extended to the area above the knee and the intravenous fluid was running very slowly. At 10 a.m. nurse Terazawa called Margen's office and was able to contact his partner, Dr. Leon Lewis. Upon being informed of the condition of respondent's leg, Dr. Lewis came to the hospital at 11 a.m. and removed the "cut-down" [sic] (undoubtedly refers to catheter). By this time respondent's right leg was swollen to approximately twice its normal size. As a result of this massive infiltration, respondent suffered "necrosis" or death of certain of the tissues in her leg.

The expert testimony relative to the sequence of events occurring subsequent to the "cut-down" procedure may be summarized as follows: Margen testified that the injury to respondent's leg would not have occurred if the "cut-down" had been properly performed and if respondent had been carefully observed during the period following the "cut-down" in a manner consistent with the standard of care generally possessed and exercised by reputable physicians in the community. He also testified that a nurse who observes swelling or redness at the site of a "cut-down" is under a duty to either notify the physician in charge of the case or turn off the intravenous fluid. He stated that respondent's injury would not have occurred if the intravenous solution had been turned off when the swelling of her leg had reached a critical point. In his opinion, respondent's injury was the result of the failure of the hospital nurses to perform their duties in a manner consistent with the standard of care ordinarily exercised by nurses of good standing in the community. He also testified, however, that only a trained physician possessed the professional judgment necessary to determine whether the good to be derived from a given medication is offset by the degree of infiltration which he observes to be occurring.

The testimony of the Alta Bates nurses relative to the standard of care generally exercised by reputable nurses in the community was to the effect that a nurse who observes swelling or other danger signs in the area of a "cut-down" is under a duty to notify the doctor in charge but that she may only cut off the flow of intravenous solution upon orders from the doctor.

This evidence supports the contention of appellant Lewis that the evidence was insufficient as a matter of law to support a judgment against him. . . . Lewis' connection with this case began and ended with the performance of the "cut-down." Although it is true that the vein wall was punctured by the catheter during the course of this operative procedure, it is apparent that neither the cause of the puncture nor the question whether it was probably the result of negligence was a matter of common knowledge among laymen. The record contains no medical testimony that the "cut-down" was performed in a manner contrary to good medical practice. Although Lewis did state it was unusual for a vein to be punctured by a catheter, he also stated that he had inserted the catheter into the vein in an entirely proper manner and that he was at a loss to explain the cause of the puncture. There was no medical testimony that the occurrence of the puncture was more probably than not the result of negligence. There was similarly no medical testimony that the decision to leave the catheter in place despite the puncture in the vein was contrary to good medical practice. Indeed, Margen specifically stated that good medical practice did not require removal to a new site upon the occurrence of a puncture. . . .

The sole question remaining is whether the evidence was sufficient to support a judgment against Margen or Alta Bates Hospital. The evidence requires an affirmative answer as to both appellants.

The record discloses ample medical testimony that respondent's injury would not have occurred if the condition of her leg had been carefully observed during the period following the "cut-down" and if the intravenous fluid had been stopped when the leg became dangerously swollen. There was also uncontradicted testimony that the condition of respondent's leg underwent a marked change between 3 p.m. on April 5, and 7 a.m. on April 6, but that the "cut-down" was not removed until 11 a.m. on April 6. In the face of such testimony, there was clearly ample evidence upon which the trier of fact could find that Margen, the hospital nurses, or both, were negligent in their duties.

Although the nurses testified that the condition of respondent's leg grew increasingly worse during the afternoon and evening of April 5, no attempt to contact Margen was made until 6:55 on the morning of April 6. At that time, according to the testimony of Margen, nurse Mello informed him only that the leg was "still edematous." This evidence was clearly sufficient to support a finding that the hospital nurses were derelict in their duty to observe the condition of respondent's leg and promptly report all unfavorable symptoms to the doctor in charge. On the other hand, the trier of fact could have believed nurse Mello's testimony that she did inform Margen of "increasing edema." This testimony would have justified a finding that he was negligent in failing either to order the intravenous infusions discontinued or to come to the hospital and ascertain for himself whether respondent's health would be endangered by continuing the infusions. As yet a third possibility, the trier of fact might conclude that respondent's injury was the result of the combined negligence of Margen and the hospital nurses. It must be recalled that Margen testified that only a trained physician was qualified to determine whether the good to be derived from a given intravenous medication was offset by the degree of infiltration which he observed to be occurring. On such a record, the trier of fact would be entitled to conclude that even if the nurses were negligent in their duty to observe and report accurately, Margen was also negligent in failing to examine respondent's leg himself more frequently and in choosing to rely, for long periods of time, solely upon the information provided by the nurses.

The order granting respondent a new trial against appellant Lewis is reversed, and the order granting respondent a new trial against appellants Margen and Alta Bates is affirmed.

## ANALYSIS

1. In the fact pattern of this case, in what areas would you say the conduct of the nurses indicated a continued awareness of a distinct duty to the patient? At what point did the nursing care appear to deteriorate through the nurses' failure in their duty to foresee possible harm to the patient?

2. Where in the evidence is indicated a lack of decisiveness on the part of the nurses in reporting to the physician? Where in the evidence is indicated an inconclusive reaction on the part of the physician? Which party was the primary one in precipitating the reaction of the other?

3. Hypothesize the communication that should have taken place between the physician and the nurse. When in the series of events was the crucial time for it to have taken place?

4. In the text, it was indicated that a measure of the duty of the nurse to foresee harm to her patient would depend on her knowledge of physical and biological (as well as social) science. Describe the knowledge in physical and biological science the nurses should have had in dealing with the Mundt situation.

5. In what areas did the conduct of the nurses fail to meet the professional, if not legal, standards?

## CASES FOR FURTHER ANALYSIS

### Methodist Hosp. v. Ball, 50 Tenn. App. 460, 362 S.W.2d 475 (1961)

This was an action against a hospital for the alleged wrongful death of plaintiff's son. Charles Ball, together with his mother and his friends, was riding in an automobile that was struck from the rear by another car. All the occupants of the plaintiff's car were taken to the emergency room of the Methodist Hospital. All except the deceased and his friend John Moore were treated for cuts and bruises. It appeared to the intern and the nurses in charge of the emergency room that young Moore had suffered a brain injury, and he was assigned to the one available bed in the hospital, where he died the following day. Charles Ball remained on a stretcher in the emergency room near the door for forty-five minutes, at which time the intern instructed the ambulance driver to take him to another hospital, where he died shortly after arrival.

The plaintiff sued the defendant hospital for the negligent failure of the employee intern to exercise reasonable and ordinary care toward plaintiff's son as his condition required.

Plaintiff's evidence was that the boy had sustained serious injuries, including a lacerated liver, which caused severe hemorrhage into the abdominal cavity and shock. The employees of the hospital failed to examine the boy or administer treatment, and falsely accused him of being drunk. They caused him to be forcibly strapped to the stretcher and evicted him from the emergency room.

Several physicians and two registered nurses, one the night supervisor and the other the nurse on duty in the emergency room, testified. A pathologist who performed the autopsy testified, as an expert witness, that the cause of death was due to the ruptured liver and further that the forceful treatment in the emergency room, including someone placing his knee in the boy's back, had further damaged the liver.

The court affirmed a verdict for the plaintiff.

### Williams v. Menehan, 191 Kan. 6, 379 P.2d 292 (1963)

An action was brought by parents against three physicians for injuries resulting in the death of their son. When the boy was about three, it was noted by the mother that the child began to show some cyanosis and lassitude after exercise. He was examined by the family physician, who referred him to a pediatrician. The pediatrician made a tentative diagnosis of congenital cardiac defect and recommended that a cardiac catheterization be performed by a team of specialists to further confirm the diagnosis. During the procedure the child died. No evidence was introduced to show medical error in the diagnostic procedure or the manner in which it was performed nor was there any evidence of error in the choice or the amount of the anesthetic administered. The case turned on the point of disclosure, whether the parents were given sufficient information of the risk involved in the procedure. In its decision, the court followed its reasoning in an earlier case [*Natanson v. Kline*, 186 Kan. 393, 350 P.2d 1093 (1963)] and said:

... it is the duty of a doctor to make a reasonable disclosure to his patient of the nature and probable consequences of the suggested or recommended treatment, and to make a reasonable disclosure of the dangers within his knowledge which are incident or possible in the treatment he proposes to administer. But this does not mean that a doctor is under an obligation to describe in detail all the possible consequences of treatment. To make a complete disclosure of all facts, diagnosis and alternatives or possibilities which might occur to the doctor could so alarm the patient that it would, in fact, constitute bad medical practice.

The appellate court affirmed the holding of the trial court in favor of the defendant physicians, which, in directing a verdict for the physicians, had held that the evidence submitted by the plaintiffs was insufficient to permit the jury to find a breach of duty.

### *Powell v. Fidelity & Cas. Co.,* 185 So.2d 324 (La. App. 1966)

This was an action for alleged malpractice of hospital nurses. Suit was filed by the plaintiff as a result of the death of his wife and his unborn child.

The wife of the plaintiff, Florida Powell, was sent to the hospital for a blood transfusion when in the thirty-fifth week of her pregnancy. At the hospital the physician injected the needle, administered the saline solution preliminary to the starting of the actual blood transfusion, set the stopcock for the desired rate of flow, and left the patient in charge of the head nurse and a member of the nursing staff. The physician returned once and commented that the blood was flowing nicely. The transfusion was completed when the amount ordered by the physician had been administered, the decedent was observed for five to fifteen minutes (long enough for her sister to have the car brought to the emergency door), and the patient departed. Shortly thereafter she was brought back to the hospital suffering from pulmonary edema, and despite all efforts to save her and the child, both died.

Three issues were raised on appeal: whether the rate of flow at which the blood was administered to the decedent was the proximate cause of her death, whether the registered nurses who administered the transfusion were responsible for the speed or rate at which the blood was given, and whether the registered nurses were under a duty to observe the decedent for any particular time following the transfusion. The attending physician's negligence was not at issue because he had entered into a separate settlement with the plaintiff.

The court held that the nurses had no right or duty to change the rate of flow of the blood once it had been set by the physician, nor was there any evidence to show they had done so, and further held that, in the absence of orders from the physician, the nurses had no responsibility or duty to keep the patient under observation for a longer period than was done.

The court affirmed the judgment that the nurses had not been negligent.

## *Williams v. New York*, 18 N.Y. 2d 481, 223 N.E.2d 343 (1966)

Suit was brought by the guardian of an infant who was born out of wedlock to a mentally deficient mother as a result of sexual assault on the mother.

Claim was made against the State of New York for negligence in the care and custody of the infant's mother while the latter was a patient at a state hospital for the mentally ill, and more particularly for failing to provide proper care and supervision over her while she was in the custody of the state. The claimant's charge was that, as a result of the neglect of the state, the child has been "deprived of property rights; deprived of normal childhood and normal home life; deprived of proper parental care, support and rearing; caused to bear the stigma of illegitimacy."

In its denial of the child's right of recovery, the court stated that the impossibility of entertaining this suit came not so much from difficulty in measuring the alleged damages as from the absence in our legal doctrines of any such idea as a *wrong* to a later-born child caused by permitting a woman to be violated.

## Recommended Source Material

TEXTS

Gregory, C., and Kalven, H., Jr., *Cases and Materials on Torts*, 252–89 (Boston: Little, Brown & Co., 1959).

Harper, F., and James, F., *The Law of Torts*, 1105–1107 (Boston: Little, Brown & Co., 1956).

Prosser, W., *Handbook of the Law of Torts*, 331–57 (St. Paul: West Publishing Co., 3rd ed., 1964).

Shartel, B., and Plant, M., *The Law of Medical Practice*, 4–10 (Springfield: Charles C Thomas, Publisher, 1959).

PERIODICALS

Bohlen, F., *The Moral Duty to Aid Others as a Basis of Tort Liability*, 56 U. Penn. L. Rev. 217 (1958).

Brody, F., *Negligently Inflicted Psychic Injuries: A Return to Reason*, 7 Vill. L. Rev. 232 (1961).

Bryan, S., *Good Samaritan Laws—Good or Bad*, 15 Mer. L. Rev. 477 (1964).

Feldbrugge, F., *Good and Bad Samaritans: A Comparative Survey of Criminal Law Provisions Concerning Failure to Rescue*, 14 Am. J. Com. L. 630 (1966).

Gordon, D., *The Unborn Plaintiff*, 63 Mich. L. Rev. 579 (1965).

Magruder, C., *Mental and Emotional Disturbance in the Law of Torts*, 49 Harv. L. Rev. 1033 (1936).

Minor, C., *The Moral Obligation as a Basis of Liability*, 9 Va. L. Rev. 420 (1923).

# Chapter Five

## Causation

In the preceding chapter, we have examined two basic ideas of tort liability, negligence and breach of duty. We have seen that, in the ordinary situation, the question of whether a particular act is negligent is determined by comparison of the actor's conduct with that of the hypothetical reasonable man. In cases involving persons acting in a professional capacity, we have seen that a different standard prevails, and in such cases, the applicable standard requires the professional or expert person to conduct himself, at least, upon the average level achieved by the members of his profession in his community. Furthermore, we have seen that every person owes to every other person the duty to conduct himself in such a fashion as to avoid injury, that the breach of that duty may lead to liability, and that the scope of the duty is measured by the foreseeability of harm. The present section is concerned with another basic element of tort liability, that of causation.

Wild Rose Road, located in Spokane County, Washington, washed away on a rainy afternoon in 1957. Prior to the washout, the county officials responsible for maintenance of the road should have taken measures, but did not, to avoid a washout and to warn users of the hazard of using the road. Several hours after the washout occurred, a car in which Mrs. Marion Trickey was a passenger drove headlong into the washout, and the resulting accident caused severe injuries to Mrs. Trickey's head and face, including fractures of her nose, facial bones, shoulder, and finger, a concussion of the brain, and several facial lacerations. Approximately a year after the accident, Mrs. Trickey unsuccessfully attempted suicide and repeated the attempt on two more occasions. Finally, twenty months after the accident, she took her own life by a massive dose of sleeping pills. Her family thereupon brought suit against Spokane County, alleging that the county's negligent failure to prevent or warn of the washout resulted in Mrs. Trickey's death. At the trial, the county successfully

171

contended that its negligence was not the cause of the suicide. The Washington Supreme Court reversed, and held that the testimony of a neuropsychiatrist to the effect that the type of brain damage resulting from an injury like that suffered by Mrs. Trickey could result in a state of insanity causing an uncontrollable impulse toward suicide. Therefore, said the court, the causal relationship between the failure to warn of the washout and the suicide was sufficiently established [*Orcutt v. Spokane County*, 58 Wash. 2d 846, 364 P.2d 1102 (1961)].

Neither negligent conduct, nor conduct in breach of duty, without more, subjects anyone to liability. This is readily apparent when one considers that nearly every day of his life every person does something that is less than thoughtful, and that unreasonably endangers other persons. Fortunately, however, the vast majority of these acts do not result in any harm to family members, fellow workers, or citizens at large, and therefore no liability results. It is only when our negligent or wrongful conduct *causes harm* to someone else that the law will place the loss from such harm upon the person acting negligently or wrongfully. It follows that a plaintiff, seeking to obtain recovery for his economic losses from another person, must show that his injuries were caused by the other person's act and, therefore, that liability falls on the one who caused the injury.

Merely showing injury and negligent conduct is not enough: the plaintiff must establish a link between the two. Thus, assume that a homeowner negligently allows a watering hose to remain across a public sidewalk, and assume that a passerby falls in the vicinity of the hose. Is there liability? There is if the passerby tripped over the hose, for in that case the injury was the direct consequence of the negligent act of leaving the hose in a dangerous spot. There is not if he stubbed his toe and fell, for the hose then had nothing whatever to do with the injury. The crucial question presented in this simple hypothetical situation, and in every negligence case, is: was the injury in fact caused by the negligent conduct?

That the causation requirement should exist, or, in other words, that the law requires an injured party to prove the fact of causation, is implicit in the primary function of tort law, namely, the fair allocation of financial responsibility for accidental injury among various persons connected with the injury in question.

Thus, if one person is responsible *in fact* for injury to another, fairness and justice require that the financial responsibility be shifted. By the same reasoning, however, if there is no factual responsibility, it would be unfair to impose financial responsibility, regardless of the irresponsibility of behavior. If factual responsibility were not a predicate for financial responsibility, the law would be imposing a financial burden for negligence alone, without regard to whether adverse consequences followed. This would be, in effect, simply a penalty or a punishment for negligent conduct, rather than a means of compelling the one at fault to compensate the injured party for his injury.

## The Tests of Causation

Causation is a question of fact, and in each lawsuit it is incumbent upon the party seeking to recover for injury to establish the existence of this fact element. Reaching the conclusion that a causal connection must be shown does not yet determine what kind of causal connection the law requires. Clearly, no event or happening, be it injury, death, or anything else, has one cause only. In any situation in which a person is injured, a long chain of circumstances culminates in the event, and in some respects it is readily possible to say that, were any one of those circumstances absent, the situation might not have developed to bring a particular person into a particular place at a particular time, thereby resulting in injury to himself or to another. Clearly also, no plaintiff could ever show that a defendant was responsible for *all* the circumstances contributing to an injury, and if such a showing were required, no plaintiff could ever recover.

### "BUT FOR" TEST

Standards, or tests, have developed in the law to attempt to define and specify the causal link that must justify the imposition of legal liability. This causation test can be described as a "but for," or *sine qua non*, test, that is, *whether the injury would not have occurred if the defendant had not been guilty of a negligent act*. Stated another way, if, "but for" defendant's negligence, plaintiff's harm would not have occurred, then the "but for" test is met, and the defendant's negligence was a legal cause of such harm. Under this test, no attempt is made to determine what is, in the last analysis, a philosophical question: what is the "true cause" of an injury? The test considers only those actions of the defendant that are claimed to be negligent. The test asks the question: if the defendant had not committed the acts that he in fact did commit, would the injury to plaintiff nevertheless have occurred? If the answer to the test question is "yes," the plaintiff has *not* succeeded in forging the causal link necessary to shift the loss to the defendant. On the other hand, if the answer is "no," that is, if the plaintiff would not have been harmed were it not for the defendant's actions, the test is satisfied, and causation in fact has been established. In a famous old case applying this rule, *Stacey v. Knickerbocker Ice Co.*, 84 Wis. 614, 54 N.W. 1091 (1893), an ice company failed to give adequate warning that a hole had been cut in the ice on a lake, and failed to fence or otherwise guard the hole. Plaintiff's horses bolted, fell through the hole in the ice, and were drowned. Even though defendant's negligence in failing to protect the hole was clear, it was held not liable, because the evidence showed the horses were uncontrollable and could not in any event have been stopped. Therefore, the court found that the "but for" test was not met, because the injury would have occurred even if there had been no negligent conduct.·

### "SUBSTANTIAL FACTOR" TEST

A second test which has currency among courts and scholars is called the "substantial factor" test. Under this test, the requirement of causation is fulfilled if *the defendant's negligent conduct was a substantial factor in bringing about the harm to the plaintiff.* If the conduct was a substantial factor, causation is established. If it was only a very minor factor, or no factor at all, there is no causal connection between the conduct and the injury. Conduct may be a substantial factor in an injury without being the sole factor; moreover, it need not be the predominant factor. The "but for" and "substantial factor" tests do not lead to different results; they are alternative ways of verbalizing the degree of relationship required between an act and an injury for there to be legal cause. The "but for" test is most readily applied in relatively simple fact situations, whereas the "substantial factor" test lends itself well to more complicated fact patterns.

## Multiple Causation

The problem of causation is simplest when *one* plaintiff is seeking to recover from *one* defendant for an injury *all* of which is attributable to that defendant, and that would not have occurred but for the one defendant's conduct. When two or more defendants are involved in a factual setting in which an injury occurs, the problem becomes more complex. Here, each defendant may claim, often with some justice, that the other defendant was at fault, and therefore that the other should bear the loss. (It must be kept in mind throughout this discussion of causation problems involving several parties that each party must always be found guilty of negligent conduct before he can be held liable, even though causation is established and, conversely, if the causation element is missing, no liability will follow even though clear negligence is shown.) When the actions of two persons coincide in such a way that a third person is injured, the "but for" test may still be applied, and in this situation separately applied, to each person's conduct. If the application of this test results in the conclusion that the injury would not have occurred without a particular defendant's conduct, that defendant is liable for the injury, and this without regard to whether anyone else may also be liable.

But what if injury would have occurred from some other cause as well? In other words, what if the defendant's conduct would have harmed plaintiff, but it is shown that injury would have occurred anyway, either because of the wrongdoing of some other person or because of the operation of natural forces. A classic instance arises where plaintiff's home is destroyed by a fire resulting from a combination of two fires each negligently set by separate defendants, where each fire alone would have burned the house. Here, the "but for" test is not met, because the injury would have occurred even if one defendant had not been negligent, namely, because of the other defendant's negligence. Nevertheless, in such a situation both are held liable for the injury on the theory that liability for genuinely negligent conduct cannot be avoided by the happenstance that someone else was equally at fault, and that each defendant's wrongful act was a "substantial factor" in the harm.

A variation occurs when one of the two forces is a natural force. Thus, in the example given, one of the two fires destroying the home may have been started by lightning. Courts divide on the issue of whether the defendant would be liable for negligently setting the fire when the house was doomed anyway because of the natural forces of the lightning bolt, and the result therefore varies from jurisdiction to jurisdiction. Some courts refuse to grant a plaintiff relief when the injury of which he complains was inevitable through no fault of anyone, whereas other courts refuse to relieve a defendant of the consequences of his negligence by the accident of nature's intervention. Which interpretation do you think best? Should the fact that insurance frequently protects against loss through natural forces affect the law's view of this situation?

## APPORTIONMENT

In the foregoing discussion of multiple causation, we have assumed that the plaintiff's injury was one that could not be fairly divided or apportioned in any way among various defendants. Sometimes, however, a basis for apportionment can be found, and each defendant can be held responsible for that portion of the injury caused by him, but no more. Thus, in the illustration of two fires burning plaintiff's property, if one defendant had set a fire that destroyed a barn, and the other had set a fire that destroyed a house, an apportionment could be made of the total injury (loss of house and barn) suffered by the plaintiff, i.e., each defendant would pay for the portion of the total damage caused by him.

Whether an injury is divisible, and therefore whether the responsibility for compensation for that injury can be divided among several persons, is a question for determination by the trier of fact, who decides the question (as all others), on the basis of the evidence presented to it. If an apportionment can be made, each defendant is responsible only for that portion of the harm that he caused; if it cannot be made, each defendant is liable for the whole.

The rule of apportionment applies to cases of successive acts of negligence as well as to concurrent ones. Here it frequently happens that the first actor is liable for an entire injury, and the second actor is liable for only a portion. A typical instance is when a person is negligently injured by A., and a doctor who treats him negligently aggravates the injury. The first defendant, because the "but for" causation test is satisfied, and because it is reasonably foreseeable that an injured plaintiff will be treated by a doctor, will be responsible for the original harm, plus the aggravation; the doctor, however, will be responsible only for the aggravation.

The idea of apportionment is not limited to situations where a division among defendants may be possible. Apportionment of damages also may become involved even though there is only one negligent actor, in a circumstance where a plaintiff's injury is a composite of harm caused by the defendant and some pre-existing condition that may contribute substantially to the final result. In this situation, too, a defendant is responsible only for that portion of the injury attributable to his conduct, provided that a valid basis for apportionment is shown to exist. To return to the plaintiff whose home was burned, assume that three days before the defendant set fire to it, a tornado had blown away the roof. The defendant then would have to compensate the plaintiff only for the value of a roofless house, not a complete one. In other words, even though plaintiff's house was totally destroyed by a combination of events, the damages would be apportioned so that the defendant would be responsible only for that portion actually caused by him.

A significant application of this rule arises in personal injury cases. Every person who receives injuries is affected by such injuries in a way partially dependent upon his existing physical condition at the time of the accident. Every person has his own unique physical makeup; he may be healthy or decrepit, strong or weak. What is a minor nosebleed to one man is fatal to the hemophiliac; what is but an irritation to one may cause lasting pain to another. The principles of apportionment come into play here also, and where division is possible, an injured party is entitled to compensation only for the portion of his injuries caused by the defendant. It is, nevertheless, fundamental that the bare fact that pre-existing conditions play a part in determining the ultimate severity of any injury affords no ground for limiting liability unless some way appears for fairly apportioning the damage. In a well-known case, *Vosburg v.*

*Putney*, 80 Wis. 523, 50 N.W. 403 (1891), a latent bone disease turned a slight impact into the loss of a limb, and the defendant was held fully responsible.

## Independent Intervening Cause

Situations can arise in which a person is injured following an act of negligence, but where some other event has taken place after the negligent act which can also be said to have caused the injury. In such cases, the negligent actor offers as a defense to liability for his negligence the contention that the injury was really caused by the later event. In other words, the claim is made that the first wrongdoer, though negligent, is free of responsibility for the injury because it was in fact the result of something that happened subsequent to his negligence and over which he had no control.

Thus in *Morril v. Morril*, 104 N.J.L. 557, 142 Atl. 337, 60 A.L.R. 102 (1928), the defendant had negligently left unrepaired a defective latch on his garage door. During a children's football game near the garage, a gust of wind blew open the door and immediately thereafter one of the children ran into the door and seriously injured his eye on the latch. In a suit against the garage owner, the court held that the wind was a factor which could not have been anticipated and that its intervention in the chain of circumstances absolved the defendant from liability.

The legal principle applied in such cases is known as the doctrine of "independent intervening cause." An intervening cause has been defined by a leading authority as "one which comes into active operation in producing the result after the actor's negligent act or omission has occurred." [Prosser, W., *Handbook of the Law of Torts*, 266 (St. Paul: West Publishing Co., 2nd ed., 1955).]

Even if he is successful in convincing the court that his act of negligence was independent and unrelated to the intervening force, however, the first actor will not be relieved from liability where the intervening cause was foreseeable or a normal incident of the risk created. Thus, when one negligently causes an automobile accident which leaves a person lying slightly injured in the road, the negligent person will also be responsible if a second driver runs over the victim and inflicts an additional injury. The theory of such recovery is that injury from a second driver on the highway is a foreseeable risk of the conduct of the first driver causing the initial accident.

## Causation as a Factor in Medical Malpractice

In the day-to-day practice of the nurse, negligence of itself is not a sufficient cause of legal action. The conduct of the nurse may fall below that of a reasonable practitioner or may breach a duty, but if no injury occurs to the patient, she has only her conscience to deal with. However, when an injury is suffered by the patient and it can be said that "but for" the negligent conduct of the nurse, the harm would not have occurred, then it is obvious that the negligence of the nurse was the cause in fact of the injury. Once the causal relationship has been found, a monetary assessment of damages is made by the court or jury and imposed on the one responsible for the harm.

At times, the conduct of the nurse or nurses stands out as a critical factor that led to the injury or death of the patient. An instance is *Bugden v. Harbor View Hosp.*, 2 D.L.R. 338 (1947), where suit was brought against two nurses, a doctor, and a hospital. The evidence was that William Bugden was admitted to the hospital for treatment of an injured thumb, and the doctor requested procaine to be used as a local anesthetic in setting the dislocation. A nurse dispensed the drug from the operating room supply and a second nurse carried the bottle to the ward and handed it to the doctor, from which he filled a hypodermic syringe and injected the thumb. After a few minutes, as the thumb was not sufficiently anesthetized, he injected another quantity. The thumb was set and the doctor left to attend to other duties. In less than thirty minutes the patient died. It was then discovered that a mistake had been made and the bottle from which the physician had drawn the drug for the local anesthetic contained a solution of epinephrine hydrochloride, and what had been administered amounted to a fatal dose. Neither the physician nor either of the nurses had read the label on the bottle. The court stated that the plaintiff need not show that negligence of any one of the defendants was the cause of Bugden's death in the sense that it was the only cause. The question before the court was which one of the defendants was liable for the death? The physician was the immediate cause of death because he administered the drug when he gave the hypodermic. The court could find no negligence on his part, however, stating that a surgeon visiting a hospital to treat a patient had a right to assume that the nurses were competent. In the absence of negligence on his part, liability could not be established. The nurses were either incompetent or careless and, in either event, they failed to exercise a recognized duty to read the label on the bottle. It was through this conduct that they were found to be the cause of death. "But for" the breach of duty of the nurses, the patient would not have died and they were therefore liable for the harm. In commenting on duty, the court said:

Persons (nurses) who are in charge of dangerous things under which category, I think, drugs are included are under a duty to handle them with such care that harm will not arise to those who depend upon their skill. At least they must exercise reasonable care to avoid such harm. The liability of any particular case arises from the foreseeability of damage, and the duty to take care.

If negligence cannot be established as a cause of the injury complained of, no liability can be found. Such was true in the case of *Connellan v. Coffey*, 122 Conn. 136, 187 Atl. 901 (1936). The plaintiff sustained a compound fracture of the arm and was treated at home for one week by the defendant physician. He was then taken to the hospital where it was necessary to amputate the arm because an infection had developed caused by a gas bacillus. It was alleged by the plaintiff that the infection and its consequences resulted because of the negligent treatment of the physician. The jury verdict for the defendant was upheld because the plaintiff failed to prove that the doctor's conduct was a substantial factor in producing the injuries suffered.

### SOLE RESPONSIBILITY V. SHARED RESPONSIBILITY OF MEDICAL TEAM

There are times when the nature of the nursing judgment is so independently exercised that, should harm come to the patient, the presence of a causal relationship between the conduct of the nurse and the injury incurred is indisputable. Such a situation may be the result of the environmental setting in which the nurse works alone, as the industrial or public health nurse. Or, although she may not be alone physically, the exigencies of the situation leave the nurse no time to consult a fellow worker or to seek medical support. Illustrations of sole responsibility are:

The public health nurse on a home visit who must decide when she can safely leave a patient following a treatment, knowing that rapid medical assistance is not available.

The nurse in an outpatient clinic who has the responsibility of evaluating a patient's history of allergies and who must decide when to give an immunizing dose or when to refer the information for medical consideration.

The nurse in the coronary care unit who must take appropriate action when confronted with the extreme emergency of cardiac arrest and when time does not permit awaiting medical assistance.

The opposite of highly individualized practice is the complex medical and nursing team relationship. The existence of the relationship poses varying problems in determining the cause of harm, because functions may be blurred and individual responsibility diffused within the composite act called patient care. It is true that in spite of a high degree of group interaction, it is possible, at times, to find a single practitioner solely responsible; usually, however, the circumstances are such that the conduct of two or more persons may contribute to a single injury or even a series of injuries where the negligence of one is compounded by the negligence of another. Difficulty in the establishment of a causal relationship when responsibility flows from one practitioner to another is illustrated by a hypothetical example: A nurse gave a hypodermic injection, which was followed by an infection at the site of the introduction of the needle. Within a few days the condition was such that it was necessary for the surgeon to open the abscess that formed, and when the wound was healed, there had developed a marked loss of function in the arm. What was the cause in fact of the injury to the arm? A contaminated needle? Poor technique in the administration of the injection? Improper surgery? Contaminated drug? What evidence might be found for a single causative factor? Or multiple causes? If multiple causation were established, what evidence might lead a court to conclude that each wrongdoer was liable for the entire harm? What evidence might lead the court to decide that the injury was divisible and apportionment could be made?

Another way in which the conduct of members of the medical and nursing team can converge to produce a single injury is when two or more actors have been negligent and the negligence of each has made a substantial contribution to the injury. This situation arose in *French v. Fischer*, 50 Tenn. App. 587, 362 S.W.2d 926 (1962). The plaintiff, Rebecca Ann Fischer, when less than one month of age, was admitted to the Baptist Memorial Hospital for surgery to reduce a pyloric stenosis. About one month after surgery, when the child was taken to another physician, it was discovered that a sponge had been left in the abdomen at the time of the first surgery, and that gangrene had developed; it was necessary to remove two thirds of the small intestine including the ileocecal valve. Issues at trial centered on the functions of each member of the surgical team and who was in control of the team as a basis of proof of legal liability. The evidence supported the fact that both the surgeon and the nurses were responsible for making an accurate sponge count and, therefore, each shared in bringing about the harm. The surgeon and the hospital (for its nurses) were responsible for damages.

We have seen that at times one member of the medical or nursing team may be found to be the single causative agent producing the harm from which the patient suffered. Again, and more frequently, two or more members of the team may have shared in the conduct which brought about the undesirable results. A third doctrine of causal relationship has significance for medical and nursing practice. It is known as the doctrine of the independent intervening cause. Here the negligence deals with a time sequence in which the later act of one person supersedes and is independent of the negligent act or omission of the other. In patient care, the physician initiates the medical plan of care and the nurse implements this plan. Negligent as the physician might be, the nurse could be guilty of independent action—of itself the primary cause of the harm— and in this event, the nurse's act could take precedence over the conduct of the medical practitioner.

In the case of *Norton v. Argonaut Ins. Co.*, *infra*, p. 189, counsel for the physician proposed in his defense to the court that the negligence of the nurse was "so inconceivable, gross and unpredictable as to constitute an independent intervening cause thereby relieving the insured [the physician] of liability." The court found this argument without merit under the facts of this particular case.

UNCERTAINTIES IN MEDICAL PROOF OF CAUSATION

As was discussed earlier in this section, the crucial point in the establishment of a cause in fact is proof. There must be proof, first, that an injury was sustained and, second, that the injury came about through the negligent conduct of the defendant. Proof of causation is complicated in medical malpractice cases, for unless the facts are within the comprehension of a lay jury, the testimony of a medical expert is necessary. This testimony usually is highly technical in nature, and because medical science is not an exact science, it does not lend itself to precise factual determination of cause. Often the combination of factors that could have brought about the harm are so nebulous and interrelated that proof is not possible. The injury to the plaintiff may be indisputable, but the law is firm that the defendant is liable only for the damage he has caused or to which he has made a substantial contribution. In *Brown v. Shannon West Texas Memorial Hosp.*, 222 S.W.2d 248 (Tex. Civ. App. 1949), plaintiff, in response to a request for blood donors, went to the Shannon Hospital. Supplies from the Baylor University Hospital were used, and two nurses performed the phlebotomy, at which time some difficulty was encountered in inserting the needle into the vein. Following the phlebotomy, the plaintiff experienced constant pain in her arm, was hospitalized at Shannon and at other hospitals, and was attended by several doctors. It was not disputed in the trial court that Mrs. Brown had sustained a serious injury. One medical expert testified:

There is an area here approximately an inch and a half by three inches in diameter which is crusted over and it's safe to assume there is some type of chronic infection present there; . . . there is an obvious contracture of the elbow and that is a shortening of the muscles so that I don't believe she can extend this arm.

Plaintiff contended that a nonsterile needle had been used. Several expert witnesses testified to the difficulty of pinpointing the source of an infection. Plaintiff failed to discharge the burden of proof resting on her to establish the proximate cause of the injuries complained of, and mere proof that infection followed the use of needles or that it could have resulted from the use of a nonsterile needle was held insufficient.

Another difficult area in proof of causation arises when a serious or fatal complication occurs so close to a medical or surgical treatment that a causal relationship is suggested and medical or hospital liability is sought. In this area are numerous instances of cardiovascular accidents, cardiac arrest, and emboli.

Illustrative is the case of *Michael v. Roberts*, 91 N.H. 499, 23 A.2d 361 (1942), in which the plaintiff's decedent died of a pulmonary embolism following a tonsillectomy. The facts were that after a tonsillectomy the patient hemorrhaged and was returned to the operating room where the bleeding was stopped; later, when it started again, efforts to locate the surgeon failed and two other physicians responded but were unable to revive the patient. The recorded cause of death was pulmonary embolism. A malpractice action was brought against the surgeon. The plaintiff's case failed because the evidence did not establish a causal connection between the alleged negligent tonsillectomy and the patient's death for the evidence permitted no conclusion other than that the immediate cause of death was a pulmonary embolism.

When several medical causes, either concurrent or successive, have converged to produce a harm, apportionment of damages is a difficult problem for the trier of facts. For example, the patient is in the hospital being treated for an aggravated diabetic ulcer of the leg, and an attendant leaves a wheelchair where the patient falls over it in the dark, striking his leg. Diabetic gangrene follows and amputation is necessary. Clearly, a question would arise whether the hospital was responsible for the total damage or whether the pre-existing condition could be evaluated from the medical testimony and the medical record, and apportionment made.

## NOTES

### (1) Divergent Views on the Meaning of Causation

On the trial level, a preponderance of all litigated cases requires medical proof. This proof frequently centers on whether a causal relationship can be established between the nature and extent of the injury and the negligent conduct of the defendant. The need to establish the relationship necessarily puts the medical expert witness in a difficult position, for the weight and clarity of his testimony may determine the outcome of the case. He knows that seldom is there a precise cause of an injury, for there are always individual differences, the obscure variables of human physiology, and the influences of the environmental setting. Legal counsel, on the other hand, is not interested in intangibles but wants a straightforward answer that will establish as firmly as possible the proof he is seeking. Because of this gap, there is a lack of identification with the point of view, each with the other, interfering with communication and not alleviated by the highly technical medical vocabulary that the expert witness tends to use. In these well-established, socially oriented professions it is unfortunate that smooth interrelationships do not exist, for their absence may interfere with a just settlement of a claim, and the client is the one who suffers. The professional nurse, as an expert witness, will bring to her testimony a medically oriented approach. It is important in terms of her value as a witness that she also identify with the legal purposes and procedure of proof.

One reason for the differing views between medicine and the law is that the term "causation" varies in meaning in terms of the operational framework in which it is used. To the physician, cause and etiology are synonymous, and may include those many factors that have contributed to the interruption in the health pattern of the individual. To seek a medical cause may lead to a differential diagnosis, which is a scientific step-by-step procedure of highly complicated laboratory tests, x-rays, tissue examinations, and physical findings. When these data are assembled, a causative factor is determined and a diagnosis is made. In some instances of obscure conditions, the physician may be forced to work on an empirical basis and to make his diagnosis from an appraisal of objective and subjective symptoms and proceed with therapy even though the actual cause of the condition is not known to medical science.

The physician makes an easy adaptation to facts that may shift from day to day as the symptoms of the patient change or as more scientific data become available to the physician, which might lead him to establish a totally different cause (diagnosis) of the condition. He is not too concerned with the circumstances that precipitated the condition or the injury, for this has spent itself; instead, he gives his attention to the prevention of such complications as nonunion of bones or the invasion of microorganisms.

With an equally clear rationale, causation as the law views it is concerned with the violation of the rights of the individual, which brought about the harm, and whether one or more persons acted severally or in concert. The lawyer, too, is vitally concerned with the facts, and is equally zealous in pursuing every possible clue to add to the facts, but these facts are static, unchanging, and in the past. His skill in developing the fact picture is as highly technical as is the physician's in making a differential diagnosis. However, the lawyer's is a vastly different skill. He is concerned with the working of the human mind, with value judgments of human conduct so that he may recapture the situation leading to the injury and present it vividly to the jury. Thus he seeks a causal relationship to persuade the jury to find liability, assess financial responsibility, and redress a harm.

Whether the expert witness be a doctor or a nurse, he should identify with the purposes of the law and endeavor to deal with those facts bearing on the injury sustained and refrain from introducing vague uncertainties of medical causation or etiology and confusing medical issues. When, for instance, the injury has aggravated a pre-existing condition, the medical witness can better serve justice in the courts by giving his full attention to legal variables of estimates of disability and the amount of pain and suffering, which will have a bearing on the apportionment of damages. When asked the direct question, if in his opinion the defendant was responsible for the harm the plaintiff suffered, the answer, insofar as possible, should be in terms of legal not medical causation, or etiology.

## (2) Malingering

Malingering interferes with a rational process in determining causation. It is a medicolegal condition, psychiatrically oriented, defined as a willful, deliberate imitation or exaggeration of illness, intended consciously or unconsciously to deceive the observer. In personal injury cases, it poses difficult problems of proof in that the evidence to support the suspected medical condition is often tenuous and uncertain.

It has been found that the intent to deceive can manifest itself in one of several forms: the malingering person may fraudulently invent symptoms he does not have, or he may have had genuine symptoms that have abated and he fraudulently alleges them to continue. Again, although his symptoms may be real, he fraudulently makes them worse than they are. In still another category is the person who has genuine symptoms that he attributes to a cause other than the cause in fact.

The etiology and therapy for this condition are far-reaching and beyond the bounds of this Note. From a legal standpoint, malingering is suspected in many courtroom situations involving personal injuries; seldom, however, is there an allegation either expressed or implied, possibly because it is a sensitive medical area in which the evidence for proof rests with the medical witness. Whether a witness be a doctor or a nurse, it is essential to guard against an easy solution to the effect that this is simply another case of "compensation neurosis." This assumption reduces all clinical manifestation to malingering supposedly motivated by a desire for money. This could be a dangerous oversimplification that might result in an injustice by belittling the actual conditions and even denying the possibility of its existence. By contrast, the medical witness might give credence to symptoms that magnify the injuries and resultant ill effects.

Often it is difficult for a medical examiner to distinguish between malingering and an actual posttraumatic condition. An inventor, unless he is very knowledgeable in the field of medical science, frequently falls into a trap devised by the careful medical examiner, and the nature of his condition can be recognized. The exaggerator who cannot walk or who complains of headache from a blow on the head or discomfort from an injury to a soft part of the body, none of which can be determined by x-ray, presents a clinical picture in which the etiology is obscure. In the consideration of the suspected malingerer, the limitations of medical science should be recognized and those opinions guarded that imply that a condition is being feigned for an ulterior motive, when in reality a deep-seated condition may exist that eludes present diagnostic measures and scope of medical science.

The industrial or public health nurse is likely to be in a position to assist in the collection of objective data that might aid the plaintiff in a fair settlement or, under other circumstances, could assist the defendant in not being held for an unjust claim. Psychiatry and pathology are areas of medical science on which the law relies heavily. As medical science advances in knowledge of human behavior and its reaction on the human body, medicine may well lead the way for the law in the *scientific* detection of this condition, which, although a sickness, is not necessarily one that falls within the field of compensation for personal injuries.

## (3) Monetary Appraisals of Personal Injuries

To this point in the text we have discussed in some detail the legal pre-requisites to the establishment of liability for negligence. For there to be liability, there must be conduct falling below a certain standard, and a causal connection between that conduct and an injury. Then, as we say, "liability" is established. What, in practical terms does this mean? A "liability" for what? The answer, of course, is clear: it is the obligation to pay a certain sum of money to the injured party. Once a jury has reached its determination of liability—and found the presence of the factors of negligence and causation—it must turn its attention to another question: how much money should the plaintiff receive to adequately compensate him for his loss. From the plaintiff's point of view, liability alone is of no interest to him; he wants money. The principle underlying the entire process of litigation is that the plaintiff should receive a sum of money such that he will be compensated for the wrong done to him. We will turn our attention in this Note to a brief consideration of how the jury can make a determination of what the plaintiff is entitled to receive as a result of a typical personal injury.

There are three broad categories for which a plaintiff is entitled to be recompensed. First, he is entitled to have his medical and hospital expenses paid, including doctor's fees, medications, and special expenses of various kinds. Moreover, plaintiff not only is entitled to those medical expenses he has already incurred to cure or alleviate his injury, but also is entitled to compensation for those the future holds for him. Second, a plaintiff is entitled to the full amount of any economic loss suffered by him as a result of the injury of which he complains. This includes both lost income resulting from time away from work or professional practice as a consequence of an injury and also an amount to compensate for a loss or lessening of future earning power. Third, an injured person is entitled to be compensated for his pain and suffering, both past and future.

There is a great element of the subjective in the consideration of any of these damage awards. In the first place, each of the three elements includes a prediction as to the future, which, making the assumption that a jury in its jury room has no more of a crystal ball than any of the rest of us, involves uncertainty and guesswork. Prediction of future medical expenses is difficult; even more difficult is prediction of future economic loss. Many difficult questions arise; is the plaintiff entitled to the benefit of the doubt when he might have taken a better job at higher pay, or continued education that would result in an increase in earning power? What of the case of a child, who has not established an earnings record and whose potentialities are neither developed nor predictable? The most uncertain of all, however, is the amount of money that will adequately compensate for pain and suffering. What the dollar equivalent is to pain or suffering from disfigurement or the loss of a limb is anybody's guess, and the court in this area typically leaves a very large discretion in the jury. Barring a completely unjustified jury verdict, the appellate courts will rarely if ever take issue with the jury's determination of the amount of money needed to compensate for pain and suffering.

The law has found it difficult to describe any standard the jury should apply in computing the pecuniary worth of pain and suffering. Indeed, even in medical terms, the quantity of pain and its impact on individuals are exceedingly difficult entities to measure. In an attempt to provide the jury with some basis for its verdict plaintiff's counsel will frequently adopt a per diem approach, and will suggest to the jury an equivalent for pain on an hourly or daily basis, and then multiply this out over the projected life expectancy of the plaintiff. Per diem computation usually results in a rather high figure, and for that reason is sternly resisted by defense counsel. For example, if a man with a thirty-year life expectancy is awarded $4 per day for his pain, he would be entitled to recover $43,820. This figure appears rather large to arise from what appears to be a rather low amount to compensate for serious pain, $4 a day. Generally speaking, the courts allow counsel to make this kind of argument. The technique used in the hands of a skillful attorney is described in the following passage.

Consider as you read the article whether the per diem approach is a fair one and should be permitted in the courts. If not, what alternatives would you suggest? What reason, if any, can you give on the basis of your medical training for disallowing entirely any recovery for pain and suffering? Can you think of any reasons based upon social policy why recovery for pain and suffering should not be allowed?

## Belli, M., *The Use of Demonstrative Evidence in Achieving the More Adequate Award,* 32–37 (San Francisco: 1952)\*

Yet you have not considered anything for general damages of pain and suffering. Recall again, "all this man does is live." What compensation is going to be accorded to the man by way of general damage whose right to live out his life free from pain and suffering has been traumatically infringed by the negligent defendant?

It is not such a difficult job to interpret pain and suffering into the necessary dollars and cents that go to make up the personal injury award. It is the lawyer's duty to do this.

### BREAK DOWN INTO FINITE PERIODS

This is the key: You must break up the 30-year life expectancy into *finite* detailed periods of time. You must take these small periods of time, seconds and minutes, and determine in dollars and cents what each period is worth. You must start with the seconds and minutes rather than at the other end of thirty years. You cannot stand in front of a jury and say, "Here is a man horribly injured, permanently disabled, who will suffer excruciating pain for the rest of his life, he is entitled to a verdict of $225,000."

You must start at the beginning and show that pain is a continuous thing, second by second, minute by minute, hour by hour, year after year for thirty years. You must interpret one second, one minute, one hour, one year of pain and suffering into dollars and cents and then multiply to your absolute figure to show how you have achieved your result of an award approaching adequacy at $225,000. If you throw a novel figure at a jury or an appellate court of $225,000, without breaking it down, you are going to frighten both your trier of facts and your reviewer of facts.

Now how do you break this down?

I heard my good friend Jim Dooley of Chicago, another of our great trial lawyers do it this way. He advised the jury that the doctors testified there would be continual pain throughout the rest of the plaintiff's life. He drew a line across the blackboard and said, "My plaintiff won't have surcease from pain between 11:59 and 11:60 in the morning; he won't be free from pain between one in the afternoon and two in the afternoon. I can't interrupt this life line of his and say, 'here,' or 'here,' there will be surcease from pain. My doctors have testified that from the

\* Reprinted with permission of Melvin M. Belli.

very beginning of this accident to the end of his life he is going to have pain. This line represents thirty years—there is no break in it. Their will be pain from the beginning of this line to the end of this line. Sixty seconds in a minute, sixty minutes in an hour, twenty-four hours a day, three hundred sixty-five days a year, thirty-one million seconds a year of conscious pain and suffering times thirty years!"

So let's put on the board $60,000 for pain and suffering. Of course in your opening statement you are only privileged to say that you are going to explain to the jury and ask for $60,000 as pain and suffering in order to make up your total figure. It would be improper to argue, this must be reserved for the final summation.

The jurors must start thinking in days, minutes, and seconds and in five dollars, three dollars, and two dollars, so that they can multiply to the absolute figure. Maybe your juror will feel that five dollars a day is not enough, that it should be ten dollars per day. They may feel that it should be four dollars or three dollars a day. At least you have started them thinking; and when they follow your mechanics of multiplication, they must by this procedure come to some substantial figure if they are fair. A jury always tries to be fair; never forget this.

Let me give you another illustration in breaking down the thirty years and the absolute figure of $225,000 to the smaller figures and smaller periods. Start at the beginning: Suppose your client has traumatic arthritis. Do you know what it means to lie awake all night, to get into one position in bed and not be able to move because of the pain and torture that an arthritic spine gives?

I had a client who told me about it. He told me that for the first couple of months after the accident he would lie awake at night, maybe doze off, hear the clock strike hour after hour. Six months later he heard the clock striking the minutes. He couldn't doze off. Then about a year later he said he would lie there on his back, looking at the ceiling, lie still; he heard the grandfather's clock in the hallway tick, tick, tick. . . . Heard every tick from the time he went to bed until the time that he was lifted out of bed in the morning, until he was given sedative upon sedative to put him to sleep.

Pain and suffering is a continuous thing. With a life expectancy of thirty years, it is 15,768,000 minutes! How much of each minute of pain and suffering? The fact of the pain and suffering has been proved, the fact of 60 seconds in a minute is within judicial knowledge, all that remains is the computation in general damages once time has been reduced to the finite.

So on the blackboard now we have the figure of $186,000. I say again to you that this is an ascertainable figure. When your jury starts computing with their pencil and paper, minutes and seconds and life expectancy, they are going to have to achieve the figure at least of this amount.

# CASES

In each of the cases that follow, a causal relationship was established or failed, for want of proof, to be established; unless the conduct of the nurse or physician can be determined to be the proximate cause of the injury, no liability can be found for the plaintiff. Bear in mind in your analysis of these cases that in seeking a causal relationship there are three steps in the establishment of liability:

1. There must have been an injury.
2. There must have been negligent conduct or complaint of such conduct.
3. There must have been proof that the negligent conduct was the proximate cause of the injury.

*Only when the evidence is sufficient to support these three criteria can liability be found.*

Also dealt with in the cases is the subject of a pre-existing condition that is aggravated by the injury which poses a problem in assessing apportionment of damages, an area important in its implications for the physician and the nurse.

### *Norton v. Argonaut Ins. Co.,* 144 So. 2d 249 (La. App. 1962)

[This was an action against the respective insurance carriers of a hospital and an attending physician, and against a registered nurse by the parents of a three-month-old infant who had died of an overdose of digitalin.

The doctor contended that he was not negligent; the nurse contended that she merely followed the doctor's orders and in so doing was exercising the requisite degree of professional skill.

The child was admitted for examinations in connection with proposed surgery for congenital heart disease. The defendant cardiologist prescribed Lanoxin, a digitalis preparation, to be administered orally, and wrote on the order sheet "Elixir Pediatric Lanoxin 2.5 cc (0.125 mg) q6h×3 then once daily." After the child was digitalized, the child's mother was instructed in the administration of the maintenance dose and the patient was discharged. Two weeks later, the child's condition deteriorated and she was readmitted. The doctor noted on the admission orders that special medication was being administered by the mother, but did not indicate what it was. Thereafter, he instructed the mother to increase the daily dose to 3 cc and noted "Give 3.0 cc Lanoxin today for 1 dose only." He did not note any means of administration, nor did he indicate that the medication was being given by the mother. Later that day, the assistant director of nursing services visited the pediatric unit and found the only registered nurse fully occupied with an emergency patient. She summoned a senior student nurse to assist and began herself to check the charts. Upon so doing, she noted the doctor's order for 3.0 cc Lanoxin.

Although a registered nurse of many years' experience, the assistant supervisor had for several years been employed principally in an administrative or supervisory capacity, and she was not aware that Lanoxin was manufactured for oral administration, and was familiar only with administration by injection. Nevertheless, she thought that 3 cc of Lanoxin by injection to a three-month-old infant appeared to be a rather large dose. She consulted briefly with the student nurse, and inquired of the registered nurse in charge of the pediatric unit whether the child had previously received Lanoxin. She also inquired of a doctor who was a consultant on the child's case, who advised her that if the prescribing physician had said 3 cc, he meant 3 cc. The nurse inquired of another pediatrician who told her that if the doctor had prescribed said amount she could give it. She then injected 3 cc into the child, causing its death.

The jury found that the doctor, the nurse, and the hospital had been negligent, and that their respective negligence had caused the death of the infant. On appeal, the verdict was affirmed, the court holding that the facts recited above sufficiently established negligence on the part of the nurse and the doctor. The issue with respect to the doctor was whether or not his notation on the order sheet constituted negligence, when the order was subsequently misinterpreted by the nurse to apply to Lanoxin by injection as opposed to Lanoxin to be administered orally. The doctor admitted that the notation was improper because it failed to note that 3 cc of Lanoxin had already been given by the mother, and that the child was thereby subjected to the possibility of a double oral dose. The doctor contended, however, that the nurse was at fault because she failed to call the attending physician to clarify the ambiguity as to the mode of administration, and that in any event the purpose and effect of the drug was so well known that no registered nurse could conceivably interpret the order to call for the administration of what should be readily recognized as a lethal dose. Therefore, the doctor contended that it was the nurse's negligence rather than his own that led to the death, or, in other words, that the nurse's conduct constituted an independent intervening cause relieving the physician of liability.

The nurse contended that the failure of the doctor to designate the means of administration was responsible for the administration of injectible Lanoxin because the order as written, without any specification of means, meant that the route was to be intramuscularly by hypodermic. Therefore, the nurse contended that she had acted properly and in accordance with the practice in the community of interpreting an order in the form written.

Eight witnesses testified in addition to the two defendants. The two doctors of whom the nurse had made inquiry testified that they had no conception that she was considering administering the drug by hypodermic. One of the doctors made it clear that in his opinion a nurse who is unaware of the fact that Lanoxin is prepared in oral form is not properly trained and instructed for duty in a pediatric ward.

Five nurses testified that they always contacted a physician with respect to an ambiguous order. The nurses generally refused to testify in support of the defendant's contention that hypodermic administration was indicated when no other means were shown by the doctor.] (Summary of facts prepared by authors.)

After stating the facts, the court continued:

Although there have been instances in our jurisprudence wherein the alleged negligence of nurses has been made the basis of an action for damages for personal injuries resulting therefrom, we are not aware of any prior decision which fixes the responsibility or duty of care owed by nurses to patients under their care or treatment. The general rule, however, seems to be to extend to nurses the same rules which govern the duty and liability of physicians in the performance of professional services. Thus in Volume 70 C.J.S. Verbo, Physicians and Surgeons, § 41, page 946 we find the rule stated as follows:

. . . The same rules that govern the duty and liability of physicians and surgeons in the performance of professional services are applicable to practitioners of the kindred branches of the healing profession, such as dentists, and, likewise, are applicable to practitioners such as drugless healers, oculists, and manipulators of X-ray machines and other machines or devices.

The foregoing rule appears to be well founded and we see no valid reason why it should not be adopted as the law of this state. Tested in the light of the rule hereinabove enunciated the negligence of Mrs. Evans is patent upon the face of the record. We readily agree with the statement of Dr. Ruiz that a nurse who is unfamiliar with the fact that the drug in question is prepared in oral form for administration to infants by mouth is not properly and adequately trained for duty in a pediatric ward. As laudable as her intentions are conceded to have been on the occasion in question, her unfamiliarity with the drug was a contributing factor in the child's death. In this regard we are of the opinion that she was negligent in attempting to administer a drug with which she was not familiar. While we concede that a nurse does not have the same degree of knowledge regarding drugs as is possessed by members of the medical profession, nevertheless, common sense dictates that no nurse should attempt to administer a drug under the circumstances shown in the case at bar. Not only was Mrs. Evans unfamiliar with the medicine in question but she also violated what has been shown to be the rule generally practiced by the members of the nursing profession in the community and which rule, we might add, strikes us as being most reasonable and prudent, namely, the practice of calling the prescribing physician when in doubt about an order for medication. True, Mrs. Evans attempted to verify the order by inquiring of Doctors Beskin and Ruiz but evidently there was a complete lack of communication with these individuals. The record leaves no doubt but that neither Doctor Beskin nor Doctor Ruiz was made aware of just what Mrs. Evans intended to administer. Dr. Beskin was of the impression she referred to oral Lanoxin and Dr. Ruiz was of the impression she intended only 1 cubic centimeter of the injectible. For obvious reasons we believe it the duty of a nurse when in doubt about an order for medication to make absolutely certain what the doctor intended both as to dosage and route. In the case at bar the evidence leaves not the slightest doubt that whereas nurses in the locality do at times consult any available physician, it appears equally certain that all of the nurses who testified herein agree that the better practice (and the one which they follow) is to consult the prescribing physician when in doubt about an order for medication. With regard to nurses consulting any available physician when in doubt about an order for medication, the testimony of Drs. Beskin and Ruiz indicates clearly that in their experience such inquiries are generally restricted solely to interpretation of the doctor's handwriting and are not usually related to dosage or route. Having elected to deviate from the general and better practice of consulting the physician who ordered the medication in question, Mrs. Evans was under the duty and obligation of making herself understood beyond the possibility of error. This she did not do as has herein previously been shown. It appears reasonably clear that had she consulted Dr. Stotler and advised him of her intention to administer the 3 c.cs. of Lanoxin hypodermically he would have warned her of the danger and this tragic accident would not have occurred.

Aetna's defense predicated on the ground that because the negligence of the nurse was so inconceivable, gross and unpredictable as to constitute an independent intervening cause thereby relieving its insured of liability is without merit under the facts of the instant case.

The evidence in the case at bar leaves not the slightest doubt that when Dr. Stotler entered the order for the medication on the chart, it was the duty of the hospital nursing staff to administer it. Dr. Stotler frankly concedes this important fact and for that reason acknowledged that he should have indicated on the chart that the medication had been given or was to be given by the mother, otherwise some nurse on the pediatric unit would give it as was required of the hospital staff. Not only was there a duty on the part of Dr. Stotler to make this clear so as to prevent duplication of the medication but also he was under the obligation of specifying or in some manner indicating the route considering the drug is prepared in two forms in which dosage is measured in cubic centimeters. In dealing with modern drugs, especially of the type with which we are herein concerned, it is the duty of the prescribing physician who knows that the prescribed medication will be administered by a nurse or third party, to make certain as to the lines of communication between himself and the party whom he knows will ultimately execute his orders. Any failure in such communication which may prove fatal or injurious to the patient must be charged to the prescribing physician who has full knowledge of the drug and its effects upon the human system. The duty of communication between physician and nurse is more important when we consider that the nurse who administers the medication is not held to the same degree of knowledge with respect thereto as the prescribing physician. It, therefore, becomes the duty of the physician to make his intentions clear and unmistakable. If, as the record shows, Dr. Stotler had ordered Elixir Lanoxin, or specified the route to be oral, it would have clearly informed all nurses of his intention to administer the medication by mouth. Instead, however, he wrote his order in an uncertain, confusing manner considering that the drug in question comes in oral and injectible form and in both forms dosage is prescribed in terms of cubic centimeters. . . .

The doctrine of independent, intervening cause invoked by defendant Aetna herein on the ground that conceding Dr. Stotler's negligence, the independent, intervening negligence of Mrs. Evans was so unforeseeable and unpredictable as to render Dr. Stotler's negligence a remote rather than a proximate cause of the child's death is without foundation in the record. . . .

. . . We believe that under the foreseeability rule . . . the doctrine of independent, intervening cause is unavailable to defendant Aetna in the case at bar. That the negligence of Dr. Stotler was a substantial factor in bringing about the death of the Norton child appears so obvious as to warrant little discussion. In this connection we believe it suffices to say that if the order had been written so that it could be clearly understood the untimely death of the child would not have resulted therefrom. Moreover, it appears from the testimony of at least two of the nurses who testified herein that prescribing the drug in cubic centimeters indicated to them that it was to be administered by intramuscular injection. We believe it safe to say that except for the manner in which the prescription was written, the accident upon which this litigation is predicated would not have occurred.

Moreover, however, what appears to us to be the more logical conclusion is that the negligence of Aetna's insured foreseeably produced the death of plaintiff's child. We believe the testimony of Doctors Bombet and Beskin make it clear that the better practice is to specify the route of administration to avoid the possibility of error in dealing with a drug of the nature and character with which we are herein concerned. Failure to specify the route of a drug which, measured in c.cs. may be administered either orally or by injection is, in our view, calculated to produce confusion and uncertainty which may foreseeably result in the drug being administered in either form one of which may prove fatal. Misinterpretation of the order as written being foreseeable under the circumstances, such misconstruction cannot serve as the basis of rendering the physician's negligence remote rather than proximate. Rather than being incomprehensible and inconceivable as defendant Aetna contends, it appears such misconstruction is foreseeable and likely under the circumstances shown in the case at bar. . . .

Amended and affirmed.

## ANALYSIS

1. What were the facts that led to a wrongful death action? Do facts flow in an unbroken sequence from cause to effect? Apply the "but for" and the "substantial factor" tests to the facts of this case.

2. What reasons did the doctor give for exonerating himself? How did the court deal with this defense? Had the court recognized this defense, what might have been the effect of the precedent on doctor–nurse responsibility and relationships?

3. An attempt was made to use custom and practice to show that the doctor's conduct was not the legal cause of death. How did the court deal with this?

4. The case against the nurse apparently turned on her failure to call the doctor about an ambiguous and uncertain order; well ahead of this need, what were the points at which the quality of nursing care fell below reasonable standards? Why do you suppose the court did not take note of the knowledge that a professional nurse should have had about the mode of administration of an *elixir*? Draw together a chain of events common to good nursing practice that could have served to prevent litigation.

### *Newbury v. Vogel,* 151 Colo. 520, 379 P.2d 811 (1963)

Pringle, Justice.

Plaintiff in error Newbury was the plaintiff in the trial court and defendants in error Vogel and Fittipaldi were the defendants. The parties will be referred to as they appeared in the trial court or by name.

The complaint alleged that each of the defendants had so negligently operated a motor vehicle as to result in permanent injuries to the plaintiff. He demanded special damages, including medical and hospital expenses incurred, and loss of wages in the amount of $6,616.87. Compensation was also asked for diminished earning capacity, for past and future disability, and for past and future pain and suffering in the amount of $35,383.13, making a total of $42,000.00.

Upon trial, the jury returned a verdict for the plaintiff in the sum of $5,000.00 against the defendant Vogel, and exonerated the defendant Fittipaldi from liability. Judgment was entered on the verdict and the plaintiff is here by writ of error, contending that errors committed by the trial court affected the amount of the award returned by the jury, which he contends is inadequate. He seeks reversal and remand for a new trial on the issue of damages only. He does not complain of the verdict exonerating Fittipaldi.

Defendant in error Vogel does not assert error by the trial court with respect to the issue of liability or to the exoneration of Fittipaldi, but contends that the rulings of the trial court with respect to the issue of damages do not constitute reversible error.

It is plaintiff's contention that the trial court erred in:

1. Failing to give an instruction embodying his theory of the case with respect to present and future disability, pain and suffering; and

2. Unduly limiting the scope of plaintiff's closing argument by refusing to allow a "per diem" suggestion to the jury on the elements of past and future pain and suffering.

Since the errors assigned deal only with the question of damages, we need not discuss the facts relating to the accident upon which the claim for damages is based, but will deal only with the evidence pertinent to the issue of damages.

Medical testimony concerning the nature and extent of Newbury's injuries was offered by each party. The testimony of Newbury's medical witness was to the effect that as a result of the accident Newbury had suffered an acute spinal sprain which had been superimposed on a pre-existing arthritic condition. It was his opinion that at the time of the trial Newbury had a permanent disability which would be manifested primarily by pain, stiffness and chronic discomfort; that a part of this disability was attributable to the original arthritis and a part to the accident, but how much was due to the effect of the trauma incurred in the accident was "the question."

The testimony of Fittipaldi's medical expert was essentially the same, this witness stating that no one could say with certainty what limitation of motion, and what portion of the pain, could be attributed to the original arthritic condition and what portion to the trauma. Vogel's medical expert agreed that there had been a sprain as a result of the accident, but it was his opinion that all of the effects of the sprain had subsided and that all of Newbury's complaints were now due to a pre-existing arthritic condition.

Newbury testified that prior to the accident he had no pain in either his neck or his back and that although he was at the time of the trial working regularly he did suffer from pain in his neck and back at the conclusion of his day's work which became worse toward the end of the work week.

Newbury's wife testified that he rarely participates in activities which were his wont before the accident and that at the time of the trial he was continually applying a heating pad to his neck.

I. *Did the instructions given by the trial court sufficiently present the plaintiff's theory of the case with respect to the damages which might be awarded him by reason of limitation of motion in his neck and back and past and future suffering?*

We hold they did not. Instruction No. 17 given by the trial court provides:

> You are instructed that if you find from the evidence that before the accident the plaintiff had an osteoarthritic condition, and further find that because of the accident this condition was aggravated, then the plaintiff is entitled to recover because of disability or pain proximately due to such aggravation; but is not entitled to recover for any physical ailment or disability which may have existed prior to the accident, or for any ailment or disability which plaintiff now may be suffering which was not caused or contributed to by reason of the accident.

Newbury contends that this instruction, while proper as far as it went, did not sufficiently cover plaintiff's theory of the case and the evidence in support thereof. . . .

It was plaintiff's theory that the pre-existing arthritis caused him no pain before the accident; that the accident aggravated the pre-existing arthritis; that he now has permanent disability consisting of a limitation of motion, pain and soreness; and that it is impossible to determine the amount of such disability attributable to the prior arthritic condition and that caused by the accident. In accordance with this theory, plaintiff submitted his tendered Instruction No. 9, which in part pointed out to the jury that if in truth they could make no apportionment between the amount of his present and future disability due to the pre-existing arthritis, and the amount due to the accident, the defendant was liable for the entire disability.

Two of the medical experts testified that a portion of plaintiff's permanent limitation of motion, pain and soreness was due to the accident and a portion was due to the pre-existing arthritis, but they both stated that they could not apportion between the two.

We find the law to be that where a pre-existing diseased condition exists, and where after trauma aggravating the condition disability and pain result, and no apportionment of the disability between that caused by the pre-existing condition and that caused by the trauma can be made, in such case, even though a portion of the present and future disability is directly attributable to the pre-existing condition, the defendant, whose act of negligence was the cause of the trauma, is responsible for the entire damage. Here the plaintiff was entitled to an instruction advising the jury that if they could not apportion the disability between the pre-existing arthritis and the trauma then the defendant was liable for the entire damage resulting from the disability. Under the instruction given the jury was advised that the plaintiff could recover only that portion of his damage which was due to aggravation. If the jury could not make such apportionment (and it might well be that they could not, since two of the medical experts could not) they were left without an instruction as to the law which would apply in such circumstances.

II. *Did the court err in refusing to allow plaintiff's counsel to suggest a per diem method of arriving at the amount to be awarded for pain and suffering?*

Whether it was proper for counsel for plaintiff in his closing argument to illustrate or to suggest to the jury the method by which he arrived at his demand for compensation for pain and suffering, by breaking the request down to a per diem or time segment basis has not previously been decided by this Court. . . .

The authorities appear to be rather evenly divided among (1) those who hold the argument is proper; (2) those who refuse to allow it; and (3) those who declare it to be a matter in the discretion of the trial court. In our judgment, the cases which recognize the propriety of the argument are based upon the better reasoning.

Most of the jurisdictions which have refused to allow the argument rely upon Botta v. Brunner, 26 N.J. 82, 138 A.2d 713, 60 A.L.R.2d 1331 as a landmark case supporting their position. It is to be noted that in Botta, the New Jersey Court also forbade advising the jury of the total amount requested by the plaintiff for pain and suffering on the theory that the jury should hear nothing equating pain and suffering with money. Such is not the rule in Colorado. An integral part of the instructions given by the trial court in this state to the jury contains the amount of compensation sought by the plaintiff for pain and suffering. Generally instructions also advise the jury of the life expectancy of the injured party. If the total amount claimed and the life expectancy can be argued, what logical reason is there for refusing to permit counsel to engage in the mathematical process of computing the gross amount sought for pain and suffering, based upon the life expectancy of the claimant and reducing it to the units by which it is endured; that is by segments of time?

In all probability no element of damages defies monetary admeasurement so elusively as does pain and suffering. Nevertheless, pain and suffering are compensable and must be translated into money by the jury. The very absence of a fixed standard by which pain can be measured and translated into compensation by a jury is a persuasive reason why counsel should be permitted to illustrate to the jury the manner in which he arrived at the total sum claimed for pain and suffering.

The jury must reach its verdict by the process of reasoning and upon the inferences to be drawn from the facts before it. That pain and suffering will continue permanently and that the plaintiff has a certain life expectancy is before the jury. The per diem argument is nothing more than a course of reasoning suggested by the plaintiff for translating pain and suffering into reasonable compensation.

It is contended that jurors often mistake the argument of counsel for evidence and are thereby misled into making excessive awards. Juries in this jurisdiction are always instructed that arguments of counsel are not evidence and the jury in this case was so instructed. We are not inclined to attribute to any jury a lack of sufficient mentality or discrimination to recognize the difference between evidence and argument. If the impact of such argument should at one time or another result in an excessive verdict, the trial and appellate courts of this state have ample means to correct such a verdict.

The judgment is reversed and the cause remanded to the trial court for a new trial on the issue of damages only in accordance with the views above expressed.

Moore, J., not participating.

ANALYSIS

1. Personal injuries have been dealt with in numerous preceding cases. What was the theory unique to this case concerning present and future disability?

2. If called as an expert nurse witness, what problems are posed in weighing pre-existing conditions and present trauma? Hypothesize on numerous similar situations that could occur, varying the pre-existing condition and the trauma.

3. In dealing with accident cases, how might the nurse assist in observing, reporting, and recording information of value in the settlement of cases similar to *Newbury*?

4. What are the salient points made in judicial reasoning concerning a monetary measurement of pain and suffering? Can you see certain advantages to the per-diem method?

5. When the precedent of this case is followed in future decisions, what may be the impact on medical and nurse expert testimony in the establishment of causation?

## *Barnes v. Bovenmyer*, 255 Iowa 220, 122 N.W. 2d 312 (1962)

Garfield, Chief Justice.

This is a law action by Leo V. Barnes to recover from Dr. D. O. Bovenmyer, M.D., an eye specialist in Ottumwa, for loss of plaintiff's left eye alleged to have resulted from defendant's negligence in diagnosing and treating an injury thereto. At the close of plaintiff's case the trial court directed a verdict for defendant because of claimed insufficient evidence. From judgment thereon plaintiff has appealed....

This leaves the two questions which are present in so many actions to recover for injury to the person—sufficiency of the evidence of defendant's negligence and, 2) if there is such, that it was the proximate cause of the injury....

III. About 6:30 in the evening of Sunday, June 29, 1958, a small piece of steel pierced plaintiff's left eye and lodged in it. It flew from a hammer or hatchet used by another person. The eye colored up and blood from the wound went clear to plaintiff's belt. Defendant, an ophthalmologist or eye specialist, was immediately called but could not be reached. Plaintiff then called the Ottumwa hospital and arrived there not later than 7:15. Dr. Emerson, a general practitioner for a year in Ottumwa, was on call, examined the eye externally and with an ophthalmoscope, saw an injury to the eye which was externally apparent, ordered X-rays taken of the eye and then called defendant.

An ophthalmoscope is an instrument for viewing the interior of the eye. Seven X-rays of the eye were taken, at least some of which showed the foreign body in the eye.

When defendant arrived he also examined the eye externally and with the ophthalmoscope, looked through the eye for possible foreign bodies in it and for damage to the eye that might be detected. Defendant, Dr. Emerson and the radiologist then examined the X-rays. Dr. Emerson testifies none of them saw the foreign body in the eye nor in the X-rays thereof. The two named doctors did see a red spot on the sclera, white part of the eye, which Dr. Emerson says could have been a bruise and could have been a point of entry into the eye of a foreign body. "It was possible either way. You never know for sure."

There was also an injury to the lower eyelid into which defendant probed and removed therefrom a small piece of steel. Dr. Emerson and, apparently, defendant thought this was the only foreign body in the region of plaintiff's eye and no attempt was made that evening to remove the piece of steel imbedded in the eyeball.

Dr. Emerson, called as a witness by plaintiff, testifies on cross-examination that after defendant removed the foreign body from the eyelid defendant told plaintiff he thought the foreign body was removed and he would probably be all right but he wanted him to return to his office the next morning. "I heard Dr. Bovenmyer urge the patient to return to his office the next morning. *I figure that is part of the treatment.* I did not object to that direction or treatment. *I regarded that treatment as usually customary and the standard of care for treatment of such patients in June, 1958.*"

We regard the quoted testimony as of vital importance on the issue of defendant's negligence. There is no evidence contrary to the part we have emphasized. However, there is a sharp dispute as to what defendant told plaintiff when he left the hospital that evening. Plaintiff denies defendant said he wanted to see him the next morning, he insists he asked defendant if he cared to see him again, defendant told him it was not necessary and there was no reason he could not go to work the next evening. Plaintiff also says he was in the building where defendant's office was on an errand the following (Monday) morning but did not go in because of what defendant told him the evening before.

Plaintiff worked nights at an Ottumwa plant, from 11 p.m. to 7 a.m. He worked Monday night as he says defendant told him he could. Before the night was over he suffered almost unbearable pain in his eye. He went to defendant's office about 8:15 Tuesday morning but was unable to contact defendant. The lady in charge of the office told him defendant would be there that afternoon and plaintiff could contact him then.

Plaintiff returned to the office a little after 4. Defendant examined the eye, sent him to another office in the same building to get more X-rays promptly, plaintiff went right to the radiologist as directed, after the X-rays were taken he was told to return promptly to defendant's office and he did. "Very shortly after my return, Dr. Bovenmyer told me there was a foreign body in my eye and I should go very promptly to Iowa City and have that foreign body removed and I did. He told me we would call the hospital at Iowa City. . . . He said we are going to Iowa City *and we want to get there as quick as we can.*"

Dr. Emerson testifies defendant told him on or after July 2 (Wednesday) he saw plaintiff Tuesday afternoon, sent him for his follow-up X-ray, appearance of the eye was not right, "on the X-rays taken July first there was still the foreign body present that it showed on the original X-rays on June 29th." Also that defendant told him plaintiff did not report back Monday morning as the witness understood plaintiff was to do, defendant saw the eye Tuesday afternoon "and ordered it re-X-rayed immediately."

Plaintiff's father drove him to Iowa City Tuesday evening. He went right to the eye ward at the State University hospitals, physicians examined the eye, found a metallic foreign body in it, more X-rays were taken, an eye surgeon was called that same evening, an incision was made in the sclera of the eye and in 10 or 15 minutes a piece of steel was removed through the incision with a magnet. The piece was shaped somewhat like a half moon, about $\frac{1}{16}$-inch wide and $\frac{1}{8}$-inch long.

The eye was inflamed from infection in it. After treating this condition for 18 days in the University Hospitals in an attempt to save the eye, it was found necessary to remove it on July 19. Plaintiff was sent home from the hospitals on July 24.

The University Hospitals' record of plaintiff for July 1 contains this statement: "Dr. Bovenmyer removed a piece from lower lid Sunday night & let go." Whether the information defendant let plaintiff go Sunday night was obtained from plaintiff or defendant does not appear. The exhibit referred to was admitted in evidence without objection. It tends to corroborate plaintiff's version of what defendant told him before they parted Sunday night. Another part of the University Hospitals' record describes plaintiff's eye injury as "perforation."

The roentgenologist's report of the X-rays taken in the Ottumwa hospital contains this: "Views of the orbit reveals evidence of a sharp metallic foreign body measuring approximately 2 mm. in length and 1 mm. in width, in the region of the left orbit. Metallic density appears to be in the anterior and lateral quadrant of the eyeball."

IV. We hold there is substantial evidence of defendant's negligence as alleged by plaintiff. . . .

We have said at least three times that malpractice may consist in lack of skill or care in diagnosis as well as in treatment. A patient is entitled to a thorough and careful examination such as his condition and attending circumstances will permit, with such diligence and methods of diagnosis as are usually approved and practiced by physicians of the same school of medicine, of ordinary learning, judgment and skill, under like circumstances and in like localities.

And a physician who, like defendant, is a specialist, is required to exercise that degree of skill and care ordinarily used by similar specialists in like circumstances, not merely the average skill and care of a general practitioner.

V. Of course proof of defendant's negligence did not entitle plaintiff to go to the jury. There must also be substantial evidence it was the proximate cause of plaintiff's damage. Plaintiff's brief furnishes us no help on this phase of the case. No error is assigned on this issue. It is not discussed except for two unrelated sentences at different places in the body of the argument. Loss of an eye, however, is no trivial matter. Hence, as a matter of grace, we have searched the record long and hard for evidence of proximate cause. We can't find it. We don't think it is there.

The issue of proximate cause boils down to this: The jury could find defendant was negligent in not discovering and advising removal of the piece of steel from the eyeball before late afternoon July 1, and that with ordinary skill and care he would have done this the morning of the preceding day. It may even be conceded the piece in the eye should have been discovered Sunday evening. Is there any evidence this delay of 36 or 48 hours probably caused loss of the eye? As indicated, we are compelled to hold there is none. Further, the evidence on the question is that the delay probably did not cause loss of the eye.

The matter of causal connection between defendant's negligence and loss of plaintiff's eye is not within the knowledge and experience of ordinary laymen. It is a question upon which only a medical expert can express an intelligent opinion. It is a question essentially within the domain of expert testimony.

This is ordinarily the rule in actions of this kind. Annos. 141 A.L.R. 5, 6–12; 13 A.L.R.2d 11, 31–34. We are fully aware there are exceptions to the rule. See annotations last above. One exception we have recognized several times is where the harmful result of the negligence is so obvious as to lie within common knowledge. This exception cannot be applied here.

The accepted method of proving proximate cause would be by expert testimony that defendant's delay in discovering the piece of steel in the eye was the probable cause of its loss. Some decisions say it is sufficient to furnish substantial evidence upon which a reasonable basis for inference may be had, provided the matter is not left to conjecture and speculation.

The only expert witness was Dr. Emerson, called by plaintiff. He proved to be a much better witness for defendant than for plaintiff on the issue of proximate cause. Plaintiff's counsel did not question the doctor on this issue but asked some questions on the issue of negligence. On cross-examination Dr. Emerson more than once expresses the opinion failure to remove the foreign body at an earlier time in all probability did not cause loss of the eye, infection entered it when the piece of steel did and removal of the steel would not remove the infection which caused loss of the eye. There may be circumstances to cast doubt on this negative testimony. However, even if it were not accepted, it would not supply the requisite affirmative proof of proximate cause.

An extended annotation in 13 A.L.R.2d 11, 98, on proximate cause in malpractice actions contains this appraisal of those similar to this: "A large proportion of eye injuries arise from the accidental introduction into the eye of foreign objects, and a number of malpractice cases have been based on the doctor's allegedly negligent failure to discover and remove such objects. These cases have frequently turned upon the question whether prompt removal would have been helpful in any event, since, if not, the failure to remove the object creates no liability even if negligent. In most of the instances involving eye injuries from foreign objects causation has been held not to have been established."

Our conclusion on the question of proximate cause leads to an affirmance.

Affirmed.

All Justices concur.

## ANALYSIS

1. What were the two major issues that were presented on appeal? Evidence was assembled through facts and expert testimony. What was the contribution of each in establishing or denying negligence of Dr. Bovenmyer? How did the court establish a standard from which to judge the doctor's conduct?

2. How did the court say the plaintiff had to prove causation? Why?

3. Why is it said that proof of negligence does not entitle the plaintiff to submit the question to the jury?

4. In the attempt to show that the delay in removing the foreign body resulted in the loss of the eye, what evidence was presented? What are the medical and legal variables that make such a determination very difficult? Was this area of doubt identified by the court? What were its comments? As a nurse, can you support the reasonableness of this uncertainty?

5. Other than to use a practitioner of medicine as an expert witness, where might the plaintiff have turned for scientific medical opinion when the primary question was the length of time a foreign body can remain in an eye and not be a predisposing factor to infection?

6. What was the holding of this case? Upon what did it turn?

## CASES FOR FURTHER ANALYSIS

### *Ruvio v. North Broward Hosp. Dist.,* 186 So.2d 45 (Fla. App. 1966)

This was an action by a wife against a hospital for death of her husband who was refused admission to the hospital on the grounds that no emergency existed.

The plaintiff's husband suffered a coronary infarction approximately 48 hours before going by cab to the emergency room of the hospital. The nurse who first saw him testified that he was pale, short of breath, sweating, and appeared to have a head cold. When she asked about chest pains, he said that he ached all over. The nurse then told him that it was not an emergency case and gave him a list of doctors' names from which to choose one to consult. The doctor whom he saw immediately found audible wheezing sounds during breathing and blueness of the lips in addition to the signs found by the nurses. He decided that it was an emergency case and sent him at once to the hospital, where he was placed in an oxygen tent. He died 48 hours later.

The plaintiff charged that the nurses were superficial in their examination and even told her husband to "get out." The nurses testified that they were careful in their examination and that the friend who came with the patient was excited and did not understand their explanation of the situation; further, they contended that they were justified under the circumstances in not reporting their findings to the doctor who was on call at the time.

In directing a verdict for the defendant hospital, the court found that the plaintiff had failed to show that any action or inaction on the part of the hospital or its employees was the proximate cause of her husband's death and had failed to show any negligence on the part of the nurses.

### *Thompson v. Louisville & N. R. Co.,* 91 Ala. 496, 8 So.406 (1890)

An action was brought to recover damages for injuries alleged to have been wrongfully inflicted by the defendant railroad and to have resulted in the death of the plaintiff's husband. The deceased, a railroad employee, fell from a railroad car and, according to the testimony of some physicians, the injury was mortal and he would have died from the effects of the injury within a short time. Medical testimony to the contrary tended to show that the wounds were not necessarily mortal. By mistake, the deceased's wife gave him 4 or 5 grains of bichloride of mercury (corrosive sublimate) by mouth, it having been left for an irrigation. It was proved that the poison would have caused the death of a well person and that it was the immediate cause of the man's death. The railroad's defense was that the conduct of the wife constituted a new and independent intervening cause of death, and that the administration of the bichloride of mercury broke the chain of causation. The court rejected the railroad's theory of causation, saying that if the wound was mortal in the first place, then the one causing it could not seek shelter under the idea that erroneous treatment was the cause, even though the treatment may have contributed to the death. The railroad was held liable, the court saying:

It does not follow that, because a man cannot die but once, there cannot be two or more concurrent, cooperative, and efficient causes to effect one killing. A person may be killed by "beating and starving." There may be contributing causes. . . . If, as the testimony tended to show, the injury received was mortal, and caused decedent to die "sooner" or "quicker" from the effects of the poison than he would have died, had he not been injured, it is difficult to perceive how the poison can be regarded as the "sole" cause of death at the time it occurred.

### Offensend v. Atlantic Ref. Co., 322 Pa. 399, 185 Atl. 745 (1936)

An action was brought to recover damages for injuries sustained in a head-on collision of automobiles.

There was no dispute of the facts, and the defendant conceded that there had been negligence on his part and that the plaintiff in no way contributed to the accident. Further, the evidence showed that following the accident, on examination, the plaintiff was in shock, complained of pain in the chest, and had abrasions on both knees, and had minor lacerations. X-rays disclosed a fracture of the right fourth rib and an inflammatory or tubercular condition immediately below the fracture. Following a seven-month period of treatment of the lung condition together with complete rest, x-rays showed no improvement and if anything the condition was worse. Expert medical testimony was that the tubercular condition had been aggravated by the injury. One expert admitted that the tubercular condition could have resulted from other causes, but reiterated it was likely that the chest injury was the efficient cause, as nothing had intervened in the interval between the injury and the finding of aggravation to give rise to a contrary belief.

At issue was whether this evidence was sufficient to sustain the finding that the accident had aggravated the pre-existing condition and therefore the plaintiff was liable. The court held that the evidence was sufficient.

*Helman v. Sacred Heart Hosp.,* 62 Wash. 2d 136, 381 P.2d 605 (1963)

This was an action to recover for injuries sustained by patient as a result of a *Staphylococcus* infection contracted while in defendant's hospital.

Plaintiff was injured in an automobile accident, his chest was crushed, and his left hip dislocated in addition to multiple fractures in the area of the left hip socket and pelvic region. After one month in another hospital he was transferred to the defendant hospital for the purpose of hip surgery. He was placed in a two-bed ward with a patient who had a fractured back.

Following surgery plaintiff was returned to the same ward. About nine days later, the patient in the adjoining bed developed an abscess under the right arm, followed the next day by purulent drainage. The discharge was cultured, and in three days the laboratory reported a positive *Staphylococcus aureus* coagulase and the patient was immediately moved to the isolation unit.

During the three-day interval between the appearance of the drainage and the laboratory report, the nurses and attendants moved from one patient to the other in giving routine patient care, without observing sterile techniques or precautions as prescribed by the hospital when an infection is suspected. On the day the patient in the adjoining bed was moved to the isolation unit, plaintiff's surgical wound erupted discharging a large amount of purulent drainage that when cultured indicated *Staphylococcus aureus* coagulase. The infection penetrated the hip socket destroying bone tissue and ligaments. The resulting condition required further surgery two months later and resulted in an immobilization of the joint.

The major issue at trial was whether plaintiff had contracted his infection by cross-infection from the patient in the adjoining bed. Unless it was proved that each suffered from the same strain of the microorganism, cross-infection would be a medical impossibility. From extensive medical testimony it was established there were some 30 to 50 strains of this organism, some of which have not been categorically identified. The defense pointed out that all modern, well-run hospitals, of which the defendant was one, are alert to the dangers of cross-infection. Personnel are instructed in the techniques to be observed in order not to transmit the microorganisms from one patient to the other. The court reasoned that proof of cross infection beyond a reasonable doubt was not required nor was proof by direct and positive evidence. It was only necessary to show a chain of circumstances from which the ultimate fact of cross infection could be reasonably inferred.

A verdict in favor of plaintiff was affirmed.

## Recommended Source Material

### TEXTS

Gregory, C., and Kalven, H., Jr., *Cases and Materials on Torts*, 5–20 (Boston: Little, Brown & Co., 1959).

Harper, F., and James, F., *The Law of Torts*, Vol. 2, 1108–61 (Boston: Little, Brown & Co., 1956).

Louisell, D., and Williams, H., *Trial of Medical Malpractice Cases*, 135–44 (Albany: Matthew Bender & Co., 1966).

Prosser, W., *Handbook of the Law of Torts*, 240–330 (St. Paul: West Publishing Co., 3rd ed., 1964).

Shartel, B., and Plant, M., *The Law of Medical Practice*, 147–48 (Springfield, Ill.: Charles C Thomas, Publisher, 1959).

### PERIODICALS

Gerber, S., *Causation in Death After Trauma with Pre-existing Cardiac Disease*, 15 Clev-Mar. L. Rev. 461 (1966).

James, F., and Perry, R., *Legal Cause*, 60 Yale L. J. 761 (1951).

Lipman, F., *Malingering in Personal Injury Cases*, 35 Temp. L. Q. 141 (1962).

McLaughlin, J., *Proximate Cause*, 39 Harv. L. Rev. 149 (1925).

Morris, C., *Proximate Cause in Minnesota*, 34 Minn. L. Rev. 185 (1950).

Note, *The Status of Proximate Cause in Virginia*, 41 Va. L. Rev. 991 (1955).

Probert, W., *Causation in the Negligence Jargon: A Plea for Balanced "Realism,"* 18 U. Fla. L. Rev. 369 (1965).

Recent Decisions, *Torts-Negligence-Concurrent*, 26 Geo. L. J. 167 (1937).

# Chapter Six

# Res Ipsa Loquitur

In the negligence cases we have analyzed, the plaintiff has proved, or tried to prove, negligence by showing specific conduct by the defendant that, when measured against the reasonable man standard, constituted negligence. In some cases plaintiff has been required to prove that the defendant's conduct did not reach a professional standard, established by expert testimony, prevailing in a community. We now consider an additional method of proving negligence, where, instead of proving a standard of conduct and specific conduct not in conformity with the standard, the plaintiff proves facts that bring into play a legal doctrine that may give rise to an inference of negligence, called the doctrine of *res ipsa loquitur*, translated as "the thing speaks for itself." Under this doctrine, when certain circumstances exist, negligence may be found without proof of a defendant's actual actions. In this section, we will study the principles of *res ipsa loquitur* and examine what circumstances must exist before these principles will be applied.

In the course of a stroll along the public street, Mr. Bryne came upon a flour warehouse belonging to Mr. Boadle. As Mr. Byrne passed the warehouse, a barrel of flour fell from one of the warehouse windows, striking and seriously injuring him. Mr. Byrne sued Mr. Boadle and at trial proved only a few simple facts. He proved that he was injured by the falling barrel; he proved that it was defendant's place of business and proved that he himself did nothing that would tend to have led to his injury. He did not show any unreasonable actions or conduct on the part of Mr. Boadle, and he did not prove any specific behavior by Mr. Boadle that placed Mr. Byrne in foreseeable risk. In fact, he did not show any conduct by Mr. Boadle at all. Mr. Boadle contended that no negligent conduct on his part had been proved and therefore he should not bear responsibility for the accident. The court, however, said that there are cases where *res ipsa loquitur*, "the thing speaks for itself," and that in such cases no direct and specific evidence of negligence need be offered. Mr. Byrne was allowed to recover from Mr. Boadle because, as the court said, "a barrel could not roll out of a warehouse without some negligence," and because Mr. Boadle was responsible for whatever negligence there was. [*Byrne v. Boadle*, 159 Eng. Rep. 299 (1863).]

## The Elements of *Res Ipsa Loquitur*

Proof of negligence by the use of the doctrine of *res ipsa loquitur* is a departure from the traditional notion that negligence is proved by showing specific acts by a defendant that fail to meet the standard set by the hypothetical conduct of the reasonable man. Thus, a typical negligence case may involve an apartment house owner who had permitted a steep stairway to remain unlighted, or a supermarket operator who had failed to clean up a broken bottle of syrup and thereby left a dangerous slick spot on the floor. If someone should fall, either down the dark stairway or on the slippery floor, he would seek to prove negligence by showing specific acts; he would try to show that the apartment house owner knew of the darkness and danger, had received warnings about it, neglected to provide lighting because it was too expensive, and so forth. Similarly, the unfortunate victim of the syrup would try to show, for example, that the breaking of the bottle was observed by the store employees, that they picked up the glass and left the syrup, or any one of numerous variations. The proof, however, would be about the acts and conduct of the defendant. The jury in such a case would make a two-step analysis. They would first decide what actually occurred: did the landlord receive warnings; did the supermarket employees see the bottle break? They would then determine whether the conduct was negligent by weighing the conduct against the applicable standard.

But proof of this nature was lacking in *Byrne v. Boadle*; there, no negligent behavior, no careless action was shown. That case illustrates the doctrine of *res ipsa loquitur*, which permits a plaintiff to establish a defendant's negligence without proving specific conduct; the plaintiff proves three conditions instead. These three conditions are (1) that the injury was of such a nature that it would not normally occur unless there was negligent conduct on the part of someone; (2) that the injury was caused by an agency within the control of the defendant; (3) that the plaintiff did not himself engage in conduct that would tend to bring about the injury.

*Proof by plaintiff that each one of these factors existed in a given situation permits the jury to conclude that the defendant was negligent. No further proof is required.*

The doctrine, says a leading authority [Harper, F., and James, F., *The Law of Torts*, Vol. 2, 1076 (Boston: Little, Brown & Co., 1956)]*,

. . . is generally saved for cases where many of the important proven facts are pretty general, although the use of the term is far from precise. As it has been put in a series of notes, "in the situations to which res ipsa loquitur as a distinctive rule applies, there is no evidence, circumstantial or otherwise, at least none of sufficient probative value, to show negligence, apart from the postulate—which rests on common experience and not on the specific circumstances of the instant case—that physical causes of the kind which produced the accident in question do not ordinarily exist in the absence of negligence."

Let us examine the three conditions.

THE ACCIDENT WOULD NOT OCCUR WITHOUT NEGLIGENCE

The first condition requires an analysis of how the injury occurred. To satisfy the condition, the plaintiff must establish that the best and most plausible explanation of how the injury came about is that someone was careless. If it is equally possible that the accident is of a type that can and often does occur without negligence, the condition remains unfulfilled. In the case of the fall in the apartment or supermarket, it would probably not be possible for the plaintiff to show that falls happen only after negligence; it is common experience that people fall in the most carefully ordered surroundings.

In Mr. Byrne's case, however, the court said—and most courts would agree—that barrels do not generally fall out of windows unless someone was negligent; therefore, the condition was met in that situation. A classic monument to an injury clearly the result of negligence stands in the well-known case of *Pillars v. R. J. Reynolds Tobacco Co.* 117 Miss. 490, 78 So. 365 (1918). There, the unfortunate Mr. Pillars contracted ptomaine poisoning after chewing a plug of tobacco containing a putrefying human toe. Upon his recovery he was understandably indignant, and brought suit against the tobacco manufacturer. Having lost in the trial court on a technicality (to the effect that tobacco was not a "food" and therefore the tobacco company was not required to keep it toe-free), he obtained his just due in the appellate court, which held that the presence of the toe, without more, rendered undeniable that the maker had been negligent in the manufacture of its wares.

To sum up, the first condition means that injuries that are in common experience explanable as pure accidents, occurring without fault, do not give rise to an inference of negligence and therefore cannot lead to the use of *res ipsa loquitur* by the plaintiff. That a man is found dead by a railroad track is not proof that the passing train was carelessly operated; there are too many

* Reprinted with permission of Little, Brown & Co.

alternative explanations for death to conclude that the first condition for *res ipsa loquitur* was met. (The reader should consider what hypothetical additional circumstances might exist that could render this death by the railroad one that "would not normally occur unless there was negligent conduct.") Typical cases of injury normally resulting only from negligence are falling elevators, the sudden startup of machinery, and explosions of boilers. In contrast are cases where the injury was held not the type that occurs only where there is negligence, including a fall downstairs, a tire blowing out, a bursting flywheel.

AGENCY IN DEFENDANT'S CONTROL

The second condition deals with the question of *who* is responsible for negligent conduct. Recall that, in a lawsuit, the plaintiff is not after a mere declaration that he has been wronged. He has brought a particular defendant, or defendants, into court and he is trying to make *them* pay *him*; he is trying to shift the loss to their shoulders. Plaintiff says to them, in effect: "It is your fault, not mine, that I am hurt; therefore it is your responsibility." Normally, of course, plaintiff involves them in his suit by showing that their conduct and not someone else's is at issue; if that conduct was negligent, and the cause of harm, they must pay the plaintiff.

How, though, does the plaintiff connect his injury to a particular defendant in a situation where he wishes to invoke *res ipsa loquitur*, that is, where plaintiff has not shown the particular conduct of anyone? Even though the first condition is satisfied, and therefore there appears to be negligence lurking somewhere in the circumstances surrounding an injury, plaintiff must still bring it to rest at the defendant's door. He does this by fulfilling the second condition, namely, by showing that the injury must have come about through an agency within the control of the defendant, or that the circumstances of the injury are such that the defendant would be responsible for any negligence connected with it. In Mr. Byrne's case, he showed that the warehouse belonged to the defendant and therefore that Mr. Boadle was responsible for what happened in it. His second requirement was therefore met. Similarly, in the *Pillars* case the toe got into the tobacco during the manufacture of the plug, and the manufacturer was naturally in control of the process. Therefore, the negligence, if any, was his and no other's, and the control requirement was satisfied.

NO CONTRIBUTING CONDUCT BY PLAINTIFF

If the first and second conditions are satisfied, there is an inference of negligence and there is an inference that the negligence was that of the defendant. The third condition must also be satisfied: that the plaintiff must not have contributed to the injury. Unless the plaintiff can establish that his own conduct was blameless, he will not be permitted to use the first two conditions to particularize defendant's conduct. In other words, if plaintiff cannot show lack of involvement on his part, the inference that it was defendant's negligence alone is no longer valid, for then it is also possible to infer that plaintiff's actions materially contributed to the injury. Thus, Mr. Byrne was able to show that he had nothing to do with the fall of the barrel by showing that he was merely walking along the street; in this way he satisfied the third of the conditions.

There is a fourth factor that is not a condition but is frequently present in cases involving *res ipsa loquitur*, namely that in many cases, the injuries cannot be traced to any specific acts of negligence, and the evidence of what actually occurred is more readily available to the defendant than to the plaintiff. The resulting difficulties of proof faced by a plaintiff may influence the courts to apply the doctrine, in order to reach a just result in a given situation.

## The Adverse Medical Incident—*Res Ipsa Loquitur*

As the nurse considers the legal theory of the doctrine of *res ipsa loquitur*, she can see its many implications for her practice. In few situations in life is one person so dependent on another as is the patient in his relationship to the nurse or the physician. The patient may not be conscious when vitally important action is taken for his welfare; frequently, even though the patient is conscious, the action is so complex that he does not understand what is being done for him. Likewise, even though the patient can judge results, particularly unfavorable ones, he is usually not able to judge whether an unfavorable outcome is due to the negligent conduct of the physician or the nurse. He may assume that pain or discomfort or immobility is an inevitable part of the therapeutic or healing process of his recovery and so may not complain or inquire for some time.

The basic theory of the law is "he who accuses must prove," and in most malpractice cases a significant part of the proof involves medical expert testimony. The nurse is more and more frequently called upon to share in expert testimony in those cases where patient care is of evidential importance. We have considered many instances in which the patient has accused the physician, hospital, or nurse of negligent conduct and at trial the plaintiff is required to prove the actual conduct of the medical practitioner and the causal connection between the conduct and the injury. The doctrine of *res ipsa loquitur* is an exception to this basic rule of proof, for the plaintiff need only present evidence of an injury from which an inference of negligence can be drawn, and that the medical practitioner is the likely causative agent. When this is done, the defendant nurse or physician must come forward, describe his conduct, and state why what happened did happen. Thus, proof in the sense of going forward with the evidence is shifted to the defendants. Once facts have been proved sufficient to bring the doctrine into play, the plaintiff has a procedural advantage in that the defendant will normally be required to justify and explain his conduct. Placing the physician in the position of defending his conduct in the face of an undenied injury gives the plaintiff a psychological advantage as well.

The three conditions necessary to establish *res ipsa loquitur* are common in situations in which the nurse or the physician may be principal actors. The classic sponge-in-the-abdomen is illustrative. First, in this instance, it is not necessary to prove negligent conduct by expert testimony, for it would be common knowledge to a lay jury that in the absence of negligence a sponge would not be left in the abdomen after surgery; therefore, the injury is one which would not normally occur without negligence, and an inference of negligence can be drawn. Second, the instrument or act that brought about the harm must be in the control of the defendant nurse or physician, which in this example is apparent. Third, the patient could not have contributed to the injury, because he was under anesthesia. Once these three conditions are met, the usual procedure of proof is reversed and the defendant is called upon to rebut the plaintiff's inference of negligence.

Not all cases are so simple, however. In many instances an injury or unfavorable result need not necessarily give rise to a presumption of negligence. If the nurse or physician were called upon to explain every untoward reaction, whether or not the patient was conscious, it would indeed be a harsh doctrine. In spite of utmost care and skill, numerous factors can contribute to unfavorable medical results; for example, individual predisposition might account for a wholly unexpected drug reaction. Again, inherent in any surgery is a certain risk, and sometimes under the most skillful hands, what may appear to be a negligent injury occurs. In *Siverson v. Weber*, 22 Cal. Rptr. 337, 372 P.2d 97 (1962), it was held that the doctrine of *res ipsa loquitur* was not applicable with respect to the alleged negligence of the surgeons in the performance of a hysterectomy. Following surgery the patient developed a vesicovaginal fistula, which caused considerable discomfort; and several months later surgery was required to correct the condition. The medical expert witness stated that fistulas may occur even though the surgeon has exercised care and skill and, although rare, are considered a risk of the operation. The decision stated:

> To permit an inference of negligence under the doctrine of *res ipsa loquitur* solely because an uncommon complication develops would place too great a burden upon the medical profession and might result in an undesirable limitation on the use of operations or new procedures involving an inherent risk of injury even when due care is used.

In some instances the burden of proof may be placed upon the nurse to explain how the occurrence could have happened in the absence of negligence on her part. In *South Broward Hosp. Dist. v. Schmitt*, 172 S.2d 12 (Fla. App. 1965), an action was brought against the hospital to recover for injuries sustained by a patient who fell from the hospital examining table in the emergency room. Following a heart attack, the patient was admitted to the hospital's emergency room and placed upon the examining table where the nursing supervisor adjusted a belt and raised the side rails. She then left the room to arrange for a hospital bed. Upon hearing a thud she returned to the room to find the patient lying on the floor having suffered head and facial injuries in the fall. The patient could not remember anything concerning the incident, but the nurse testified that the patient was conscious on admission and that she conversed with the patient regarding her medications. On appeal the court held that the trial judge properly refused to invoke the doctrine of *res ipsa loquitur* because the plaintiff had failed to present evidence of an injury from which an inference of negligence could be drawn and had also failed to show that the means by which the injury was sustained was in the sole control of the defendant.

Whether or not the doctrine may be invoked depends upon the facts of a particular case and the strength of the inference that can be drawn. Judicial decisions in some courts consistently refuse to apply the doctrine, whereas others show a tendency to see strong reasons for its application. Even in those courts where the doctrine is viewed with favor there are certain categories in the field of medical practice in which the doctrine does not apply, according to Louisell and Williams. [Louisell, D., and Williams, H., *Trial of Medical Malpractice Cases*, 437, 438–41. (New York: Matthew Bender & Co., 1968).]*

When the facts show no more than

. . . 1) a mistake in diagnosis [as surgery for presumed appendicitis],

2) unsuccessful treatment or an adverse result of medical procedures [as facial paralysis following mastoidectomy],

3) choice of a wrong method of treatment ["cold" treated, plaintiff had tuberculosis],

4) an adverse result of a medical procedure which is known to produce some bad results even when all reasonable precautions have been taken (the so-called "calculated risk") [as injury to peroneal nerve at time of knee surgery].

It is debatable whether all these categories will continue to hold as medical knowledge advances and as diagnostic measures become more precise.

Louisell also lists those categories in which common knowledge among laymen is sufficient to support an inference of negligence in medical practice without proof of conduct.

---

* Reprinted with permission of Matthew Bender & Co., 235 E. 45th St., New York.

1) objects left in the patient's body at the time of surgery [as sponges];

2) injury to a healthy part of the body in the treatment area, or to a part remote from the treatment area, whether healthy or not [as maxilla fractured by mouth gag during tonsillectomy];

3) removal of the wrong part of the body when another part was intended [as wrong tooth removed];

4) teeth dropped down the windpipe (trachea);

5) burns from a) hot water bottles, b) diathermy machines, c) heat lamps, d) X-rays, particularly when used for diagnostic purposes, e) steam vaporizers, f) chemicals, g) bedside lamps;

6) infection resulting from unsterilized instruments [as infection in jaw following dental extraction];

7) failure to take X-rays to diagnose possible fractures;

8) a fracture set so badly that the deficiency of the workmanship is apparent to anybody;

9) disability directly resulting from injection of drugs into the body [as injection of vitamin solution into deltoid muscle region of arm];

10) explosion of anesthetic gases.


It must always be kept in mind that, while an inference of negligence is permitted in medical mishaps listed above, many times these inferences are successfully rebutted by the defendant.

It may be of interest to the reader to speculate on nursing situations that might fall into either one of the two categories differentiated by Louisell. For example, a patient develops a decubitus ulcer leading to an extensive and damaging necrosis. Would this be an instance in which common knowledge among laymen would be sufficient to support an inference of negligence in nursing practice? Or, might this be a category in the field of nursing practice where the doctrine would not apply, in that an adverse result does not necessarily lead to an inference of negligence? What other examples may be identified?

When the doctrine is applied, the facts of the situation may be such that the necessary inference of negligence can easily be drawn, but because of the complex relationships in medical and nursing practice it is not possible to name a single defendant who could be charged as solely responsible. The plaintiff then charges several members of the medical team. In *Oldis v. La Société Française*, 130 Cal.App.2d 461, 279 P.2d 184 (1955), an action was brought by a hospital patient for burns sustained during a period of post-operative care. Defendants named included the physician who referred the patient to the surgeon and who had made calls during the critical period, the surgeon, the nurses in whose custody the defendant was placed, and the hospital. The plaintiff suffered a third-degree burn in the lower-right quadrant of the abdomen following surgery when he was semiconscious from drugs administered over a three-day period. Evidence of the injury was amply supported. One or more of the defendants may have had control over the instrumentality that caused the injury, but it was uncertain what the causative agent really was. Those proposed varied all the way from hot packs, or a hot-water bottle, to a cautery unit used during surgery. Defendants who came forward to testify included the special duty nurse, the staff nurse, the physician, and the surgeon, all of whom failed in a satisfactory rebuttal of the inference of negligence. The decision for the plaintiff against all the defendants was affirmed by the appellate court. All members of the medical team, then, may be held under the doctrine of *res ipsa loquitur* for a single injury to a patient.

Another requirement for defendant responsibility under this doctrine is *control*. The "Vicarious Liability" chapter will discuss the "captain of the ship doctrine" under which control for all that occurs in the operating room is considered to be under the control of the surgeon. In *Jensen v. Linner*, 260 Minn 22, 108 N.W.2d 705 (1961), an action initiated by a patient and her husband for an injury sustained in the course of an operation, it was held that a *res ipsa loquitur* instruction was proper. The plaintiff was admitted to the Swedish Hospital to have a hysterectomy. After the surgery was completed, it was decided to remove the appendix. A phenol solution was needed to cauterize the stump of the appendix. The solution was brought by the circulating nurse and handed to the surgeon by the instrument nurse by means of an applicator that had been dipped in the solution. At some point before the patient left surgery, she suffered a third-degree burn on her ankle from phenol. The three essentials necessary to invoke the doctrine of *res ipsa loquitur* were clear except the control of the instrumentality that brought about the harm. The trial court after relieving the Swedish Hospital of responsibility stated that at the time of the accident hospital personnel in the operating room were under the control of the doctor and not the hospital and therefore he was responsible. This decision was affirmed by the appellate court.

In all instances of the application of the doctrine of *res ipsa loquitur* cited, there has been one element in common: proof that established an inference of negligent conduct without proof of the actual conduct itself. In the situation in which the one who is injured is not aware of the facts surrounding the injury, whether he be conscious or not, he is then in a difficult position to obtain proof necessary to support an inference of negligence. Expert medical testimony may be required which places the attorney for the plaintiff in the position of combatting the reluctance of physicians to testify or deal with their guarded testimony when they do so. In order not to impede justice in situations of this kind there appears to be a tendency for courts to invoke the doctrine, which places the defendant physician in the position of giving evidence to explain why what happened did happen and of assuming the burden of going forward with the evidence.

## NOTES

### (1) Res Ipsa Loquitur as a Rule of Sympathy

Suggested in the following article are some of the reasons why the doctrine of *res ipsa loquitur* is feared by the medical profession.

## Morris, R. C., "Res Ipsa Loquitur"—Liability Without Fault, *J.A.M.A.*, 163:1055 (1957)*

### INTRODUCTION

Throughout the United States and England medical malpractice lawsuits are alarmingly on the increase. So are the size of the verdicts rendered therein.

Newsweek Magazine reports: "Some 5,000 cases are now being tried each year with thousands of other cases settled out of court. Since 1950, one out of every 35 doctors insured under the New York State Medical Society's group-insurance plan has been sued in the courts for malpractice."

The chairman of the District of Columbia Medical Society Professional Liability Insurance Committee (where recently 115 malpractice cases were pending and the doctors found all group insurance withdrawn from them) states: "Only about one in seven or eight of the district cases shows any voluntary negligence on the doctor's part. Nonetheless, the doctor loses about one in four cases."

England's experience is the same: "The flood of claims against doctors which has been steadily rising during the past few years, shows no sign of subsiding. In fact, in the year under review, the number of such claims has again shown an increase."

Verdicts are even more alarming. In a very recent case, a San Francisco jury returned a malpractice verdict in the sum of $250,000. A few months before, a San Diego jury returned a malpractice verdict in the sum of $210,000. A Tennessee jury returned a malpractice verdict of $200,000, a federal jury one of $123,000, a Texas jury one over $100,000, and a Wisconsin jury one of $97,000.

In fact, the medical malpractice picture is changing so catastrophically that one wonders if the law itself is changing: "The increase in the number of actions against hospitals and doctors has given rise to the feeling in some quarters that the law of negligence, in so far as it affects doctors has undergone a drastic change."

We submit, and earnestly hope, that it has not, and that our courts will continue to adhere to those safeguards of the law requiring legal proof of negligence by expert testimony in medical malpractice cases. The rationale of recent cases extending the doctrine of *res ipsa loquitur*, however, alarms us and commands our serious attention.

* Reprinted with permission of the *Journal of the American Medical Association* and R. C. Morris.

THEORY OF THE LAW

The basic theory of our law is that he who accuses must prove. In medical malpractice cases this means *"must prove by expert medical testimony,"* for the jury, which alone is empowered to determine all disputed questions of fact, can have no opinion upon complicated medical questions unless furnished that opinion by doctors themselves testifying in the case. Nothing is more fundamental to the law than that a jury must not be permitted to speculate: "Under our law it is just as pernicious to submit a case to a jury and permit the jury to speculate with the rights of citizens when no question for the jury is involved, as it is to deny to a citizen his trial by jury when he has the right."

Jury speculation in medical malpractice cases means that the jury must guess whether or not a physician's particular course of conduct constituted malpractice, that is, whether the defendant-doctor "in the performance of his service either did some particular thing or things that physicians and surgeons of ordinary skill, care, and diligence would not have done under the same or similar circumstances, or that the defendant failed or omitted to do some particular thing or things that physicians and surgeons of ordinary skill, care, and diligence would have done under the same or similar circumstances." For manifestly, a lay jury of men and women, untrained in medicine, can have no opinion as to what "thing or things" a physician or surgeon of ordinary skill would or would not have done under similar circumstances save as a physician or surgeon tells the jury by testifying in open court. To prevent jury speculation with the rights of the medical profession, the law has always required that the patient prove his claims against the doctor by expert medical testimony of other doctors of the same school of medicine. Such testimony must be that in the opinion of the doctor-witness the defendant-doctor did (or failed to do) some particular thing or things that physicians and surgeons of ordinary skill, care, and diligence would not have done (or would have done) under similar circumstances. If the patient failed to produce such testimony, then the case was withdrawn from the jury's speculation and judgment entered for the defendant-doctor as a matter of law by the court.

Once the patient has produced such testimony, however, then it becomes the province of the jury to weigh the probative value of such testimony and, in the event other doctors have expressed contrary opinions on behalf of the defendant-doctor, to determine from a consideration of all such opinions and all the other evidence what it finds the medical fact to be in the case before it, namely, whether the defendant-doctor "did (or failed to do) some particular thing or things that physicians and surgeons of ordinary skill, care, and diligence would not have done (or would have done) under similar circumstances." When doctors' opinions differ, the jury and only the jury has the power and the duty to resolve those differences.

There has long been an exception to this rule, inherent in the rationale of the rule itself, namely, that when the act complained of by the patient is so simple as to be within the lay knowledge of the average citizen-juror, then the patient need not produce expert medical testimony but is entitled to have his case submitted to the jury for determination without such proof. For example, such claims as severe burn following a mere x-ray picture to reveal a fracture, foreign bodies left in the tissues, hot-water bottle burns, failure of the doctor to attend the patient frequently enough, have been held to fall within this exception. The rationale is clear: in such cases "the particular thing or things" complained of is within the lay experience of the average juror and therefore the jury can form an intelligent opinion without the guidance of expert medical testimony, whereas in the case of a complicated medical procedure the jury, without medical testimony to give it a yardstick by which to measure the defendant-doctor's conduct, can form no opinion beyond mere guess or speculation.

There is a second exception in the law to the fundamental rule that he who accuses must prove, which has sometimes been applied to malpractice cases. That exception is known by the Latin phrase *res ipsa loquitur*.

## "RES IPSA LOQUITUR"

Originally the offspring of a casual word of Baron Pollock during legal argument, the phrase translated means nothing more than "the thing speaks for itself." Around this phrase there has evolved a legal doctrine that has been severely criticized: "It adds nothing to the law, has no meaning which is not more clearly expressed for us in English, and brings confusion to our legal discussions. It does not represent a doctrine, is not a legal maxim, and is not a rule."

Basically the doctrine is simply this:

Negligence may be proved by circumstantial evidence. One type of circumstantial evidence to which the courts have given the name res ipsa loquitur, arises where

(a) the accident is of a kind which ordinarily does not occur in the absence of someone's negligence, and

(b) It is caused by an instrumentality within the exclusive control of the defendant, and

(c) The possibility of contributing conduct which would make the plaintiff (patient) responsible is eliminated. . . .

Historically, this principle has been applied to cases of falling objects, explosions, railroad derailment, etc., wherein the object was in the exclusive control of the defendant and the accident was of a kind that does not ordinarily occur in the absence of someone's negligence.

The doctrine has also been invoked, however, in cases where from the very occurrence of the events themselves the injured party knew and could know nothing of what has happened to him, but the defendant had such knowledge available to him. To invoke the general rule that he who accuses must prove in such circumstances seemed so harsh and unfair that some courts uttering the phrase *res ipsa loquitur* turned to the defendant requiring him to furnish the explanation of what happened and to show that the occurrence was due to no negligence on his part. This extension of the doctrine would seem to make of *res ipsa loquitur* merely a rule of sympathy rather than a rule of law and has been severely criticized in many quarters. When extended to medical malpractice cases, this "rule of sympathy" becomes exceedingly unfair to the defendant-doctor, for it can be applied to every case of an untoward result following any operation wherein the anesthetized patient knows nothing of what occurred to her, whereas the surgeon has some knowledge, with the result that the jury is forced to speculate with the rights of the surgeon— more often than not with disastrous financial consequences to the surgeon. . . .

What is alarming is the recent tendency in some courts toward extending this perversion of the doctrine of *res ipsa loquitur*, which for lack of a better term we have characterized as a "rule of sympathy," into the medical malpractice field wherein untoward results may occur during conditions (such as found in every operation wherein the patient because of the anesthetic knows nothing of what occurred) appealing to the natural sympathy of the courts. The outcome is often disastrous to the medical profession because the "rule of sympathy" removes the safeguard of the law preventing jury speculation, that he who accuses a doctor of malpractice in his chosen profession must prove that malpractice by expert medical testimony from members of that same profession, qualified by training and experience to have intelligent opinions, not guesses, concerning the propriety of the acts complained of. For when forced to speculate, the jury's natural sympathy for a personal injury with its attendant pain and suffering often colors its guesswork to the detriment of the defendant-doctor. . . .

## COMMENT

Thus the fallacy inherent in the rule of sympathy is that whenever a bad result follows an operation (where of course normally no such bad result occurs) it is presumed by the courts that the reason for the bad result must be some negligence on the part of the operating surgeon and therefore a lay jury is entitled to weigh the defendant-doctor's explanation of his conduct against such presumption without proof by expert testimony from another doctor of just what the defendant-doctor did wrong. In this situation the lay jury is forced to speculate between the defendant-doctor's explanation and the natural sympathy for the injured patient—with disastrous results to the defendant-doctor. . . .

## CONCLUSION

We have examined in some detail the cases of one jurisdiction—namely California—in order to show the recent trend towards liberalization and extension of the doctrine of *res ipsa loquitur* far beyond its original purpose to the dangerous point of a "rule of sympathy" wherein an untoward result is the only proof required to force the defendant-doctor to run the gauntlet of jury speculation, with disastrous consequences approaching financial ruin. This trend appears in other states as well, (although California seems to have gone the farthest in this direction) but fortunately so far has remained a distant minority view. However, inroads are being made upon the sound principles of the law protecting the medical profession from the evils of jury speculation and resultant liability without fault; pressure groups are exerting influence upon courts and legislatures alike to relax and abolish these safeguards of the law. The time has come to exert an organized and effective pressure upon both courts and legislatures in defense of the rule requiring proof of negligence by expert testimony in malpractice cases.

To do so will be to defend not only the medical profession but also the rights of the public, for, if this trend continues, it is the public, as potential patients and beneficiaries of the advancement of medical science, that will suffer. For the medical profession cannot be asked to underwrite the cost of the advancement of medical science at the risk of personal financial ruin. As an English court has said:

We should be doing a disservice to the community if we imposed liability on hospitals and doctors for everything that happens to go wrong. Doctors would be led to think more of their own safety than of the good of their patients. Initiative would be stifled and confidence shaken. A proper sense of proportion requires us to have regard to the conditions in which hospitals and doctors work. We must insist on due care for the patient, but we must not condemn as negligence that which is only misadventure. . . .

It is easy to accuse; it is difficult to defend. The safeguard of the law that "he who affirms must prove" and, in malpractice cases "must prove actual negligence by expert testimony," is sound and should be preserved. To do otherwise is to force the medical profession into the role of insurers, a burden which it cannot and will not bear, with the resultant loss of useful techniques and retardation of the progress of medical science. Ultimately, this loss will fall upon the patient himself—who sooner or later may be any one of us.

## CAVEAT

While the medical profession can justly complain that the courts have gone too far in converting the doctrine of *res ipsa loquitur* into a rule of sympathy, thus forcing the defendant-doctor to run the gauntlet of speculation by a lay jury ignorant of "the medical facts of life," there is one aspect of this problem that perhaps bears mention if the medical profession in turn is to understand "the legal facts of life" confronting the courts and the entire legal profession. Occasionally there is a justified malpractice lawsuit. Some doctor was negligent and from that negligence there arose an injury. Such a patient deserves redress. She is entitled, if justice means anything, to her day in court. Yet when she turns to the courts she finds the door to recovery barred by the safeguards of the law, that she who affirms must prove, and in malpractice cases must prove by expert medical testimony. When she reaches for that key, the medical expert, she finds difficulty in persuading any competent doctor to give testimony against a fellow-doctor in any malpractice lawsuit. Deprived of the key, she must batter at the door as best she can hoping to find a way to make it yield. Courts are keenly aware of her dilemma.

Courts are human beings, swayed by natural sympathy for such a patient. In the face of the medical profession's unwillingness to furnish the key, the courts are finding a way to forge a key of their own to unlatch this door for the rightfully injured patient. That key is the rule of sympathy—an illogical but humanly understandable distortion of the doctrine of *res ipsa loquitur* beyond its original intended purpose, for it dispenses with the necessity of the medical expert. The danger to the medical profession is obvious. It runs the risk of being condemned for problems never rightly understood in cases completely unmerited if the medical truth were only known. . . .

The medical profession cannot have its cake and eat it too. This is a live and let live world. Justice is a two-way street. If the medical profession wishes to retain the safeguards of the law requiring proof of malpractice, by medical testimony, it must make available to rightfully injured patients such medical proof in turn. Whatever the medical truth, patients are entitled to it too. For if the door is not unlocked by the one key, it most assuredly will be by the other. Perhaps this is a problem the medical profession will have to answer for itself. From the medico-legal point of view, in the face of astronomically rising *res ipsa loquitur* verdicts against defendant-doctors without proof of fault, some sort of answer would seem to be a necessity; from the long range public relations point of view, it would seem to be a virtue.

## (2) Res Ipsa Loquitur as a Rule of Justice

The following excerpt presents the other side of the coin from the preceding note.

**Louisell, D., and Williams, H.,** *Trial of Medical Malpractice Cases,* **418 (Albany: Matthew Bender & Co., 1968)\***

PROBLEMS OF PROOF IN MALPRACTICE CASES: THE INHERENT DILEMMA

The dilemmas presented by problems of proof in a malpractice action are succinctly and fairly stated by Rutledge, J. in *Christie v. Callahan* [124 F.2d 825 (D.C.Cir. 1941)]

Malpractice is hard to prove. The physician has all of the advantage of position. He is, presumably, an expert. The patient is a layman. The physician knows what is done and what is its significance. The patient may or may not know what is done. He seldom knows its significance. He judges chiefly by results. The physician has the patient in his confidence, disarmed against suspicion. Physicians, like lawyers, are loath to testify a fellow craftsman has been negligent, especially when he is highly reputable in professional character. . . . In short, the physician has the advantage of knowledge and of proof. . . . What therefore might be slight evidence when there is no such advantage, as in ordinary negligence cases, takes on greater weight in malpractice suits. On the other hand, malpractice is a serious charge. The physician is not an insurer of health. He undertakes only for the standard of skill possessed generally by others practicing in his field, and for the care which they would give in similar circumstances. He must have latitude for play of reasonable judgment, and this includes room for not too obvious or gross errors according to the prevailing practice of his craft. Generally the standard must be shown by experts and so must the departure from it. But there are cases in which the result of medical or surgical treatment, considered in the light of the circumstances attending and following it, may warrant an inference of negligence.

THE "CONSPIRACY OF SILENCE" IN MALPRACTICE CASES: IMPETUS TO *RES IPSA LOQUITUR*

Clearly there is a general reluctance of physicians to testify to facts or to give opinions which likely will involve their brethren in legal liability or professional embarrassment growing out of alleged malpractice. It is apparent that this reluctance customarily has led to refusal by physicians voluntarily to participate in malpractice cases on behalf of plaintiffs. Of course, mere reluctance or refusal of physicians voluntarily to testify for a plaintiff does not establish a "conspiracy of silence," certainly not in any precise sense of the word "conspiracy." But the reluctance has been so general and notorious as to be equivalent in a practical sense to a concert of purpose and action. Moreover, courts, lawyers, and the public have seen the consequences of this reluctance result in miscarriage of justice in certain fact situations as to which the conclusion of malpractice, even of gross negligence, is rationally inescapable. Sometimes the picture is compounded by serious suspicion

\* Reprinted with permission of Matthew Bender & Co., 235 E. 45th St., New York.

that the defendant's experts have blinded themselves to the realities, even to the point of wilful misrepresentation or perjury.

Courts have always recognized that the practice of a profession involves intangibles and many unknown quantities. The existence of uncertainties in the practice of medicine has received specific recognition in the judicial doctrine that the degree of skill and the standard of care required of a physician may be evaluated only by others in the profession. At one time courts were persuaded that practically all features of medical diagnosis, treatment and results were subject to interpretation by physicians only. The likely range of possible results was so wide that this line of thought was reasonable in most situations fifty or sixty years ago.

As the courts increasingly realized that the inability of plaintiffs to procure medical experts was producing injustice in certain malpractice cases, perceptive judges began to veer away from the rule invariably requiring expert testimony for a plaintiff's case. The most convenient and feasible vehicle of escape from the rule in a number of cases was the doctrine of res ipsa loquitur.

The principal factors motivating the increasing acceptance of the doctrine in malpractice cases, in addition to the general feeling of unfairness caused by inability of plaintiffs to get medical testimony, have been the constantly developing lay comprehension of medical techniques and practice, the growing judicial awareness that the progress of medical science is in substance withheld from the victims of malpractice by the profession's self-imposed rule of silence about acts of malpractice, and the inclination to reaffirm the common law's hard-headed distrust of expertise that runs counter to the observations of common sense.

# CASES

Note that in the cases that follow another legal approach is used in establishing proof of injury. Arguments for and against the application of the doctrine of *res ipsa loquitur* in medical malpractice cases have been presented in the cases and the text. As you analyze these cases, determine which of the doctor-nurse-patient interests are best served by the *res ipsa loquitur* doctrine. Try to identify from the facts a point in which the quality of patient care failed to meet reasonable standards. Can the assumption that lowered quality of care precipitated the litigation be equally well supported in this section?

## *Ybarra v. Spangard,* 25 Cal. 2d 486, 154 P.2d 687, 162 A.L.R. 1258 (1944)

Gibson, Chief Justice.

This is an action for damages for personal injuries alleged to have been inflicted on plaintiff by defendants during the course of a surgical operation. The trial court entered judgments of nonsuit as to all defendants and plaintiff appealed.

On October 28, 1939, plaintiff consulted defendant Dr. Tilley, who diagnosed his ailment as appendicitis, and made arrangements for an appendectomy to be performed by defendant Dr. Spangard at a hospital owned and managed by defendant Dr. Swift. Plaintiff entered the hospital, was given a hypodermic injection, slept, and later was awakened by Drs. Tilley and Spangard and wheeled into the operating room by a nurse whom he believed to be defendant Gisler, an employee of Dr. Swift. Defendant Dr. Reser, the anesthetist, also an employee of Dr. Swift, adjusted plaintiff for the operation, pulling his body to the head of the operating table and, according to plaintiff's testimony, laying him back against two hard objects at the top of his shoulders, about an inch below his neck. Dr. Reser then administered the anesthetic and plaintiff lost consciousness. When he awoke early the following morning he was in his hospital room attended by defendant Thompson, the special nurse, and another nurse who was not made a defendant.

Plaintiff testified that prior to the operation he had never had any pain in, or injury to, his right arm or shoulder, but that when he awakened he felt a sharp pain about half way between the neck and the point of the right shoulder. He complained to the nurse, and then to Dr. Tilley, who gave him diathermy treatments while he remained in the hospital. The pain did not cease but spread down to the lower part of his arm, and after his release from the hospital the condition grew worse. He was unable to rotate or lift his arm, and developed paralysis and atrophy of the muscles around the shoulder. He received further treatments from Dr. Tilley until March, 1940, and then returned to work, wearing his arm in a splint on the advice of Dr. Spangard.

Plaintiff also consulted Dr. Wilfred Sterling Clark, who had X-ray pictures taken which showed an area of diminished sensation below the shoulder and atrophy and wasting away of the muscles around the shoulder. In the opinion of Dr. Clark, plaintiff's condition was due to trauma or injury by pressure or strain applied between his right shoulder and neck.

Plaintiff was also examined by Dr. Fernando Garduno, who expressed the opinion that plaintiff's injury was a paralysis of traumatic origin, not arising from pathological causes, and not systemic, and that the injury resulted in atrophy, loss of use, and restriction of motion of the right arm and shoulder.

Plaintiff's theory is that the foregoing evidence presents a proper case for the application of the doctrine of *res ipsa loquitur*, and that the inference of negligence arising therefrom makes the granting of a nonsuit improper. Defendants take the position that, assuming that plaintiff's condition was in fact the result of an injury, there is no showing that the act of any particular defendant, nor any particular instrumentality, was the cause thereof. They attack plaintiff's action as an attempt to fix liability "en masse" on various defendants, some of whom were not responsible for the acts of others; and they further point to the failure to show which defendants had control of the instrumentalities that may have been involved. Their main defense may be briefly stated in two propositions: (1) that where there are several defendants, and there is a division of responsibility in the use of an instrumentality causing the injury, and the injury might have resulted from the separate act of either one of two or more persons, the rule of *res ipsa loquitur* cannot be invoked against any one of them; and (2) that where there are several instrumentalities, and no showing is made as to which caused the injury or as to the particular defendant in control of it, the doctrine cannot apply. We are satisfied, however, that these objections are not well taken in the circumstances of this case.

The doctrine of *res ipsa loquitur* has three conditions: " (1) the accident must be of a kind which ordinarily does not occur in the absence of someone's negligence; (2) it must be caused by an agency or instrumentality within the exclusive control of the defendant; (3) it must not have been due to any voluntary action or contribution on the part of the plaintiff." Prosser, Torts, p. 295. It is applied in a wide variety of situations, including cases of medical or dental treatment and hospital care.

There is, however, some uncertainty as to the extent to which *res ipsa loquitur* may be invoked in cases of injury from medical treatment. This is in part due to the tendency, in some decisions, to lay undue emphasis on the limitations of the doctrine, and to give too little attention to its basic underlying purpose. The result has been that a simple, understandable rule of circumstantial evidence, with a sound background of common sense and human experience, has occasionally been transformed into a rigid legal formula, which arbitrarily precludes its application in many cases where it is most important that it should be applied. If the doctrine is to continue to serve a useful purpose, we should not forget that "the particular force and justice of the rule, regarded as a presumption throwing upon the party charged the duty of producing evidence, consists in the circumstance that the chief evidence of the true cause, whether culpable or innocent, is practically accessible to him but inaccessible to the injured person." 9 Wigmore, Evidence, 3d Ed., § 2509, p. 382.

In Maki v. Murray Hosp., [91, Mont. 251, 7 P.2d 228 (1932)], an unconscious patient in a hospital received injuries from a fall, the court declared that without the doctrine the maxim that for every wrong there is a remedy would be rendered nugatory, "by denying one, patently entitled to damages, satisfaction merely because he is ignorant of facts peculiarly within the knowledge of the party who should, in all justice, pay them."

The present case is of a type which comes within the reason and spirit of the doctrine more fully perhaps than any other. The passenger sitting awake in a railroad car at the time of a collision, the pedestrian walking along the street and struck by a falling object or the debris of an explosion, are surely not more entitled to an explanation than the unconscious patient on the operating table. Viewed from this aspect, it is difficult to see how the doctrine can, with any justification, be so restricted in its statement as to become inapplicable to a patient who submits himself to the care and custody of doctors and nurses, is rendered unconscious, and receives some injury from instrumentalities used in his treatment. Without the aid of the doctrine a patient who received permanent injuries of a serious character, obviously the result of some one's negligence, would be entirely unable to recover unless the doctors and nurses in attendance voluntarily chose to disclose the identity of the negligent person and the facts establishing liability. See Maki v. Murray Hospital, 91 Mont. 251, 7 P.2d 228. If this were the state of the law of negligence, the courts, to avoid gross injustice, would be forced to invoke the principles of absolute liability, irrespective of negligence, in actions by persons suffering injuries during the course of treatment under anesthesia. But we think this juncture has not yet been reached, and that the doctrine of *res ipsa loquitur* is properly applicable to the case before us.

The condition that the injury must not have been due to the plaintiff's voluntary action is of course fully satisfied under the evidence produced herein; and the same is true of the condition that the accident must be one which ordinarily does not occur unless some one was negligent. We have here no problem of negligence in treatment, but of distinct injury to a healthy part of the body not the subject of treatment, nor within the area covered by the operation. The decisions in this state make it clear that such circumstances raise the inference of negligence and call upon the defendant to explain the unusual result.

The argument of defendants is simply that plaintiff has not shown an injury caused by an instrumentality under a defendant's control, because he has not shown which of the several instrumentalities that he came in contact with while in the hospital caused the injury; and he has not shown that any one defendant or his servants had exclusive control over any particular instrumentality. Defendants assert that some of them were not the employees of other defendants, that some did not stand in any permanent relationship from which liability in tort would follow, and that in view of the nature of the injury, the number of defendants and the different functions performed by each, they could not all be liable for the wrong, if any.

We have no doubt that in a modern hospital a patient is quite likely to come under the care of a number of persons in different types of contractual and other relationships with each other. For example, in the present case it appears that Drs. Smith, Spangard, and Tilley were physicians or surgeons commonly placed in the legal category of independent contractors; and Dr. Reser, the anesthetist, and defendant Thompson, the special nurse, were employees of Dr. Swift and not of the other doctors. But we do not believe that either the number or relationship of the defendants alone determines whether the doctrine of res ipsa loquitur applies. Every defendant in whose custody the plaintiff was placed for any period was bound to exercise ordinary care to see that no unnecessary harm came to him and each would be liable for failure in this regard. Any defendant who negligently injured him, and any defendant charged with his care who so neglected him as to allow injury to occur, would be liable. The defendant employers would be liable for the neglect of their employees; and the doctor in charge of the operation would be liable for the negligence of those who became his temporary servants for the purpose of assisting in the operation.

In this connection, it should be noted that while the assisting physicians and nurses may be employed by the hospital, or engaged by the patient, they normally become the temporary servants or agents of the surgeon in charge while the operation is in progress, and liability may be imposed upon him for their negligent acts under the doctrine of respondeat superior. Thus a surgeon has been held liable for the negligence of an assisting nurse who leaves a sponge or other object inside a patient, and the fact that the duty of seeing that such mistakes do not occur is delegated to others does not absolve the doctor from responsibility for their negligence.

It may appear at the trial that, consistent with the principles outlined above, one or more defendants will be found liable and others absolved, but this should not preclude the application of the rule of *res ipsa loquitur*. The control at one time or another, of one or more of the various agencies or instrumentalities which might have harmed the plaintiff was in the hands of every defendant or of his employees or temporary servants. This, we think, places upon them the burden of initial explanation. Plaintiff was rendered unconscious for the purpose of undergoing surgical treatment by the defendants; it is manifestly unreasonable for them to insist that he identify any one of them as the person who did the alleged negligent act.

The other aspect of the case which defendants so strongly emphasize is that plaintiff has not identified the instrumentality any more than he has the particular guilty defendant. Here, again, there is a misconception which, if carried to the extreme for which defendants contend, would unreasonably limit the application of the *res ipsa loquitur* rule. It should be enough that the plaintiff can show an injury resulting from an external force applied while he lay unconscious in the hospital; this is as clear a case of identification of the instrumentality as the plaintiff may ever be able to make.

An examination of the recent cases, particularly in this state, discloses that the test of actual exclusive control of an instrumentality has not been strictly followed, but exceptions have been recognized where the purpose of the doctrine of *res ipsa loquitur* would otherwise be defeated. Thus, the test has become one of right of control rather than actual control. Finally, it has been suggested that the hospital cases may properly be considered exceptional, and that the doctrine of *res ipsa loquitur* "should apply with equal force in cases wherein medical and nursing staffs take the place of machinery and may, through carelessness or lack of skill, inflict, or permit the infliction of injury upon a patient who is thereafter in no position to say how he received his injuries," where the court refers to the "instrumentalities" as including "the unconscious body of the plaintiff."

In the face of these examples of liberalization of the tests for *res ipsa loquitur*, there can be no justification for the rejection of the doctrine in the instant case. As pointed out above, if we accept the contention of defendants herein, there will rarely be any compensation for patients injured while unconscious. A hospital today conducts a highly integrated system of activities, with many persons contributing their efforts. There may be, e.g., preparation for surgery by nurses and internes who are employees of the hospital; administering of an anesthetic by a doctor who may be an employee of the hospital, an employee of the operating surgeon, or an independent contractor; performance of an operation by a surgeon and assistants who may be his employees, employees of the hospital, or independent contractors; and post surgical care by the surgeon, a hospital physician, and nurses. The number of those in whose care the patient is placed is not a good reason for denying him all reasonable opportunity to recover for negligent harm. It is rather a good reason for re-examination of the statement of legal theories which supposedly compel such a shocking result.

We do not at this time undertake to state the extent to which the reasoning of this case may be applied to other situations in which the doctrine of res ipsa loquitur is invoked. We merely hold that where a plaintiff receives unusual injuries while unconscious and in the course of medical treatment, all those defendants who had any control over his body or the instrumentalities which might have caused the injuries may properly be called upon to meet the inference of negligence by giving an explanation of their conduct.

The judgment is reversed.

## ANALYSIS

1. What were the facts presented by the plaintiff's counsel? From these facts, how did counsel support the proposition that the three conditions essential to invoke the doctrine of *res ipsa loquitur* had been met? Did the fact that the patient was unconscious have added weight, and if so, why?

2. In invoking this doctrine, an inference of negligence is drawn. In your experience, does it necessarily follow that, if an injury appears to flow from positioning a patient on the operating table, it is due to negligence? What elements are present that might lead to an injury that could be beyond the control of any member of the surgical team? As one of the defendant nurses called as a witness, develop your testimony using your knowledge of anatomy and physiology to show that unfavorable results that occur under rare circumstances are not necessarily due to negligence. What are the implications for medical and nursing practice if this doctrine is extended?

3. Viewing this case from the opposite position, wherein does this doctrine place the injured one in a better position in seeking a just recompense for the wrong done him? It has been contended that this method of establishing proof expedites justice. Give illustrations that would support this position.

4. How did the court dispel the defendant's contention that the number of nurses and doctors participating on the surgical team prevented liability in tort for any of them? The court chose to use right of control of the instrumentality causing the harm, rather than actual control. Considering the way a surgical team works, is this a fair differentiation?

## *Ayers v. Parry,* 192 F. 2d 181 (3d Cir. 1951)

Marsh, District Judge.

This action was instituted against a surgeon and an anesthetist for malpractice. Jurisdiction arises from diversity of citizenship and a claim for damages in excess of the statutory amount. At the conclusion of the evidence presented on behalf of plaintiff the court below entered judgment in favor of the defendants and plaintiff appeals. The question raised by this appeal is whether plaintiff made out a prima facie case. A careful examination of the record convinces us that he did not, and the action of the learned trial judge should be sustained.

Since all the operative facts have a New Jersey setting the tort law of that State governs.

Viewing the evidence in the light most favorable to the plaintiff, as we are required to do, Newman v. Zinn, supra, the following appears to be the factual situation. Since February, 1947, plaintiff had been treated for gallstones by Dr. Louis F. Albright of Spring Lake, New Jersey. Within the preceding two years, he had undergone two abdominal operations in which spinal anesthesia was used. On September 20, 1947, plaintiff suffered a severe attack and at 3:15 p.m., was removed to the Fitkin Memorial Hospital in Neptune, New Jersey, to undergo an emergency operation for an obstruction to the common bile duct. Plaintiff was seriously ill. His temperature was 103.6 degrees and he had an acute infection. Dr. Albright engaged the defendant, Dr. O. K. Parry, as the surgeon. The other defendant, Dr. Emerson Haines, chief anesthetist at the hospital, undertook to administer the anesthetic. During the afternoon and evening, morphine and scopolamine were administered at the direction of Dr. Albright. Spinal anesthesia was selected because the doctors were of the opinion that ether would be harmful to this patient's liver. Dr. Haines administered the anesthetic agent through a needle inserted between the second and third lumbar vertebrae. This treatment was started at 9:50 p.m. The operation began at 10:10 p.m. and ended at 1:30 the next morning. During the operation gas, oxygen, and ether supplemented the spinal anesthetic. The common duct was located at about 1:00 a.m. whereupon the obstructing stones were removed and the cause of the infection was corrected.

Plaintiff testified that he was placed on the operating table and assumed a "curled up" position to receive the anesthesia. He stated he "felt this jabbing of pain into my spinal column, and from that point on I had this terrific pain radiating down my [right] leg, such as a heavy electrical shock. I remember stiffening out. I remember screaming, and from that point on I fainted and do not know what happened until the next morning in bed." He also said he fainted from the pain. The next morning plaintiff found he could not move his right leg and partial paralysis, marked atrophy, and sensory changes in this leg and in adjacent organs have persisted to the time of trial and probably will be permanent.

Dr. E. A. Rovensteine, an expert anesthetist, hypothesized that if the pain was experienced it was caused by the needle striking the nerve roots. Dr. Denker, a neurologist, testified that a painful reaction to the puncture needle was a "common experience." Dr. Rovensteine further stated that if a patient has pain on the insertion of the needle, followed by stiffening and unconsciousness, the recognized procedure is for the anesthetist to try to determine what caused the unconsciousness and further action would depend on what he learns. As to whether or not defendants should have proceeded with this operation under the circumstances, Dr. Rovensteine was unable to express an opinion.

According to Dr. Denker "this patient suffered an injury to the nerve roots in the lower end of the spinal cord." He said, "The particular region is known as the cauda equina. That is called a cauda equinal neuritis. That condition was produced by the spinal anesthesia. . . . The following nerve roots were injured, on the right side from the eleventh thoracic, all the lumbars and all the sacrals right down to the fifth sacral nerve root." He further said that the anesthetic agent "had a toxic effect on these nerve roots . . . and that has given him the resultant paralysis, atrophy, and sensory changes which are manifest on examination."

On cross examination Dr. Albright agreed that the unfavorable reaction of plaintiff to the administration of the anesthetic was something that could not be predetermined and that it was one of the hazards of this anesthesia. He stated that the anesthetic solution produced a condition called "arachnoiditis, which is an inflammation about the spinal cord . . . that constricts and damages the nerves, . . . and which occurs due to some unusual reaction on the part of the patient to that solution."

The parties seem to agree on the principles of law enunciated by the courts of New Jersey as they relate to physicians in the treatment of their patients; they, of course, disagree on their application to the facts.

It is generally held that the physician undertakes in the practice of his profession that he is possessed of that degree of knowledge and skill which usually pertains to the other members of his profession and he has a duty to use that standard of knowledge and skill in treating his patient. One holding himself out as having special knowledge and skill has a duty to exercise the special degree of knowledge and skill possessed by physicians who are specialists in the particular field involved in the light of the present state of scientific knowledge.

The physician is liable for a failure to exercise the requisite skill or for omitting to exercise the proper care, but without an express contract he is not a guarantee of good results.

It is presumed that a physician or surgeon exercised the ordinary care and skill required of him in treating his patient.

The lack of due care, or lack of diligence on the part of a physician in diagnosis, method and manner of treatment ordinarily must be established by expert testimony and the alleged negligence must be the proximate cause of the injuries.

Occasionally expert testimony is not required where an injury results to a part of the anatomy not being treated or operated upon and is of such character as to warrant the inference of want of care from the testimony of laymen or in the light of the knowledge and experience of the jurors themselves. This situation arises when an ulterior act or omission occurs, the explanation of which does not require scientific opinion.

But where, as here, an injury to healthy tissue within the region of treatment constitutes an occurrence beyond the realm of the knowledge and experience of laymen, the issue of negligence with respect to that injury must be determined by expert testimony.

We think it is beyond dispute that the nerve roots which were damaged in the process of producing anesthesia by injecting the drug into the spinal cord are within the region of treatment and that the cause of this injury to the nerve roots and its effect on the leg and adjacent organs must be explained by experts. When the expert testimony offered by the plaintiff ascribes the cause to the toxic quality of the injected drug as distinguished from the negligence of the anesthetist, that evidence is binding upon the court and the jury would not be permitted to speculate to the contrary.

The gravamen of plaintiff's argument is that Dr. Haines negligently failed to follow the proper procedure in that he injected the anesthetic agent without first determining the cause of plaintiff's unconsciousness and that this was the proximate cause of the injury. It was not proved affirmatively that this defendant failed to ascertain the cause of unconsciousness, but, even if we assume this to be the fact, the causal connection between the omission and the injury was not shown and cannot be inferred. Since Dr. Rovensteine was unable to render an opinion as to whether the operation should have proceeded or whether it should have been stopped, a matter which clearly calls for expert testimony, it is axiomatic that a jury should not be permitted to hazard a guess.

In his reply brief, plaintiff attempts to remedy lack of proof by invoking the doctrine of *res ipsa loquitur*. We do not think the doctrine is available to him.

*Res ipsa loquitur* does not apply in malpractice cases where the injury is one which may occur even though proper care and skill are exercised. From the medical testimony, this seems to be the case sub judice.

The doctrine does not apply where common knowledge or experience is not sufficiently extensive to permit it to be said that the patient's condition would not have existed but for the negligence of the doctors. Here the record is barren of any accident, or ulterior act or omission, which produced the injury such as a "slip" or "awkward thrust" of an instrument, or the injection of a harmful substance into the spinal canal. The painful reaction to the puncture needle is described as a "common experience."

Nor is the doctrine available in a case based upon want of skill in diagnosis, method or manner of treatment. Here, the process of treating the nerve roots by a drug to produce anesthesia in an operation to remove an obstruction to the common duct certainly requires technical knowledge and skill. Because the unfortunate consequences suffered by plaintiff in themselves do not as a matter of common knowledge and experience reveal lack of skill in the anesthetist, scientific opinion is clearly necessary to throw light on the subject. Seldom, indeed, would physicians administer a spinal anesthetic if they are to be held responsible solely for an adverse reaction of the anesthetic on the nerve roots.

In view of the foregoing, we are not required to consider the interesting question of the liability of the surgeon for negligence of the anesthetist.

The judgment will be affirmed.

## ANALYSIS

1. What were the facts upon which the plaintiff contended that the doctrine of *res ipsa loquitur* should be invoked?

2. The court in denying the use of the doctrine as a means of proof for the plaintiff pointed out that it did not apply where proper care had been used. Using the three basic steps necessary to invoke the doctrine of *res ipsa loquitur*, can you from the facts support that none of the required criteria were met? Do you agree that the doctrine was properly denied?

3. What does the court say about an inference of negligence?

4. In further reasoning denying the doctrine of *res ipsa loquitur*, how does the court deal with diagnosis and manner of treatment?

## CASES FOR FURTHER ANALYSIS

### *Sherman v. Hartman*, 137 Cal.App.2d 589, 290 P.2d 894 (1955)

The plaintiff was admitted to the hospital for a hysterectomy to be performed by the defendant surgeon. During the operation a blood transfusion was started by the anesthetist. On the patient's return to the room, both the surgeon and the anesthetist evaluated her condition and the rate of flow of the transfusion. The surgeon instructed the nurse to watch the patient's blood pressure and, because the patient would not be conscious for two hours, assumed that a nurse would be in constant attendance. About half an hour later, when the nurse had left the patient with an orderly to go to lunch, the needle came out of the vein. The surgeon was not called, and an unnamed physician came in and started the transfusion again. When the surgeon called in two hours, the patient had a "painful infusion of blood into the right arm from leaking blood" (about 200 ml had infiltrated into the soft tissues). The patient sued the doctor and the hospital for injury to the arm.

The jury found for the defendant doctor and, on appeal, the refusal of the trial court to invoke the doctrine of *res ipsa loquitur* as to him was upheld. The court agreed that two of the three conditions of the doctrine were met, namely, that (1) the accident was one that did not ordinarily occur in the absence of someone's negligence, and (2) the accident was not due to any voluntary conduct by the plaintiff, but the court found the third element missing, i.e., that at the time of the injury the defendant did not have the exclusive control of the instrumentality causing the harm. The defendant had determined that the transfusion was working properly and, in accordance with good practice, left the patient in the hands of the registered nurse provided by the hospital. Therefore, the court concluded, the control was not in the defendant's hands but in those of the hospital employees; he had a right to assume that the nurse had the requisite training and knowledge to watch the transfusion and to call the surgeon if the needle slipped. Moreover, the court noted that there was direct evidence of negligence on the part of the nurse. The hospital took the position that it is common for needles to come out of the vein during a transfusion and that *res ipsa loquitur* should not apply here. Such contention, said the court, overlooks the evidence that such a common occurrence does not result in the condition the plaintiff suffered. It is, in this instance, the unsual result that causes the doctrine to apply and to require explanation from the defendant hospital.

### *Renrick v. City of Newark,* 74 N.J. Super. 200, 181 A.2d 25 (1962)

This was an action against the city based on the alleged malpractice of doctors and nurses at the hospital operated by the city. The suit was dismissed and the plaintiff appealed.

Plaintiff was admitted to the hospital in critical condition suffering from a ruptured gastric ulcer and diffused peritonitis requiring surgery; she was in complete shock during the operation and moribund during the postoperative period; her condition was so grave that multiple blood transfusions were given. A drug was given intravenously to overcome circulatory collapse, which was so extensive as to constitute a complete failure of the peripheral circulation. Plaintiff contended that the medication was given in such a negligent manner that severe burning and sloughing followed that required skin grafts and resulted in scarring. The plaintiff offered no expert testimony and relied on the common knowledge or experience of the lay jury to infer that the injury that occurred was caused by negligence in the administration of the drug. The court concluded this was not a proper case to invoke the aid of the doctrine of *res ipsa loquitur*, for it lacked the first essential requirement because the occurrence did not bespeak negligence. For all that laymen could properly infer, the damaging effect might well have followed the exercise of ordinary professional care. Judgment in favor of the defendant was affirmed.

### *Hurt v. Susnow,* 192 P. 2d 771 (Cal. App. 1948)

A malpractice action was brought against the surgeon for damages incurred in the course of his medical treatment of the plaintiff.

The plaintiff-patient entered a hospital for surgery to strip varicose veins; the evening before the operation the surgeon had the patient stand beside the bed while he outlined the veins to be removed with a silver nitrate pencil which he procured from the nurse and then dipped in water. Shortly thereafter, the area became inflamed, blisters appeared, and the surgery was canceled. The patient lost work as a result of the burn, suffered considerable pain, and some thirteen months after the date of the burn was still scarred. The surgeon testified that plaintiff had a very fair skin, that he knew that some people were susceptible to silver nitrate burns, that he had made no tests and had not inquired as to the strength of the silver nitrate solution. He also testified that it was common practice of the doctors in San Francisco to mark off the area to be operated upon with silver nitrate solution without first making tests.

On this evidence, the trial judge dismissed the case because in his view the plaintiff had failed to prove that the surgeon was negligent in any way. The plaintiff appealed on the grounds that she was under no obligation to prove negligence because the doctrine of *res ipsa loquitur* applied to the facts, because the injury was not one that would usually occur in the absence of negligence, and because the instrumentality causing the action was under the control of the defendant. The appellate court held that the doctrine of *res ipsa loquitur* was applicable under these circumstances, because severe burning of patients was not the normal result of the preparatory treatment for surgery to remove varicose veins, and that although the instrument causing the injury was not under the exclusive control of the defendant, the burden would be placed on both the nurse and the doctor to come forward with an explanation of what happened. Thus, the court said that an inference of negligence was raised. The court also said that because of the bias and prejudice of the defendant, his testimony alone in his defense would not suffice to rebut the inference of negligence.

The defense makes a forceful argument that under the facts of this case, negligence on the part of the physician or surgeon may not be presumed from the mere happening of an injury to the patient. The defense took the view that, although what happened could not be contended to be a normal result, it need not necessarily be attributed to negligence.

Suit was dismissed because the plaintiff failed to prove that the defendant surgeon was negligent and that he had not used the degree of learning and skill ordinarily possessed by physicians in his locality.

### Davis v. Memorial Hosp., 26 Cal. Rptr. 633, 376 P.2d 561 (1962)

Here, an action was brought against hospital for perirectal abscess and resulting fistula allegedly caused by an enema given by a nurse. A judgment was rendered for the defendant and the plaintiff appealed contending that refusal to give instructions on the doctrine of *res ipsa loquitur* was an error.

The plaintiff entered the hospital for surgery, and a preoperative enema was given. The patient stated that the enema was painful, that four attempts were made to insert the tube, and each time there was a sensation that some trauma had been inflicted. A few days after surgery a perirectal abscess was diagnosed that required several weeks of treatment and surgery to close the fistula. One medical expert witness testified that in his opinion the condition was due to a break in the mucous membrane, which permitted an infection to develop. Another expert denied that the enema was a causative factor. Since the applicability of the doctrine of *res ipsa loquitur* depended on the determination of a factual issue whether the giving of the enema was the cause of the plaintiff's injuries, it was for the jury to weigh the conflicting testimony. The decision was that there was sufficient evidence to permit an inference of negligence and to have withheld a conditional instruction on *res ipsa loquitur* was an error. The judgment was reversed.

## Recommended Source Material

TEXTS

Harper, F., and James, F., *The Law of Torts*, Vol. 2, 1075–1107 (Boston: Little, Brown & Co., 1956).

Louisell, D., and Williams, H., *The Parenchyma of Law*, 261 (Rochester: Professional Publications, 1960).

Louisell, D., and Williams, H., *Trial of Medical Malpractice Cases*, 87 (Albany: Matthew Bender & Co., 1960).

Prosser, W., *Handbook of the Law of Torts*, 215–39 (St. Paul: West Publishing Co., 3rd ed., 1964).

Shartel, B., and Plant, M., *The Law of Medical Practice*, 3–19 (Springfield, Ill.: Charles C Thomas, Publisher, 1959).

Stetler, C., Stetler, J., and Moritz, J., *Doctor, Patient and the Law*, 376–90 (St. Louis: C. V. Mosby Co., 4th ed., 1962).

PERIODICALS

Johnson, R., *Medical Malpractice—Doctrines of Res Ipsa Loquitur and Informed Consent*, 37 U. Colo. L. Rev. 182 (1965).
Markels, M., *Conspiracy of Silence*, 14 Clev. Mar. L. Rev. 520 (1965).
Prosser, W., *Res Ipsa Loquitur*, 37 Cal. L. Rev. 183 (1949).

# Chapter Seven

# Vicarious Liability

In the preceding chapters, detailed consideration has been given to the standards by which individual liability for negligence and breach of duty are determined in legal proceedings. These areas of the law have been analyzed to determine when and under what conditions a person may be said to be negligent, or in breach of duty. Throughout, we have concerned ourselves with the responsibility of an individual for his own actions. This individual responsibility has been developed in the previous discussion as the fault principle, that is, that liability is dependent upon fault, and without fault there is no legal responsibility.

Also discussed was the causation requirement, namely, that before liability is imposed upon an alleged tort feasor, a plaintiff must show not only wrongful conduct but also that the injury would not have occurred had it not been for the defendant's conduct.

We turn now to the idea of vicarious liability, where liability may be imposed without personal fault and without a causal connection between the actions of the one held liable and the injury. This takes place where one person— we shall call him A—is held legally responsible for another's—call him B— neglectful actions, even though A's conduct is above reproach. Such a situation occurs when there is a relationship of some kind between A and B. Usually, this relationship is one of the various species of employment; that is, A has hired B to do something in furtherance of A's interests. When, in the course of endeavoring to accomplish the result for A, B wrongfully or negligently injures a third person, A may have to bear the loss, that is, A may be held liable to the third person and be forced to compensate him for injuries suffered at B's hands.

The Houston Transit Company operated a bus line in Houston, Texas, and had in its employ a driver by the name of B. F. Goodson.

Mr. Guy Felder was driving his car one day through the Houston streets and doing such a poor job of it that he ran into the rear of one of the Transit Company buses, which was being driven by Mr. Goodson. Mr. Goodson alighted from his driver's seat, stepped back to Mr. Felder's car, and struck him full in the face with a money-changing box. Upon suit against the transit company for the wrongful conduct of its driver, the company contended that it did not hire its drivers to be pugilists and that as soon as Goodson hit Felder, the driver was no longer acting within the scope of his employment. The court rejected this argument, holding that the company was responsible for assaults by its employees, where the assault is closely connected with the performance of the employee's duties. [*Houston Transit Co. v. Felder*, 146 Tex. 428, 208 S.W.2d 880 (1948).]

The historical basis for vicarious responsibility has been attributed to the Romans, to the Germans, to the English, and to a combination of these. Early instances are found in ancient law making slave owners responsible for the actions of their slaves. The legal rule imposing liability on an employer in some circumstances is often referred to as the rule of *respondeat superior*, a Latin phrase meaning "let the master answer." The phrasing clearly reflects the fact that it is the employer, or master, whose liability is at issue. When and under what conditions liability under the doctrine of *respondeat superior* may be visited on an employer will occupy us in this chapter.

One factor must remain clear throughout this discussion: *in considering vicarious liability we are concerned with an expansion of liability to include the master as well as the employee and not a shift of liability from the employee to the master.* Nothing in the law of vicarious liability changes the unvarying principle that every person bears full responsibility for his own wrongful conduct; this principle applies regardless of how many other persons may also be liable. Therefore, when a person through negligence injures another, he is and remains fully responsible. Whether his employer is also liable depends upon the principles of vicarious liability, and the actor is not exonerated regardless of whether his employer is or is not held.

## Rationale of Vicarious Liability

What significance, then, does the whole matter have? If each of us is always liable for our own wrongful conduct, why does anyone care whether his employer is liable as well? Usually, the answer is obvious: money and the ability to pay. Because in any litigation where compensation is sought in dollars—and this includes all but a small percentage of civil litigation—actual compensation will be obtained if and only if the defendant can in fact pay. It is in the interest of every plaintiff to have as many financially responsible persons as defendants as he can legitimately find.

Damage awards for serious injuries can easily run into tens of thousands of dollars and relatively few persons are able to pay such amounts. However, it seems to be true in general that employers as a class are more able to respond to damage liability than are employees as a class. Thus, it becomes important in many cases for an injured party to establish existence of vicarious responsibility to avoid bearing the entire loss himself, because the prime actor in the drama is wholly unable to respond to a judgment running to very high sums.

Although this "deep pocket" theory gives sufficient reason for a victim to *want* to expand the scope of liability, it is clearly not sufficient reason for the courts to take the actual step and do it; if the wishes of plaintiffs determined the outcome of litigation, there would be very few verdicts for defendants. We must, therefore, search for the explanation and justification of the theory.

The first and perhaps the most persuasive justification is that such liability stems from the "feeling of justice which every man has." [Wigmore, J., *Responsibility for Tortious Acts*, 7 Harv. L. Rev. 383, 404 (1894).] If A. hires a person to do his business, and while doing it he injures another, should A. be permitted to disclaim responsibility? Why should A. not have to accept the burdens of his servant's actions, as well as the benefits? People may differ in their answer to be sure, but the strong reaction appears to be on the side of liability, not exoneration.

At the present time, the notion of fairness that seems to require employer liability can be expressed in economic terms; namely, that the employer is in a better position to bear the risk of loss because he can treat such losses as a cost of operating his business and can price his goods or services at such a level that this cost, like other costs, will be returned to him in the course of his business. In other words, his customers will, by paying slightly higher prices, provide the funds to finance payment of claims based on the wrongful conduct of his employees. The employer's competitors, so the theory goes, will not be unfairly advantaged because they will naturally have to follow the same course, at the risk of a money judgment against them which would seriously impede their operations. And furthermore, because all business enterprises will be compelled to do the same, the risks will be spread among all customers, which, because everyone is someone's customer, is the same as saying that the risk is spread throughout society as a whole. Thus, diffusion of the risk accomplishes two ends: it increases the likelihood that innocent victims will be compensated, and it leads to a broad distribution of costs so that no one group is crippled or hampered by the need to pay them.

The institution of readily purchasable liability insurance provides a perfect means for this risk spreading, because as a practical matter, employers can and will bear such costs by purchasing insurance rather than by building a fund for payment of claims. This makes the risk of spreading rationale for vicarious liability all the more valid because an existing business device is at hand to provide an easy way to obtain protection without an unreasonably high cost.

A second justification for the doctrine of vicarious liability arises from an analysis of how injuries can be prevented. It seems to be generally agreed that an employer is able and willing to bend his efforts toward eliminating accidents by and among his employees if he knows in advance that he will have to pay for their derelictions. He can do this by increased care in the initial selection of employees, by requiring safety measures to be adopted, and by generally insisting that his enterprise be conducted as safely as possible. Since prevention is the most socially desirable way of dealing with the accident problem, a legal rule imposing liability upon the employer, and thereby stimulating efforts toward accident prevention, is clearly desirable.

## Master-Servant Relationship and the Principle of Control

We have said that vicarious liability depends upon a relationship between the negligent person and the person or firm who may be liable under the doctrine of *respondeat superior*. Relationships among people naturally take a myriad of forms. Parent-child, the bonds of friendship, and employer-employee are simple illustrations. Unless we are prepared to say, as the law is not, that any such relationship leads to vicarious responsibility, a test must be devised to guide the determination of what relationships do, and what ones do not, lead to vicarious liability. The fundamental test of vicarious liability is *whether one party has the right to control the actions and conduct of the second*, and the basic relationship giving rise to the vicarious liability is known as the master-servant relationship. Here, the term "master" is used to designate the vicariously liable party, who possesses the right of control, and the term "servant" to designate the person whose conduct gives rise to the injury and whose actions are subject to control.

The so-called servant can perform duties from the most mundane to the most intellectually sophisticated duties; the range of activities of the master can be equally wide. By the control test, the research scientist working in company laboratories is as equally a servant as the keeper of the grounds, for though the details of the scientist's research are assuredly not controlled in any immediate sense, his projects and research efforts are subject to the right of control of his employer.

Although a simple idea of control suffices in many situations, a mere statement concerning right to control is not very refined when analysis is made of borderline cases. What, for example, of the salesman working on commission and driving his own car, who does not see his superior except at long intervals? If, in the course of driving from one prospective customer to the next, he negligently causes an accident, can it be said that he was controlled by his company? The company, perhaps, was wholly unaware of his activities, his customers, or even his whereabouts. What of a business consultant, who may be taking a trip on behalf of several clients? The answer to the question of whether an employer is liable in these and other marginal situations may be the subject of sharp dispute, and therefore, the only way to reach a conclusive determination is to examine all the circumstances, to view the relationship in all its intricacies, and to reach a determination after, and only after, weighing the various factors at work.

In practice, the question arises in the course of a lawsuit, where all the factors are brought to light in a trial. It becomes, then, a job for the jury, or other trier of fact, to say whether the requisite control can be found. In other words, the jury determines, after having heard all the evidence, whether the employer is vicariously liable. The factors which bear on the decision in a given case have been categorized in the following way [Restatement (Second) Agency §220 (1954)]:

Definition of Servant—(1) A servant is a person employed to perform services in the affairs of another and who with respect to the physical conduct in the performance of the services is subject to the other's control or right to control.

(2) In determining whether one acting for another is a servant or an independent contractor, the following matters of fact, among others, are considered:

(a) the extent of control which, by the agreement, the master may exercise over the details of the work;

(b) whether or not the one employed is engaged in a distinct occupation or business;

(c) the kind of occupation, with reference to whether, in the locality, the work is usually done under the direction of the employer or by a specialist without supervision;

(d) the skill required in the particular occupation;

(e) whether the employer or the workman supplies the instrumentalities, tools, and the place of work for the person doing the work;

(f) the length of time for which the person is employed;

(g) the method of payment, whether by the time or by the job;

(h) whether or not the work is a part of the regular business of the employer;

(i) whether or not the parties believe they are creating the relation of master and servant; and

(j) whether the principal is or is not in business.

One aspect is to be clearly understood: the many factors may make determination of the question difficult, but the grays become pure black and white when the jury reaches its conclusion. However many the factors, only two conclusions are possible: either there is liability or there is not. From the employer's point of view, therefore, either he is entirely responsible for what may be a large judgment or he goes scot-free; there is no generally accepted legal notion of partial control, or partial responsibility.

## SCOPE OF EMPLOYMENT

Even though control be found to exist, however, it would obviously be unfair and unjust to render the employer liable for *everything* that any of its employees might do to injure another person. If, for example, an employee negligently operated his car while on a weekend fishing trip, it would scarcely occur to anyone that his regular employer would be liable for his weekend activities. Some tests must therefore be devised to distinguish between the situation where an employee is clearly on his own time, and the other extreme where the employee, while engaged on the business expected by the employer, injures another. This test is broadly described as whether the conduct is "within the scope of employment." If it is within the scope of the employment, then vicarious liability exists and the employer, as well as the employee, will be liable for the torts of the employee. On the other hand, if the tort is committed by a person when he is not engaged on the master's business and when the tort is outside the scope of his employment, the mere fact that in the business world a person is an employee will not serve to render his employer liable.

Again, the decision may be difficult, and the result uncertain. Many factors can be involved in the determination of whether actions are within the scope of the employment. Obviously, there will be in many cases no unanimity in the conclusion, for different persons will attach different weight to the various factors. Some of the factors that may be taken into account are (1) the purpose of the allegedly negligent act and whose interest it was designed to serve, (2) the time and locale of the action and the circumstances generally surrounding it, (3) whether the action is frequently done by persons properly considered servants or whether it is normally done by each person for himself, (4) the degree to which the act departs from other actions of other servants, (5) whether the action is typical or whether it is abnormal and unusual, (6) whether in the past the servant has performed similar actions, (7) whether the master knew that the servant was performing such acts or whether he had reason to believe that the servant would in the normal course of events perform such acts, (8) whether the result sought in doing the act was a result authorized by the master, even though the means of obtaining such result might have been not authorized, (9) whether or not the instrument causing the harm was furnished by the master to the servant or whether it was the servant's own, (10) whether the act is criminal in character, and (11) what, in general, the employment was designed to be. In a law suit, the trier of fact will analyze and weigh all the factors and make the final determination as to whether a particular act is within the scope of the employee's employment.

### FROLIC AND DETOUR

Even when an employee is found to act within the scope of his employment generally speaking, there are still some limitations upon the liability of his employer. If, even though many of the tests of scope of employment are met, the employee was engaged in a frolic or detour of his own, the master will not be liable. A typical case raising this problem is that of a truck driver who leaves his assigned route for personal reasons. He may go around the block to buy a pack of cigarettes, or he may drive 100 miles to see his girlfriend. The question arises in these cases whether he has so far left the business for which he was employed that he can no longer be considered to be acting within the scope of employment. Likewise, a question may sometimes arise as to whether the employee has totally abandoned the business of his employer. An employee driving a company car may decide to steal the car and try to disappear. In the course of such efforts, he might be found to have abandoned the employer's business and therefore the employer would not be liable on vicarious principles, even though his employee, who had started out performing his day-to-day task, was guilty of negligence. Another limitation imposed in some jurisdictions is that the master is not liable for the intentional torts of his servants. Thus, when an employee insults or assaults the customer, the employer will in most jurisdictions in the United States not be held liable if it can be shown that the employee acted from purely personal motives. However, the converse may be true when the intentional tort is so intimately related to the employment as to be within its scope; e.g., a bouncer in a nightclub.

## Doctrine of the Borrowed Servant

As is frequently the case in the application of legal rules, there are exceptions to the basic proposition that an employer is liable for the negligence of his employee within the scope of employment. The exception occurs when the employee is temporarily engaged in performing his services not for his regular employer but for a second employer, because the two *employers* have agreed between themselves upon this allocation of the employee's efforts. Then the problem arises as to which of the two employers should be liable in the event that the servant commits a tort while engaged in the temporary service. The determination of this liability for the servant's torts is made through the "borrowed servant" doctrine, which states that when control of specific acts of a servant passes temporarily to a second master, that second master will be liable for the torts of the servant committed during the time the right of control lies with the second master. Note that we are here concerned with a *shift* in liability from the regular employer to the temporary one, and not with an expansion of liability to include both employers. (The employee, as always, remains liable for his own torts.) This borrowed servant issue arises frequently in cases involving nurses where the permanent employer of the nurse is a hospital and the temporary employer is a physician or surgeon.

In connection with the borrowed servant problem, consider the following hypothetical illustration.

A company—which we can call Crane Co.—is in the business of renting large cranes. Crane also hires and supplies the operators, who are highly trained in the use of the equipment. Construction Co., in the business of building skyscrapers, enters into a rental agreement with Crane, and upon the arrival of the crane at the construction site, its operator becomes subject to the orders and direction of Construction's foreman. In fact, Construction personnel are in complete charge of how the crane is to be used. While the crane is being used, the operator negligently drops a concrete slab, injuring a passerby below, who then sues both Crane and Construction. Assuming the crane operator was negligent, which company is liable?

There are valid arguments supporting the liability of Crane. Crane, after all, is in the crane business. It reaps the benefits of the operator's conduct, in the form of rental payments for its crane. Therefore, it would be in a position to treat the costs of potential tort liability as its cost, and charge accordingly. In other words, it is in a position to spread the risk. Likewise, it is in the best position to take preventive measures, in the form of better selection of employees, careful training, installation of safety devices, and the like.

On the other hand, Construction's business interests are also being furthered, in that it is, through the use of the crane, engaged in performing its construction contract. It too could spread the risk. Moreover, practically speaking, the right of control rests with it, not with Crane. Construction, in other words, really tells the operator what to do.

As might be expected, different courts reach different conclusions in assessing these considerations. Some cases would hold Crane; some Construction. The majority would be inclined to give the most weight to the control factor and permit recovery against Construction, rather than Crane.

## Independent Contractor

A very significant limitation upon the doctrine of vicarious responsibility is found in the rule that persons standing in the relationship of an independent contractor to an employer do not by tortious actions render their principal liable. An independent contractor is said to be one who has a relationship to another whereby he performs services for another, but where his physical activities in the performance of such services are not controlled by, or subject to the control of, the principal. Thus, in an action against an employer for the torts of an alleged servant, the employer may defend the suit on the grounds that the employee was not a servant but rather an independent contractor. It therefore frequently becomes important to set out guidelines for making this classification. As noted, the primary distinction is one of the right of control or control itself, and the factors entering into this decision are set forth *supra*, p. 237.

## Employer Responsibility for the Conduct of the Nurse Employee

The discipline of nursing is primarily one of concern for people; in fact, all of nursing practice revolves around people, those people to whom the nurse renders a direct service and those employing her to give this service. Being human, the nurse sometimes makes mistakes, and unhappy relations, to the point of legal involvement, can enter into her people-to-people contacts. When mistakes and injuries do occur, not only the nurse but also her employer may be held accountable. The employer may know little or nothing of the intricacies of nursing practice; he exercises no supervision over her practice and probably had no means of preventing the injury that did occur, and yet, he may be held responsible under the doctrine of vicarious liability. As has been pointed out, this is an expansion of liability and in no way relieves the nurse of her individual liability. Indeed in many instances, the physician, the nurse, and the employing agency of the nurse are all joined as defendants in lawsuits and at trial the employer-employee relationships as shown by the evidence will then determine who shall bear the cost of the harm done.

The agency that hires the nurse may be held responsible in two ways, one known as corporate liability and the other as vicarious liability. In the case of *Darling v. Charleston Community Hosp.*, *supra*, p. 139, the hospital was held liable both for its corporate negligence in failure to follow the organization channels it purported to have to effectuate good patient care and vicariously for the conduct of the nurses who failed to take affirmative action in the face of the deteriorating condition of the patient. At times, these two areas of legal responsibility are not so easily distinguished and the corporate negligence of the hospital may be such an intangible factor that the injury appears to be one of nursing mismanagement. For example, in hospitals, as in every other business endeavor, management is responsible for providing qualified personnel and equipment necessary to render safely the service it purports to give, and thus an injury occurring because of their lack may actually be due to failure on the part of administration.

To illustrate some situations that might lead to corporate liability: (1) a hospital, for the sake of economy, may digress from recognized standards and hire a preponderance of nonprofessional nurses with the result that an un-qualified worker might perform a task that brought about an injury to the patient; (2) a hospital might fail to recognize the need for continuing education for the nursing staff, such failure, leading to failure to provide for an active in-service program and failure to recognize the need for leaves of absence for study and attendance at workshops, could indefensibly limit the nursing staff in its efforts to keep abreast with advances of medical science to the point that a practitioner might be told to assume a responsibility for which she had not been given available preparation; (3) a hospital might fail to select qualified personnel and fail to instruct them in the theory and use of new equipment, thereby depriving the personnel of the necessary scientific knowledge and training in the mode of operation of the machine, both of which would be necessary for the safety of the patient.

We now move away from the role in which management itself may be the offending party to vicarious liability in which management may be innocent but nonetheless held responsible for the harm. The statement of an early English decision is equally appropriate today, "For whoever employs another, is answerable for him" [*Jones v. Hart* (Kings Bench, 1689)]. When the nurse explores her practice as it lies within the bounds of the legal doctrine of vicarious liability, certain legal principles fall into place, for the nurse has always been, and no doubt will continue to be, an employee in the true sense of the word. She also sees certain ambiguous relationships, largely uncategorized by the courts, that come about as a result of increasingly complex team practice and such a high degree of specialization that almost defies application of a concept of unified control. To seek some of the certainties and to identify the areas in nursing in the process of change are a part of viewing law as an essential component of patient care and nursing practice.

FACTORS DETERMINING LIABILITY IN EMPLOYER–NURSE RELATIONSHIPS

*Respondeat superior* is the legal doctrine by which the employer is held liable for the negligence of his employees that occurs within the scope of the employee's duties and in the process of furthering the employer's interests. On first reading this seems a clear and simple statement of a relationship.

Within the context of nursing practice, there is little doubt that legally the nurse is an employee. Among criteria the courts have developed to test employer-employee status, the most significant for the nurse is control. Control in this sense means that the employer has the power to hire, discharge, and determine the scope of employment for which he pays the employee a salary. For an employee to "control" another does not mean that the employer need have the knowledge or skills necessary to do the work himself or the ability to supervise or evaluate the quality of service being rendered, particularly in such highly specialized areas as medicine or nursing. That legal control is vested in another in no way dims professionalism, or freedom of creative action. As illustrated in the cases to follow, the subject of control is many times the legal issue upon which the case turns and one that frequently is a question for the jury.

In *Moeller v. Hauser*, 237 Minn. 368, 54 N.W.2d 639 (1952), an action was brought by the father for negligent treatment of his minor son by residents, interns, and nurses employed by a hospital managed by a county welfare board. The plaintiff, a five-year-old boy, sustained a simple fracture of the middle third of the right femur and was admitted to the defendant hospital where his leg was placed in traction. His care was chiefly under the resident doctor, interns, and nurses, with some indirect supervision of the chief of staff of the service. About a month after his admission the boy complained of pain, and when the leg was taken out of traction it was found that a severe pressure sore had developed with ulceration, necrosis, and tendon involvement to the degree that surgery was necessary. The result was a partial permanent disability. The decision to hold the hospital liable turned on the fact that the resident, interns, and nurses received compensation from the hospital while they provided routine hospital care and as such the hospital was liable for their negligence under the doctrine of *respondeat superior*.

A basic requirement that must be met before a nurse's employer will be liable for the negligent conduct of the nurse is that the negligent conduct fall within the scope of employment. In ordinary nursing situations, questions concerning the "scope of employment" test might not be raised as frequently as for traveling employees who carry on activities far from a central base of operation, but the same tests nevertheless apply. For example, consider the nurse who is invited to speak in another part of the state on a nursing phase of coronary care being implemented under her direction in the hospital where she is employed. En route to the meeting, she is negligent in her driving and collides with another car, injuring several people. Did the accident fall within the scope of her employment and could her employer be held accountable? It is probable that most courts would take the position that she was so acting. The scope of employment of the public health nurse working on a state or regional basis might allow for a wider geographic area but would be as clear in employer relationship as that of the nurse acting within the immediate range of the employer's office in a hospital.

Instances are numerous in which the courts have recognized both control and scope of employment and applied the doctrine of *respondeat superior*. In *Goff v. Doctors General Hosp.*, 166 Cal. App. 2d 214, 333 P.2d 29 (1958), the court stated:

> Any liability of the appellant hospital must necessarily be predicated on the doctrine of respondeat superior so we must determine whether there is any evidence in the record which would support a finding that either of the nurses was negligent, since Doctor Ashley was not an employee of the hospital. . . . A hospital is liable for want of ordinary care whether from incompetency of a nurse or failure in duty by a fully qualified nurse. . . .

Another illustration of the use of this doctrine is in *Norton v. Argonaut Ins. Co. (supra*, p. 189):

> . . . it is settled jurisprudence of this state that a hospital is responsible for the negligence of its employees including, inter alia, nurses and attendants under the doctrine of respondeat superior.
>
> In the case at bar it was not disputed that Mrs. Evans was not only an employee of the hospital but that on the day in question she was in charge of the entire institution as the senior employee on duty at the time.

If the question of the role of the nurse is disputed, it will usually be left to the jury to decide, as in *O'Neill v. Montifiore Hosp.*, 11 A.D.2d 132, 202 N.Y.S.2d 436 (1960), where it was held that it was a jury question whether the nurse in the emergency room who called the physician was doing so as a favor to the deceased or as an employee of the hospital.

SHIFTING CONTROL—A FACTOR IN SHIFTING LIABILITY

In the application of the doctrine of *respondeat superior*, seldom is the issue of control more difficult to resolve than in problems that arise concerning physician-hospital-nurse relationships. Interns, residents, and nurses are primarily the employees of the hospital, but under certain conditions, the employee may become the borrowed servant of another master. The basic test of legal responsibility then is not whether the servant was in the actual employ of the master, but rather who exercised the control at the time of the negligent act. The surgical team in the operating room has so frequently been under legal scrutiny, in terms of control, that a concept called the "captain of the ship" doctrine has grown from the legal decisions; the doctrine simply sets forth that the surgeon is responsible for the conduct of all members of the team while in the operating theater. This holding is exemplified by *Beadles v. Metakya*, 135 Colo. 366, 311 P.2d 711 (1957), in which the surgeon was held for giving conflicting instructions to an orderly and the orderly carried them out without giving due consideration to the safety of the patient, with the result that the patient rolled from the operating table and was injured. With present-day advances in medical science and surgery, the surgical team is becoming complex and highly specialized in its functioning, and justification of one-man control will be increasingly difficult. It can be expected that the law will be sensitive to these changing relationships, will take into account the diffusion of medical responsibility, and, as time goes on, will look with less favor on the "captain of the ship" doctrine. Thus in *Thompson v. Lillehei*, 164 F.Supp. 716 (D.Minn. 1958), the court held that evidence was insufficient that the defendant surgeon, responsible only for a heart operation on a patient, had vicarious responsibility for actions taken by other doctors who were allegedly negligent in respect to the plaintiff, who was to act as donor in a controlled cross-circulation heart operation on the patient. If in a complicated surgical procedure such as the one in the *Thompson* case a nurse was negligent and the hospital exonerated for such negligence under the borrowed servant doctrine, it would have to be determined, on the basis of allocation of responsibility within the surgical team, which physician, if any, would be responsible for her conduct.

It is a debatable question whether the nurse as a member of a surgical team is a borrowed servant, responsive only to the orders of the surgeon, or whether she carries on certain independent functions which the surgeon does not direct but which he relies upon her to perform as a part of the total surgical process. In the case of *Rural Educ. Ass'n. v. Bush*, 42 Tenn. App. 34, 298 S.W.2d 761 (1956), a sponge case, the court's conclusion was that the nurse was the employee of the hospital and not the borrowed servant of the physician. It stated:

It is the custom and practice that the operating surgeon is in complete charge of the surgery room and all personnel connected with the operation. In matters of professional skill or decision, it is the duty of the personnel (nurses, the anesthetists, and any others who may assist) to obey explicitly the orders of the surgeon. There are many matters, however, which do not involve professional skill or decision on the part of the surgeon. It is the custom and practice for the nurses to count the sponges which are taken into the surgery room. After the operation, and before the incision is closed, the nurses again count the sponges which have not been used, then count the sponges which have been used, and see if they total the number originally brought into the surgery room. . . . The surgeon relies upon the nurses for this sponge count. Before closing the incision, the surgeon inquires of the nurses about the sponge count. If they assure him the sponge count is correct, he closes the incision.

In the case at trial, Dr. Schuler made such inquiry about the sponges and was informed by the scrub nurse that the sponges were accounted for. Whereupon the surgeon closed the incision. The nurse, however, made a mistake.

At what point in patient care does a nurse cease to be an employee of the hospital and come under the control of the physician? The case of *Clary v. Christensen*, 54 Ohio L.Abs. 254, 83 N.E.2d 644 (Ohio Ct. App. 1948), deals with this issue. There, the plaintiff suffering from an abscess of the lung was sent to the operating room where a special type of machine was to be used. In preparation for the operation, the surgeon had stated which of two kinds of machines he chose to use; when he arrived at the hospital the operating room was in readiness and the machine was in place. The surgeon tested it and found it in good condition and left to scrub for the operation. In his absence, the machine was replaced for another and the doctor was not advised. In that the machine was operated by foot pedals and the patient was draped, the surgeon had no way of knowing he was using a machine other than the one he had tested. The result was that the patient received a severe burn on the outer surface of the right thigh where the leg rested on an electrode of the machine.

The decision was that the scrub nurse was an employee of the hospital charged with the duty of preparing the operating room and instruments and that the surgeon was not liable for the injury for he did not direct the manner or mode of preparing the room for operation.

This decision reflects the general rule in borrowed servant cases involving nurses, namely, that if the surgeon is vicariously held for the nurse's misconduct as a borrowed servant, it will be for conduct in an operating room or emergency room situation. Errors made by nurses in preoperative preparation, and in postoperative care, even if made in the course of carrying out the doctor's instructions, are generally held to be the responsibility of the primary employer, the hospital, rather than the doctor.

Fragmentation of the surgeon's responsibility for the actions of others in the care of the patient will undoubtedly continue as surgery and medicine become increasingly specialized. If this development represents a danger to the patient in terms of financial recovery, it is offset by increasing recognition of the vicarious liability, through elimination of charitable and sovereign immunities, of the hospital and other health agencies.

INDEPENDENCE OF NURSING CONDUCT VERSUS STATUS AS AN INDEPENDENT CONTRACTOR

To this point the nurse's position has been analyzed as falling within one of two categories in her employment relationships, either that of the direct employee of the hospital or another community agency, or as the borrowed employee of the physician. In either instance, the employer may be held vicariously liable for her negligent conduct.

For members of some professions there is a third employment category, the independent contractor. The independent contractor contracts to render a service but is not subject to specific direction from the contractor, such as the private practitioner of medicine, the house painter, the lawyer, or the taxicab driver. Whether or not the nurse ever functions in the capacity of an independent contractor is an open question. However, before discussing the position of the nurse within the legal framework of the independent contractor, the way the term is used in nursing practice should be clarified. Even though the nurse exercises numerous independent functions, as she frequently does in observing, reporting, making complex judgments, and teaching others, she is nonetheless the legal employee of the agency that hired her. Although it is true that the independence of her practice more and more places her in situations where she is likely to become involved in litigation, this independence in no way minimizes the vicarious liability of her employer. Contrast this point of view with that of the legal concept of the independent contractor. A question could be raised whether the nurse is ever hired to render nursing service free from control of her employer. If such were the case, she could well be held to be an independent contractor, and her employer would not be liable for her misconduct. If she were at fault in the care of her patient, she alone would bear the cost of the injury.

The courts have occasionally taken the attitude that the physician or surgeon is an independent contractor, even though employed and paid by the hospital, reasoning that so specialized is his preparation in this area that he could not be regarded as acting as a servant or in an employee capacity. The opposite position has been taken in holding the hospital responsible for the acts of its employed physicians, however specialized. Here courts, with much more force and logic, reason that failure to exercise the right of control does not diminish its power, and that the hospital like all other employers is in a superior position to distribute the risk for the tortious conduct of its employees.

By contrast, the self-employed surgeon who agrees to remove the appendix of the patient is an independent contractor of the patient, who is selling the product of his service free from any stipulation on the part of the patient-employer regarding how the surgeon intends to carry out the work. Similarly, even though he has staff privileges at hospitals, he diagnoses and treats his patients essentially free from direct hospital control.

From the standpoint of the nature of the calling, the nurse is sometimes viewed as an independent contractor. The analogy to the legal status is weak, however, unless the role of the private duty or special nurse is considered. Here she is hired by the patient and it could be argued clearly that her relationships conform to the criteria for an independent contractor, in that except for personal requests, the patient has no control over the manner in which her work is done. It is true that when the patient is in the hospital, the nurse is under the nominal supervision of the hospital nursing service staff, but this does not usually change her relationship with her patient, and does not make her subject to the direct control of the hospital. Although the control of the hospital might be limited, another factor clouding the nurse's status as an independent contractor is that she is at all times working under the medical orders of the physician who is himself an independent contractor. Therefore, she could under proper circumstances be the physician's employee rather than an independent contractor of the patient.

A developing legal theory that could reverse reasoning exonerating hospitals from liability for the torts of private duty nurses is that if the hospital is to be considered legally responsible for all medical care given within its walls, as in *Darling v. Charleston Community Hosp., supra*, p. 139, then it must concern itself with the selection and the conduct of the private duty nurse. If the trend is toward increasing liability for the hospital, administrative policy in this area might well be examined, in the interest of the hospital's own defense, if an injury should occur to a patient.

Louisell and Williams bring together conflicting reasoning [Louisell, D., and Williams, H., *Trial of Medical Malpractice Cases*, 502 (New York: Matthew Bender & Co., Inc., 1968)]:*

Perhaps in this area the safest generalization is: increasing realistic judicial appraisal of such problems today makes it unlikely that a private duty nurse will be held to be an agent of the patient unless it is clear that the patient himself made arrangements for her employment and her negligence was committed beyond the boundaries of ordinary supervision by the physician or regular hospital employees.

## Immunities: An Exception to Liability

The liability of the employer for the wrongful conduct of his employees is not absolute but is subject to some exceptions. In other words, some employers are better off than others because they can avoid liability for the torts of those who carry on the day-to-day operation of their business. These employers are two basic kinds: governmental entities and charitable organizations. Because they are protected, or immunized, from liability by virtue of their status, the legal principles establishing and defining the boundaries of that protection are referred to as the doctrines of sovereign or governmental immunity and charitable immunity, respectively.

* Reprinted with permission of Matthew Bender & Co., 235 E. 45th St., New York.

The doctrine of *respondeat superior* and the liability of employers for the employees' torts is a very significant one in today's world. Much tort litigation names employers as defendants, and often the imposition of liability on an employer is essential to the plaintiff, because the employer will be the only party with sufficient financial resources to respond to a judgment, or the employer will be the only one who carries insurance. From the frequency of cases in which the employer is the only one able to provide fair compensation for injuries, it follows that doctrines permitting some employers to escape liability on an immunity theory are also important. By such rules, the entire economic burdens of a negligently caused injury may be shifted from the employer, a financially responsible party, to the injured person. The result, of course, will be that the injured party, through absolutely no fault of his own, will bear the entire loss arising from an injury. Such a result is out of step with legal thinking that allocates loss in accordance with the principle that the person who is in a position to distribute loss should in the first instance bear legal responsibility. We should expect the courts, therefore, to be extremely reluctant to grant immunity from liability, or at the very least, if such immunity is granted, to do so only on the basis of the clearest possible policy and the soundest reasoning. Unfortunately, our expectations along these lines will not be borne out, and we will find that the legal problems involved in various forms of immunity are complex and highly variable from jurisdiction to jurisdiction. Therefore, it is exceedingly difficult to say what "the law" of sovereign immunity or charitable immunity is. We will in this section only attempt to present some general principles and theories behind the immunity rules, and not to describe with precision the law of any particular jurisdiction.

## SOVEREIGN IMMUNITY

Generally speaking, federal, state, and local governments are held to be immune from liability for the wrongful acts of their agents or employees, even though those wrongful acts are committed in the scope of the governmental employment.

This is somewhat paradoxical, in view of the emphasis we have placed on the theory of vicarious liability and on the ability of the employer to distribute the risk, for federal and state governments are probably better able than any private employer to spread the burden of tort liability among all those who use or benefit by governmental services. That is, the government could, if it chose, pay for the compensation of those persons injured by the actions of its employees by taxation of the entire citizenry, so that the burden on any one person arising from the torts of government employees would be minimal, and in no event would it be borne by a single person, i.e., the victim.

Governmental immunity derives from historical origins, not from logic or policy. The basis for governmental immunity can be traced to the old English idea that "the king could do no wrong." Because the king, that is, the sovereign, the government, was incapable in the ancient view of committing a tort, naturally no liability could be imposed upon him. The doctrine jumped to America in the early days of independence. Since that time, unless federal, state, or local governments consent to be sued, the immunity rule has had wide acceptance. The case for and against immunity has been concisely stated by one authority in the tort field. [Harper, F., and James, F., *The Law of Torts*, Vol. 2, 1611–12 (Boston: Little, Brown & Co., 1956)]:*

Governmental immunity has sometimes been defended on grounds of policy. The argument is fourfold: (1) funds devoted to public purposes should not be diverted to compensate for private injuries; (2) "the public service would be hindered, and the public safety endangered, if the superior authority could be subjected to suit at the instance of every citizen, and, consequently, controlled in the use and disposition of the means required for the proper administration of the Government"; (3) that liability would involve the government "in all its operations, in endless embarrassments, and difficulties, and losses, which would be subversive of the public interests"; and (4) that unlike private enterprise, the government derives no profit from its activities. To these arguments it may be answered in part (1) that since the public purposes involve injury-producing activity, the injuries thus caused should be viewed as a part of the activity's normal cost, and no one suggests that it is a diversion of public funds to pay the costs of public enterprise even if payment is made to private persons; (2) that while control of government activity by private tort litigation may be involved where the alleged tort is legislative action or the making of some high-level policy decision, no such thing is involved in ordinary accident cases; (3) that the direct cost of making compensation by the government will not exceed the sum of the losses suffered by the hapless victims of government activity, and that it is better to distribute these losses widely among the beneficiaries of government than to let them rest on the individual victims; that the embarrassments and expenses incidental to defending accident suits are also a part of the just social cost of operations that cause injuries and have never stifled comparable private enterprise; and finally (4) that, though the government as an entity does not profit from its enterprises, yet (it is devoutly to be hoped) the taxpaying public does, and it is the taxpaying public which would bear the costs of government tort liability.

### FEDERAL TORT CLAIMS ACT

The federal government has waived its sovereign immunity in many situations by the passage of the Federal Tort Claims Act.

The basic provision of the Act is found in 28 U.S.C. §2674, which provides in part:

* Reprinted with permission of Little, Brown & Co.

The United States shall be liable, respecting the provisions of this title relating to tort claims, in the same manner and to the same extent as a private individual under like circumstances. . . .

It follows from this provision that the United States, as an employer, is liable for the tortious conduct of its employees, just as we have seen the private employer bears legal responsibility for his employees guilty of negligent conduct within the scope of their employment. By a separate section of the statute, 28 U.S.C. §2671, members of the military forces are expressly included among those to be categorized as employees of the government, for the purposes of imposing tort liability.

As in many cases involving private employers, usually there is no dispute about whether a particular tortfeasor was an employee of the United States or not. A salaried employee, at whatever level of government, easily fits within this category, and salaried employees naturally constitute an overwhelming percentage of governmental employees who become guilty of torts. Only in certain marginal situations, such as employees of national guard units not on active duty, are there questions raising directly the issues of whether the United States bears such a relationship to an alleged tortfeasor to render it liable.

Many of the activities of the United States are not those normally found in the private sector of our country. Perhaps the farthest removed from private activities is the maintenance by the United States government of military forces. The question therefore arises whether the United States is liable to military personnel who are injured in the course of performing their military service by torts of other government employees.

As the final arbiter of interpretation of the acts of Congress, the Supreme Court has answered the question in the negative. In a series of cases, it is held that servicemen on active duty may not recover from the government for injuries incurred that were incident to the military service. The contrary result is reached when the injuries are not incident to the military service of the victim, or are incurred after discharge of the individual from the military service.

This result is justified on two principal grounds. First, there is no relationship in private life like that of a member of the military service to his government. Therefore, because United States government liability under the terms of the act is predicated upon "like circumstances," the act's terms are not complied with. Second, an elaborate and complete compensatory scheme is in effect for injured servicemen, ranging from disability payments and pensions to death benefits. The dependents, or survivors, of deceased military personnel are the beneficiaries of similar statutes. Given the fact, therefore, that Congress has already enacted a comprehensive scheme of compensating for injuries, there is no need for additional compensation to be provided by the Federal Tort

Claims Act. Therefore, according to the reasoning of the Supreme Court, the Act does not apply to those in military service.

In addition to the military exception, the statute itself provides a long list of exceptions to the application of the Act. These include claims arising from loss of mail, detention of goods by the customs officers, torts arising in foreign countries, damages for imposing quarantine, damages allegedly arising from the operation of the monetary system, and other exceptions. Two exceptions are of special significance to nurses. These are 28 U.S.C. §2680(a), which provides that the consent to suit embodied in the Federal Tort Claims Act shall not apply to

Any claim . . . based upon the exercise or performance or the failure to exercise or perform a discretionary function or duty on the part of a federal agency or an employee of the Government, whether or not the discretion involved be abused.

It is clear that nearly every activity performed by humans can be said to involve some discretion. The operation of a motor vehicle, perhaps the single most frequent cause of tort claims against the government, involves many discretionary decisions by the driver every minute throughout a trip. Similarly, the policy decisions made at the cabinet level of government equally involve exercise of discretion by those entrusted with the responsibility of making them. The second of these types of decisions is within the scope of the exception, whereas the discretion involved in the operation of a motor vehicle is clearly outside the scope of the exception. All the various decisions made by governmental employees can be ranged somewhere along this scale. In each individual case, therefore, when the government urges upon a court that suit under Federal Tort Claims Act is barred by the discretionary-function exception, the court must make a determination whether or not the activity allegedly engaged in by the government employee is of the type that should be insulated from suit, or whether the reverse is true. Broadly speaking, the courts have tried to draw the line between "operational" decisions—those involved in the day-to-day business of doing whatever it is the employee is to do—and "policy" decisions, which are basically decisions as to overall courses of governmental action. The line, though fuzzy, appears to be workable in practice.

The second principal exception is for certain kinds of intentional torts, particularly assault and battery. These are set forth in 28 U.S.C. §2680(h), which excepts from governmental liability

Any claim arising out of assault, battery, false imprisonment, false arrest, malicious prosecution, abuse of process, libel, slander, misrepresentation, deceit, or interference with contract rights.

This section has been held to bar a claim for an unauthorized surgical operation, where a military veteran had been admitted to a Veterans Administration hospital in connection with a medical problem of his left leg, and his right leg had been operated on. Because operation without the requisite consent is considered to be assault and battery, the court held the claim to be barred.

Nurses working in government service are subject to these rules. A nurse in federal employment may be either the injured party, injured by another government employee in the course of her duties, or she may be the employee who negligently inflicts an injury upon a patient in one of the many and varied types of governmental hospitals. In her capacity as a plaintiff—that is, as an injured party—she will be subject to the exception from liability if she is on active duty in a military service, and if the injury is incident to her service; for example, the nurse who submits to surgery by a medical officer and the surgery is negligently done, or the nurse who is struck by a government-owned jeep when she is on her way to another ward in an adjacent building. If the injury is found to be incident to her service, she will have only the remedies provided in other compensatory statutes, and will have no remedy under the Tort Claims Act.

To the extent that the nurse is injured while acting as a government employee, but not in the military service, she will have the same rights as nonmilitary governmental employees.

Likewise, when a nurse is involved in injury to a patient under her care, the patient's ability to recover from the government will depend on whether his status is as a member of the military or a civilian. Only the latter always has a right of recovery under the act. The military man is always limited in his rights of recovery to those injuries that were not an incident to his service.

## CHARITABLE IMMUNITY

The second category of immunity is the immunity of charitable, or eleemosynary, institutions. Although this immunity is of particular importance to hospitals, where the doctrine finds its most frequent application, it applies equally to all institutions with charitable purposes.

To be classified as "charitable," an organization must fulfill two basic requirements. First, it must furnish services that benefit society as a whole, and that are generally available. Second, the profits of the organization must not inure to the benefit of private persons. In other words, to obtain the benefit of immunity, a charitable institution must not exist to further the pecuniary interest of any person or group.

It is impossible to give any brief statement of the status of the doctrine of charitable immunity that would be applicable in all jurisdictions. There are numerous qualifications and limitations, one or more of which find favor in many states. Broadly speaking, three judicial views of immunity can be found.

First, there is complete immunity from any and all liability for all negligent actions of any employees of the charity. Second, and at the other end of the spectrum, are those jurisdictions that have eliminated immunity altogether, and judge the vicarious liability of a charitable enterprise by the same standards applicable to profit-making organizations. Third, there is partial immunity, where the immunity exists in some circumstances but not in others.

The permutations of the rules conferring partial immunity are many, and the application of these rules is frequently very difficult. Thus, a common qualification is that the immunity does not apply where so-called "strangers" to the charity are injured. Thus, a motorist run down by an ambulance belonging to a charitable hospital may be entitled to compensation as a stranger, whereas the patient riding in the ambulance, as a beneficiary of the charity, would be unable to recover. A second rule applies the immunity principle only to cases not involving "corporate negligence." Corporate negligence is defined as negligent conduct involving injury to persons to whom a particular duty is owed. Under this theory, patients accepted by a charitable hospital are entitled to expect competently administered care, and are owed a duty of such care. Therefore, if this duty is breached by the hospital or its employees, no immunity will be granted, and the patient may recover. The corporate negligence theory of immunity is directly inconsistent with the "stranger" theory, for the person to whom a particular duty is owed will often be the very one who is *not* a stranger. Third, some states hold that a charitable institution is immune except where one of its employees injures another employee. Still another rule imposes liability on charity only to the extent that the charity has insurance coverage, and not otherwise. Thus, a patient injured in a hospital whose board of directors had seen fit to bear the cost of insurance premiums would be compensated, but the patient unfortunate enough to be hurt in a hospital whose directors were not so concerned with the well-being of its patients would bear the loss himself.

The reasons given by the courts for permitting any charitable immunity have been roundly and universally criticized, as have the inconsistency and difficulty of the various limitations. The rule apparently appeared first in England in 1839, but was repudiated there in 1866. In America, the doctrine gained a foothold in the middle of the nineteenth century and its scope was gradually extended until the classic case of *President and Directors of Georgetown College v. Hughes*, 130 F.2d 810 (D.C.Cir. 1942), *infra*, p. 259, which apparently initiated a trend toward the elimination of immunity by both legislative and judicial action.

The initial reasoning supporting immunity viewed liability of a charity as a diversion of funds from the purposes intended by the donors supporting the charity to one they did not have in mind when the donation was made, and thought that donations to charities would be discouraged by the imposition of liability. Other theories supporting immunity include the notion that the recipient or beneficiary of a charitable institution, i.e., a nonpaying person, implicitly waives any right of recovery, and the concept that vicarious liability is related to profit-making enterprises alone. These reasons all seem to fall before the fundamental idea that an injured party should not be required to bear the loss suffered without fault of his own. Moreover, it can be empirically observed that charities continue to prosper in states where there is no immunity, and, in any event, the basis for financial support of many charities, including hospitals, has long since shifted from donation as a major source of revenue. Therefore, a distinct trend away from immunity is seen.

## NOTES

### (1) Distinction Between Medical and Administrative Acts

From the early days of the establishment of the doctrine of charitable immunity, which granted to charitable institutions complete freedom from potential liability for the tortious conduct of their employees, there have been limitations and qualifications imposed on the doctrine, which had the effect of narrowing its scope. We have seen that the logical foundations of the doctrine were weak from the very outset, and the injustice of its application a cause for concern and comments from judges, lawyers, and citizens alike. One of these distinctions was that drawn by the courts between "administrative" acts and "medical" acts of hospital personnel. Administrative acts that led to injury were, under this theory, chargeable to the hospital under the principle of *respondeat superior*. By contrast, medical acts that resulted in injury, were not chargeable to the hospital and the charitable immunity doctrine prevented recovery by those injured. The leading case implementing the administrative-medical distinction was *Schloendorff v. Society of New York Hospital*, 211 N.Y. 125, 105 N.E. 92 (1914). In that case, the patient alleged that she had expressly notified the physician that she was not to be operated on, but in spite of this instruction she was taken at night from the medical ward to the surgical ward and prepared for an operation by a nurse. Plaintiff claimed that she told the nurse that she was not going to be operated on, but was merely going to be examined under the influence of ether. The nurse informed her that preparation for ether examination was the same as the preparation for an operation. This examination was undertaken at midnight, and the following day the plaintiff was operated on and a tumor removed. Following the operation, and apparently as a result of it, gangrene developed in the left arm and some of her fingers had to be amputated.

In spite of the fact that substantial injury had been done to the plaintiff, the court held the hospital not liable because the relationship between the hospital and the doctors and nurses was not that of master-servants, but, so to speak, of an independent contractor because of the independence and skill the physicians and nurses had to exercise in carrying out their "medical functions."

At the same time, the court recognized that many of the functions carried out by nurses and doctors are in furtherance of the hospital's duty to provide a suitable setting for treatment. This category of conduct the court referred to as "administrative," and indicated that liability would be imposed for such conduct.

The difficulty with the administrative-medical distinction was that it proved exceedingly difficult to administer consistently and fairly. No ready distinction could be drawn between conduct merely designed to further treatment, or set the stage, and the treatment itself. Consequently, the result came to be over a long period of time that different people, who would have very similar injuries, would be treated differently by the law. This difficulty, coupled with the overall objections to the immunity doctrines that were being felt throughout the country, led the New York Court of Appeals finally to over-rule the *Schloendorff* doctrine.

This they did in the case of *Bing v. Thunig*, 2 N.Y.2d 656, 143 N.E.2d 3 (1957). In that case, the patient had been severely burned during the course of an operation when, preparatory to an operation, both the anesthetist and nurses applied a benzylkonium solution to the operative area. The nurses were fully aware that the inflammable antiseptic employed was potentially dangerous, and they admitted that they had been instructed not only to exercise care to see that none of the fluid dropped on the linen, but to inspect it and to remove any that had become stained or contaminated. This they failed to do, and when the doctor began the operation with an electric cautery, "there was a smell of very hot singed linen," whereupon the surgeon doused the area with water. After the operation, examination revealed severe burns on the patient's body, and showed that several holes had been burned through the sheet under her. The case had been dismissed in a lower court, upon the theory that the nurses had been performing a "medical act," and therefore the hospital was not liable. Pointing out the difficulties and inconsistencies in the application of this distinction, the higher court held that it was no longer to be drawn, and that henceforth, in New York, immunity for medical acts was dead. With respect to some of the difficulties the drawing of a line between the two types of acts had produced, the court said, referring to its varied decisions in earlier cases,

Placing an improperly capped hot water bottle on a patient's body is administrative, while keeping a hot water bottle too long on a patient's body is medical. Administering blood, by means of a transfusion, to the wrong patient is administrative, while administering the wrong blood to the right patient is medical. Employing an improperly sterilized needle for a hypodermic injection is administrative, while improperly administering a hypodermic injection is medical. Failing to place sideboards on a bed after a nurse decided that they were necessary is administrative, while failing to decide that sideboards should be used when the need does exist is medical. [Citations omitted.]

The position that a hospital is not responsible for medical acts undertaken by its employees is carried to the fullest extreme by decisions holding that any conduct, however careless and negligent, undertaken by a physician who is an employee of the hospital is not chargeable to the hospital on a *respondeat superior* principle. An instance is *Moon v. Mercy Hosp.*, 150 Colo. 430, 373 P.2d 944 (1962), where the reasoning of the court was that the hospital was not responsible because it could not be licensed to practice medicine, that being an area solely within the skills of the doctor.

In a recent case, an attempt was made to extend this reasoning to exonerate a hospital for the conduct of an employed nurse. *Bernardi v. Community Hosp. Ass'n.*, 443 P.2d 708 (Colo. 1968). There, a seven-year-old patient in the hospital had been the subject of surgery for the drainage of an abscessed appendix. Her doctor had left a written postoperative order that she was to be given an injection of tetracycline every twelve hours. During the evening of the first day following surgery, a nurse employed by the hospital and acting under the order injected the dosage of tetracycline in the patient's right gluteal region. The complaint alleged that the nurse had negligently injected the tetracycline into or adjacent to the sciatic nerve, causing the little girl to have a complete foot drop and to lose permanently the normal use of her right foot.

Prior to trial, and without determining the facts of the case and whether the nurse had in fact acted negligently, the trial court dismissed the hospital, on the grounds that the hospital could not engage in the practice of professional nursing, and that therefore it was not responsible for the nurse's conduct. The court was thus faced with the question of whether its theory adopted earlier in the *Moon* decision should apply to nurses as well. In refusing to extend its theory to nurses, the court analyzes in detail the *Schloendorff* and *Bing* decisions. The court said:

If we were to rule that *respondeat superior* does not apply because the hospital is not licensed as a Nurse, then it would seem to follow that an airline should not be liable for the negligence of its pilot because the airline is not licensed to fly an aircraft. This and other examples are given Bing v. Thunig, *supra*. The Hospital was the employer of the Nurse. Only it had the right to hire and fire her. Only it could assign the Nurse to certain hours, certain areas and certain patients. There was no choice in the Doctor or the plaintiffs as to the identity of the nurses who would serve Lisa. In this day and age the hospital should be responsible for the acts of its nurses within the scope of their employment, irrespective of whether they are acting "administratively" or "professionally." See Rice v. California Lutheran Hospital, 27 Cal. 2d 296, 163 P.2d 860, and Dickerson v. American Sugar Refining Co., 3 Cir., 211 F.2d 200.

Some of the authorities mentioned, and others, make no distinction in application of the rule of *respondeat superior* to hospitals between employed nurses and employed doctors. Expressly, this opinion relates only to nurses. Also, it should be borne in mind that this decision relates only to the case in which the nurse acts out of the presence of the doctor.

## (2) Trends in Immunity Rules

The following excerpt gives a brief summary of legal trends in the immunity doctrines.

### Southwick, A., *Vicarious Liability of Hospitals*, 44 Marq. L. Rev. 156 (1960)*

SUMMARY

There are three recognizable trends in the law of a hospital's vicarious liability. The first is a change in attitude toward governmental immunity. The Federal Torts Claims Act, the New York statute, and other statutes cited indicate legislative activity in this area and reasonably forecast that additional statutes will follow. Furthermore, it is probable that courts in the future will be more anxious than heretofore to restrict the scope of governmental immunity at the county and municipal level by creating additional exceptions and modifications through expansion of the concept of what constitutes a proprietary function.

The second trend is the judicial reversal of charitable immunity by those courts willing to give the doctrine of *stare decisis* flexibility to serve current social philosophies. Unless legislatures follow the lead of Kansas in re-establishing immunity by statute, an event which is thought to be unlikely, it is to be anticipated that additional courts will join those who have already overruled or severely restricted the doctrine's scope.

The first two trends merely equate the responsibilities of governmental and charitable hospitals with the for-profit hospital and commercial enterprise generally. The third trend in the law of hospital liability is the most significant. It is the increasing tendency, aside from immunity, to impose vicarious liability on facts where none would have been imposed heretofore. By some leading decisions it no longer follows that a professional person using his own skill, judgment and discretion in regard to the means and methods of his work is an independent contractor. The hospital may not in any real sense control the staff physician, intern, or nurse in their medical activities but yet there is frequently vicarious liability for their negligent professional acts. By some courts the payment of a salary is more important than control over the actor's work. Gradually, the test of hospital liability

---

* Reprinted with permission of the *Marquette Law Review*.

for another's act is becoming simply a question of whether or not the actor causing injury was a part of the medical care organization.

Those courts following the theory of ostensible agency, on appropriate facts, go even further and find vicarious liability whenever the hospital has led the patient to reasonably believe that another was in its employ and under its control. As has been pointed out, this does not fit the traditional legal tests basing vicarious liability upon the existence of an actual master-servant relationship with the servant acting under the master's control in the furtherance of the latter's business. Neither does it fit the newer development of simply inquiring whether or not the actor was in fact and actuality a part of the hospital organization because it emphasizes appearance rather than the true relationship between the actor and the defendant hospital. Regardless of the social merits or de-merits of the theory as it is stated, it is submitted that courts must use care to strictly limit the concept to facts where the hospital has truly misled the patient regarding the identity of the responsible party. There must be a stopping point somewhere to the imposition of vicarious liability. To misunderstand or misapply the ostensible agency theory can only lead to an indistinguishable line of demarcation between liability and non-liability for another's tortious conduct. In any event, it would appear that the law is developing to a point where the only clear-cut line of demarcation is a situation where the patient himself has clearly and expressly employed and paid his own private physician or nurse. Otherwise the hospital's defense plea that the negligent actor was an independent contractor is likely to be unsuccessful.

# CASES

In the following cases the legal theory of vicarious liability is applied to medical litigation. If the trend for the future is a more highly organized form of group practice for the physician and the nurse, what will be the impact on this area of the law?

## *President and Directors of Georgetown College v. Hughes,* 130 F.2d 810 (D.C. Cir. 1942)

Rutledge, Associate Justice.

The appeal brings here for the first time the question whether a charitable corporation is liable for injury negligently caused by an employee acting in the course of duty. Issues of negligence and contributory negligence also are raised. . . .

### I. NEGLIGENCE AND CONTRIBUTORY NEGLIGENCE

On both issues the evidence was sufficient to go to the jury. Hence its findings for the plaintiff must be sustained.

Defendant conducts Georgetown Hospital. Plaintiff, a special nurse on duty, was struck in the back by a door hinged to swing both in and out and located between a ward and the corridor along which she was passing. The door was pushed open suddenly and violently by a student nurse coming out from the ward. The corridor ran east and west. It was a little more than six feet wide. The ward and the door were on the north. Nurses were instructed to keep to the right of the center line and to be cautious about the door. Plaintiff was walking westwardly, to the right of the center, and had already passed the door, when it was pushed open and struck her. She was thrown violently to the floor, and incurred the injuries which have permanently disabled her. There is no issue concerning the character of the injury or the amount of the damages.

The evidence to show negligence is, in part, that the student nurse and several others, in company with the head instructor, Miss Sandmaier, entered the ward just prior to the injury for an hour's work. Miss Sandmaier found some needed article was lacking and sent the student nurse for it. The latter turned and went hurriedly, not running, but walking very fast. Her own and other testimony describes her as rushing, not stopping at the door "because it was a swinging door," not looking through the wire mesh at the bottom to see if anyone were outside, not slowing or slackening her speed as she approached the door, pushing it, meeting an obstacle which fell, pushing it open again after it had swung back toward her, and finding the plaintiff lying on the floor. The testimony also showed that the morning was unusually busy, the article was needed quickly—"the work had to be done in an hour"—and the student nurse habitually rushed and hurried about her work. More need not be related.

At times things happen fast, and have to, in hospitals. When they do accidents may occur which the law must classify as negligence. The student nurse made things move. Ordinarily this would be commendable. Unfortunately that cannot relieve her act here of negligent quality. It was careless, because thoughtless and hasty. We cannot say that the jury could not find it was unreasonably dangerous to others.

The claim of contributory negligence is that plaintiff walked too closely to the door and failed to take due care regarding it, with full knowledge of the danger. The evidence, however, was not so one-sided as to require the case to be kept from the jury. The corridor was not a one-way street. It was only a few inches over six feet wide. Nurses were instructed to walk to the right of the center line. Plaintiff followed the instructions. She was told also to be cautious about the door. The distance from the center to the right side was only about three feet. Nothing shows that plaintiff was not keeping proper lookout for the door as she approached and passed it. She passed in safety. Only after she had gone by was she struck. Whatever might be true if this had taken place before she passed the door, we cannot say as a matter of law that she was bound to anticipate it would be pushed open with such violence as to strike her from behind after she had passed and throw her more than eight feet across the hall. Busy as the period was, it cannot be ruled she was required at her peril to keep her head turned or turning toward the door over her shoulder and backward to guard against so sudden, violent and wide an opening. Nor can it be said certainly that the danger to herself or others would have been greater or less, had she followed a path nearer the center or nearer the wall. There was not much leeway either way, and clearly she was not required to step beyond the center each time in passing the door. Her instructions required the contrary.

Written statements taken from various witnesses shortly after the accident were used to contradict their statements at the trial in some respects. So far as they did so, they merely created conflict in the facts or questions of credibility which also were for the jury. Taking account of all the circumstances, we cannot say plaintiff was contributorily negligent as a matter of law.

## II. LIABILITY OF CHARITABLE CORPORATIONS

We turn to the main question.

A few further facts pertinent to this issue should be stated, in view of the trial court's finding that plaintiff was a stranger to the charity, and the importance the finding has assumed on appeal. She was a special nurse. She was called to duty and assigned to the case by the hospital's superintendent of nurses. The patient was a paying one, who also paid plaintiff and paid the hospital for her meals. The hospital furnished her working facilities. The arrangement was the usual one for special nurses.

Paradoxes of principle, fictional assumptions of fact and consequence, and confused results characterize judicial disposition of these claims. From full immunity, through varied but inconsistent qualifications to general responsibility is the gamut of decision. The cases are almost riotous with dissent. Reasons are even more varied than results. These are earmarks of law in flux. They indicate something wrong at the beginning or that something has become wrong since then. They also show that correction, though in process, is incomplete.

On the other hand, scholarly treatment outside the courts is almost uniform. There is general agreement of such opinion in support of liability and against immunity. Legal scholarship finds an important function not only in research and instruction, but as the most effective agency for constructive criticism of judicial thought and action. Great names in law rest on this foundation, some as revered as any made so by the judicial function itself. One may mention among others in the common law, Blackstone, Wigmore, Mechem. A few have combined the two functions, each adding luster to the other, for example, Kent, Story, Cooley, Holmes and Stone, in addition to the great Commentator. Therefore, when opinion among scholars who are not judges is uniform or nearly so and that among judges is in high confusion, the former gives direction to the law of the future, while the latter points presently in all directions. In such circumstances scholarly opinion has more than merely persuasive effect. It is the safest guide for jurisdictions where the question has never been determined.

### A. UNDERLYING PRINCIPLES

We start with general principles. For negligent or tortious conduct liability is the rule. Immunity is the exception. Human beings ordinarily are responsible for their own legally careless action. They respond also for negligent harms inflicted by their agents and employees. So do business corporations. Likewise trustees and other fiduciaries generally are liable for their own negligence in administration and operation of the business or property committed to their control. Respondeat superior more and more has made them, as it has private corporations, responsible for wrongs done by their inferior functionaries.

Generally also charity is no defense to tort. For wrong done, it is no answer ordinarily to say, "He did not pay and was not bound to pay for the service. I gave it to him." One who undertakes to aid another must do so with due care. Whether the Good Samaritan rides an ass, a Cadillac, or picks up hitchhikers in a Model T, he must ride with forethought and caution. He is not relieved because it is his driver rather than himself who lapses into carelessness. Nor does it matter that the doer of good is a corporation, if the act of gratuitous service is fairly incidental to the business. Railroad companies, through their employees, may and often do undertake to do more for the passenger than the strict bargain or duty of carriage requires. But if they depart from normal conduct in doing it, they pay for the deviation. Charity and gratuity generally go to motive, not to duty. The automobile guest statutes show that legislation has been required to modify the common-law rule, though even in this application they do not entirely abolish it. Charity suffereth long and is kind, but in the common law it cannot be careless. When it is, it ceases to be kindness and becomes actionable wrongdoing.

Apart from charity, immunity does not turn on the technical form in which the legal interest is organized. Corporations, trustees, executors, administrators, receivers, as well as individual human beings and partnerships or their members, are responsible for negligence. Respondeat superior makes each liable for the tortious conduct of representatives acting in the course of the enterprise and not too far out of the proper sphere of duty. It is true that shareholders have limited liability and trust beneficiaries generally may not be held personally responsible. Normally, too, the trust fund cannot be reached directly, though breaches appear progressively in its classical immunity. So it is with decedents' estates and others. But the corporate liability is substituted for that of the shareholders, and the trustees' personal responsibility gives the victim of their careless action a source of indemnity. The form of legal organization may place liability here or there. But in general it does not nullify liability altogether and cast the burden of negligent injury exclusively upon its victim. Somewhere in the legal structure there is a responsible element apart from the negligent actor.

When an individual human being undertakes not simply an isolated act, but a habit or business of charity, without incorporating or casting it in the form of a trust, he does not acquire immunity. Possibly half the medical service rendered today is charity practice. So is a large share of legal service. Some physicians, and perhaps some lawyers, spend half or more of long and useful careers ministering to the sick and the troubled without pay. Many more do so habitually, but less extensively. Yet they do not have leave to be careless, notwithstanding their kindness is continuous or habitual rather than casual or occasional. Nor would they if it were conducted through or in association with others. Only when an individual institutionalizes his charitable enterprise formally, as by incorporation or possibly by creating a trust, does he succeed in casting the whole burden of its negligent operation on those it injures.

It is a strange distinction, between a charitable institution and a charitable individual, relieving the one, holding the other, for like service and like lapse in like circumstances. The hospital may maim or kill the charity patient by negligence, yet the member of its medical staff, operating or attending without pay or thought of it, dare not lapse in a tired or hurried moment. The institution goes free. The physician pays. Yet they render a common service, which the hospital could not furnish without him. The physician cannot incorporate. He cannot shield himself behind a trust. He cannot escape respondeat superior. His partner answers if he does. So it is with the lawyer.

The basis of the distinction cannot be charity. It cannot be habit or continuity in charity. If it were either, individuals would be free upon proof of the fact, or institutions would be liable upon proof of the contrary in the particular instance. The distinction reverses the general trend of responsibility in a risk-sharing and distributing age. Institutions have a survival value no individual possesses. They withstand vicissitudes individuals cannot meet. It is probable that charitable ones resist demise more stoutly than business ones. Certainly they incur no greater risks. If charity should exempt either institutions or individuals, it should be the latter. But there should be no distinction. Unless motive is to replace duty, both should be liable and liable alike. Institutions should shoulder the responsibilities all other citizens bear. They should administer as others do, within the obligation not to injure through carelessness.

Nor should the legal form in which the charitable institution is cast create immunity. It is not altogether clear that it does, except possibly when the corporate form is used. Unless the normal law of trusts is modified, the trustee must go down in his pocket as other trustees do, though he cannot dip into the fund. But when the charity is incorporated, somehow charity plus incorporation creates a certainty of immunity neither can attain apart from the other. Because the directors do not hold the legal title to the corporate property and therefore are not "principals" as trustees are, though they have all the latters' control and more, there is no personal liability of the ultimately responsible management except when its members participate personally in the negligent action. When charity is incorporated, therefore, it takes on a cloak of immunity not granted it in other guises, and not granted in that guise to other activities. . . .

## D. POLICIES SUPPORTING AND NEGATING IMMUNITY

For it are various commonly advanced arguments: Liability would violate the donor's intention; misappropriate the funds to unauthorized purposes and to persons not within the intended class of beneficiaries; and in effect indemnify the trustees, if the charity is organized as a trust, against the consequences of their own or their subordinate's misconduct. More persuasive apparently, but hardly more substantial, are the frequently expressed fears that imposing liability would dissipate the fund in damages and deprive the favored class or the public of the charity's benefit. A variant is the assumed danger that donors would be deterred from creating the charity and from adding to its funds by subsequent donations. Other considerations are mentioned, but these are the principal ones.

The confusion comes to climax when attempt is made to modify the rule in some of the ways previously mentioned and to reconcile the modifications with these reasons. It seems not to be recognized that all apply with equal force, on any basis of logic, whether the violation, misappropriation, dissipation or deterrence takes place through the negligent action of (1) the board of directors, (2) the principal or managing officers, (3) the operating superiors, as distinguished from the managers of finance and general policy, or (4) employees and representatives generally acting within their actual or apparent functions. There is the same failure to see that dissipation and deterrence also take place equally, whether damages are paid to a stranger or to a beneficiary and regardless of who falls within each class. Damage suits by employees, visitors, special nurses, physicians, and members of the general public are apt to be as frequent and as serious as those by patients. If, too, the donor's intention is controlling and he does not intend the fund to be expended for damages, but only for the purposes he specifies, the violation of his intention and the misappropriation from the objects of the trust are as great when a "stranger" collects damages as when a patient does.

These reasons therefore are not consistent with any of the modifications ordinarily made. They support general exemption and they negative one form or instance of immunity as much as another. The only sound arguments from them would be, first, for total immunity; second, for selection of the smallest class of claimants and the smallest or least-likely-to-be negligent group of agents or representatives, to whom and by whom liability would be incurred. The latter would reduce to the minimum the volume of dissipation and the deterrent effect, but would not escape, in a logical sense, violation of the donor's intention or the ultra vires effect of so applying the fund.

Taking the reasons for their logical consequence—total immunity—we find them not convincing in the light of modern conditions, both in the law and in philanthropy. Whatever its form, the doctrine of ultra vires, so strong in the nineteenth century, has shrunk constantly both in the law of private corporations and in that of trusts. This is true especially concerning responsibility for tort. From authority as a controlling premise, no corporation and no trust could possibly be guilty of tort. Corporate charters and trust indentures do not authorize corporate representatives or trustees to commit assaults, libel, slander, and negligent torts. But authority has given way to respondeat superior and "course of employment," for reasons not necessary to restate, in the highly organized society of this century. The surrender has been greater by corporations than by trusts, but with the latters' advent into business the old lines of limitation have been shaken. Breaches have been made too in the trustee's inability to secure indemnity from the fund and in the claimant's inability to reach it. Apart from charity organized in trust or corporate form, the law of ultra vires action as defeating liability has moved on from *authorized* action to conduct incidental to the enterprise and the actual or apparent function of the actor as the line of demarcation. There is no longer the same broad climate of exemption as existed when the "rule" of immunity for charitable institutions took form. Nor is the law of negligence in its swaddling clothes as it was then.

There are also reasons which take force away from the fears of dissipation and deterrence of donations. No statistical evidence has been presented to show that the mortality or crippling of charities has been greater in states which impose full or partial liability than where complete or substantially full immunity is given. Nor is there evidence that deterrence of donation has been greater in the former. Charities seem to survive and increase in both, with little apparent heed to whether they are liable for torts or difference in survival capacity.

Further, if there is danger of dissipation, insurance is now available to guard against it and prudent management will provide the protection. It is highly doubtful that any substantial charity would be destroyed or donation deterred by the cost required to pay the premiums. While insurance should not, perhaps, be made a criterion of responsibility, its prevalence and low cost are important considerations in evaluating the fears, or supposed ones, of dissipation or deterrence. What is at stake, so far as the charity is concerned, is the cost of reasonable protection, the amount of the insurance premium as an added burden on its finances, not the awarding over in damages of its entire assets.

Against this, we weigh the cost to the victim of bearing the full burden of his injury. In line with this view may be mentioned the general extension of workmen's compensation acts and social security legislation to include the employees of charitable institutions. Also, as some of the more recent cases point out, much of modern charity or philanthropy is "big business" in its field. It therefore has a capacity for absorption of loss which did not exist in the typical nineteenth century small hospital or college. While the larger hospitals generally are not operated for profit, much of their revenue comes from paying patients, who are either not at all or are only partially beneficiaries on a charitable basis. To that extent, perhaps, the institutions should not be regarded as charitable and the paying patient, if he is injured and cannot recover, pays twice that others may have healing where he has injury.

Finally, in recent years the real deterrents to donation have been taxation, despite contrary inducements in deductions, and the fears of persons well placed for the future of large individual accumulations of property, arising from economic trends much more fundamental than making charitable institutions liable for their torts.

The chief arguments, therefore, for sustaining the immunity, namely, ultra vires action marked out by authority or intent of the donor and danger of destroying or preventing the creation of charitable institutions, no longer have, if they ever had, compelling effect. Changes in the law and in the organization and mores of community life have taken away their major force. That is true, whether for full or for modified immunity.

As against the factors favoring it, may be mentioned the tendency of immunity to foster neglect and of liability to induce care and caution; the departure from the general rule of liability; the anomaly of exempting charitable corporations and trust funds, when charity is not a defense to others; the injustice of giving benefit to some at the cost of injury to others and of the injured individual's having to bear the loss wrongfully inflicted upon him, at a time when the direction of the law is toward social distribution of losses through liability for fault, liability without fault, and legislation which gives the person disabled to work what is commonly but inaccurately called "social" security. There are others we do not stop to mention.

It is hardly necessary to discuss the various theories of exemption or their application in various modifications. Whether immunity be founded on the "trust fund" theory, the rule of respondeat superior, so-called "public policy," or the more indefensible doctrine of "implied waiver," is not for us a controlling consideration. At bottom, except possibly for the last, these come down to the same thing, supported by the same considerations. They are merely different names for the same idea, cast according to the predilection of the user for technical or for broader terminology. The "trust fund theory" comprehends all that is involved in "public policy," with only an apparent difference in approach. This is true likewise of "respondeat superior" and "implied waiver." In any event the result is a departure from general, and we think right, principles of liability. The differences in foundation do not affect even the extent of the departure. We think it should be complete and that charitable corporations should respond as others do for the wrongs inflicted by persons who act in their behalf about their business and within the course of their duties, actual or apparent. Immunity, whether full or partial, is to be granted only when compelling reason requires it. If there has been, there is no longer such reason. The reasons which support governmental immunity, where it remains, are largely different, but even so they too give way gradually to liability imposed or permitted by legislation. . . .

## F. SUMMARY

We think therefore, the trial court was right in allowing plaintiff to recover. But this is not, as it held, because she was a stranger to the charity. We do not undertake to say whether she was stranger or beneficiary. She was trained in the hospital. She worked there many years. When she did, it was at the hospital's summons and she was, partially at least, under its control. In a sense she was beneficiary more than most patients. We think she should recover because she was injured by the negligence of the hospital's employee while the latter was discharging its business in the course of her employment.

We return therefore to the starting point. The law's emphasis ordinarily is on liability, not immunity, for wrongdoing. Respondeat superior has widened it in an institutionally, and to a large extent corporately, organized community. Charity is generally no defense. When it has been organized as a trust or corporation, emphasis has shifted from liability to immunity. The conditions of law and of fact which created the shift have changed. The rule of immunity is out of step with the general trend of legislative and judicial policy in distributing losses incurred by individuals through the operation of an enterprise among all who benefit by it rather than in leaving them wholly to be borne by those who sustain them. The rule of immunity itself has given way gradually but steadily through widening, though not too well or consistently reasoned, modifications. It is disintegrating. Each modification has the justification that it is a step in result, if not in reason, from the original error toward eventual correction. As more and more steps are taken, correction becomes more complete. The process is nearing the end. This leave the steps untaken standing out as the more anomalous.

In taking this view we are not unmindful that charitable institutions perform a high service in the community. In days when the state was less mindful of individual need, they gave a helping hand not otherwise held out to large numbers of people. They still do so. They recently have faced, and still face grave problems. Purse strings no longer are loose, as they were before world wars and world-wide depressions. But individuals and business institutions face similar uncertainties. It does not recompense injured persons that the loss is inflicted by charitable institutions, nor should they alone bear it because all together face a hard future. For reasons already stated we do not believe the survival of charities will turn on whether or not they must answer for their wrongs to persons they are formed to help. There may be some added expense of operation. It may be no more than the cost of litigating these claims over and over, for the issue will not down. Insurance must be carried to guard against liability to strangers. Adding beneficiaries cannot greatly increase the risk or the premium. This slight additional expense cannot have the consequences so frequently feared in judicial circles, but so little realized in experience. To offset the expense will be the gains of eliminating another area of what has been called "protected negligence" and the anomaly that the institutional doer of good asks exemption from responsibility for its wrong, though all others must pay. The incorporated charity should respond as do private individuals, business corporations and others, when it does good in the wrong way.

The judgment is affirmed.

## ANALYSIS

1. What is the primary issue in the case that is for the first time dealt with in this jurisdiction? What supportive reasoning led to the conclusion of "earmarks of law in flux?" In this opinion what weight was given to the thinking of legal scholars? In nursing, can you support that scholarly thinking precedes change in practice as it apparently did here?

2. Wherein did the evidence fail to support a claim of contributory negligence?

3. Where does the Good Samaritan doctrine come into the court's reasoning?

4. In seeking damages from a charitable institution, does there seem to be an inconsistency in the way the courts have dealt with the stranger to the charity as compared to the so-called beneficiary?

5. How is the rule of immunity an exception to the general principle of liability? What social changes have brought this doctrine under scrutiny?

6. What was the argument for holding the special nurse as a stranger? Why did the defendant advocate it?

7. The appellate court concurred with the decision of the trial court but did not adopt its reasoning. Which line of reasoning do you find most persuasive?

8. What are the implications for nursing of this carefully reasoned decision?

## *Dickerson v. American Sugar Ref. Co.,* 211 F.2d 200 (3d Cir. 1954)

Staley, Circuit Judge.

This case raises the perennial problem of the "borrowed servant" and requires that we decide whether there was sufficient evidence to justify a jury finding that the nurse who treated plaintiff was, while rendering that treatment, defendant's servant.

Defendant maintains a sugar refinery in Philadelphia. In connection with the refinery, it maintains a dispensary. The dispensary is permanently staffed by a registered nurse who is a full-time employee of defendant. A doctor is in attendance at the dispensary for a few hours a day. He testified that he was retained as a "contract physician" to treat all accident cases that came in and those which had occurred in his absence and had been given first aid by the nurse. He was to administer to injured men who were defendant's employees. His testimony was to the effect that he administered also to men injured at the refinery who were employees of third persons, but that in such cases there was a tacit understanding between himself and the stranger employer's insurance carrier that the latter would pay for such services on a fee basis.

Defendant engaged Charles Schwertners and Sons, Inc., to tear down an old stable at the refinery. Plaintiff, a carpenter, was an employee of Schwertners. While working on the stable, he ran a splinter into his hand and went to defendant's dispensary to have it removed. The nurse tried to remove it but could not and, thereupon, called in the doctor, who was then in attendance, and he removed it. Because of the danger of plaintiff's contracting tetanus, it was necessary that he be given a shot of tetanus antitoxin. This was done by the nurse, and, according to plaintiff's evidence, the jury properly could have found that it was done negligently. The testimony was conflicting as to the nurse's post-injection instructions to plaintiff, but, in any event, he returned to his work. About fifteen minutes later, he was brought back to the dispensary on a stretcher in a state of shock and was then taken to a hospital. Plaintiff's medical expert testified that, in his opinion, plaintiff's illness and his consequent disability to work as a carpenter were caused by the allegedly improper injection of the antitoxin.

After all the evidence was in, defendant moved for a directed verdict on the ground that plaintiff had not established that, while treating plaintiff, the nurse was its servant. This motion was reserved, and the court then instructed the jury, discussing the servant question and that of contributory negligence. The jury's general verdict was in favor of defendant. Plaintiff then moved for a new trial, alleging that it was error to submit the issue of contributory negligence to the jury, timely objection having been made at the trial. The court determined that excessive caution had caused it to allow the jury to pass on the servant issue and held that the question should have been decided in defendant's favor on defendant's motion for a directed verdict. The motion for a new trial was dismissed, and this appeal followed.

Diversity of citizenship is the sole basis for federal jurisdiction here, and, thus, we apply Pennsylvania substantive law.

First, we must set the stage. As we have said, the jury was told to pass upon the servant question and that of contributory negligence, among others. It is true that there was conflicting testimony as to whether the nurse told plaintiff to remain in the dispensary so that his reaction to the injection could be observed. Assuming that she did so instruct him, he disregarded those instructions and went back to his work. This was thought such evidence of contributory negligence as to require its submission to the jury. But the trouble is that there was no evidence, from layman or doctor, that plaintiff's returning to work could have been any kind of a cause of his injuries. As to the defense of contributory negligence, it is beyond question that defendant must show, not only that plaintiff failed to exercise reasonable care for his own safety, but also that such failure legally contributed to his injury. Here, there was no evidence on the causal connection and, therefore, the matter should not have gone to the jury. The result is that the case is in this posture on appeal: The jury was told to decide two questions, among others, that of master and servant and that of contributory negligence. But the latter was not a jury question. By general verdict, it found for defendant, so that we cannot tell upon which ground plaintiff lost. Hence, although the fact finder decided in favor of defendant, we must view the evidence in the light most favorable to plaintiff when we review the servant issue.

Pursuant to a request under Rule 36 of the Federal Rules of Civil Procedure, 28 U.S.C., defendant admitted that the nurse was in its employ on the day of plaintiff's injury. Plaintiff argues that the admission was enough to get him to the jury on the servant issue. Defendant's reply depends upon the status of the doctor. It is said that the doctor was an independent contractor. Defendant contends that, conceding, as indeed it must, that the nurse was in its employ as to matters generally, at the time when she was helping the doctor to treat persons who were not defendant's employees she was the doctor's servant and not defendant's. This view was accepted by the district court. We agree that it is a permissible view, but we think on this record it is not the sole permissible view and that the jury properly could have found that the nurse was defendant's servant. . . .

The law dealing with tort liability caused by the negligence of a "borrowed employee" is well settled, no matter how troublesome may be its application. We begin with the fundamental proposition that the one sought to be held is liable only if he is the master of him who was negligent. One who is in the general employ of A may, as to certain work, be transferred to the services of B so that he becomes B's servant while engaged in that work. In order to determine whether a person is the employee of A or B, the test is whether the one or the other had the right to control, not only the work to be done, but also the manner of doing it, and the person is the servant of him who has the right to control the manner of performance of the work, regardless of whether or not he actually exercises that right. Then, of course, there is a middle ground. That is, a person may be the servant of two masters, not joint employers, at the same time as to the same act, provided that service to one does not involve an abandonment of service to the other. Such is the case where the employee is transferred to carry on work which is of mutual interest to both of two employers and to effect their common purpose. The result is that, depending upon the evidence, three different conclusions are possible: The person may be the servant of A only, of B only, or of both. Factors which indicate that a person remains the servant of his original master are that the latter has the right to select the employee to be loaned and to discharge him at any time and send another in his place, that the lent servant has the skill of a technician or specialist which the performance of the work requires, that the hiring is at a daily or an hourly rate, and that the employment is for no definite period. Furthermore, there is no inference that because the general employer has permitted a division of control, he has surrendered it. None of this is new law. The opinion of Chief Justice Stern in the Mature case, supra, is a veritable mine of Pennsylvania authority and sets out most of the propositions stated above.

There were these factors which would have permitted the jury to find that the nurse was defendant's servant at the critical time. The dispensary was maintained and supplied by defendant. The latter admitted that the nurse was in its general employ. The nurse testified that she was a full-time employee at the dispensary; that her work for defendant entailed taking care of and giving first aid to all accident cases that came in and, specifically, that her duties included giving tetanus antitoxin injections. Furthermore, defendant selected the nurse and certainly had the right to discharge her and substitute another; as a nurse she had the skill of a technician which the performance of the work required; and the jury could have found that her employment was for no definite period of time. From these factors, the jury could well have inferred that the nurse remained subject to the control of defendant and, thus, was defendant's servant at the critical time, as opposed to passing into the exclusive control of the doctor.

On the other hand, there was evidence that the doctor was an independent contractor. Testifying for defendant, the nurse said that when the doctor was present at the dispensary she worked under his supervision. In addition, the doctor said that he instructed the nurse to give plaintiff a test dose of tetanus antitoxin. These elements would have justified the jury in inferring that the exclusive power to control the nurse's work had passed to the doctor, thus making her solely the latter's servant.

To complete the picture, we think it could be found that both parties had some measure of control over the nurse's work. Were the jury to credit all the testimony, that result would follow. From the nurse's testimony, it could be inferred that defendant's purpose was to supply first aid to those injured at the refinery. The doctor's services were retained for the same purpose but on a more expert level and possibly on the basis of an independent contractor relationship. Therefore, his objective, assuming he was an independent contractor, was the same as defendant's. Hence, while assisting the doctor, the nurse could be found to have been acting under the supervision, actual or potential, of both defendant and doctor, since she would be carrying on work which was of mutual interest to both and to effect their common purpose. Clearly, assisting the doctor would not necessarily involve an abandonment of her service for defendant; nor does the fact that defendant may have permitted a division of control compel the conclusion that it was given up entirely.

An essential link in defendant's case is that the doctor was an independent contractor. Arguing that he was, defendant's contention would shift the nurse from defendant's service to that of the doctor, depending upon the employment status of the patient. That is, the nurse would be defendant's servant if the patient were an employee of defendant, but the doctor's servant if the patient were an employee of a third person, since the treatment by the doctor and nurse of a total stranger could hardly be of benefit to defendant. It may well be, however, that when the nurse was treating plaintiff, her services were for the purpose of mitigating possible tort damages for which defendant might otherwise be liable.

Finally, we must reject plaintiff's suggestion that the ultimate test is whether or not the doctor was actually in the room at the time of the negligent act. Such a distinction misses the point and distorts the importance of the physical whereabouts of the doctor. It is the power to control, not the actual exercise of it, that answers the question. The doctor does not necessarily lose the power to control the nurse simply by stepping into the next room.

We think that the district court's original decision to allow the jury to pass upon the servant issue was correct and that the evidence would support any of the three possible results.

The judgment will be reversed and the cause remanded for a new trial.

## ANALYSIS

1. The fact situation is not an uncommon one for the industrial nurse. What were the major issues in this appeal?

2. What was the legal reasoning that led the court to accept or to deny the charge of contributory negligence?

3. Of the criteria presented in the discussion of vicarious liability in the text, which ones are applied in this case? How did the district court and the appellate court differ in their views of the role of the nurse at the time of the harm to the plaintiff?

What were the arguments that the nurse was: (a) The employee of the defendant? (b) The borrowed servant of the physician? (c) The servant of two masters?

To which role do you subscribe and why? How did the court decide?

4. What measures might the nurse have taken that would have prevented the harm and the resulting litigation?

## *Seneris v. Haas*, 45 Cal. 2d 811, 291 P.2d 915 (1955)

Carter, Justice.

Plaintiffs, Jessie and Jesus Seneris, husband and wife, appeal from judgments of nonsuit entered in favor of all three defendants, Dr. George S. Haas, Dr. James S. West, and Methodist Hospital of Southern California, in an action for damages for malpractice.

On March 22, 1951, plaintiff Jessie Seneris, 37 years of age, and the mother of four children, was admitted to defendant Methodist Hospital as a routine obstetrical case. Some nineteen hours after her admission, plaintiff was administered ether and other drugs which rendered her unconscious (618, 619, Pl.Ex. 1). The record shows that defendant hospital, through one of its nurses, selected defendant Dr. West, one of a panel of six anesthesiologists, to administer a spinal anesthetic to Mrs. Seneris. Within approximately twelve minutes after the anesthetic was administered (Pl. Ex. 1), plaintiff gave birth to a daughter. The delivery was spontaneous and uncomplicated. Plaintiff awakened the following morning and complained that "she couldn't move her legs; that she had pain in her back, neck, head, arms and wrist." Plaintiff left the hospital five days after the birth of the baby, but returned for examination and X-rays. She was then given a back brace and crutches and later a leg brace. Within two or three months she regained the use of her right leg but at the time of the trial was still suffering pain in her left hip and had limited use only of her left leg.

Plaintiffs brought this action on the theory that Dr. West was negligent in administering the spinal anesthetic; that Dr. Haas, the obstetrician, was liable in that he knowingly permitted Dr. West to administer the spinal anesthetic; and against the hospital on the theory that it was liable under the doctrine of respondeat superior. Plaintiffs contend that all three defendants are liable under the doctrine of res ipsa loquitur; as joint venturers; and because they failed to call in a neurosurgeon and arrange for a laminectomy after discovering the paralysis. . . .

### SUMMARY

A summary of plaintiff's evidence shows that Mrs. Seneris entered the hospital in good health and suffering from none of the complaints and difficulties with which she awakened the day following the administration of the spinal anesthetic; that she had previously had a spinal anesthetic from which she suffered no ill effects and so was presumed, medically speaking, to be non-allergic thereto; that she had no disease or condition which might have caused paralysis following a spinal anesthetic. The record also shows that defendant Haas testified that the place in the spine where the anesthetic was to be administered was an "important thing" and of "utmost importance"; that it was "safe to work" below the end of the spinal cord; that it was "bad practice" to go into the spinal canal above the first lumbar vertebra; that the insertion of a needle above the first lumbar vertebra could cause cord damage; that in general practice a doctor never went in above the second lumbar vertebra. Dr. West testified that trauma to the cord would cause paralysis; that it would be "impossible to cause trauma to the cord below the conus medullaris"; that it was his opinion that plaintiff's (spinal) nerve roots had been affected by the anesthetic solution used by him. Plaintiffs introduced in evidence hospital records which showed that Dr. West arrived in the hospital delivery room at 9:00 p.m. and that two minutes later, at 9:02 p.m., the spinal anesthetic was completely administered. Dr. West's testimony shows the various steps, in chronological order, taken in administering such an anesthetic. Plaintiffs showed that Dr. West did not wash his hands prior to administering the anesthetic to Mrs. Seneris. Plaintiffs introduced in evidence the written report of Dr. Nathan E. Carl, defendant hospital's staff neurologist, wherein he stated that Mrs. Seneris' condition "indicat[ed] *cord damage* on the left in the lumbar region." (Emphasis added.)

Plaintiffs contend that evidence shows that the spinal anesthetic was hurriedly and negligently administered and that it was the proximate cause of Mrs. Seneris' injuries. Defendant West contends that there is nothing in the record to show that plaintiff wife's injuries were caused by the anesthetic. This contention is disproved by the testimony of Dr. Haas himself when he testified: "Q. By Mr. Pollack: Doctor, I want to know, in the case of Mrs. Seneris, what is your opinion as to the level of the nerve roots, this damage or injury to the—well, it is all mixed up. Let me try it once more. What I am trying to get at is this: *The nerve roots* (to be distinguished from the spinal cord) *have been affected, you say, by the anesthetic solution that you used; is that correct?* A. I think so. It is my opinion, yes." (Emphasis added.)

Dr. West later testified that "I should say that the nerve roots have been affected below the level of my injection." He had previously testified that the solution he used was "weighted" and the table tilted so as to be sure the fluid would "go down."

From this evidence, it could have been legitimately inferred by the jury that plaintiff Seneris' injuries were proximately caused from spinal cord damage caused by a spinal anesthetic administered between the twelfth thoracic and the first lumbar vertebrae; that a spinal anesthetic administered in that location was not good medical practice, or the exercise of that care and caution expected of a practicing physician in that community. . . .

Defendant West argues that paralysis may result from a number of causes other than negligence in giving a spinal anesthetic; that in a certain percentage of cases paralysis will result from spinal anesthesia without any negligence; that plaintiffs introduced no proof that the practice used by him in administering the anesthetic was not the desirable or standard practice; that it is of "no importance" that he did not scrub since he used sterile gloves; that plaintiffs introduced no proof that the spinal anesthetic fluid was ever injected in Mrs. Seneris' spinal canal. . . .

EVIDENCE AS TO DEFENDANT HOSPITAL

Plaintiffs' first contention is that defendant hospital is liable under the doctrine of respondeat superior for the negligence of Dr. West in administering the spinal anesthetic to Mrs. Seneris.

Mr. Hoefflin, administrator of defendant hospital, testified as follows concerning the relationship between the hospital and Dr. West: That Dr. West was one of six anesthesiologists on the hospital staff; that these anesthetists were appointed by the board of directors of the hospital after having been approved and selected by the members of the medical staff (composed of doctors); that the six anesthetists constituted the medical staff of the Department of Anesthesiology "and their services were available to the members of the staff. Uniquely, they had an agreement among themselves in order to provide good anesthesia coverage to cover the hospital on a 24-hour basis by themselves. Inasmuch as there were six, as I recall, they would cover on a 24-hour basis one night themselves in six as a person on first call, and another person on second call and third call, right down the line, which meant that one man would ordinarily be staying in the hospital after he finished his anesthesia work in the regular scheduled hours in order that any emergency surgery that came into the hospital or any obstetrical case would have anesthesia coverage there"; that the anesthetists are under the control of the medical staff; that no member of the board of directors has anything to do with them; that the anesthetist himself billed the patient for the anesthetic given by him; that the hospital furnished to the anesthetist the medications given, the supplies, needles, nursing service, white clothes, gloves, telephone service and a place to rest; that the anesthetist was required to make a written report on each anesthetic given. Mr. Hoefflin further testified that if an anesthetist was found to be unsatisfactory, the medical executive committee as governing board of the medical staff recommended to the board of directors of the hospital that action be taken.

Dr. West testified that he gave anesthetics at no hospital other than defendant hospital; that he had no office of his own but took calls at his home; that it was common practice for him to be summoned by a nurse at defendant hospital to administer an anesthetic to an obstetrical case, that one of the nurses on the obstetrical floor notified him to give the anesthetic to Mrs. Seneris. Dr. West testified that he did not see Dr. Haas until after he had finished administering the spinal anesthetic to Mrs. Seneris. Dr. West explained the call system to mean that when he had "first" call, he would give all the anesthetics necessary; that if he happened to be giving an anesthetic when another was needed, the anesthesiologist on "second" call would give that one; that if he were not busy giving an anesthetic, he would give them all. Dr. West testified that after Mrs. Seneris' difficulties arose he wrote a "document" of which he had copies made; that he presented one copy to the administrator of the hospital; that this was not required and was a report other than the usual and required anesthetic report to the hospital. . . .

The judgment of nonsuit as to defendant Haas is affirmed and as to all other defendants it is reversed.

## ANALYSIS

1. What are the medical facts upon which the plaintiff charges the physicians and the hospital with negligence?

2. If you had been a member of the jury how would you have reacted to plaintiff's exhibit 5 (per full case)? From the symptoms the plaintiff suffered, can you introduce any explanation to support the defense?

3. What arguments did the hospital administrator advance to refute liability under the doctrine of *respondeat superior*? On the subject of control, wherein did his argument fail?

4. What was the decision of the appellate court?

## CASES FOR FURTHER ANALYSIS

### *St. Paul—Mercury Indemn. Co. v. St. Joseph's Hosp.*, 212 Minn. 558, 4 N.W.2d 637 (1942)

This was an action against the defendant hospital for injuries suffered by plaintiff while undergoing surgery.

Plaintiff entered St. Joseph's Hospital for the removal of her appendix. At the operation, four nurses assisted the surgeon. During the course of the operation the surgeon called for some warm water with which to irrigate the wound. Water was given to him by one of the nurses and he refused it because it was too hot. The nurse then brought another receptacle of water, which the surgeon tested with his finger. He testified later than when he tested it in this manner, he thought it was cool enough. Either the surgeon or one of the nurses under his direction poured the water into the wound; the water proved to be too hot and burned the patient.

The only question before the court, on appeal, was whether the hospital could be held liable for the acts of its nurses while they were assisting the doctor during the operation. The court held that when the general employer assigns his employee to duty for another and surrenders to the other the direction and control in relation to the work to be done, the employee then becomes the employee of the other insofar as service related to the work so controlled and directed. The evidence was clear that the surgeon had exclusive control over the acts in question and therefore the hospital could not be held even though the nurses were in the general employ of the hospital and paid by it.

Judgment against hospital was affirmed.

### *Casper v. Cooper Hosp.*, 26 N.J. Super. 535, 98 A.2d 605 (1953)

Plaintiff, a registered nurse, enrolled in a college course in nursing. The classes were conducted in rooms located on premises belonging to defendant, a charitable hospital. For the use of the rooms, the college paid the hospital $75 annually, which was applied to books and equipment for the hospital's nursing school.

After an evening class, plaintiff was injured in a fall on the hospital grounds. She then sued the hospital, claiming that the fall occurred as a result of defendant's negligent failure to light and mark the path.

The hospital contended that the doctrine of charitable immunity protected it from liability for negligence to any person other than strangers having no beneficial relation to the hospital. Agreeing with this contention, the court held that the charitable aims of a hospital are not limited to patients alone, but extended to the provision of quarters for the advancement of nurses' training. Therefore, where the plaintiff attended classes on defendant's premises, and studied nursing in a hospital environment, she was not a stranger, but a beneficiary of the hospital activities. Judgment for the hospital was affirmed.

### *Harlan v. Bryant,* 87 F.2d 170 (7th Cir. 1936)

A suit was brought against a surgeon for injuries to a child born by a cesarean section.

The parents of the plaintiff employed the physician to care for the prospective mother during pregnancy and at the time of delivery. On her admission to the hospital, after all efforts had failed to bring about a normal delivery, a cesarean section was performed and the child was delivered. The child cried and opened his eyes and was handed by the doctor to the nurse, who took the child from the operating room to the nursery where usual newborn care was given. Although not ordered by the physician, the nurse decided that the Crede treatment for the eyes should be administered. The silver nitrate solution as furnished by the Board of Health was inadvertently wasted and the nurse ordered from the pharmacy a solution of double strength. When the solution was dropped into the child's eyes, the nurse immediately noted the caustic reaction and bathed the eyes with normal saline solution. That evening the surgeon learned about the injury and ordered boric solution irrigations and later called in a specialist. For a considerable time the child was blind and under constant medical attention. At the time of the trial, three years after the injury, he had regained substantial vision.

The central issue at trial was whether or not the surgeon was responsible for the negligent act of the nurse under the doctrine of the borrowed servant. The court noted that a surgeon operates in one or several hospitals over a radius of a number of miles, and for him to have personal charge of the after-treatment until the time of the dismissal of the patient would be unreasonable and might even deter him from giving to society the benefit of his skilled services. Furthermore, the court pointed out that those who brought about the injury were not in any way acting for or in behalf of the surgeon.

The decision in favor of the plaintiff and against the surgeon was reversed.

## McConnell v. Williams, 361 Pa. 355, 65 A.2d 243 (1949)

This case considers the problem of whether a surgeon, who is a staff member at a hospital, is personally liable for the negligent conduct of a hospital intern assisting him in the performance of an obstetrical operation. The plaintiff had retained the surgeon as her obstetrician during pregnancy; a cesarean operation was found to be necessary. The surgeon requested that a certain intern be present to assist him during the operation and to take care of the baby at the time of the delivery. After a difficult operation, the intern, according to the testimony of the plaintiff's nurse, filled a syringe and instilled silver nitrate solution once into the child's left eye and twice into the right eye, putting into the latter a great many drops. He failed to irrigate the eyes for five or ten minutes while the nurse remained in the operating room, with the result that the child lost the sight of her right eye completely and suffered severe and permanent scars in her left eye.

The plaintiff did not contend that the obstetrician was in any way negligent, but conceded that he had performed a difficult operation entirely satisfactorily. Her contention was that the surgeon was liable for the negligence of the intern. The surgeon testified that he was in complete control of the operating room and the court held that, under these circumstances, the jury would be justified in concluding that the intern was acting as the surgeon's agent or servant while in the operating room, and that therefore the jury could find the surgeon to be liable for his negligence. In so holding, the court said:

[I]t can readily be understood that in the course of an operation in the operating room of a hospital, and until the surgeon leaves that room at the conclusion of the operation, . . . he is in the same complete charge of those who are present and assisting him as is the captain of a ship for all on board, and that such supreme control is indeed essential in view of the high degree of protection to which an anesthetized, unconscious patient is entitled,—a protection which Mrs. McConnell could justify claim in this case by reason of her trust and confidence in, and a necessary reliance upon, the surgeon she employed to take care of her and her child when born.

## Recommended Source Material

TEXTS

Gregory, C., and Kalven, H., Jr., *Cases and Materials on Torts,* 703–710 (Boston: Little, Brown & Co., 1959).

Harper, F., and James, F., *The Law of Torts,* Vol. 2, 1361–1428 (Boston: Little, Brown & Co., 1956).

Hayt, E., Hayt, L., Groeschel, A., and McMullan, D., *Law of Hospital and Nurse,* 74–87 (New York: Hospital Textbook Co., 1958).

Louisell, D., and Williams, H., *Trial of Medical Malpractice Cases*, 485–587 (Albany: Matthew Bender & Co., 1966).

Prosser, W.,*Handbook of the Law of Torts*, 545–91 (St. Paul: West Publishing Co., 3rd ed., 1964).

Shartel, B., and Plant, M., *The Law of Medical Practice*, 183–91 (Springfield, Ill.: Charles C Thomas, Publisher, 1959).

Stetler, C., Stetler, J., and Moritz, J., *Doctor, Patient and the Law*, 343–75 (St. Louis: C. V. Mosby Co., 4th ed., 1962).

PERIODICALS

Comment, *Surgeons' Liability and the Concept of Contract*, 9 Vill. L. Rev. 636 (1964).

Curran, W., *A Symposium on Professional Negligence*, 12 Vand. L. Rev. 535 (1959).

Letourneau, C., The Liability of Physicians for the Negligent Acts of Others, *Hosp. Manage.*, 98:52, 1964.

Note, *Torts—Nondelegable Duty—Direct and Vicarious Liability for Negligence*, 44 N.C. L. Rev. 242 (1965).

Overton, P., Rule of Respondeat Superior, *J.A.M.A.*, 163:847, 1957.

Southwick, A., *Vicarious Liability of Hospitals*, 44 Marq. L. Rev. 152 (1960).

# Part Three

---

Social Consequences of
Deliberate Acts—Intentional
Torts

# Chapter Eight

---

# Intended Interference with the Person

This chapter will consider injury-producing conduct differing from negligence or an unwitting breach of duty. Here, we will be concerned with the legal ramifications of deliberate and intentional behavior designed to bring about a result that is or may be injurious to another person or to his property.

Early in 1929, two pugilistic-minded gentlemen engaged in a prize fight in Seattle, Washington. In the course of it, one of them, Cecil Geysel, delivered a knockout blow that ended the fight and ultimately resulted in the death of the other fighter. Geysel was then sued by the estate of the deceased boxer, and it was contended that the death was due to wrongful and intentional conduct by Geysel. The court, though conceding a wrong and an intent to injure, denied recovery, holding that where the fighter had expressly consented to the fight and to the resulting physical buffeting, he was not entitled to sue for consequent injuries. [*Hart v. Geysel*, 159 Wash. 632, 294 Pac. 570 (1930).]

Intuitively, one feels a fundamental difference between conduct that has as its object the infliction of harm on a human being and that which is undertaken carelessly or without proper regard of the rights of others. Intentional misconduct seems more culpable, more reprehensible, and more subject to the imposition of sanctions by society. Less sympathy is accorded the intentional tortfeasor. Less consideration is given to his rights. The emphasis of legal thinking shifts toward compensation of the victim for his injury regardless of circumstances, and at times providing him with a windfall of a punitive damage award. This is a notion, a feeling, and not a legal rule. Its expression comes in a wide variety of subtle differences between the legal principles controlling intentional torts and those involving negligence alone. The attitude is lucidly

281

described by Prosser [Prosser, W., *Handbook of the Law of Torts*, 28–29 (St. Paul: West Publishing Co., 2nd ed., 1955)]:*

There is a definite tendency to impose greater responsibility upon a defendant whose conduct has been intended to do harm, or morally wrong. More liberal rules are applied as to the consequences for which he will be held liable, the certainty of proof required, and the type of damage for which recovery is to be permitted, as well as the measure of compensation. The defendant's interests have been accorded substantially less weight in opposition to the plaintiff's claim to protection when moral inequity is thrown into the balance. Apparently the courts have more or less unconsciously worked out an irregular and poorly defined sliding scale, by which the defendant's liability is least where his conduct is merely inadvertent, greater when he acts in disregard of consequences increasingly likely to follow, greater still when he intentionally invades the rights of another under a mistaken belief that he is committing no wrong, and greatest of all where his motive is a malevolent desire to do harm.

In considering the legal principles dealing with intentional infliction of harm, it is important to keep in mind that the same type of harm or injury may be negligently caused as well as deliberately caused. For example, some form of personal injury is the subject of nearly all the cases we have considered under unintentional torts. Because of the greater concern for the intentionally wronged person, however, the legal consequences of an intentionally perpetrated injury may be significantly different from those of a negligent act, and the student should keep in mind throughout this section that it is the intent added to an injury that brings these legal principles into action.

## The Element of Intent

Given, then, that "intent" is a critical factor in a situation in which some harm has come about, we must define and describe what the law means by the term. First, to be intentional, an act must be deliberate, the result of the exercise of the actor's will, an act of consciousness, of volition. The accidental firing of a loaded gun may bring about as fatal a result as a coldly premeditated ambush, but if it came about when a hunter tripped over a log, it will not be considered intentional. The driver who loses control of his car because he suffers a heart attack does not cause an accident as a consequence of a deliberate act; any injury caused by him is therefore not intentional.

If it is clear that an act was deliberate, it is not necessary that there be an actual intent to inflict an injury. To be sure, any injury resulting from conduct

---

* Reprinted with permission of West Publishing Co.

carried out with the design and purpose to inflict that very injury is clearly intentionally caused. The purposeful kick or the carefully aimed bullet are deliberately calculated to injure. The person guilty of such conduct obviously is guilty of an intentional tort.

But what if it can be shown that there was no intent to harm? What if a practical joker fires a shot to frighten, and instead the bullet fatally strikes? Here, too, the law would say the injury was intentionally inflicted. For conduct to be intentional, there must be *the conscious performance of an act, either for the purpose of accomplishing a particular result or where a reasonable man would believe that a particular consequence of the act would be very likely to occur*. Stated differently, there are two characteristics an action may have, either of which, in the eyes of the law, makes that action intentional. First, the act may be performed for the express, considered purpose of bringing about a desired result. Second, the result that in fact occurred could have been foreseen by a reasonable man to have been very likely to occur.

The second part of this definition of intent introduces to the field of intentional torts our friend the "reasonable man," with whom we have become so well acquainted in analyzing negligent conduct. The question arises how an intentional tort differs from a negligent tort if what the reasonable man would foresee is a part of the definition. We have defined negligent conduct as conduct undertaken when harm is *reasonably foreseeable*. However, in defining intentional conduct, we say that the result was intended where it was *very likely*. For example, one can reasonably foresee that an automobile being driven very fast on slippery streets may cause an accident, but it probably could not be said that an accident was very likely. On the other hand, when a driver swerves his car toward a pedestrian and accelerates at the same time, injury to the pedestrian can readily be said to be very likely. The difference is one of degree. All conduct can therefore be placed on a spectrum. At one end is conduct that is certain, or virtually certain, not to cause harm. This shades into conduct where harm is possible but not readily foreseeable, which in turn blends into action where harm is reasonably foreseeable. Then follows conduct that is very likely to cause injury, and finally conduct where harm is inevitable. The gray area between conduct where harm is not readily foreseeable and where it is readily foreseeable is, as we know, the area between negligent and nonnegligent conduct. Similarly, the point at which negligent conduct becomes intentional is where the possibility of harm becomes the likelihood of harm. Obviously, because such matters are not subject to precise weighing, different persons and different juries will not always agree and will reach dissimilar decisions in similar fact situations. Thus, the basic legal proposition that lines must be drawn by judge and jury between shades of conduct is illustrated once again; there is no clear line.

## Specific Intentional Torts

An intentional tort may be defined as the deliberate invasion of another's legally protected interest, and we can usefully examine the field of intentional torts by analyzing it in terms of the interests invaded. We can think of legally protected interests as a group of rights and freedoms belonging to each person, which the state endeavors to shield from invasion or restriction by another person, or if the invasion has already taken place, for which the state will provide a means of exacting compensation from the one guilty of the invasion.

There is a wide range of legally protected interests belonging to each individual. There is the interest in having one's person free from harmful or damaging physical contact of any kind, and the closely related interest in freedom from emotionally or intellectually offensive physical conduct, or, put another way, the interest in maintaining one's sense of dignity without being exposed to obnoxious contacts. The intrusion upon these interests is termed a *battery*.

There is the interest in freedom from fear of damaging or embarrassing contacts (note carefully that this interest, as sharply distinguished from the first two, does not involve bodily contact but the apprehension of the contact; thus, the interest is mentally or emotionally based). The invasion of this interest is termed an *assault*.

There is the interest in remaining free from being arrested or imprisoned in ways other than those allowed by law, the invasion of which is termed *false imprisonment*.

There is the interest in being free from misuse of the judicial process, that is, that one shall not without proper reason be subject to litigation or threat of litigation. The invasion of this interest is termed *malicious prosecution* or *abuse of process*.

There is the interest in privacy, and freedom from having one's personal life being the subject of public scrutiny, and the name given to the intrusion on this right is, not surprisingly, *invasion of privacy*.

Each of these torts has its own set of controlling legal principles. This list is not exhaustive and we shall see some instances of legal proceedings speaking of interests other than these.

### BATTERY

Battery is perhaps the most important of the torts relating to personal rights, in part at least because it is the most likely to result in serious injury with consequently high damages. Battery consists, very simply, of physical contact, brought about by the defendant and not consented to, together with intent to cause such contact. Purely accidental contacts, though caused by the defendant's conduct, are not batteries, because the defendant intended no such contact. If the defendant is unable to stop his automobile at an intersection because his brakes fail and he runs over a pedestrian, he is not guilty of a battery.

Physical contact need not be direct, of course. The firing of a high-powered rifle from a great distance is a battery if the rifle was aimed at the plaintiff and the bullet strikes him. In this regard, contact produced by any force brought into being by the defendant satisfies the contact requirement. Nor is any material damage necessary. In *Burton v. Leftwich*, 123 So.2d 766, 89 A.L.R.2d 980 (La.App. 1960), a physician was held liable for battery where he spanked a child in the course of treatment, even though no permanent distress of any kind resulted.

## CONSENT

"Invasion," the term frequently used to describe the various infringements of personal rights giving rise to intentional torts, implies a forcefulness and an overriding of another's wishes, and in this implication lies an important aspect of batteries and intentional torts in general. That is, that actions to which one has given his consent are not actionable as intentional torts. One cannot have his cake and eat it; he cannot have his interests protected by the law and at the same time agree to their violation.

The consent giving rise to this privilege may be expressed or implied. The pretty girl who whispers in the moonlight, "kiss me," will have no action for battery, however distasteful she finds the kiss when actually administered; she, it seems clear, has expressly consented to what might otherwise be a battery. Similarly, the consent may be implied. Thus, the mere fact of participating in a professional football game, or any other event or sport where injuries from contact are frequent would be considered as consenting to the inevitable contact, and therefore no action for battery would be permitted. The case arising from a boxing match summarized at the opening of this chapter graphically illustrates how courts will imply consent in such situations.

Note carefully that in these examples all the elements of a battery are satisfied: there is deliberate conduct, where harm is very likely and may be severe and result in injuries. Nevertheless, the consent is effective to preclude any liability.

Another area where consent to certain forms of contact is implied is in those parts of everyday life where contact is reasonably to be expected and is commonly experienced by all. Jostling during the rush hour, generally acceptable gestures of friendship, mild attention-getting contacts—all these do not give rise to torts because consent is presumed, and it would be utterly impractical for the courts to offer legal redress for such matters. In this area, however, if one knows that certain forms of usually innocuous contact are in fact repulsive to another, the consent will not be implied by the courts, and the deliberate initiation of contact known to be offensive gives rise to a battery.

To be effective, consent must be given by one in full possession of all relevant facts and able through mental capacity and experience to make his consent a true one. Young children, insane persons, and those under the influence of drugs cannot give legal consent; in other words, even if such persons expressly consent to a battery, or other invasion of interest, the consent is ineffective to relieve a defendant of legal responsibility.

## ASSAULT

Assault differs from battery in that in battery the fear of immediate contact is substituted for the contact itself. In other words, to assault another is to place him in fear of an immediate battery. The classic assault occurs where menacing gestures are made with a weapon, to frighten the person who is their object. It is the fright of the victim that is crucial, not the ability, or lack of it, of the perpetrator to carry out his threats. Thus, if threats are made while a gun is pointed, it matters not that in fact the gun is unloaded; the fear is perfectly real if the gun is believed by the victim to be loaded, regardless of whether it is or not.

In the tort of assault we find a clear expression of the fact that significant differences exist between intentionally inflicted injuries and negligently caused ones. In the intentional tort of assault, all recoveries are for a purely emotional or mental harm: fear. However, the circumstances are quite limited in which recovery for emotional disturbances is permitted in negligence suits.

## MALICIOUS PROSECUTION

Instituting or causing the institution of legal proceedings against an innocent person without probable cause and with an improper motive results in the tort of malicious prosecution, when the proceedings are terminated favorably to the accused. Most frequently, the proceedings giving rise to an action for malicious prosecution are criminal in character; that is, one person falsely accuses another of the commission of a crime. They can, however, be civil in nature, such as the malicious institution of an action to have a person adjudicated an incompetent or committed as insane.

## INVASION OF PRIVACY

The right to be let alone is, to a degree, a legally protected right. Since early in the twentieth century, courts have expressly held that this right will receive the protection of the law; that is, the courts will provide a means of compensation for the violation of such right. The sympathetic treatment the courts give is based upon a deep-rooted feeling that each person is his own master and that his personal dignity, freedom, and independence are deserving of the fullest protection.

Intrusion by one person into the private life of another may take an infinite variety of forms, and a legal action for damages may be proper for the emotional and mental distress caused [Harper, F., and James, F., *The Law of Torts*, Vol. 1, 677–78, (Boston: Little, Brown & Co., 1956)]:*

It is not every invasion of a privacy interest that is actionable, of course. The mere fact of living in a social order implies certain annoying contacts with others which even the least fastidious member of the community may on occasion resent. Nevertheless, such experiences are the price of social intercourse. It is only when these annoyances become unreasonable by offending against prevailing standards of decency that the law takes cognizance of them. With maturity and refinement in civilization there comes a rise in the level of decency. One may be expected to tolerate less in a society which has improved its manners over hundreds of years than in the crude social order of the frontier. Rough men may pay little attention to conduct which proves highly annoying in a cultured community.

The protected interests can be divided into four principal categories. These are (1) the right of solitude, which can be invaded in such ways as window peeping or wire tapping; (2) the right of dignity and self-respect, invaded by publication of debts, or unpleasant or startling facts about an individual that would normally be considered to be no one's business but his own; (3) the right of privacy in name and likeness, intruded upon by the unauthorized use of one's name or picture for advertising purposes; and (4) the right of privacy in sentimental relations, invaded by publication of letters, mementos, and the like. In the case of public figures, political or otherwise, the privacy rights of the individual come into conflict with the freedom of the press and sometimes with the right of the electorate to be informed about its representatives. So there has grown up a doctrine of "fair comment," whereby one who is constantly in the public eye is deemed to have waived some of the usual perquisites of privacy; similarly, perhaps, with persons who have seen fit to publish autobiographical materials. But these exceptions obviously have little application to most of us, and we can still be assured of the right of recovery should our private affairs be wantonly exposed.

### FALSE IMPRISONMENT

The tort of false imprisonment consists of the intentional confinement of a person within a restricted area without consent or legal justification. When

* Reprinted with permission of Little, Brown & Co.

one person intentionally impedes another's freedom of movement, he has committed the tort of false imprisonment and the law will require adequate compensation to be paid for any resulting damages.

The confinement must be total, in the sense that there can be no confinement if the person has a reasonable means of egress and if he is aware of it; if two doors to a room are open, there is no false imprisonment by blocking one door alone. However, once the principal passages to freedom are sealed, it is no defense that some unusual and difficult means of egress was available. If wrongfully confined, one is not required to battle his way out, or to risk life and limb in a dramatic effort to escape.

Furthermore, distant boundaries as well as near can serve as the barriers to freedom. The point is that genuine barriers exist, erected or brought about by the defendant, and that the plaintiff suffers an actual restriction of his freedom of movement. The barriers themselves need not block physical action. Confinement may be enforced by threats as well as by locked doors. A common situation leading to claims of false imprisonment arises in department stores, when an innocent person suspected of shoplifting is directed not to leave the store, under threat of restraint rather than actual restraint. Here the courts tend to hold that the suspect need not conduct tests to see whether the threats will be carried out and that he is entitled to take the department store personnel at their word.

The confinement must be intentional. Locking a door without knowledge that someone remains inside cannot give rise to false imprisonment, because the element of intent is lacking. Such an action may, of course, be negligent, if the unwitting jailer should have known of the distress he was imposing.

## Intentional Invasions of Patients' Protected Interests

As the nurse considers the legal theory of the intentional tort and the possibility of her involvement in this area, her first thought may be that this is an area not directly related to her practice. Though she is aware that liability for a negligent act of inadvertence is an ever-present hazard in her professional practice, the idea of intentionally inflicting harm on a patient is entirely out of context of the ethical canons of her profession.

The distinguishing word in this area of tort law is *intent*, and when intent, as legally defined, is associated with the invasion of the legally protected interests of others, the application to the conduct of the nurse and the physician becomes apparent. In fact, the invasion of numerous protected interests is a part of the daily medical practice. The intent to invade a particular protected interest in the course of professional practice need not be hostile; in fact, such an invasion most often stems from a desire to bring about an ultimate good for the patient. The harm which may have occurred is not that of a physical injury, but rather that one or more of the legally protected interests of the patient have been invaded without proper consent to do so.

## CONSENT—THE PRACTICAL LIMITATION ON BATTERY

Of the several protected interests, the one that may lead to charges of battery is the one that lies at the heart of all of medical and nursing practice: individual protection from unpermitted and unprivileged contact with one's person. This contact can take place on any or all parts of the body and can range in degree from the simply physical contact necessary to apply a bandage to the surgical removal of an organ of the body. What is necessary to permit the professional practitioner to invade this interest and, under ordinary circumstances, not found to be liable? The answer lies in the legal notion of *consent*. When consent to physical contact is properly given to another person, it permits him to intrude upon this interest and no liability follows. In the case of *Schloendorf v. Society of New York Hosp., supra,* p. 255, the court acknowledged that the surgeon was an eminent one and that he, together with the nurses, had moved within the accepted standards of medical and nursing practice, but it held that a battery had been committed because the surgery had not been performed within the bounds of the patient's consent.

The importance of consent in medical practice is clear when its legal meaning is first taken into account. The patient has an acknowledged legal right to be protected, but in order that some good may accrue to him, he voluntarily chooses to surrender this right. While consent for patient care is an essential prerequisite for that care, it is sometimes difficult to obtain a true and valid consent even under usual medical circumstances. The patient is often tense and emotional over his illness or accident and the strange environment of the hospital, or other health care facility, is an ever-present factor to be recognized and dealt with by those obtaining consent.

The primary purpose in the requirement of consent, without regard for the particular form in which it is given, is to protect the patient. By consenting, the patient acknowledges that he is aware of his rights and that because of the present situation, he is willing to relinquish those rights. The legal components that make the consent sound are (1) that the patient is competent and free from such factors as may cloud his competency—an unsound mental condition, influence of drugs, nature of his illness, or his age; (2) that the patient has consented voluntarily under no coercion, knowing that he has a right to refuse and that in refusing no consequences will accrue to him other than those of his own act; (3) that he has a full understanding of what he is signing, and that, if it is a blanket consent, he realizes he is giving unlimited freedom to his physician or health agency to act in his behalf and for his welfare. If the patient is consenting to a single procedure, such as a blood transfusion, he should be aware that he is limiting the scope of the physician's diagnostic or therapeutic efforts.

The act of consent may occur in one of several forms: it may be expressed in writing or given verbally, or it may be implied by conduct of the patient, which of itself manifests consent. All three of these forms are illustrated in a frequent medical series of events. In the physician's office the patient has been told that an operation is necessary and he has verbally consented to follow the physician's advice. On the basis of this express oral consent, the surgeon schedules time in the operating room and arranges for a hospital bed. On the appointed day, the patient reports to the hospital; through his conduct he implicitly gives consent to follow the physician's recommendations. The admitting clerk then asks him to express his consent in written form, which then serves to reinforce all that has led up to this point and may also include a description of the condition to be corrected, the provision that no cure is guaranteed, the right to dispose of tissues, permission for restricted release of information, and other types of related data. Another form of expressed consent, which may accompany the general admission consent form, is the blanket written consent for surgery that authorizes the surgeon to conduct the operation in the best interests of the patient.

Implied consent is nonverbal and is a simple willingness that the act should occur, which is usually manifested by the actor's conduct. In *O'Brien v. Cunard S.S. Co.*, 154 Mass. 272, 28 N.E. 266 (1891), action was brought by the plaintiff for assault when one of the defendant's employed physicians vaccinated her in order for her to qualify to pass quarantine. The facts showed that the plaintiff voluntarily entered the line of those being vaccinated, had ample time to watch the procedure being administered to others, and could have withdrawn at any time. The court in holding for the defense noted that no force was used, that the behavior of the plaintiff indicated consent on her part, and that whatever her unexpressed feelings may have been, the surgeon was guided by her overt acts.

Voluntary submission to a procedure does not imply consent if known dangers are minimized to the patient in obtaining consent. In *Scott v. Wilson*, 396 S.W.2d 532 (Tex Civ. App. 1965), an action was brought against a surgeon for malpractice in performing a stapedectomy. The evidence brought out that the patient, prior to the surgery, had not been properly informed of the risk of surgery. The operation was elective and had the surgeon informed the plaintiff that one of the hazards of the surgery was a total loss of hearing, the patient might have decided to live with his impaired hearing. In reversing a decision that had been rendered in favor of the surgeon, the appellate court said:

If Dr. Wilson did not have Scott's informed consent to operate upon him he would be guilty of assault and battery on Scott, and liable for the damages caused by the operation.

The value of the written consent to the health agency or to the physician is that it can be offered as evidence to refute the claim that a consent was not given. When consent is presented to the court in written form, it places the plaintiff in the position of asserting why this form did not constitute consent; it may also serve to clarify a dispute over the facts of what was actually included in the consent as given. All too frequently, in medical and hospital practice, the patient may be informed verbally by his doctor and the anxiety over the impending operation may cloud his comprehension or block his memory.

The method of securing a written consent may of itself decrease its value as evidence. If the person responsible for securing the patient's signature views it as another routine clerical matter and urges the patient to sign quickly because it is simply a matter of form, or if she has not been taught adequately to explain the form, the signing may be done in such a way that the patient does not comprehend what is taking place. A meticulously constructed form can be invalidated as evidence by hasty or ineffectual administration. Nonverbal or implied consent is more difficult to support in evidence, although there are times when conduct of itself is strong evidence of the patient's willingness to submit to treatment.

It is clear that a fundamental principle of the law is that consent must be obtained from the patient, or one legally authorized to give it for him, but even having given it, then privilege is extended only for those acts that are substantially similar to those to which consent has been granted. This legal requirement has, in numerous instances, been overlooked or ignored by the physician or surgeon and thus he has been found liable for assault and battery. Instances in which consent could be exceeded are those in which the operation consented to was not the one performed or when the surgeon disregarded the limitation stated in the consent to the removal of certain pelvic organs; or where the operation consented to may have been performed on the opposite side of the body.

Although the surgeon can refuse to operate if the patient does not give him freedom to exercise judgment, when he accepts a restricted consent he is liable if he disregards it and exceeds an expressed wish in the action which he takes, even though it may be for the patient's ultimate good. When an appendectomy is consented to, the surgeon may not exceed consent and remove the tonsils, even though the patient's history is clear and the removal of the tonsils should have been included in the original consent.

On the other hand, there are times when an extension of consent can be reasonably implied; if, for example, an appendectomy is consented to and at the time of the operation a diseased gallbladder is also found, it might well be that the patient would have no abatement of symptoms unless the gallbladder were removed. Under such circumstances, where a surgeon finds an unexpected condition with a clear medical relationship to the condition the surgeon was seeking to correct, the courts would be apt to hold that the patient had impliedly consented to the correction of the unanticipated condition. However, the surgeon faces a difficult choice with no clear legal answer. He can proceed to deal with the new condition in an effort to cure the basic disease, and hope that the patient will not take issue with his decision, or he can proceed with his original plan, ignore the newly discovered problem, and then subject his patient to a second operation at a later date. In such a situation, legal liability would depend upon all the facts of the situation and the reasonableness of the action taken and in litigation might be left to the jury to decide.

A plausible medical solution to a problem and highly skilled surgery to correct it may not serve as a defense when consent is exceeded. In *Franklyn v. Peabody*, 249 Mich. 363, 228 N.W. 681 (1930), an action was brought against a surgeon for operating on the plaintiff's thigh to obtain fascia for repair of superficial and deep tendons in the hand. When the need for fascia to sheath the tendons was discovered, the patient was unconscious and after discussing the problem with two doctors present, the surgeon decided to make an incision in the thigh. The patient in her claim stated that the operation on the thigh resulted in a muscle hernia causing her pain and disability. The trial court found the surgeon liable. On appeal, the court recognized that the surgeon could be found to have gone beyond the authorization of his patient.

An opposite view of a claim of exceeding consent was taken by the court in the case of *Kennedy v. Parrott*, 243 N.C. 355, 90 S.E. 2d 754, 56 A.L.R. 2d 686 (1956), an action against a surgeon for an unauthorized puncture of cysts on the left ovary, which occurred while an authorized appendectomy was performed. The plaintiff contended that the puncture of the cyst led to phlebitis and that the surgeon admitted to her that in the process of puncturing the cyst he had cut a blood vessel, which brought on the complication. The defendant denied the accusation. The court held that evidence was insufficient for the jury to pass on issues of negligence, assault, or trespass. The court also took issue with the strict common law interpretation that limited the right of the surgeon to extend the operation without the expressed consent of the patient, and subscribed to the position that the law should encourage self-reliant surgeons to whom patients may safely trust their bodies and not men who may shirk from duty for fear of lawsuit:

In short, where an internal operation is indicated, a surgeon may lawfully perform, and it is his duty to perform, such operation as good surgery demands, even when it means an extension of the operation further than was originally contemplated, and for so doing he is not to be held in damages as for an unauthorized operation.

Inherent in the right of consent is the right to refuse consent or, having given it, to withdraw it. When a competent person refuses any aspect of patient care, this refusal should be honored whether it be for reasons of religion, fear of pain, or lack of confidence in the physician or the nurse. Cases discussed elsewhere represent instances in which this refusal has been a focal point, as in *Schloendorf* and *Erikson, supra,* p. 255, and *supra,* p. 132.

In a somewhat different legal context are the decisions made by parents for their minor children, which could make a difference between life and death for them. Here the courts have stated that the rights of religion and the rights of parenthood are not without limitation. Parents may be free to become martyrs themselves, but it does not follow that they are free, in identical circumstances, to make martyrs of their children before they have reached the age when they can make that choice for themselves. *Hoener v. Bertinato,* 67 N.J. Super. 517, 171 A.2d 140 (1961), was an action in which a county case supervisor of a child welfare agency sought custody of an unborn child for the purpose of having a blood transfusion administered immediately after birth. The unusual circumstances surrounding the medical aspects of the case led the county to intervene to protect the child. The blood of the expectant mother was Rh negative; for religious reasons, she refused to have a blood transfusion for the child, in spite of undisputed medical evidence that without it the child would die soon after birth, or in the remote possibility of its survival, it would be physically and mentally deformed for life. The mother's history of previous pregnancies bore out this prognosis; a second child who had been transfused under compulsion was living and well, and a third child who was not transfused had died. In granting custody of the unborn child to the case worker, the court noted that:

> Failure or refusal to take necessary steps to protect a child's life is obviously neglect of the child, even if the parents have not failed in their duty to the child in other respects and even if such failure or refusal is grounded on genuine religious beliefs. The parents' constitutional freedom of religion, although accorded the greatest possible respect, must bend to the paramount interest of the State to act in order to protect the welfare of a child and its right to survive. . . .
>
> '. . . [M]edical authorities recognize that an unborn child is a distinct biological entity from the time of conception, and many branches of the law afford the unborn child protection throughout the period of gestation.'

The increasing use of experimental drugs raises questions concerning the legal aspects of consent in still another area. Legally, the position is clear; the patient is entitled to a full discussion of the procedure planned and should be permitted to decide whether he wishes to risk the experimental treatment and allow his body to be used for experimental purposes. The reasons offered against acquainting the patient with his part in the research are those discussed in an earlier section, *supra*, p. 131, of the psychological impact on the patient and the possible distortion of the therapeutic results. However, in spite of these reservations, the patient's consent must be an integral part of drug research and the acceptance or refusal to participate rests with him.

In an emergency, consent may not be required, where circumstances demand immediate action for the preservation of the life or health of the patient when it is impossible to obtain the consent of the patient, his spouse, the parent or guardian, or any other person authorized to assume such responsibility. Illustrative of such a situation is *Luka v. Lowrie*, 171 Mich. 122, 136 N. W. 1106 (1912). An action was brought against a surgeon for amputating the foot of a boy without the consent of his parents. The plaintiff, a fifteen-year-old boy, in crossing a railroad track was knocked down by an engine and thrown under its wheels. His foot was mangled and crushed; shortly after his arrival at the hospital the boy lapsed into coma. When the surgeon learned of the distance to the boy's residence and the time it would take to bring the parents to the hospital, he consulted with four house surgeons and in view of the shock from which the boy was suffering and the condition of the foot, he amputated it. The plaintiff recovered and the parents sued the surgeon. Two claims were made, first that the foot need not have been amputated and second that it should not have been done without the parents' consent. In affirming the decision in favor of the defendant, the court stated:

> The fact that surgeons are called upon daily, in all our large cities, to operate instantly in emergency cases in order that life may be preserved, should be considered. Many small children are injured upon the streets in large cities. To hold that a surgeon must wait until perhaps he may be able to secure the consent of the parents before giving to the injured one the benefit of his skill and learning, to the end that life may be preserved, would, we believe, result in the loss of many lives which might otherwise be saved.

It is clear that consent, under other than emergency situations, is the legal keystone in avoiding liability for battery. Seldom, if ever, would a nurse be accused of assault, for it is improbable that she would ever be led to provoke in the patient such a feeling of apprehension of harmful contact that she might be held liable. It could be hypothesized that in a situation where the patient was competent but resistant, the nurse in her zeal to administer a medication or treatment for the patient's own good might threaten him. If the apprehension she created posed a threat of battery, she might be found guilty of assault, even though she was not capable of and had no intention of carrying out a threat, and even though she may have made no move to touch the patient.

Thus far the discussion of the medical implications of the intentional tort has focused on the protected interest of the patient in freedom from physical contact without his consent. When the situation is reversed and it is the patient who invades this interest to the point of physical violence or injury to the medical practitioner, what is the legal recourse? Such a situation is not uncommon when the patient is mentally ill, delirious, or reacting violently to drugs, and the person who tries to intervene, many times to keep the patient from harming himself or others, is the one who is injured.

When the patient is sued by the injured practitioner, questions of precautions arise. A common question is whether the nurse was cautioned that the patient was potentially dangerous and whether she violated instructions. In *Van Vooren v. Cook*, 273 App. Div. 88, 75 N.Y.S. 2d 362 (1947), the plaintiff was an attendant and not a nurse, but some of the statements of the court are equally applicable. The patient was subject to recurrent attacks of hyperactivity in which he showed a predisposition to attack people. The attendant had been advised not to go to the patient's room alone but was not told that he was dangerous. The attendant was told to go to the patient's room to summon him to dinner; the attendant complied, and while there acceded to the patient's request to help him off the bed. The attendant was then violently attacked and sustained injuries. In permitting recovery from the patient by the attendant, the court stated that a summons to dinner was not an "invitation" for the attack as proposed by the defense. It also stated:

... [P]ublic policy places on one suffering from defective reasoning the same liability for torts of this type as it places upon those who are of normal mentality.

A second point of legal inquiry into injuries inflicted by patients on nursing personnel is whether in accepting the responsibility for the care of the mentally ill, the nurse assumes risk and actually invites injury if it occurs. If so, the patient would not be liable. In *Mullen v. Bruce*, 8 Utah 2d 290, 333P.2d 945 (1959), the plaintiff, a private duty nurse, was called to a sanitarium to care for a patient suffering from acute alcoholism. When she reported for duty, she was told that her patient was suffering from *delirium tremens* and that she (the nurse) would probably have a "rough night." Later the patient made two attempts to leave the sanitarium. In the first instance she was persuaded to return to bed, but she tried the second time, and in the encounter she tripped the nurse, knocking her to the floor and causing a severe fracture of the shoulder and the upper part of the humerus. The nurse had a period of hospitalization, medical expense, and loss of employment. The nurse alleged that the defendant assaulted her and caused her to fall. In holding for the nurse, the court denied that in accepting employment she had assumed the risk of injury and stated that she was subject to call and to have refused to accept the case might have affected her standing with the sanitarium and the medical profession. If the hospital, nurse, or physician is able to show that due precautions were observed in conformity with those which would be adopted by "reasonably" prudent practitioners, the patient may not raise his own insanity or other mental disorder as a defense in an action for a battery committed by the patient on the medical personnel caring for him.

PERSONAL PRIVACY—THE PATIENT'S RIGHT

The invasion of the right of privacy is not a new tort; in fact, it is based on a long-recognized principle of the right of the individual to exist and to enjoy life, free from interference except when this freedom impinges upon the rights of others. This tort can be distinguished from that of assault and battery, in that it is an intrusion on a human personality that may destroy individual dignity, freedom, and independence. The right of privacy may be waived, either by expressed consent or by implication, but the waiver authorizes an invasion of the right only to the extent that it accomplishes the purpose for which it is given. For example, a person on admission to the hospital may consent to have his medical history and surgical findings discussed at a medical staff meeting in the particular hospital, but such consent would not necessarily permit a similar presentation at a meeting of the state medical society.

In daily practice the physician or professional nurse may become legally involved in an alleged invasion of the right of privacy in which the plaintiff charges improper exposure resulting in shame and mortification to him, as for example careless exposure during a physical examination in a clinic or in the delivery room. In *De May v. Roberts*, 46 Mich. 160, 9 N.W. 146 (1881), a physician took an unprofessional unmarried man with him to attend a case of confinement and, where no real necessity existed for the latter's assistance, both were liable in damages. Although the decision was made well over 75 years ago, the language of the court in rendering this decision still shows a clear recognition of the individual right of privacy and the legal consequences when this right is invaded:

. . . It would be shocking to our sense of right, justice and propriety to doubt even but that for such an act the law would afford an ample remedy. To the plaintiff the occasion was a most sacred one and no one had a right to intrude unless invited or because of some real and pressing necessity which it is not pretended existed in this case. The plaintiff had a legal right to the privacy of her apartment at such a time, and the law secures to her this right by requiring others to observe it, and to abstain from its violation.

In *Brazemore v. Savannah Hosp.*, 171 Ga. 257, 155 S.E. 194, (1930), the parents of a deceased child brought suit against the hospital, a photographer, and a local newspaper. A male son of the plaintiffs was born at home, with his heart on the outside of his body. He was taken immediately to the hospital for surgery where he subsequently died. Disregarding the right of privacy of the parents, the hospital allowed photographs to be taken and gave to the *Savannah Press* certain facts without the permission or knowledge of the parents. This was held to amount to an actionable invasion of privacy.

The nursing and medical implications of the tort of the invasion of privacy lie in a continuing recognition by the nurse practitioner that the right of privacy is acknowledged for each and every patient in his day-to-day care.

### RESTRAINTS ON PATIENTS' FREEDOM

Deeply rooted in history, and one of society's early means of punishing the wrongdoer, the act of imprisonment is broad in scope and has many legal ramifications. In common parlance, imprisonment meant an enclosure of stone with iron bars, but in law it has more liberal connotations and imprisonment can be said to have occurred in a hospital, home, or by any structured form of restraint of one's freedom of movement. Freedom from unlawful restraint is an individual freedom protected by law just as freedom from physical contact and right of one's privacy. Restraint to any degree, unless authorized by law or voluntarily consented to, constitutes a false imprisonment and is a tort for which the courts offer legal redress.

The broad area of restraint is closely allied to nursing and medical practice and requires careful consideration so that the protected rights of others may not be invaded. Routine care in hospitals and nursing homes poses many restraints on the patient's freedom just in his ordinary day-to-day period of hospitalization. For example, the patient may be told that he may not leave his bed, or if given permission he may be permitted to move only within a certain restricted area. This restriction of one's freedom is usually a reasonable one that takes into consideration the person's own physical limitations and is not actionable because the patient expressly or implicitly consents to it.

Restraints are common in medical and nursing practice and may vary all the way from the indefinite detention in a psychiatric ward to the temporary use of side rails for a sedated or elderly, confused patient. Restraints for children are routine depending on age and may be applied only long enough to permit a treatment or may be maintained during the entire time of hospitalization. The primary reason for most restraints of this type is to protect the patient from injuring himself, and, except for the mentally ill, restraints are seldom applied to protect others. A restraint, whether ordered by a physician or applied on the basis of a nursing judgment, should not be regarded as an easy solution for nursing problems; in fact, it may compound them. The possibility that the patient who is in a restraint may harm himself is an ever-present danger; for example, there is the danger of the constricture of a part and the trauma of resulting pressure or of a fall from the bed while confined in vest or ankle straps. The dangers point to the need for more rather than less nursing surveillance when a patient is in a restraint of any type. An incident was reported (*Colo. Nurse*, August, 1968, p. 17) involving the negligent rather than the intentional misuse of restraints, which was not taken to a higher court, of a six-year-old child who had eye surgery. Restraints were ordered by the physician and applied to both arms but they were not properly checked, and after eighteen hours it was found that undue pressure and constriction of the circulation had caused muscle damage to the left arm.

If a hospital or nursing home is charged with false imprisonment there must be proof of all the elements of the tort before any determination of illegality can arise. Points that would undoubtedly enter into the determination of whether false imprisonment did or did not take place would be whether the patient had given his consent, actual or implied, usually the reasons for limiting freedom, and the amount of coercion exercised in bringing about the alleged tortious confinement. However, if liberty were in fact denied, the length of time and the manner of restriction of freedom would not be considered by the courts.

Three defenses to interference with freedom close to professional practice are, first, that the restraint may have been authorized by an administrative official pursuant to the law that compels the person to accept medical procedures such as the commitment of the mentally ill or, in some states, quarantine for smallpox or venereal disease. Second, the restraint may have been applied in an emergency, as with a dangerously insane person or with an attempted suicide—in either instance the restraint would be limited to that necessary to prevent harm to the individual or to others, and of a sufficient length of time necessary to secure the assistance of the police or a member of the family. Third, the restraint may have been consented to by the patient himself or by one responsible for him; such consent could vary in duration from the time necessary for anesthesia during surgery to days or weeks of restraint for the treatment of drug addiction or alcoholism. At any point in the treatment the consent may be withdrawn and the physician is obligated to honor the request for withdrawal, unless there is a controlling statute that would supersede such a request.

## NOTES

### (1) The Child Abuse Problem and Its Legislative Solution

When the state intervenes in situations of child abuse by parents, should it be to punish the parents or to provide if possible a means of rehabilitating family relationships? The note that follows discusses the provisions of a typical statute, that of Florida, that takes a positive approach to the solution of this all too common problem. Should the child be able to sue his parent for the battery? What are the arguments for and against civil liability of a parent for assaulting a child?

## The Battered Child: Florida's Mandatory Reporting Statute, 18 U. Fla. L. Rev. 503 (1965)*

Florida Statutes, section 828.041 requires "any physician, including any licensed doctor of medicine, licensed osteopathic physician, intern and resident" to report all instances of nonaccidental physical injury to children to an appropriate juvenile judge. At the present time forty-eight states have similar legislation. Common features in these reporting statutes are the naming of a state agency or agencies to which reports are to be directed, the requirement of specific contents of the report, the abolishment of the physician-patient privilege with regard to these contents, and the granting of immunity from both civil and criminal liability to those who file reports under the statute if the reporter acts in good faith. Some statutes are mandatory, as is Florida's; others are permissive. Beyond these features there is variation in the statutes.

The purpose of these reporting statutes is to protect children by bringing what would normally be a low-visibility occurrence of parental abuse, one that is not often seen by those outside the family, to the attention of proper state authorities. Through these statutes the state, acting as *parens patriae*, emphasizes the limitations of parental authority. The statutes announce that parental conduct that produces physical injury—exposes the family to state intervention.

Historically there has been a reluctance by the state to interfere with the integrity of the family. In the United States, particularly, the family has been considered a preferred method for rearing children. There is also the feeling that the family unit should be preserved. Yet society realizes that certain intra-family conduct may be detrimental not only to family members, but to the community as a whole. Normally, only extreme conduct or total disregard for parental functions triggers state intervention into the family unit, and then only when it is publicly visible. Battered child reporting statutes provide the opportunity for better visibility when none or very little existed.

Why are instances of nonaccidental physical injury to children singled out as sufficiently crucial to warrant aggressive state action? The answer lies in the fact that the discovery of a battered child might also lead to finding a dysfunctioning family. If a goal of society is to preserve the family as well as to protect children then the state has a vital interest in requiring the investigation of these injuries.

### THE HISTORY OF BATTERED CHILDREN

"Battered children" are not recent phenomena that can be attributed solely to the increasing pressures on parents and the difficulties in coping with their roles. Cases of a "battered child" nature are noted in legal reports as early as 1840. Many

* Used by permission. Copyright 1966 by the *University of Florida Law Review*.

of these cases are perceived as questions regarding the limitations of a parent's right to punish his child; only those cases that threatened the child's life or put him in danger of extreme bodily harm were deemed to exceed these limitations.

One of the earliest cases on record involved a prosecution in Tennessee of parents for criminal assault due to alleged excessive punishment. One parent had held the child while the other struck the child with her fists and pushed the child's head against a wall. The court said the "right of parents to chastise . . . disobedient children is so necessary to the government of families . . . that no moralist or lawgiver has ever thought of interfering with its existence. . . ." The court further noted that although "the law has created and preserved this right, in its regard for the safety of the child it has prescribed bounds beyond which it [chastisement] shall not be carried."

Early textbooks on domestic relations recognized parental immunity with regard to punishment. Tort concepts, such as causal factors, mental attitudes (intentional or unintentional), sufficient impact, and so on were used as guides for determining the presence of excessive punishment. Parental conduct considered so extreme as to subject parents to state intervention was defined as punishment "unreasonably severe, or in manner inhuman and shocking to the senses."

Today, however, research in child development has brought out more sophisticated views of punishment; these views are particularly helpful in providing guides for state intervention. Young distinguishes punishment that may require societal involvement as that which is "without regard for its cause or its purpose." Katz makes the point that some parental actions can be considered "deliberate, calculated, consistent and tortuous, in other words cold blooded," and thus go beyond the bounds of parental authority, rather than normal parental reactions to some stimulus, which he regards as "spontaneous, indirect, impulsive and loving."

Battered children are the result of abnormal or perhaps irrational behavior on the part of their parents or of those in whose custody they are placed. The result of this behavior may take the form of bone fractures in the child, in various stages of healing. Other manifestations of a parent's deliberate injury to a child might take the form of subdural hematoma, skin bruising, and so on.

It was not until the early 1960's that the medical profession, particularly pediatricians, became aware of certain peculiar unexplained injuries to children. The term "battered child syndrome" was coined to characterize a clinical condition in young children who had received serious physical abuse, generally difficult to explain in and of itself. In other words, the clinical history as given by the parents did not justify the extent of injury.

Not only are there medical aspects to battered child cases, but psychiatric ones as well. Sufficient data are now available to provide accurate descriptions of parents who abuse their children and the behavior patterns of these children. This information is important for purposes of understanding reasons for parents' behavior and its effects, both present and future, on the child's physical and emotional health. Data on the parents are particularly relevant in deciding questions of child custody, for example, whether a child should be temporarily or permanently removed from his home.

Parents who batter children may suffer from feelings of inadequacies, immaturity, and an inability to cope with everyday problems. These parents often overreact to their own unmet needs. It is likely that when these unmet needs conflict with the needs of their children or the children are misperceived as being the cause of the parents' own need frustration that the children may suffer.

A study by the Massachusetts Society for the Prevention of Cruelty to Children provides helpful insights into the personality characteristics of parents who abuse their children. These characteristics fell into one minor and three major groupings:

1. Characteristics of hostility and aggressiveness. A continual anger rules these parents' lives, its source seemingly derived from present conflicts or early childhood experiences in a home where emotional rejection and deprivation were severe.

2. Characteristics of rigidity, compulsiveness and lack of warmth, reasonableness and pliability in thinking and beliefs. Primary concern with their own pleasures as well as inability to feel love and protectiveness toward their children were also exhibited. Excessive cleanliness and strict discipline ruled these parents in their attitudes toward sex, dirt, and bodily processes generally; and, children who violated these standards were unhesitatingly punished. In many cases there existed no rational relationship between the nature of the child's infraction and the severity of the punishment meted out.

3. Characteristics of passivity and dependence. These parents competed with their children for the love and attention of their spouses and seemed continually sad, moody, unresponsive, and unhappy.

A minor, but significant, grouping were the families in which the mother was the breadwinner while the formerly active father, who became incapable of supporting his family because of some physical disability, remained home acting as the mother figure.

Other studies have highlighted additional characteristics of the abusing parent. Many abusing parents have been found to be of low intelligence; frequently they were involved in minor criminal activities; alcoholism, sexual promiscuity, and unstable marriages evidenced themselves in many cases. Much of the brutality occurred in slum families in which economic deprivations and hardships created situations that were unbearable. This is not to say that parents in middle and upper class families have not battered their children. It is in the latter area that the cases are generally more difficult to discover and the least amount of information is available.

Typically, the battered child is under three years of age. His behavior patterns and emotional makeup are generally different from children reared in a functioning family. During childhood such noticeable characteristics as the following arise: a tendency to overreact to hostility, depressed and generally passive personality, destructiveness, and fear of parents.

It has been suggested that battered children have difficulty maturing emotionally unaffected by the abuse. During the period of abuse, the child's inner psychic life may be suspended. In adulthood, reactions to this abuse may be manifested in such feelings as hostility toward adults and the community in general and a propensity toward battering their own children.

## THE PHYSICIAN AND THE BATTERED CHILD

Physicians have always occupied a unique position in regard to physically abused children. Quite often they are the only persons outside of the family to witness closely the results of child battering and question the parent concerning the cause. As a consequence, physicians have reported a large number of battered child cases to state authorities. The number reported, however, probably has never approached the total number of battered child cases that physicians necessarily treat. There are many reasons for this disparity.

Battered child cases are extremely difficult to diagnose as intentionally inflicted harm. Parents rarely state that the injuries were caused by punishment, and even more infrequent are the cases in which the parents say that they inexplicably inflicted the injuries. The cover-up explanations, on the other hand, may sound quite truthful and be compatible with the nature of the injuries especially in cases in which no outward manifestation is shown and parents are extremely cooperative. Questionable explanations, such as crib falls, accidental droppings, and peer or sibling encounters may create doubt in the physician's mind, but there may be little else to support his feelings. Infants are usually too young to articulate the cause of their injuries or are afraid to tell what happened. Further, difficulty in obtaining any type of history is often encountered. As a result of these problems, recognition of a battered child usually depends on the physical examination, X-ray findings, and a high index of suspicion on the part of the physician.

Once a physician accurately diagnoses an injury as part of the battered child syndrome, a further question remains in his mind: what, other than medical treatment, should be undertaken? Before the passage of reporting statutes, many physicians undoubtedly felt no compulsion to report a battered child to a state authority. They saw their functions merely in terms of making decisions about the medical aspects of the case rather than in deciding to invoke the criminal process or make referrals to state welfare agencies. Fear of defamation suits as well as notions of the confidentiality of the physician-patient relationship probably influenced many physicians. Other considerations may have been influential: time loss due to involvement with state agencies and appearance in court, decline in practice due to parents' fear of being reported, and a less than full commitment to the over-all well-being of the child patient. It is also possible that, prior to the reporting statutes, many physicians were reluctant to bring state intervention into the family sphere of authority. In any event, the passage of reporting statutes, especially mandatory ones, has had the twin purpose of alleviating the fears and emphasizing the responsibilities of physicians in battered child cases. Secondarily the acts may also serve to sensitize the diagnosis of physicians who are faced with a battered child case.

## EVALUATION OF FLORIDA'S MANDATORY ACT

The Florida statute is mandatory, a feature found in a majority of the other acts. For at least three reasons, the mandatory feature is desirable. First, if the protection and aid of the state is truly directed to the battered child, then all battered children should have an equal right to "claim" this protection. The decision to withhold or to provide this protection should be made by a state officer rather than by a physician who is largely unaware of the protective steps that would be taken. Nonmandatory statutes actually treat the physician as the person being primarily protected with the interests of the battered child contingent on his decision. Second, more complete records of the battered child cases can be kept under a mandatory reporting system. Even if state action is not taken in every reported case at least the battered child's injuries are noted so that recurrences may reveal a pattern of child abuse. Third, the absence of discretion on the part of the physican should undoubtedly insulate him from community criticism in the unpopular case and may also minimize the extent and effect of parental pressure to withhold a report.

Despite the mandatory feature of the statute, which makes willful violations a misdemeanor, noncompliance still exists. Ignorance and misconceptions of the statute are largely responsible for the remaining gap between cases seen by physicians and those reported. Accurate disbursement of information, which impresses upon physicians the great need for immediate reporting of suspected cases and reveals the effective handling of these cases when reported, is needed.

Another feature on which state statutes vary concerns the agency to which reports are to be directed. The Florida statute requires that the reports be made to "the appropriate juvenile judge." This provision is subject to criticism. It is doubtful whether the juvenile courts have enough properly trained personnel to handle effectively the battered child caseload. Florida's juvenile courts were encountering serious personnel shortages prior to the enactment of the statute. These conditions would lead one to believe that the courts deal with the serious cases and let others remain unattended until they finally reach a degree whereby they themselves demand immediate attention. This procedure is dangerous because child abuse tends to be repetitive with its degree becoming more severe.

The juvenile court may call upon the Child Welfare Unit of the State Welfare Agency to investigate reported battered child cases. This agency investigates such cases whenever requested to do so by the court or institutions that encounter them. There are many problems in this arrangement. There is no mandatory requirement that the welfare unit make the investigation or, for that matter, that an investigation be made at all. The recommendations of the welfare unit need not be followed by the juvenile judge; he may handle the case as he sees fit. In many instances, follow-up studies are not made.

Many states utilize a department of welfare as the agency to which reports are directed. A recent Illinois act, for example, uses that state's Department of Children and Family Services. The necessity for employing a social service agency is apparent. Since child abuse is viewed as a symptom of family dysfunctioning with the twin goals of state intervention being protection of children and the preservation of the family unit, personnel trained in family counseling matters is required. In addition, social workers recognize the importance of continual contacts with clients and thus follow-up studies are ordinarily considered a routine function. A further advantage lies in the centralized files that could be kept on child abuse cases. This arrangement largely negates attempts by parents to conceal hospital aid rendered their children on different occasions. Important, too, is the public image that the department maintains as opposed to that of the juvenile court or police authorities. Less resistance normally is met by social workers of a welfare department than that faced by officers of the courts or police.

Another feature of the Illinois act is worthy of special notice. While the act requires that a report be made immediately to the nearest office of the Department of Children and Family Services, it provides that "reports may in addition be made to the local law enforcement agency." Presumably, the immunity provisions of the act apply equally to both the mandatory and discretionary reports. In this feature of its act, Illinois seems to have attained the best possible blend of mandatory and discretionary reports—its physicians *must* report all cases to the specialized department that provides children and family services, but *may* report any case directly to the law enforcement authorities without fear of criminal or civil liability.

The Florida statute grants immunity from liability for anyone participating in the making of a report or in a judicial proceeding resulting from a report. This covers both civil and criminal actions and would eliminate possible liability from defamation suits. The individual covered by this section is presumed to have acted in good faith. This is a rebuttable presumption, but the burden of proof is on the initiator to show that the person acted in bad faith or with malicious purpose.

Although Florida does not recognize the physician-patient privilege, the act provides that the privilege shall not be grounds for excluding evidence in judicial proceedings resulting from a report. This provision was undoubtedly included as a prophylactic against possible future recognition of the privilege. The physician-patient privilege is not truly applicable to battered child cases, in any event, because the privilege is for the protection of the *patient* and not his parent. It would be an anomaly to allow an abusing parent to gain protection under this privilege, thus excluding the physican's testimony regarding the cause or extent of a child's injuries in any judicial proceeding resulting from a report under the statute.

CONCLUSION

The needs of the battered child and his family justify state intervention into the family unit. Battered children are children in danger. They sometimes suffer daily physical abuse at the hands of an emotionally unstable parent. Unless the abuse is halted and other remedial steps taken, the result may be lasting physical and emotional impairment or death. Abusing parents may also need psychotherapy if they are to be helped to solve their own problems.

In response to these needs, the Florida Mandatory Reporting Statute was enacted. The statute is designed to remove the obstacles to better visibility in battered child cases. With this basic purpose, the statute aims too low. While the act does much to improve visibility, it does nothing to provide for the very specialized treatment required in these cases. In fact, it may even burden the inadequately equipped juvenile courts to such an extent that the handling of other types of cases may suffer.

The Florida statute should be amended to provide the following:

1. that mandatory reports be made directly to the Child Welfare Unit of the State Welfare Agency;

2. that physicians may, in addition, file a report directly with an appropriate law enforcement agency;

3. that the Child Welfare Unit be granted full power to investigate all reported cases, to take remedial action within its competence, and to petition the appropriate court for any judicial assistance necessary to accomplish the most satisfactory results, such as a change in custody;

4. that the Child Welfare Unit shall maintain a central registry of cases reported under the statute.

These amendments would assure that state intervention would be effective in helping to solve the problems revealed by the increased visibility of battered child cases. Their enactment will fulfill the stated purpose of the existing statute by causing "the protective services of the state to be brought to bear on the situation in an effort to prevent further abuses, protect and enhance the welfare of these children and preserve family life wherever possible."

## (2) Right to Privacy

The many difficulties faced by the medical profession in determining when and under what circumstances the patient's desire for privacy may be disregarded are discussed in this Note.

### *Medical Practice and the Right to Privacy,* 43 Minn. L. Rev. 943 (1959)*

The right to privacy is the "right of the individual to be let alone," and to be free from unwarranted and undesired publicity, whether true or false. Law books and legal periodicals teem with cases and articles on the right to privacy, and the state of the law developing around the protection of that right is aptly described as that of a "haystack in a hurricane."

Cases where a patient alleges that his right to privacy has been violated by his physician often involve a difficult balancing of conflicting interests. To enable proper diagnosis and treatment of his physical or mental disorders, the patient must reveal to his doctor information concerning intimate personal matters. His right to prevent undesired public disclosure of this information very often collides head on with the public interest in having it disclosed to further the progress of medical science, to protect some third person likely to be affected by the patient's condition, or to aid in the care and treatment of the patient himself.

This Note will (1) examine the privacy problems raised by the doctor-patient relationship; (2) analyze the types of privacy interests involved in these problems, and the legal defenses or justifications for many privacy invasions; and (3) suggest some possible improvements in the law regarding enforcement of a patient's right to privacy.

### THE DOCTOR'S DILEMMA

The physician's ethical duty to keep secret all confidential information obtained from his patients is founded on the Hippocratic oath, in which he pledges that "What I may see or hear in the course of the treatment or even outside of the treatment in regard to the life of man, which on no account one must spread abroad, I will keep to myself holding such things shameful to be spoken about." The duty of professional secrecy has been adopted by the American Medical Association in its Principles of Medical Ethics; the British Medical Association has taken an even stronger position on this professional duty.

The duty of professional secrecy is not based merely on an altruistic ideal of "sacredness of the relationship"; nor is it based solely on interests of common

* Reprinted with permission of the *Minnesota Law Review.*

decency in protecting the patient's reputation or his peace of mind, although these factors are both important underlying reasons for keeping confidential information secret. The principal reason is that without some assurance that information given to the doctor will be kept in confidence, a patient might be reluctant to reveal embarrassing facts which could be vital to proper diagnosis or treatment. And so the physician has a very serious obligation, both to his patient and to his profession, to keep all the information he acquires during the course of his professional relationships absolutely secret.

But occasionally a doctor may learn that some third person will be exposed to danger from the peculiar disease or disability of his patient, or that someone is about to commit a crime, or even that a crime has already been committed. In these cases, if his patient insists on secrecy, the doctor is in a very unenviable position; his ethical duty to remain silent may be at war with his "moral inclinations and duty as a citizen . . . to do all in his power to prevent harm to others." Furthermore, even legal compulsion to speak may not ethically justify disclosure of the confidential information in a particular case. Two eminent medical ethics authorities have recently asserted that "The principal element of a doctor's judgment should be concern for his patient. . . . Conscience must be above even law when it confronts political dictates that are unjustifiable from the medical standpoint." What then should the doctor do? Although both legal and ethical problems are raised in these cases, this Note will discuss only the extent to which the patient can *compel* his doctor *as a matter of law* to respect his personal interest in privacy. . . .

## DEFENSES TO THE PATIENT'S PRIVACY ACTION

A doctor may raise any of three principal defenses to a patient's privacy action: (1) The patient may have consented to the particular privacy invasion; (2) the doctor may be required by law to invade the patient's privacy; and (3) the doctor's duty not to invade his patient's privacy interests may be outweighed by a more compelling duty to protect some other sufficiently important interest.

### Consent

Consent to a particular privacy invasion, by a patient who fully understands all the relevant circumstances, will *always* be an absolute defense to any subsequent action based on that privacy invasion. But even expressed consent will be insufficient to protect the doctor if, under the circumstances, he should have realized that the patient did not fully understand what he was consenting to, and that if the patient had understood he might have refused the consent. In *DeMay v. Roberts* the court held:

The fact that at the time, [the plaintiff] . . . consented to the presence of [the defendant's layman friend] . . . supposing him to be a physician, does not preclude her from maintaining an action and recovering substantial damages upon afterwards ascertaining his true character. . . . [The defendant was] guilty of deceit, and the wrong thus done entitles the injured party to recover the damages afterwards sustained.

Furthermore, even when valid consent has been obtained, the doctor will be liable for any privacy invasion exceeding that consent.

Of course, consent will be implied to any privacy invasion that the patient can reasonably expect to be necessary for proper diagnosis or treatment of his case. For example, by consulting a doctor, the patient impliedly consents to the doctor's keeping ordinary medical records of the patient's case, and to the customary and foreseeable use of these records. However, in most cases no consent would be implied to photographing the patient, since normally he would not expect to be photographed by the doctor.

## Duty Imposed by Law

A doctor can be forced to disclose confidential information whenever he is called as a witness in a lawsuit, unless his patient properly asserts the physician-patient privilege. And in almost all states, a doctor is required by statute to inform designated public officials whenever he finds a patient suffering from certain highly contagious diseases: these statutes often apply specifically to venereal diseases or to tuberculosis. Some states also have enacted legislation requiring that whenever a doctor treats a woman for injuries caused by a criminal abortion, he must report the facts of the case to health authorities or to the police. Physicians who strictly comply with these statutes will not be liable for invasion of the patient's right to privacy.

## Overriding Competing Interests

One British authority, curious whether doctors themselves feel they should violate their duty of professional secrecy under some circumstances by disclosing confidential information, has questioned a large group of doctors practicing in the area near Derby, England. The results of his study indicate overwhelmingly that most practicing physicians are willing to disclose confidential information in certain compelling cases, and that a sizable minority of them would do so in cases that arguably are *not* very compelling.

A patient's legal right to enforce his doctor's duty of professional secrecy quite obviously cannot be absolute. Like any other personal right, it must bow before more important competing interests. The problem is simply to determine what interests are "more important"; that is, to provide guides to help a doctor or an attorney decide whether an interest dictating disclosure in a particular case is sufficient to justify violating the patient's confidence.

*(1) Protecting Others Endangered by the Patient's Condition. Simonsen v. Swenson* is probably the strongest case for allowing the doctor to disclose confidential information. In that case, the patient was exposing other roomers in the hotel to his highly contagious disease. The court held that disclosure of this information to the hotel owner was justified. It would be unreasonable to expect the doctor, whose professional efforts are directed almost exclusively to preventing or relieving disease, to remain silent while one of his patients obstinately subjects others to the danger of being infected with a serious disease.

Doctors are often called upon to protect some third person by disclosing information concerning one of their patients. In *Berry v. Moench*, a recent Utah case arising out of this type of situation, a psychiatrist was asked by another physician for "your impression of" one of his former patients. The letter explained that the patient was courting a young girl, and that the girl's parents had come to the physician for advice. The psychiatrist replied, in part:

Dear Doctor ———,

Since I do not have his authorization, the patient you mentioned in your last letter will remain nameless.

He was treated here in 1949 as an emergency. Our diagnosis was manic depressive depression in a psychopathic personality. . . .

He had one brother as a manic, and his father committed suicide. . . .

The patient was attempting to go through school on the G.I. bill. . . .

Instead of attending class he would spend most of the days and nights playing cards for money.

Because of family circumstances, we treated him for a mere token charge (and I notice even that has never been paid).

During his care here, he purchased a brand new Packard, without even money to buy gasoline.

He was in constant trouble with the authorities during the war, . . .

. . . did not do well in school, and never did really support his wife and children.

Since he was here, we have repeated requests for his record indicating repeated trouble. . . .

My suggestion to the infatuated girl would be to run as fast and as far as she possibly could in any direction away from him.

Of course, if he doesn't marry her, he will marry someone else and make life hell for that person. The usual story is repeated unsuccessful marriages and a trail of tragedy behind.

This letter was given to the girl's parents, who gave it to the girl herself. The Utah court said, "[The girl's] concern for her well-being and happiness was a sufficient interest to protect, and . . . it was within the generally accepted standards of decent conduct for the doctor to reveal the information which might have an important bearing thereon."

But not every case involving protection of others will justify disclosure. *Kitson v. Playfair*, indicates that protecting the doctor's own wife and family from associating with immoral women is not a sufficient interest to override the duty of secrecy.

*(2) Serving Various Interests of Society.* Fairly clearly, neither publication of "newsworthy" material nor advancement of medical science will justify an invasion of the patient's right to privacy. Some years ago, the Attorney General of New York was forced to balance these social interests against the patient's interest in privacy. The State Department of Health had sought an opinion on the legality of displaying at a state fair photographs of cancer victims "for educational purposes without the consent of the subjects of the photographs and without altering the photographs so as to make them unidentifiable." The Attorney General concluded that this display would violate the cancer victims' privacy:

While it is true that the contemplated use may have a distinct social value for the general instruction and information of the public, yet I believe that the unauthorized use of such pictures is barred by the provisions of the [privacy] statute. . . . The unfortunate person afflicted with a malignant disease such as cancer may very well have a perfectly natural and readily understandable aversion to having a photograph or picture showing his condition displayed before the public. Apart from the legal question involved, it seems improper, to say the least, to add to the mental anguish of one so afflicted the fear that photographs portraying his condition will be publicly displayed.

Ordinarily, of course, these interests of society can be fully satisfied without disclosing the identity of the patient whose case is described or discussed.

But it would be a mistake to conclude that interests of society never justify disclosing confidential information. For example, the situation posed in Question 3 of the Dawson study, where the doctor knew that his patient's claim for relief from a state fund was fraudulent, could very easily be held to justify such a disclosure. Although the interest in protecting a state fund from small fraudulent claims might be considered relatively insubstantial, it probably outweighs the patient's interest in making fraudulent personal gains. Furthermore, confidence in the integrity of the doctor-patient relationship is not likely to be substantially impaired if patients learn that their doctors could speak up whenever they fraudulently misrepresent the nature of their injuries.

*(3) Protecting the Patient Himself.* Only one case, *Iverson v. Frandsen*, raises the issue whether protection of the patient himself will justify invading his privacy, although the court's holdings turned on a different issue. In that case, the parents had taken the child patient to a mental hospital for help in overcoming her claustrophobia. The results of an I.Q. test and several other tests given to the patient at the hospital were recorded in a standard hospital report. These tests revealed that she was a "feeble-minded" high-grade moron, and the report predicted that "at the time she is about sixteen, she should have progressed to about the fourth grade level in reading, arithmetic, writing, etc." A copy of the report was sent to the guidance director of the child's school, on his request, and a while later embarrassing rumors about the child's mental ability spread throughout the school.

The doctor could reasonably feel that for the good of the child, information about her mental and emotional problems should be given to the officials at her school. When they understand these problems, they can plan special instruction to help the child make the greatest possible use of the abilities she has. But the serious harmful effect on the child from embarrassing rumors likely to follow disclosure of this information could outweigh the advantages from informing the school authorities. Since in this type of case both of the competing interests concern only the welfare of the patient, he is best able to decide which is more important *to him*. Absent consent, then, the doctor should not be justified in revealing the confidential information. . . .

Conclusion

It is appropriate now to suggest a few general rules to govern lawsuits based on unauthorized disclosure of confidential information. As a basic principle, the law should honor the judgment of a doctor who reasonably decides that he must reveal certain information to protect an interest that he believes, in good faith, is more important than his patient's interest in keeping the information secret. The doctor, after all, is the one who must balance the conflicting interests in these cases, and as a practical matter his discretion in each case must be accepted. A court should inquire only whether, under the circumstances, the doctor exercised his discretion reasonably; preceding sections of this Note have discussed the reasonableness of disclosure in some of the more common situations. Any decision to divulge confidential information, however, should be subject to the following limitations:

1. The doctor must first explain to the patient that disclosure is necessary, except when he would hurt the patient by doing so. The patient should have an opportunity to determine to whom the information will be revealed, and the manner of disclosure.

2. The doctor must use all reasonable care to know that the information is both accurate and true.

3. The doctor must not disclose any confidential information unnecessary to protecting the competing interest.

4. The doctor must not disclose such information to anyone who is unnecessary to protecting the competing interest.

5. The doctor must take all reasonable precautions to avoid any foreseeable harm to the patient from the disclosure of this information.

So long as the doctor complies with these rules he can and must rely on his own good conscience.

# CASES

The following cases are illustrative of inadvertent involvement of the nurse and the physician in litigation, even though there was no question concerning the skill and the quality of care given. Had the nurse or the physician been fully aware of the legal implications of their acts might they in each instance have changed the course of events?

## *Mohr v. Williams,* 95 Minn. 261, 104 N.W. 12 (1905)

Brown, J. Defendant is a physician and surgeon of standing and character, making disorders of the ear a specialty, and having an extensive practice in the city of St. Paul. He was consulted by plaintiff, who complained to him of trouble with her right ear, and, at her request, made an examination of that organ for the purpose of ascertaining its condition. He also at the same time examined her left ear, but, owing to foreign substances therein, was unable to make a full and complete diagnosis at that time. The examination of her right ear disclosed a large perforation in the lower portion of the drum membrane, and a large polyp in the middle ear, which indicated that some of the small bones of the middle ear (ossicles) were probably diseased. He informed plaintiff of the result of his examination, and advised an operation for the purpose of removing the polyp and diseased ossicles. After consultation with her family physician, and one or two further consultations with defendant, plaintiff decided to submit to the proposed operation. She was not informed that her left ear was in any way diseased, and understood that the necessity for an operation applied to her right ear only. She repaired to the hospital, and was placed under the influence of anaesthetics; and, after being made unconscious, defendant made a thorough examination of her left ear, and found it in a more serious condition than her right one. A small perforation was discovered high up in the drum membrane, hooded, and with granulated edges, and the bone of the inner wall of the middle ear was diseased and dead. He called this discovery to the attention of Dr. Davis—plaintiff's family physician, who attended the operation at her request—who also examined the ear, and confirmed defendant in his diagnosis. Defendant also further examined the right ear, and found its condition less serious than expected, and finally concluded that the left, instead of the right, should be operated upon; devoting to the right ear other treatment. He then performed the operation of ossiculectomy on plaintiff's left ear; removing a portion of the drum membrane, and scraping away the diseased portion of the inner wall of the ear. The operation was in every way successful and skillfully performed. It is claimed by plaintiff that the operation greatly impaired her hearing, seriously injured her person, and, not having been consented to by her, was wrongful and unlawful, constituting an assault and battery; and she brought this action to recover damages therefor. The trial in the court below resulted in a verdict for plaintiff for $14,322.50. . . .

We come then to a consideration of the questions presented by defendant's appeal from the order denying his motion for judgment notwithstanding the verdict. It is contended that final judgment should be ordered in his favor for the following reasons: (a) That it appears from the evidence received on the trial that plaintiff consented to the operation on her left ear. (b) If the court shall find that no such consent was given, that, under the circumstances disclosed by the record, no consent was necessary. (c) That, under the facts disclosed, an action for assault and battery will not lie; it appearing conclusively, as counsel urge, that there is a total lack of evidence showing or tending to show malice or an evil intent on the part of defendant, or that the operation was negligently performed.

We shall consider first the question whether, under the circumstances shown in the record, the consent of plaintiff to the operation was necessary. If, under the particular facts of this case, such consent was unnecessary, no recovery can be had, for the evidence fairly shows that the operation complained of was skillfully performed and of a generally beneficial nature. But if the consent of plaintiff was necessary, then the further questions presented become important. This particular question is new in this state. At least, no case has been called to our attention wherein it has been discussed or decided, and very few cases are cited from other courts. We have given it very deliberate consideration, and are unable to concur with counsel for defendant in their contention that the consent of plaintiff was unnecessary. The evidence tends to show that, upon the first examination of plaintiff, defendant pronounced the left ear in good condition, and that, at the time plaintiff repaired to the hospital to submit to the operation on her right ear, she was under the impression that no difficulty existed as to the left. In fact, she testified that she had not previously experienced any trouble with that organ. It cannot be doubted that ordinarily the patient must be consulted, and his consent given, before a physician may operate upon him. It was said in the case of Pratt v. Davis, 37 Chicago Leg. News, 213, referred to and commented on in Cent. Law J. 452: "Under a free government, at least, the free citizen's first and greatest right, which underlies all others—the right to the inviolability of his person; in other words, the right to himself—is the subject of universal acquiescence, and this right necessarily forbids a physician or surgeon, however skillful or eminent, who has been asked to examine, diagnose, advise, and prescribe (which are at least necessary first steps in treatment and care), to violate, without permission, the bodily integrity of his patient by a major or capital operation, placing him under an anaesthetic for that purpose, and operating upon him without his consent or knowledge." 1 Kinkead on Torts, § 375, states the general rule on this subject as follows: "The patient must be the final arbiter as to whether he will take his chances with the operation, or take his chances of living without it. Such is the natural right of the individual, which the law recognizes as a legal one. Consent, therefore, of an individual, must be either expressly or impliedly given before a surgeon may have the right to operate." There is logic in the principle thus stated, for, in all other trades, professions, or occupations, contracts are entered into by the mutual agreement of the interested parties, and are required to be performed in accordance with their letter and spirit. No reason occurs to us why the same rule should not apply between physician and patient. If the physician advises his patient to submit to a particular operation, and the patient weighs the dangers and risks incident to its performance, and finally consents, he thereby, in effect, enters into a contract authorizing his physician to operate to the extent of the consent given, but no further. It is not, however, contended by defendant that under ordinary circumstances consent is unnecessary, but that, under the particular circumstances of this case, consent was implied; that it was an emergency case, such as to authorize the operation without express consent or permission. The medical profession has made signal progress in solving the problems of health and disease, and they may justly point with pride to the advancements made in supplementing nature and correcting deformities, and relieving pain and suffering. The physician impliedly contracts that he possesses, and will exercise in the treatment of patients, skill and learning, and that he will exercise reasonable care and exert his best judgment to bring about favorable results. The methods of treatment are committed almost exclusively to his judgment, but we are aware of no rule or principle of law which would extend to him free license respecting surgical operations. Reasonable latitude must, however, be allowed the physician in a particular case; and we would not lay down any rule which would unreasonably interfere with the exercise of his discretion, or prevent him from taking such measures as his judgment dictated for the welfare of the patient in a case of emergency. If a person should be injured to the extent of rendering him unconscious, and his injuries were of such a nature as to require prompt surgical attention, a physician called to attend him would be justified in applying such medical or surgical treatment as might reasonably be necessary for the preservation of his life or limb, and consent on the part of the injured person would be implied. And again, if, in the course of an operation to which the patient consented, the physician should discover conditions not anticipated before the operation was commenced, and which, if not removed, would endanger the life or health of the patient, he would, though no express consent was obtained or given, be justified in extending the operation to remove and overcome them. But such is not the case at bar. The diseased condition of plaintiff's left ear was not discovered in the course of an operation on the right, which was authorized, but upon an independent examination of that organ, made after the authorized operation was found unnecessary. Nor is the evidence such as to justify the court in holding, as a matter of law, that it was such an affection as would result immediately in the serious injury of plaintiff, or such an emergency as to justify proceeding without her consent. She had experienced no particular difficulty with that ear, and the questions as to when its diseased condition would become alarming or fatal, and whether there was an immediate necessity for an operation, were, under the evidence, questions of fact for the jury.

The contention of defendant that the operation was consented to by plaintiff is not sustained by the evidence. At least, the evidence was such as to take the question to the jury. This contention is based upon the fact that she was represented on the occasion in question by her family physician; that the condition of her left ear was made known to him, and the propriety of an operation thereon suggested, to which he made no objection. It is urged that by his conduct he assented to it, and that plaintiff was bound thereby. It is not claimed that he gave his express consent. It is not disputed but that the family physician of plaintiff was present on the occasion of the operation, and at her request. But the purpose of his presence was not that he might participate in the operation, nor does it appear that he was authorized to consent to any change in the one originally proposed to be made. Plaintiff was naturally nervous and fearful of the consequences of being placed under the influence of anaesthetics, and the presence of her family physician was requested under the impression that it would allay and calm her fears. The evidence made the question one of fact for the jury to determine.

The last contention of defendant is that the act complained of did not amount to an assault and battery. This is based upon the theory that, as plaintiff's left ear was in fact diseased, in a condition dangerous and threatening to her health, the operation was necessary, and, having been skillfully performed at a time when plaintiff had requested a like operation on the other ear, the charge of assault and battery cannot be sustained; that, in view of these conditions, and the claim that there was no negligence on the part of defendant, and an entire absence of any evidence tending to show an evil intent, the court should say, as a matter of law, that no assault and battery was committed, even though she did not consent to the operation. In other words, that the absence of a showing that defendant was actuated by a wrongful intent, or guilty of negligence, relieves the act of defendant from the charge of an unlawful assault and battery. We are unable to reach that conclusion, though the contention is not without merit. It would seem to follow from what has been said on the other features of the case that the act of defendant amounted at least to a technical assault and battery. If the operation was performed without plaintiff's consent, and the circumstances were not such as to justify its performance without, it was wrongful; and, if it was wrongful, it was unlawful. As remarked in 1 Jaggard on Torts, 437, every person has a right to complete immunity of his person from physical interference of others, except in so far as contact may be necessary under the general doctrine of privilege; and any unlawful or unauthorized touching of the person of another, except it be in the spirit of pleasantry, constitutes an assault and battery. In the case at bar, as we have already seen, the question whether defendant's act in performing the operation upon plaintiff was authorized was a question for the jury to determine. If it was unauthorized, then it was, within what we have said, unlawful. It was a violent assault, not a mere pleasantry; and even though no negligence is shown, it was wrongful and unlawful. The case is unlike a criminal prosecution for assault and battery, for there an unlawful intent must be shown. But that rule does not apply to a civil action, to maintain which it is sufficient to show that the assault complained of was wrongful and unlawful or the result of negligence.

The amount of plaintiff's recovery, if she is entitled to recover at all, must depend upon the character and extent of the injury inflicted upon her, in determining which the nature of the malady intended to be healed and the beneficial nature of the operation should be taken into consideration, as well as the good faith of the defendant.

Order affirmed.

## ANALYSIS

1. In the trial court the defendant was found guilty of assault and battery. A major issue was whether, if the patient had consented to an operation on her right ear, it would then follow that no consent was necessary for surgery on the left ear. How did the court reason and decide the issue?

2. Another contention of the defendant was that absence of negligence or evil intent relieved the defendant from charges of unlawful assault and battery. Do you believe that the fact that an operation was competently performed and based on good medical judgment should be considered when the issue is whether the plaintiff consented?

3. Under what circumstances discussed in the decision might the surgeon have been justified in extending the operation?

4. The presence of the family physician, at the request of the patient, was used as evidence in what way and what was response of the court?

5. What considerations did the court propose in allowing plaintiff to recover?

## *McGuire v. Almy,* 297 Mass. 323, 8 N.E.2d 760 (1937)

Qua, Justice.

This is an action of tort for assault and battery. The only question of law reported is whether the judge should have directed a verdict for the defendant.

The following facts are established by the plaintiff's own evidence: In August, 1930, the plaintiff was employed to take care of the defendant. The plaintiff was a registered nurse and was a graduate of a training school for nurses. The defendant was an insane person. Before the plaintiff was hired she learned that the defendant was a "mental case and was in good physical condition," and that for some time two nurses had been taking care of her. The plaintiff was on "24 hour duty." The plaintiff slept in the room next to the defendant's room. Except when the plaintiff was with the defendant, the plaintiff kept the defendant locked in the defendant's room. There was a wire grating over the outside of the window of that room. During the period of "fourteen months or so" while the plaintiff cared for the defendant, the defendant "had a few odd spells," when she showed some hostility to the plaintiff and said that "she would like to try and do something to her." The defendant had been violent at times and had broken dishes "and things like that," and on one or two occasions the plaintiff had to have help to subdue the defendant.

On April 19, 1932, the defendant, while locked in her room, had a violent attack. The plaintiff heard a crashing of furniture and then knew that the defendant was ugly, violent and dangerous. The defendant told the plaintiff and a Miss

Maroney, "the maid," who was with the plaintiff in the adjoining room, that if they came into the defendant's room, she would kill them. The plaintiff and Miss Maroney looked into the defendant's room, "saw what the defendant had done," and "thought it best to take the broken stuff away before she did any harm to herself with it." They sent for a Mr. Emerton, the defendant's brother-in-law. When he arrived the defendant was in the middle of her room about ten feet from the door, holding upraised the leg of a low-boy as if she were going to strike. The plaintiff stepped into the room and walked toward the defendant, while Mr. Emerton and Miss Maroney remained in the doorway. As the plaintiff approached the defendant and tried to take hold of the defendant's hand which held the leg, the defendant struck the plaintiff's head with it, causing the injuries for which the action was brought.

The extent to which an insane person is liable for torts has not been fully defined in this Commonwealth. Dickinson v. Barber, 9 Mass. 225, 6 Am.Dec. 58, turned upon questions of evidence in an action for slander. However, the implication of the case seems to favor liability. . . .

Turning to authorities elsewhere, we find that courts in this country almost invariably say in the broadest terms that an insane person is liable for his torts. As a rule no distinction is made between those torts which would ordinarily be classed as intentional and those which would ordinarily be classed as negligent, nor do the courts discuss the effect of different kinds of insanity or of varying degrees of capacity as bearing upon the ability of the defendant to understand the particular act in question or to make a reasoned decision with respect to it, although it is sometimes said that an insane person is not liable for torts requiring malice of which he is incapable. Defamation and malicious prosecution are the torts more commonly mentioned in this connection. A number of illustrative cases appears in the footnote. These decisions are rested more upon grounds of public policy and upon what might be called a popular view of the requirements of essential justice than upon any attempt to apply logically the underlying principles of civil liability to the special instance of the mentally deranged. Thus it is said that a rule imposing liability tends to make more watchful those persons who have charge of the defendant and who may be supposed to have some interest in preserving his property; that as an insane person must pay for his support, if he is financially able, so he ought also to pay for the damage which he does; that an insane person with abundant wealth ought not to continue in unimpaired enjoyment of the comfort which it brings while his victim bears the burden unaided; and there is also a suggestion that courts are loath to introduce into the great body of civil litigation the difficulties in determining mental capacity which it has been found impossible to avoid in the criminal field.

The rule established in these cases has been criticized severely by certain eminent text writers both in this country and in England, principally on the ground that it is an archaic survival of the rigid and formal mediaeval conception of liability for acts done, without regard to fault, as opposed to what is said to be the general modern theory that liability in tort should rest upon fault. Notwithstanding these criticisms, we think, that as a practical matter, there is strong force in the reasons underlying these decisions. They are consistent with the general statements found in the cases dealing with the liability of infants for torts, including a few cases in which the child was so young as to render his capacity for fault comparable to that of many insane persons. Fault is by no means at the present day a universal pre-requisite to liability, and the theory that it should be such has been obliged very recently to yield at several points to what have been thought to be paramount considerations of public good. Finally, it would be difficult not to recognize the persuasive weight of so much authority so widely extended.

But the present occasion does not require us either to accept or to reject the prevailing doctrine in its entirety. For this case it is enough to say that where an insane person by his act does intentional damage to the person or property of another he is liable for that damage in the same circumstances in which a normal person would be liable. This means that in so far as a particular intent would be necessary in order to render a normal person liable, the insane person, in order to be liable, must have been capable of entertaining that same intent and must have entertained it in fact. But the law will not inquire further into his peculiar mental condition with a view to excusing him if it should appear that delusion or other consequence of his affliction has caused him to entertain that intent or that a normal person would not have entertained it.

We do not suggest that this is necessarily a logical stopping point. If public policy demands that a mentally affected person be subjected to the external standard for intentional wrongs, it may well be that public policy also demands that he should be subjected to the external standards for wrongs which are commonly classified as negligent, in accordance with what now seems to be the prevailing view. We stop here for the present, because we are not required to go further in order to decide this case, because of deference to the difficulty of the subject, because full and adequate discussion is lacking in most of the cases decided up to the present time, and because by far the greater number of those cases, however broad their statement of the principle, are in fact cases of intentional rather than of negligent injury.

Coming now to the application of the rule to the facts of this case, it is apparent that the jury could find that the defendant was capable of entertaining and that she did entertain an intent to strike and to injure the plaintiff and that she acted upon that intent. We think this was enough.

The defendant further argues that she is not liable because the plaintiff, by undertaking to care for the defendant with knowledge of the defendant's condition and by walking into the room in spite of the defendant's threat under the circum-stances shown, consented to the injury, or, as the defendant puts it, assumed the risk, both contractually and voluntarily. Without considering to what extent consent is in general a defence to an assault (see American Law Institute Restatement, Torts, § 13), we think that the defendant was not entitled to a directed verdict on this ground. Although the plaintiff knew when she was employed that the de-fendant was a mental case, and despite some show of hostility and some violent and unruly conduct, there was no evidence of any previous attack or even of any serious threat against anyone. The plaintiff had taken care of the defendant for "fourteen months or so." We think that the danger of actual physical injury was not, as matter of law, plain and obvious up to the time when the plaintiff entered the room on the occasion of the assault. But by that time an emergency had been created. The defendant was breaking up the furniture, and it could have been found that the plaintiff reasonably feared that the defendant would do harm to herself. Something had to be done about it. The plaintiff had assumed the duty of caring for the defendant. We think that a reasonable attempt on her part to perform that duty under the peculiar circumstances brought about by the defendant's own act did not necessarily indicate a voluntary consent to be injured. Consent does not always follow from the intentional incurring of risk. "The degree of danger, the stress of circumstances, the expectation or hope that others will fully perform the duties resting on them, may all have to be considered." Judgment for the plaintiff on the verdict.

## ANALYSIS

1. In the charges of assault and battery, what was the reasoning of the court in dealing with the element of intent to harm with respect to an insane person and with his accountability for his act?

2. In tort liability why is there special treatment for malicious acts? Do you agree?

3. If the act of intervention by the nurse were viewed as one of consent, what might be the implications for the nursing care of the mentally ill? How did the court reason on the act of intervention by the nurse?

4. Reasoning that liability should rest on fault is said to be yielding to considerations of public good. How would you apply this to the facts of this case? Inasmuch as the rule imposing liability rests on public policy, how would it be justified in this and similar instances?

5. What was the decision in this case? Was this one of the unavoidable risks of psychiatric nursing or might the harm and resulting litigation have been avoided?

## *Geddes v. Daughters of Charity of St. Vincent De Paul, Inc.,* 348 F.2d 144 (5th Cir. 1965)

Sheehy, District Judge:

... The case was tried before a jury. At the close of the plaintiff's evidence the trial court, on motion of the defendants, directed a verdict in favor of the defendants and entered judgment accordingly. The sole question on appeal is whether the district court erred in granting the directed verdict. . . .

Miss Geddes was a life-long resident of Natchez, Mississippi, who was 59 years of age at the time of the trial of this case. Prior to the events which gave rise to the present litigation, Miss Geddes was retired and lived in her family home supported by the income from an inherited trust, which was administered by Francis Geddes, her brother and closest living relative. Miss Geddes had a long history of a number of ailments including alcoholism, drug addiction, and a series of abdominal problems. The last mentioned problems resulted from a ruptured appendix which she suffered when she was a teenager. She had no history of previous treatment for a mental disorder.

In 1959, Miss Geddes was taken by her brother to the Natchez Sanitarium at Natchez, Mississippi, for treatment after he had been summoned to her home by her maid when the maid was unable to arouse Miss Geddes. At this institution she was under the care of a Dr. Stowers who had treated Miss Geddes before her other illnesses and who diagnosed her present condition as a probable addiction to a sedative. After several weeks of treatment at the Natchez Sanitarium, Dr. Stowers concluded that psychiatric care would be required and recommended that Miss Geddes be transferred to the De Paul Hospital in New Orleans. After consultation with Dr. Stowers and with her brother, Miss Geddes agreed to be taken to the De Paul Hospital for treatment.

Miss Geddes was driven to the De Paul Hospital by her brother, accompanied by two nurses. Upon their arrival she was taken directly to the room assigned her while her brother took care of the details of the admission procedure. A psychiatrist, Dr. William Sorum, was given charge of Miss Geddes' case and saw her at regular intervals during her hospitalization at De Paul Hospital which lasted for one year and 22 days.

Miss Geddes testified, in effect, that when she was discussing with her brother and Dr. Sorum the matter of her going to the De Paul Hospital, she was not told that said hospital was a mental institution nor was she told that she had a mental condition and was going to receive psychiatric treatment at De Paul's; that at the time she entered De Paul's she did not know it was a mental institution and thought it to be a general medical hospital at which she was to receive medical treatments for the abdominal adhesions which had troubled her for a number of years; that she never requested nor authorized anyone to administer treatment to her for a mental condition; and that she did not realize that the hospital was a mental institution until some two days after her admission when she heard some of the other patients discussing their various ailments and was asked by them the nature of her own mental problems. This testimony was substantiated, at least to some degree, by the hospital record wherein an entry note made by a nurse on the date of Miss Geddes' admission to the hospital shows that Miss Geddes at that time stated to the nurse: "I had adhesions. That's what I'm in here for now."

Following Miss Geddes learning that the De Paul Hospital was a mental institution she requested of Dr. Sorum and the various nurses and nuns on the staff that she be released and allowed to leave the hospital. These requests were viewed by the hospital as the customary and usual complaints almost universal among psychiatric patients and were ignored. On a few occasions Miss Geddes was permitted to leave the hospital to go shopping and/or attend various entertainment attractions in New Orleans. However, on each of said occasions she was accompanied by an employee of the hospital as an attendant and was given by the hospital staff a small amount of money which was sufficient only to cover her expenses for the day.

In August 1960 Miss Geddes sent a letter to an attorney in Natchez, Mississippi, asking that he assist her in getting out of the hospital. Shortly thereafter there was instituted on behalf of Miss Geddes in a civil district court of the Parish of Orleans a habeas corpus proceeding naming the Daughters of Charity of St. Vincent De Paul, Inc., as the respondent. A hearing in that proceeding resulted in the court ordering and directing the hospital to release Miss Geddes. Subsequent to the conclusion of that proceeding Miss Geddes instituted this action seeking to recover the damages she suffered and expenses incurred as a result of her alleged false imprisonment at De Paul Hospital.

Under Louisiana law there are two essential elements to the tort of false imprisonment, namely, (1) there must be a detention or restraint of the person, and (2) such detention or restraint must be unlawful.

As to the first element the defendants contend that the restraint of Miss Geddes was not sufficient to meet the requirements of a false imprisonment in that there were reasonable means of escape available to Miss Geddes which she failed to exercise. While there is evidence that would support a finding that there were reasonable means of escape available to Miss Geddes which she failed to exercise, there is evidence that would support a finding that no such means of escape were available. The evidence reflects that while Miss Geddes was in the hospital there were at least two locked doors barring her from leaving the institution, and there is ample evidence from which the jury could reasonably infer that the hospital personnel would have prevented Miss Geddes from leaving the hospital had she attempted to do so. As to the trips Miss Geddes occasionally was permitted to take to downtown New Orleans, the evidence shows she was always escorted on said trips by a nurse or other attendant and was given only five to ten dollars in money to cover her expenses of the trip which was not sufficient money to get her back to Natchez, her hometown, and she knew no one in New Orleans to whom she could turn for help had she been able to elude her companion. Such facts as those coupled with her ill health, age, and weakened condition are such that we must conclude that reasonable men in an impartial exercise of their judgment could reach different conclusions as to whether there were reasonable means of escape available to Miss Geddes during all or any part of the time she was confined in the De Paul Hospital.

It is without dispute that Miss Geddes was not confined in the De Paul Hospital as a result of formal commitment proceedings. As to the lawfulness of the detention of Miss Geddes, the defendants maintain that the restraint which was imposed, if sufficient to constitute an imprisonment, was lawful because Miss Geddes voluntarily presented herself for treatment at the hospital and, therefore, consented to such restraint as may have been imposed. Thus, the lawfulness of the detention or restraint of Miss Geddes by the defendant hospital rests upon whether such detention or restraint was consented to by Miss Geddes.

While it is true that Miss Geddes agreed to be taken to the De Paul Hospital and entered said hospital without any objection on her part, she contends that she did not *voluntarily* enter the hospital or consent to be treated there because she was not aware of the fact that the hospital was a mental institution at the time she entered and did not learn such fact until about two days after she was admitted. If Miss Geddes, at the time she entered the hospital, did not know it was a mental institution and that she was to receive psychiatric treatments there, it cannot be said that she voluntarily entered the hospital and consented to receive psychiatric treatment. As above demonstrated, there was sufficient evidence to warrant a jury finding that Miss Geddes at the time she entered the De Paul Hospital did not know that it was a mental institution and did not consent to receive psychiatric treatment there.

Furthermore, as above indicated, there is evidence to the effect that commencing approximately two days after her admission to De Paul's, Miss Geddes, on four or five occasions, "begged" Dr. Sorum to release her from the hospital and in addition thereto on several occasions requested both the head nurse and the nun in charge of her ward in the hospital to release her and let her go home. This evidence is of itself sufficient to authorize a jury finding that, at some point subsequent to her entry in the hospital and during her stay therein, Miss Geddes withdrew her consent to detention in the hospital given on her original entry and that further detention at the hospital subsequent to such withdrawal of the consent constituted a false imprisonment, even though the jury might have believed and found that Miss Geddes, upon her original entry in the hospital, consented to be detained therein and to be given psychiatric treatments.

For the reasons above stated, we are convinced that the evidence required that the issues as to the false imprisonment of Miss Geddes and her damages, if any, resulting therefrom be decided by the jury and that it was error for the court to decide them as a matter of law and direct a verdict in favor of the defendants.

The judgment of the trial court is reversed and the case is remanded for further proceedings not inconsistent with this opinion.

## ANALYSIS

1. From the facts identify necessary legal criteria that were fulfilled in establishing that false imprisonment occurred.

2. Under the Louisiana law two essential elements are cited in the decision as necessary to support a charge of false imprisonment. From the facts what was the argument for and against the charge that a reasonable means of escape was available to the plaintiff, which she failed to use? What are the facts that cloud the issue that the plaintiff voluntarily consented to being taken to the mental hospital? What is the evidence of withdrawal of consent, if in fact it was given?

3. The act of imprisonment may be said to be privileged if there is evidence that the person was a danger to himself or to the community. Would the facts in *Geddes* support the exercise of privilege for either of these reasons?

4. At one time restraint of the insane was an end in itself; today there is definite social interest in providing psychiatric treatment. To what extent was this interest recognized?

5. Hypothesize regarding the point at which the nursing staff might have taken action that might have prevented litigation?

6. What was the decision?

# CASES FOR FURTHER ANALYSIS

## *Banks v. King Features Syn., Inc.,* 30 F.Supp. 352 (S.D.N.Y. 1939)

This was an action against a New York newspaper for money damages for the alleged invasion of the plaintiff's right of privacy.

In the course of a physical examination and treatment, an x-ray of the patient's pelvis revealed a six-inch steel hemostat that had been carried by the plaintiff for four years as a consequence of surgery in another city. The hemostat was removed. The physicians without the patient's consent turned over the x-ray to a local newspaper reporter, who in turn, for a consideration, passed it to a newspaper syndicate, which then wrote a feature article and sold it to a New York newspaper. Plaintiff alleged she was humiliated and suffered agony, and loss of social prestige by the publicity. Neither the physician nor the local reporter was sued.

Apparently recognizing the right of privacy, the court ordered that a motion to dismiss be deferred until trial where all the facts could be adduced as to where the plaintiff's name and x-ray were first made public.

### *Rogers v. Lumbermens Mut. Cas. Co.,* 119 So.2d 649 (La. App. 1960)

This was an action brought by a patient and her husband against physicians and their insurer for unauthorized removal of the patient's reproductive organs when she had intended to submit to an appendectomy.

The patient had one daughter by her first marriage. In her second marriage, when she failed to become pregnant she consulted the defendant physicians and submitted to the treatment. Several months later she was admitted to the hospital by the defendant physicians to have an appendectomy performed. During the course of the surgery, it was necessary because of an unanticipated condition and for the patient's best interest and well-being, to perform a bilateral salpingo-oophorectomy.

No question of medical ethics or malpractice arose; the case turned on the point of consent. The evidence showed that the patient had never at any time given consent for other than the removal of the appendix and further that she was ignorant of any possibility of further surgery. When admitted to the hospital for the surgery, she signed a blanket consent form that authorized the physician and surgeon "to perform this operation which is advisable in the treatment of this patient" and also to administer such anesthetics as found necessary. In its review of the consent form the court stated:

We think the . . . so-called authorization is so ambiguous as to be almost completely worthless, and, certainly, since it fails to designate the nature of the operation authorized, and for which consent was given, it can have no possible weight under the factual circumstances of the instant case.

In addition, even though the husband of the patient and other members of her family were present in the hospital all during the operation, no effort was made to secure an extension of the consent upon finding a condition that warranted further surgery.

A decision in favor of the plaintiff patient was affirmed.

### Sarlat v. State of New York, 52 Misc.2d 240, 275 N.Y.S.2d 293 (Ct. Cl. 1966)

Here, an action was brought against the State of New York for injuries sustained by patient as result of assault of attendant.

Robert Sarlat had had several periods of hospitalization for a mental illness diagnosed as dementia praecox, catatonic type. His admission record reported his physical health as good, his mental state unstable, restless, and distractable, and noted his repetitive compulsion to touch people by means of light taps on the shoulder or arm. The supervising psychiatrist noted on the record that hospital personnel had been instructed to understand the patient's needs and to expect and to permit this compulsive touching.

A ward attendant, who stated he had not been informed of the patient's condition, told him to stop tapping the floor and threatened him if he continued. At the same time the patient had a compulsive desire to touch the attendant and did so, which led to an exchange of blows that resulted in the patient's sustaining a fractured mandible. A period of hospitalization followed that included oral surgery to wire teeth dislocated by the force of the blow to the head and the face.

The state was found liable for damages inflicted by the ward attendant, on the ground that the hospital authorities failed to acquaint an attendant who served in the plaintiff's ward with plaintiff's condition and propensities.

### Petition of Nemser, 51 Misc.2d 616, 273 N.Y.S.2d 624 (Sup. Ct. 1966)

This is an application by two of three sons for an appointment as temporary legal representative of their mother for the purpose of executing a consent to a transmalleolar amputation of the right ankle and foot. The facts showed that two of three sons had concluded that their mother required the specified medical treatment to save her life, and that there was a question as to her ability to understand the proceeding. The court appointed a psychiatrist and a guardian *ad litem* to investigate her condition, and each concluded that she was incapable of fully understanding the essentials of the operation and its potential effect on her, but each recommended that the court not intervene. The son opposing the procedure was a doctor, who took the position that it was not an emergency, and that the mother, a diabetic, might not be materially aided by the operation. The court concluded that intervention was not desirable, and in the course of the opinion made repeated strong statements criticizing the medical profession for failure to use its own judgment in such circumstances.

## Recommended Source Material

TEXTS

Gregory, C., and Kalven, H., Jr., *Cases and Materials on Torts*, 21–63 (Boston: Little, Brown & Co., 1959).

Harper, F., and James, F., *The Law of Torts*, Vol. 1, 211–99 (Boston: Little, Brown & Co., 1956).

Prosser, W., *Handbook of the Law of Torts*, 28–62, 829–51 (St. Paul: West Publishing Co., 3rd ed., 1964).

Shartel, B., and Plant, M., *The Law of Medical Practice*, 10–28, 171–80 (Springfield, Ill.: Charles C Thomas, Publisher, 1959).

Stetler, C., Stetler, J., and Moritz, A., *Doctor, Patient and the Law*, 121–72 (St. Louis: C. V. Mosby Co., 4th ed., 1962).

PERIODICALS

Berlow, L., Recognition and Rescue of the "Battered Child," *Hospitals*, 41:58, 1967.

Note, *Unauthorized Rendition of Life-Saving Medical Treatment*, 53 Cal. L. Rev. 860 (1965).

Note, *Civil Liability of Persons Participating in the Detention of the Allegedly Mentally Ill*, 1966 Wash. U. L. Q. 193 (1966).

Note, *Dispensing with Parental Consent in Indiana Adoption Proceedings*, 40 Ind. L. Rev. 378 (1965).

Note, *Extrajudicial Truthful Disclosure of Medical Confidences: A Physician's Civil Liability*, 44 Denver L. J. 463 (1967).

Oppenheim, M., *Informed Consent to Medical Treatment*, 11 Clev.-Mar. L. Rev. 249 (1962).

Paulsen, M., *Child Abuse Reporting Laws: The Shape of Legislation*, 67 Colum. L. Rev. 1 (1967).

# Part Four

Sanctions and Social Justice in the Criminal Law Process—Criminal Law

# Chapter Nine

# Criminal Law

In the domain of the criminal law, the state stands in a different relationship to its citizens than in that of the civil law. In civil law, the state provides an impartial and independent means whereby private disputes between private persons can be resolved in a manner that is both fair to the parties and consistent with the treatment accorded others in similar factual circumstances. Put another way, the state in the area of civil law acts as umpire in a game governed by the rules of law. The events that bring about the litigation and the impetus to resolve it in the courtroom always come from the private person and not from the state. The objective of the civil law is generally to compensate an injured party when a violation of a standard of conduct is found. Rarely is it to punish, or deter others from misconduct, although it may have this indirect effect.

Criminal law, on the other hand, is created by the state through the enactment of statutes; it prohibits certain conduct and disciplines those who ignore the prohibitions. The state takes an active role in enforcing these laws and punishing transgressors. The state provides a means of supervision of the public at large, through police forces and investigatory agencies. The state takes immediate action when conduct appearing to be in violation of the law is perceived, by arrest or, on occasion, by even more forceful measures such as preventing conduct through the use of dangerous, sometimes lethal, weapons. The state takes the initiative in bringing the case to the attention of the court, through the office of the prosecuting attorney. If a violation of law is found, the state provides the means for punishment, through the prison system, and sometimes is instrumental in imposing the ultimate sanction of death and in acting as executioner.

A wide range of prohibited conduct is encompassed by the criminal law. Among the activities the state attempts to control through the use of the criminal law are crimes between individuals, such as robbery, murder, and other acts of violence; crimes against the state, such as treason or income tax fraud; and crimes having detrimental social effects on others, such as illicit sale of narcotics.

The study of the criminal law involves consideration of the social policies that lead to laws banning certain conduct and an analysis of what conduct is banned. In analyzing the materials that follow, the student must keep before him the questions of why the legislature has chosen to proscribe certain conduct; whether the purposes of the criminal law are achieved by the proscription and penalties; and whether the laws make social sense in terms of the groups most likely to run afoul of their provisions. Particularly in dealing with these latter questions, criminal law draws close to the behavioral sciences; much light is shed on criminal behavior through the efforts of sociologists, psychologists, psychiatrists, and others dealing with the actions and reaction of groups and individuals.

An effort is made here to give the reader a broad view of the criminal process as a whole without regard to particular crimes. The source and purpose of the law are briefly dealt with, and the rationale of sanctions considered. Attention is then directed to certain aspects of several forms of prohibited conduct. The selection of materials is designed to lead the reader to ponder some—by no means all—of the legal and social problems raised by the criminal process.

Mr. Gantz found a revolver with one bullet in its chamber lying in the road near his house. Having tried and failed to shoot out the bullet, and to punch it out, he set the weapon aside. His brother-in-law, Hardie, commented that he would not be afraid to have the gun snapped at him all day, and everyone in the house regarded the weapon as harmless. Some five years later a neighbor visited the house and Hardie said he would frighten her with the revolver and picked it up. Then the revolver discharged, killing the neighbor. Hardie was convicted by a jury of manslaughter through criminal carelessness. On appeal, he argued that the killing had been accidental, or at most was the result of ordinary carelessness. The court, commenting that the conduct was "grossly reckless and without palliation or excuse," affirmed his conviction. [*State v. Hardie*, 47 Iowa 647 (1878).]

## Source of the Criminal Law

Whereas the common law—a body of judicial decisions outlining general principles—is all-important to the area of the civil law, there are no analogous kinds of legal rules in the criminal field. *All criminal law is statutory law;*

*whatever is not expressly forbidden by one or more statutes is permitted, and conduct that does not contravene the terms of a statute cannot give rise to criminality.*

Consider for a moment some of the implications of this state of affairs. A legislative body, be it a council of the smallest village, the Congress of the United States, or something in between, must examine the whole of human affairs and select from the infinite possibilities and permutations of human interaction those types of conduct that the state must or should in one way or another inhibit. Moreover, a re-examination of the situation must be continually in progress, so that artificial and outmoded limitations are not placed upon activities that are basically beneficial, or at the very least not actually detrimental to society. It must then describe such conduct and determine what penalties will attach for engaging in the prohibited conduct.

The responsibility is great and the possibility of error considerable; the enormous power of the state is not lightly to be set in motion. What one person can view as criminal, another can readily view as necessary for his personal or intellectual freedom. What to one person is thought control is to another the exercise of the right of the state to protect itself. What to one person is an odious restriction upon his personal liberty is to another necessary to protect the public at large. The legislature therefore bears grave responsibility to engage in reasoned lawmaking and not to persecute or pursue or turn into criminals those whose conduct or beliefs are merely unorthodox rather than truly harmful.

One of the reasons written statutes are needed is described in the case of *McBoyle v. United States*, 283 U.S. 25 (1931). There, a person had been convicted of the crime of transporting an airplane across state lines. The government contended that this act was rendered criminal by a statute making it a crime to transport across state lines "a motor vehicle." The act provided:

The term "motor vehicle" shall include an automobile, automobile truck, automobile wagon, motorcycle, or any other self-propelled vehicle not designed for running on rails; . . .

The Supreme Court of the United States reversed the conviction on the grounds that the definition was not intended by the Congress to include airplanes. Mr. Justice Holmes said:

Although it is not likely that a criminal will carefully consider the text of the law before he murders or steals, it is reasonable that a fair warning should be given to the world in language that the common world will understand, of what the law intends to do if a certain line is passed. To make the warning fair, so far as possible the line should be clear. When a rule of conduct is laid down in words that evoke in the common mind only the picture of vehicles moving on land, the statute should not be extended to aircraft simply because it may seem to us that a similar policy applies, or upon the speculation that if the legislature had thought of it, very likely broader words would have been used.

Other ends of justice are also achieved by an accurate statutory description of conduct punishable by the state. These include consistency of application of the laws, so that imposition of sanctions does not turn on whims of judge or jury; and the fact that the legislative purpose in enacting the statute will best be furthered by clearly prohibiting the particular antisocial conduct, while allowing all other without a large gray area where conduct is neither clearly illegal nor clearly permitted.

## Sanctions in the Criminal Process

In enacting criminal legislation, the state does much more than merely describe criminal conduct. It takes the highly significant additional step of penalizing persons who are found guilty of criminal acts. The state can punish in numerous ways. It can take a citizen's property by imposing a fine. It may take his liberty by imprisonment; it may restrict his activities, as in the case of probation or parole. Finally, it may take life itself by solemn, organized killing.

These are weighty matters and the criminal law must justify itself in its use of these penalties by understanding, defining, and then fulfilling the purposes achieved by the sanctions. There are four of these purposes. By imposing sanctions, the state can *restrain* persons who represent dangers to others; it can *rehabilitate* those convicted of crimes and make them less disruptive and more useful members of society; it can, by the example of punishment, *deter* others from criminal conduct, and, last, the state can *seek revenge*, which appears to be the attaining of a collective public satisfaction in the observation of the suffering of a wrongdoer. There are these four, and no more. We can examine every crime and every punishment to see if one or more of these purposes are adequately served.

Restraint is straightforward. If a person through his action has demonstrated that he represents significant danger to society as a whole, it is perfectly appropriate to forcibly, and against his will, prevent him from carrying out his propensities. If a person is a repeated thief, the protection of society's property may require, and in any event justifies, restraint. Likewise, the infliction of physical harm on another justifies protecting other persons from similar harm. The primary question in analyzing the purpose of the imprisonment sanction is what the duration of such imprisonment should be. A person may present every likelihood of further offense; is it therefore justified to imprison him for life? Generally it is thought not, and for few crimes have legislatures in general provided for imprisonment of long and extended duration. Note that the legislature does a balancing job; it balances the needs of society against the rights of the individual to be free, regardless of the degree of likelihood that his criminal conduct will continue.

Rehabilitation is a commendable goal. To the extent that criminal personalities can be remolded and reformed into persons who can take a standard place in the workaday world, society has made a great stride. It has changed a liability into an asset. This purpose is sought to be achieved by various educational and training programs in our prison systems. However, it makes no sense to talk in terms of rehabilitation of persons subjected to criminal sanctions unless in fact resources for rehabilitation are available. Too many of our prison systems lack effective means for training and rehabilitation. They need more funds for continuing supervision in the systems, for equipment, and for further education. It follows that, in a state or jurisdiction where such programs are not available, the criminal law in that jurisdiction does not and cannot be argued to fulfill its rehabilitation function.

Perhaps the most obvious purpose served by the criminal law is to deter others from similar conduct. Society has a strong interest in limiting the amount of disturbing activity that goes on within its borders. Continued crimes of violence and crimes endangering the safety and security of individuals can create a major disruption in an organized society. One of the ways thought effective to prevent such occurrences is to make an example of those who are found and convicted of this kind of conduct. The example of punishment, in itself, will frighten or deter others from following such paths. Deterrents are effective only to the degree to which the public is aware of the fact of the imposition of punishment. To be deterred one must be aware, consciously or unconsciously, of unpleasant consequences of a wrongful act. One of the peculiarities of the function of deterrence in the criminal process is that it may be independent of the true guilt of the person on whom the punishment is imposed. Thus, the public hanging of a person announced to be a murderer is effective as a deterrent to others, even though he, in fact, was not the guilty party.

The fourth purpose, revenge, comes under severe criticism in the modern day and age. Is it proper, the question is heard, for an enlightened society to seek its vengeance merely for the self-satisfaction of enforcing the ancient maxim of an eye for an eye and a tooth for a tooth? Perhaps there is a collective tension that builds up at the sight and awareness of crime; perhaps this tension needs to be discharged by a black-type headline that the supposed wrongdoer has met his just fate. Each person can examine himself to see if he is satisfied with this as one of the purposes of the criminal law.

## A Study of Particular Crimes

We will in this section give attention to the details of three selected types of human conduct: the killing of human beings, abortion, and the possession, use, or sale of narcotics. Every state has legislation that makes these acts criminal under certain circumstances and imposes penalties that extend to life imprisonment and death.

With respect to these types of conduct, there are some situations where society condones and even encourages the conduct, and some situations where the conduct is absolutely prohibited. In each instance, the legislature (and occasionally the courts) has made choices and has attempted to draw lines separating the legal from the illegal, or, more simply, the good from the bad. It has also selected the penalties to be inflicted by the state when the conduct is found to fall on the wrong side of the line.

In each of these three crimes the drawing of the line is difficult and is the subject of analysis, debate, and strong feelings. They are particularly important to the person engaged in some phase of medical practice. Each practitioner should consider the material presented in the light of her knowledge and experience and debate with herself and others the question of whether the lines have been properly drawn in the best interests of society and from the standpoint of their practical application to nursing and medical practice. She should consider whether the sanctions are appropriate or whether reform is indicated. Furthermore, the exceptions to criminal acts in these areas, that is, the various ways of taking human life for which no sanctions are imposed, and the circumstances under which abortions and narcotics utilization are permitted should be analyzed to see how they were fixed, whether they should be expanded, and, if so, whose responsibility it is to make efforts so that the necessary changes will be brought about.

### THE PERMITTED TAKING OF LIFE

Although murder is a spectacular crime in its effect on the individual victim and in its overall disruptive influence on the normal patterns of life in our society, it has never been universally prohibited in any culture. At least one distinction is always made, between *wrongful* killing and some other kind. It is easy in our society to think of several kinds of killings that are viewed with equanimity, even approbation. Sanctioned killing on the largest scale takes place in organized warfare, whether declared or undeclared; here, killing is not prohibited.

A second kind of killing given formal sanction is the organized execution by the state, through the use of the electric chair, the noose, the gas chamber, or the firing squad. There are no borderline cases here; if the preliminaries of conviction and sentencing are carried out, no blame attaches to the perpetrators.

Other situations may be posited where *some* killing is certain, although the identity of the victim is shrouded in the shades of the future. When a large bridge is to be built, a contractor may know from past experience that one or more of his men will accidentally die in the process. When an automobile manufacturer puts his cars in the showrooms, he does it with the full understanding that some of the buyers will end their days in the wreckage. Firearm makers are aware that some of their products will be used to put persons to death.

There is also a class of situations where a death may or may not be wrongfully caused, depending on variables in the surrounding circumstances. Killing to protect oneself or one's loved ones from serious harm is not a criminal killing, although questions arise as to whether the need to use deadly force was apparent or whether some less extreme measure would have adequately filled the protective role.

Killings by police officers in the line of duty are justified when, and only when, a serious offense has been committed and the person whom the officer is seeking to arrest resists arrest and flees. The officer is then exonerated from criminal responsibility if the fleeing criminal is killed in the process of pursuit and arrest. Naturally, killing in self defense is also permitted.

Similarly, certain kinds of provocation will excuse some homicide. One who, in the heat of passion, responds to a violent blow with deadly force may be excused of his act.

### THE CRIMINAL TAKING OF A LIFE

Prohibited killings are not treated uniformly by the state. The man who conceives, plans, and carries out a cold-blooded killing of his spouse in order to pocket the insurance proceeds is treated differently from the hunter who carelessly fires at and kills his hunting companion, mistaking him for the quarry. Different states adopt different divisions; the discussion here is therefore very general in nature and is not intended to apply in any particular jurisdiction.

Homicides are designated generally in three classes: murder, manslaughter, or negligent homicide. The three acts of homocide are progressively less serious. Murder, the most serious in the sense that the penalties are the heaviest, is a homicide which is the result of a deliberate and malicious attempt to inflict injury. The intentional character is the factor rendering it subject to heavy penalties.

Manslaughter is a homicide without malice, but without justification or excuse. A common form of manslaughter is death caused while engaging in unlawful acts, such as driving while intoxicated.

The third classification is homicide that is the result of negligence. In such deaths, there is never a desire or an intent to kill; likewise malice is invariably lacking.

We have in an earlier section of this text examined at length the concept of negligence, and studied the rules whereby an injured party is financially compensated when he is injured as a consequence of that negligence. To repeat, negligent conduct is conduct that fails to meet the standard of the reasonable man, or that creates a foreseeable risk to others.

The negligence principle has a place in criminal law as well, and *if a person's conduct departs from the reasonable man standard in a very substantial way, that person may be criminally responsible for injury caused to another.* Such conduct is often called wanton or reckless. In particular, if wantonly or recklessly negligent conduct results in the death of another, the person responsible will be guilty of the crime of negligent homicide, as well as civilly liable in money damages for the death. Negligence that leads to criminal responsibility is frequently referred to as "culpable negligence."

The difference between civil and criminal responsibility for negligence lies in the degree of carelessness of the actions. Any deviation from the reasonable man standard can result in civil liability, but only a gross deviation will render a person guilty of a crime. The latter conduct may be described as reckless, or in wanton or willful disregard of the consequences, or as needless indifference to the safety and rights of others; "mere" carelessness or thoughtlessness is not enough. An authority on criminal law sums up the problem in this way [Perkins, R. M., *Criminal Law and Procedure, Cases, and Materials*, 411 (Brooklyn: The Foundation Press, Inc., 1959)]:

> The social purpose underlying the requirement of compensation to the person harmed is not identical with that which forms the basis of punishment. Conceivably, therefore, the standard adopted in the criminal law of negligence might be entirely different from that used in civil cases. This is not exactly the answer since the "measuring stick" here, as well as there, is the conduct of a reasonable man under like circumstances. But whereas the civil law requires conformity to this standard, a very substantial deviation is essential to criminal guilt according to the common law. To express this greater degree of deviational behavior it has been common to modify the word "negligence" with some such epithet as "criminal," "culpable," "gross" or "wicked." Needless to say this is a field not subject to exact measurement. What it amounts to as a practical matter is a caution to the jury not to convict of crime, where other elements of culpability are lacking, except where the conduct causing the harm represents a rather extreme case of negligence.

### ABORTION

Under some circumstances, abortion is a crime in every state. Abortion consists of the performance of an operation, or the administration of a drug, designed to induce miscarriage in a pregnant woman. Generally, it is not necessary actually to induce a miscarriage; the operation or administration is the unlawful act regardless of its effects. In all or nearly all states, there is an exception to the illegal abortions, which applies to abortions necessary to save the life of the pregnant woman, or (in some states) to prevent serious and permanent injury to her. To invoke the exception, it is also required that a physician advise of the need for the abortion.

Everyone is familiar with the tragic results that so frequently follow the work of the illegal abortionist. Operating under dangerously unsanitary conditions, in secret, without training, and indifferent to the welfare of those who seek him out, he is a despicable character. No one doubts that he and his kind should be eliminated from society. Any physician or nurse performing, participating in, or in any way assisting in abortions without clearly understanding the circumstances and without ascertaining the legality in each case exposes himself to criminal prosecution.

However, there is considerable ferment among physicians, social workers, religious leaders, and others concerning what society's real responsibilities are in this area, and how the legislature should act to fulfill them.

The basic problem stems from the fact that the lifesaving exception of the typical statute is not nearly broad enough to take care of the many other problems stemming from pregnancies. What of the forcible rape that results in pregnancy? What of incest? What of a pregnant woman who is suicidally psychotic, who is unable to properly care for another child, for either financial or psychological reasons? All these seem to many to be justified cases for therapeutic abortion, and there is considerable sentiment for a general relaxation of the abortion laws. Other groups feel equally strongly that abortion should remain a serious crime, except in limited circumstances. These cite the sanctity of life and religious and moral precepts in support of their views. The materials set out in the Notes to this section raise and develop both points of view.

## NARCOTICS

Narcotics regulation takes place on both the federal and the state levels. On the federal level, the Harrison Act, initially adopted in 1914, regulates medical use of drugs through reporting and revenue requirements. At the state level, each state has enacted narcotics control legislation, generally patterned after the Uniform Narcotic Drug Act. The state statutes uniformly prohibit the possession and sale of drugs except under certain specified conditions. Physicians and nurses are, of course, free to use and prescribe drugs in the course of their practice. The Harrison Act has been interpreted to permit doctors to prescribe drugs to addicts.

Like the other problems considered in the criminal law portion of this text, the illicit use of narcotics poses a problem with dominating social as well as legal overtones. The choices of approach to regulation must be made by the legislative branch of government. Some of the differing considerations and viewpoints are set out in the note materials. As shown there, the primary problem is how the addict should be treated. Should he be regarded and treated as a criminal, or is he the victim of social forces? Those who adopt the former view urge that heavier penalties and tighter laws are the answer. Those with the latter outlook feel that rehabilitation centers and broad attacks on social evils would be the most effective ways to handle the narcotics problems so common in large urban areas.

## Insanity and Its Interaction with Criminal Law

That mental problems contribute to crime is doubted by no one. The psychotic with strong homicidal tendencies, the kleptomaniac appropriating spools of thread, the arsonist following the dictates of sexual drives—all are the potential perpetrators of serious crime. However, our sense of justice requires that, to be punishable by the state, an act must to some degree be rational. The idea of punishment presupposes individual responsibility in the guilty person; he suffers for crimes he need not have committed, for acts he did with a conscious exercise of "will." Where in this picture does mental disorder fit? What of acts that are at once criminal and clearly the product of a depraved mind? What does the law require in terms of mental responsibility before it will bring its penalties into operation? How is this responsibility determined? These questions pose the difficult problem of the insanity defense in criminal prosecutions. The defense states simply that *certain individuals will not be held criminally responsible for their actions, no matter how serious the crime, because of those individuals' mental states or conditions.* Having agreed, however, that the reach of the criminal law should stop short of punishing such persons as criminals, we are left with the problem of describing the distinction between those whom society will excuse on the basis of their mental state and those whom it will not. Although the word "insane" is a handy catch phrase for those who will not be held criminally responsible, it does not itself give a basis for differentiation. It is a legal term, not a medical one, and sums up any number of mental disorders; indeed, it can include the whole contents of the psychiatrist's notebook.

Modern psychiatry does not draw a clear line between the sane and the insane. A famous psychiatrist states it in this way [Roche, P., *Symposium on Criminal Responsibility and Mental Disease*, 26 Tenn. L. Rev. 221, 240–41 (1959)]:

I will say there is neither such a thing as "insanity" nor such a thing as "mental disease." These terms do not identify entities having separate existence in themselves. They are merely designations of a kind of behavior which in a given society by consensual feeling and reaction is regarded as maladaptive, disturbing and socially dangerous. "Mental illness," a medical term, borrowed from the mechanistic concepts of classical physical disease, refers to an altered internal status of the individual vis-á-vis his external world as interpreted by others. In a way the term is a misnomer, since the "mental illness" is not actually limited to a place called the "mind," but rather it is a changed interrelationship of the individual with his fellow creatures.

For many decades, the prevailing legal definition of insanity in every state but New Hampshire was based on the famous M'Naghten Rules. These rules were an outgrowth of an attempt on the life of the Prime Minister of England in 1843, in which Daniel M'Naghten, apparently a paranoiac, succeeded only in killing the Prime Minister's private secretary. At his trial, he was acquitted on the basis of medical testimony, much to the distress of the Queen and her loyal subjects. The judges were called before the House of Lords to answer questions concerning the case, and from those answers arose the M'Naghten Rules, under which an accused will be absolved of criminal responsibility *if at the time of committing the act he was laboring under such a defect of reason, from disease of the mind, as not to know the nature and quality of the act he was doing, or if he did know it, that he did not know he was doing what was wrong.* Thus the issue of criminal responsibility turns on whether an accused knows "right" from "wrong."

In modern times, the ability of an accused to discriminate right from wrong is regarded as a specialized medical matter and, like all such matters that reach the courts, is to be determined by expert testimony of professional practitioners, i.e., psychiatrists. Psychiatrists who appear as witnesses in criminal matters must therefore testify concerning the accused's ability to deal with the ideas of right and wrong. However, psychiatry does not approach its task in that fashion; ideas of right and wrong do not enter into diagnosis or therapy. As a result, the psychiatrist must somehow fit the square peg of his medical analysis into the round hole of the legal definition. This cannot be done easily and it cannot be done well. Because of the difficulty of reconciling the legal standard with the medical realities, the legal definition is often referred to as a fiction, or an artificial construct without relation to the real world, and as psychiatry has developed, there has been a rising tide of criticism of the M'Naghten Rule.

The criticism first received judicial recognition in 1955 when the United States Court of Appeals for the District of Columbia decided *Durham v. United States*, 214 F.2d 862 (D.C. Cir. 1954). In that case, the M'Naghten Rule was discarded and in its place there was created a test which made criminal responsibility turn on whether the criminal behavior was a product of mental illness. In the wake of *Durham*, other courts were lead to re-examine their adherence to the right-wrong test in M'Naghten and several courts have now rejected M'Naghten. Thoughtful and scholarly judges in *United States v. Currens*, 290

F.2d 751 (3d Cir. 1961), and *United States v. Freeman*, 357 F.2d 606 (2d Cir. 1966), have analyzed in depth the medical and legal problems and adopted in essence the view that *a person is not responsible for criminal conduct if at the time of such conduct as a result of mental disease or defect he lacks substantial capacity either to appreciate the criminality of his conduct or to conform his conduct to the requirements of the law.* There is much reason to believe that this test will gain an increasing acceptance in the future.

# NOTES

## (1) Nurse Is Convicted of Homicide Through Reckless Imprudence

A number of years ago a prosecution of a nurse that took place in the Philippine Islands captured the interest of nurses throughout the world. The following account of the case shows the reason why.

### Grennan, E. M., *The Somera Case,* Int. Nurs. Rev., 5:325 (1930)*

*The case of the Filipino nurse, Lorenza Somera, who was condemned in May, 1929, at Manila to one year's imprisonment, in connection with the death of a young girl in the operating theatre, caused much concern and deep-felt sympathy in a large section of the nursing world during the latter half of last year. Miss Somera had been accused, together with Drs. Gregoria Favis and Armando Bartolome, of "homicide through reckless imprudence." The following is a summarized statement of this important case, and describes the course of events from the time of the operation down to the movement which ultimately secured Miss Somera's pardon, granted by the Governor-General of the Philippines.*

#### FACTS AS STATED IN THE TESTIMONY

Several days previous to May 26th, 1928, Pedro Clemente took his daughter Anastacia Clemente, not yet fourteen years of age, to Dr. Gregorio Favis at Manila. After examination Dr. Favis decided to perform a tonsillectomy. He instructed the father and daughter to go to St. Paul's Hospital where he would perform the operation at 7 a.m. on May 26th.

Dr. Favis then called up Sister Mercedes at St. Paul's Hospital and had the operation fixed for the date and hour agreed. He said he would follow the same orders given in previous tonsillectomy cases done there.

The head nurse in the operating room on the morning in question was Lorenza Somera. Valentina Andaya and Consolacion Montinola were student nurses working in the operating room under Miss Somera. Consolacion Montinola was the sterile nurse, Dr. Bartolome was the assistant surgeon.

Dr. Favis arrived a little before 7 a.m., scrubbed his hands and examined the patient, who was already present. He then asked for 10 per cent. cocaine with

* Reprinted with permission of the *International Nursing Review*.

adrenalin and swabbed the throat of the patient. Before this was done, as the clock was striking 7, Dr. Bartolome arrived. He scrubbed and came to assist Dr. Favis. The sterile table was prepared with the solutions and other needed articles. Dr. Favis asked Dr. Bartolome for the novocaine solutions. Miss Montinola handed Dr. Bartolome a syringe of solution, which Dr. Favis received from him and injected into the patient. After a few minutes Dr. Favis asked for and injected more solution.

Dr. Bartolome noticed that the patient became pale and acted as if dizzy, and called Dr. Favis's attention to this. Dr. Favis said this was not unusual. Dr. Favis then asked for, received and injected a third syringe of solution. A few minutes later the patient showed symptoms of convulsions. Dr. Bartolome again called Dr. Favis's attention to the condition of the patient. Dr. Favis ordered adrenalin, which was injected. A second injection was also administered. The patient again showed symptoms of convulsions and died in a few moments.

Dr. Favis then asked if the novocaine was fresh. Miss Somera replied: "It was not novocaine but 10 per cent cocaine." Upon direct examination Miss Consolacion Montinola when questioned by the prosecution affirmed firstly that she did not know who prepared the drugs, and secondly that she heard Dr. Favis order cocaine with adrenalin for injection and also heard Miss Somera verify the order. When questioned by the defence she again testified that she heard the order given and verified. This point is important—even the prosecution brought out that Dr. Favis ordered 10 per cent. cocaine for injection and that Miss Somera verified the order.

The autopsy report and the testimony of Dr. Anzures showed that the patient was suffering from *status lymphaticus*. He also testified that such patients have been known to die with even so slight an injury as the prick of a needle; also that the organs of a person dying from this disease (after a very slight injury as the prick of a needle) which he had examined, were in practically the same condition as those of the deceased.

Facts not brought out in the trial are: that Miss Somera had only finished her training on May 20th, 1928; that she had not yet received her registration certificate and was not an experienced graduate, as stated in the prosecution; that Dr. Favis had operated for tonsilitis but once previously in St. Paul's Hospital and that Miss Somera had not been on duty in the operating room at the time; and that no order from Dr. Favis was given her before his arrival.

## DEFENCE IN THE LOWER COURT

The defence was conducted by Mr. Courtney Whitney, who has been practising law in Manila for a number of years and previous to that time was a member of the Legal Department of the United States Army.

He brought out the following points:

1. That there was no competent evidence to clothe Lorenza Somera with the crime.

2. That if the testimony of Consolacion Montinola that Miss Somera prepared the drug is accepted, it must also be accepted that she did it upon the order of Dr. Favis. Her testimony must be either accepted *in toto* or rejected *in toto*.

Dr. W. H. Waterous and Dr. Rufino Abriol, both of whom had operated for many years in St. Paul's Hospital, testified that both in that institution and elsewhere nurses are under a semi-military training and are required to carry out the orders of the doctors for drugs. That when a doctor orders a solution for injection the nurse does not know how much he intends to use of the amount prepared. That furthermore a doctor learns the action of drugs by administering them and that, therefore, the nurse's training and experience are not adequate to this knowledge and that this responsibility belongs to the doctor. They also testified that cocaine both was and had been used for injection by many doctors.

A resolution approved by the Educational Section and by the Executive Board of the Filipino Nurses' Association was presented. This resolution affirmed that nurses are taught that they must not question the order of a doctor for drugs except to verify it. The Chairman of the Curriculum Committee of the Educational Section and Principal of a School of Nursing testified to the same, and nursing text-books were presented to support the testimony.

3. That the prosecution had failed to establish whether the cause of death was due to cocaine poisoning or *thymus lymphaticus*. The testimony of Dr. Anzures, as given in the facts above, and that of Dr. Waterous indicate that the patient could have died irrespective of the solution used. "The fact that Anastacia Clemente died subsequent to surgical procedure does not in itself make any of those in professional attendance upon her *prima facie* responsible."

## DECISION OF THE LOWER COURT

The case dragged along from May 26th, 1928, to May 7th, 1929, when the following decision was rendered:

Wherefore the Court absolves the two said accused, Gregorio Favis and Armando Bartolome, of the crime of which they are accused in this case, . . . and declares Lorenza Somera guilty of the crime imputed in the complaint and in conformity with the provisions of Article 568, Section I, of the Penal Code, *without finding any modifying responsibility as none has been shown*, condemnds her to suffer one year and one day imprisonment, to indemnify the heirs of the deceased Anastacia Clemente in the sum of One Thousand (1,000) Pesos with subsidiary imprisonment in case of insolvency and to suffer further the accessories provided in Article 61 of said Code and to pay one-third of the costs.

## THE DEFENCE BEFORE THE SUPREME COURT

Mr. Whitney based his plea before the Supreme Court on six points. In these he showed that the conclusions of the Court of First Instance were not supported either by the evidence or by the actual facts of the situation, all of which had not been brought out. He pleaded the case upon professional and humanitarian as well as legal grounds, bringing in and using those facts which had escaped the Lower Court.

## THE SUPREME COURT DECISION

On December 20th, 1929, Justice Villareal with Justices Street, Ostrand, and Johns, handed down the following decision:

Wherefore, finding the decision of the Lower Court to be in accordance with the facts and law, it is confirmed in all respects with costs against the appellant.

Ten days from the promulgation of this sentence, let sentence be entered accordingly and five days later return the record to the Lower Court. . . .

[After the decision of the Supreme Court] counsel for the defence inserted the following statement in the Court record:

> Upon the confirmation of the sentence of this Court by the Supreme Court, on behalf of Lorenza Somera I sought from the Governor-General a full, unconditional pardon. This the Governor-General refused to consider on the ground that it was contrary to the policy of the Chief Executive to thus set aside the mandates of the Courts, but in view of the recommendation of two of the Justices of the Supreme Court who reviewed the case upon appeal, the unanimous recommendation of the Board of Pardons, and the petition of the Philippine Nurses' Association for executive clemency in some degree, as well as because of certain exceptional extenuating circumstances apparent to him in this case, the Governor-General remitted that part of the sentence as called for prison confinement, upon the condition that Lorenza Somera should not in the future violate any of the penal laws of the Philippine Islands.
>
> Although disappointed in not being granted the full and unconditional pardon from the Governor-General which she had through her counsel sought, Lorenza Somera has formally accepted the conditional pardon His Excellency has extended.
>
> I therefore hand the Court a signed copy of the conditional pardon of the Chief Executive and a signed copy of Lorenza Somera's acceptance thereof, and move the Court to order the release of the young nurse convicted, and the exoneration of her bond.

Would the defense raised—that the nurse was under an absolute duty to obey the doctor's order—be one likely to carry weight today? Why? Why not?

## (2) Social Concern for Taking a Life

### (A) CAPITAL PUNISHMENT

One man's view of the process of legalized homicide was presented to a jury in the following argument. Do you think the matters mentioned should bear on the sanctions provided by the criminal law? Where do they fit in the four purposes of criminal sanctions? How should the state conduct executions to achieve those purposes?

### *Tennessee v. Wash Jones:* Closing Argument for the Defense by Joe W. Henry, Jr., 46 A.B.A.J. 52 (1960)*

Mr. Henry to the Jury: . . .

You have been told in great detail just precisely how Wash Jones killed and murdered Wes Howard. Now let us see how the State of Tennessee would kill and murder Wash Jones.

At about 5:30 in the afternoon of the eve of the execution the prisoner is shaved, bathed, and his head is clipped. He must be clean so that it is unnecessary to bathe his body after the electrocution. His head must be clipped so they can apply the electrode.

Then they give him a new shirt and a new pair of pants, without a belt, and shoes without laces. No belt and no shoe laces. After all he must not hang or strangle himself and cheat the chair.

Next, the minister of his choice visits him to offer whatever words of assurance and solace he can conjure up.

Then the condemned man is given an opportunity to eat a hearty meal of his choice.

Then his family is permitted to visit with him until midnight. Then at about ten minutes to five the warden and the guards and the execution party come and they start to walk the last mile down the dim-lit corridor, which leads to the chamber of horrors to the electric chair.

They place him in the chair, roll up his trouser legs in order to clamp the electrode to his right leg. Then to his clipped head they clamp the other electrode.

Then they ask him for his last words. Only the prisoner, the warden and God are present in the room. The warden is doing his statutory duty, the prisoner paying his debt to society and as to him, I am sure he feels that God has forgotten him.

Then they place the mask upon his face—not for his benefit, but to keep the witnesses from looking upon the hideous countenance of the dying man as his facial features contort in pain and agony.

The warden looks through the little window at the man who throws the switch — $25.00 the state pays for this service—the warden has a stop watch in his hands and upon his signal the switch is thrown. Then, there comes the sound from the electrician's niche—a sound like that that comes from an X-ray machine, a crackle, a whine, a buzz as 2,300 volts, for thirty seconds and then 500 for one and one-half minutes are sent circulating through his body as it convulsively jerks and writhes.

And then when his body has cooled off enough to touch, the physician applies his stethoscope and pronounces him dead.

He is then placed in cold storage—in a deep freeze—because the state does not embalm. Now another name is added to the yellow list—the roll of horror—the state has got another pound of flesh. But it is the law of the state.

I ask you in the name of all that is sacred and holy, how can such a spectacle as this ever magnify the law or make it honorable or preserve the peace and dignity of the state?

And they say that Wash Jones killed in cold blood.

Wash didn't lock Wes Howard in a room, keep him there for weeks and months, announce ahead of time the date and time of his death, and leave the condemned man to die a thousand deaths.

Ladies and gentlemen, you and you alone can send Wash Jones to the electric chair. There can be no division of responsibility, you can never say that the rest overpowered you. It must be your deliberate, cool, premeditated act. It takes your vote.

I plead for human consideration, for charity, for mercy. Man was truly created in God's image, but humane treatment of our fellow man is necessary in order that the divine image may not be obscured.

I hope and pray that the Tennessee legislature will at this session veto this unconscionable decree of blood and write for the state, as the state has written for its citizens, the injunction—at once rational, scriptural, salutary, and humanitarian: "*Thou shalt not kill.*"

## (B) MERCY KILLING

One form of killing that is not legally justified is euthanasia. An absolute prohibition on euthanasia operates in two ways. First, it prohibits the healthy from terminating the life of another. Second, it deprives the dying person of the right to end his agony; the law, in other words, prohibits him from relieving his suffering.

The article that follows presents the arguments against euthanasia, and then seeks to refute them. Is it successful?

## Williams, G., *Euthanasia and Abortion,* 38 Univ. Colo. L. Rev. 178 (1966)*

### EUTHANASIA

The rule prevails in the United States, as in Britain, that a person who kills another with his consent for merciful reasons, when that other person is suffering from a fatal and incurable disease, is guilty of murder or manslaughter; and the rule is the same if he provides the sufferer with the means of suicide. Apparently only in Texas is the position different; there, the act of providing the means of suicide is not an offense, but directly killing the sufferer is.

Various attempts to change the law and allow voluntary euthanasia have been made both in Britain and in the United States. The moving force in this country is chiefly the Euthanasia Society of America, but its efforts, like those of its British counterpart, have so far been unavailing.

Death is the great taboo subject in our civilization—more so even than sex. Except in war, most of us seem to be unable to contemplate death calmly and rationally; at the last, we accept any circumstances of degradation for ourselves, and strain and despair for those who love us, rather than make a comfortable and dignified exit. And, until death comes, we choose to know as little as possible about it. This attitude of preferring not to think is perhaps the main reason for the general lack of support given to the cause of euthanasia. (The word itself has come to be such an unpalatable one that the Voluntary Euthanasia Society of Connecticut has hopefully changed its name to the "Humanitarian Society.")

Until the 1960's, even doctors had made no study in Britain of the physical and mental distress of the dying. Dr. J. M. Hinton's investigation in 1963 dispelled several comfortable misconceptions. It has frequently been argued that the legalization of voluntary euthanasia would have little practical effect, because most dying patients do not know they are dying, and it is not the practice of doctors to tell them. Of the 102 dying patients studied by Hinton, three-quarters were aware of the probability of death in their last month. "In the face of this," said a leading article in the British Medical Journal, "the question 'Should a doctor tell?' loses much of its force."

Another argument against legal change is that the modern armory of tranquilizing, euphoric, pain-killing (analgesic), and stupefying (narcotic, anaesthetic)

* Reprinted with permission of the *University of Colorado Law Review.*

drugs has solved the problem of painful disease. Hinton found that although pain presented no serious problem in treatment, nausea and vomiting often could not be eliminated, and dyspnoea (shortness of breath) persisted without relief in four out of five of those who had to face it. Nearly half of the dying patients had a distressing degree of depression, and several expressed suicidal ideas.

The majority of dying patients are in their own homes or in a general hospital ward, and often they do not receive the heavy sedation that alone could alleviate their misery. Fear of the law still affects the help that doctors give, particularly when death is not imminent. This is so, for example, with inoperable cancer of the throat. The patient finds it difficult and painful to swallow and even to breathe, and he can hardly speak; yet he will generally take months to die. Few doctors take the responsibility of administering the massive doses of a narcotic necessary to prevent pain when it is known that such a dosage will cause immediate death or considerably accelerate it.

One of the misfortunes of this area of controversy is that social and medical questions become entangled with divergent religious beliefs. It would be wrong to give the impression that the dispute is entirely on sectarian lines; a survey has indicated that almost as many Catholics as Protestants accept the idea of euthanasia, though a majority of both reject it. Those who reject it do so partly on religious grounds, which may be regarded as irrelevant to the question of changing the law. The legislative question is not whether euthanasia is moral but whether society has the right to punish a doctor who believes that it is. No one suggests that a doctor should be punished for *not* administering euthanasia. The main issue, therefore, is one of personal liberty.

Many people still fail to comprehend that the question whether conduct is wrong or foolish or undesirable is not the same as the question whether it ought to be punished by law. There is a sphere of conduct in which men are, or ought to be, free to act according to their consciences. This is denied only by those who cannot see that the principle of religious toleration is not confined to matters of abstract belief. If toleration has any meaning, it must be extended to the way in which belief is put into practice.

Since liberty at present is not conceded, we must look more closely at the arguments advanced to prove that voluntary euthanasia is wrong. Both compassion and honesty seem to be lacking from some of them. The main religious contentions are that the sanctity of life must be maintained, that no one can rightfully consent to being killed, and that pain may lead a sinner to repentance. "Suffering for the Christian is not an absolute evil, but has redeeming features. It may be an occasion for spiritual growth and an opportunity to make amends for sin." To anyone who is remotely acquainted with the facts of suffering in illness the argument for its redemptive effect must surely seem absurd. Nor should the intolerance of the argument be overlooked. Christians (or some Christians) find (or are alleged to find) benefit in suffering through illness; therefore those who do not share this outlook are to be required to suffer too. The argument fails to explain why all religious communions, even the Catholic, accept the use of stupefying drugs, even for patients on their death-bed. It is not for lawyers and priests to dictate to doctors and patients how to deal with suffering.

> The toad beneath the harrow knows
> Exactly where each toothpoint goes.

The butterfly upon the road
Preaches contentment to that toad.

Those who adopt a religious attitude on a social issue quite often attempt to support themselves by empirical arguments. Sometimes the secular veil is diaphanous, as when Lord Devlin supports the law against voluntary euthanasia by saying that "a murderer who acts only upon the consent, and maybe the request, of his victim is no menace to others, but he does threaten one of the great moral principles upon which society is based, that is, the sanctity of human life." Society must punish murder, and to this extent the moral principle referred to may be regarded as a necessary part of the law. But surely it is illegitimate to deduce from this the conclusion that the law against consent-killing is basic to society's existence. If euthanasia or any other consent-killing were legalized, society would in no way be imperiled.

Among the other empirical objections to legalizing voluntary euthanasia, generally advanced by those whose basic position is a religious one, are the following: that it is difficult to ascertain the patient's real consent; that there would be danger of abuse; that the doctor may diagnose a disease as incurable when it is in fact curable; that allowing voluntary euthanasia would be the thin end of a wedge leading to a general disrespect for the sanctity of life. Some of these risks are merely the ordinary risks of medical practice, and we do not normally think that the desirable solution of such problems is to forbid medical men to use their best judgment. The "wedge" argument is perhaps sufficiently answered by comparing the murder rate in two significant years. In 1939 the number of murders known to the police in England was 156. In 1947, after a war in which vast numbers of men were trained and conditioned to kill, the number of murders known to the police was 171. In 1948 the figure fell to 162. It is clear that if war had any effect on the murder rate, it was infinitesimal. In other words, active encouragement to slaughter on an immense scale does not diminish respect for the sanctity of life outside the area permitted. It is inconceivable that permission to put an end to the existence of the comparatively small number of suffering patients who positively wish for death would bring about any widespread decline in the value attached to human life and well-being. On the contrary, it would express that value. . . .

The positive argument in favor of legalizing voluntary euthanasia is that we behave cruelly in refusing merciful release to a person dying in pain, and absurdly in applying ordinary notions of the value of life to a person who, in his last illness, is afflicted not only by pain but by nausea, weakness, giddiness, a feeling of suffocation through difficulty in breathing, incontinence, and a sense of hopelessness of his condition. For the libertarian, the issue is settled by his philosophy. As Eugene Debs said, "It ought to be the privilege of every human being to cross the River Styx in the boat of his own choosing." Perhaps the most remarkable contribution to the debate is that of Dr. Eliot Slater, a biologist, who characterizes the current attitude towards death as irrational, if not neurotic.

Death performs the inestimable office of clearing up a mess too big to mend. . . . In human communities, if the aged and the sick did not die within no long span after they had ceased to be self-supporting, the burden on society would become disastrous. The position of the biologist asked to contemplate the death of the individual is that this is an end devoutly to be wished. Death plays a wholly favorable, indeed an essential, part in the human economy.

The only alleviation of the traditional attitude has been to recognize that a doctor is entitled to administer drugs in order to overcome pain, even though the result may be to shorten life. There is little judicial authority, but in England the prosecution of Dr. John Bodkin Adams for murder affords considerable assistance. The point of interest in the case is that the judge, Devlin J., gave the first judicial pronouncement in England on the legality of administering narcotics. He pointed out that although it is murder to shorten life deliberately, a doctor who administers narcotics for the purpose of relieving pain and suffering is not guilty of murder merely because the measures he takes incidentally shorten life. In such a case, he said, the death would not in law be caused by the narcotic; it would be caused by the illness.

While welcoming the result reached by the judge, I would, for my part, prefer to base it on the legal doctrine of necessity. However that may be, the important thing is that it is lawful to administer narcotics to relieve pain and suffering even though they shorten life. I am sure that no judge, in America or England, would dissent from this view.

Humanitarian feeling also prevails when considering the doctor's duty to make positive exertions to prolong life. A physician cannot be charged with manslaughter merely because, in the terminal stages of disease, he does not take exceptional measures to prolong a doomed life. This attitude has religious support; it is the only point on which religious opinion is in agreement. It can be used to provide an acceptable decision in those tragic cases where a person through brain disease or injury falls into the living death of a coma or semi-coma which can have no favorable outcome and yet may last for years. The moral decision in these cases could be aided by taking "cerebral death" (evidence by a flat EEG reading) as decisive; supportive efforts should be continued only so long as the brain shows a physiological response. Even this test may sometimes fail to give an acceptable answer. For example, if a dying patient is being kept alive only by a tracheotomy (a hole cut in the throat through which an artificial respirator is used), is it permissible (without using the EEG) to remove the oxygen in order to "let him go"? Is this a positive act of mercy-killing, or a mere omission to fight further? If it is illegal mercy-killing, would it become legal by waiting for the oxygen cylinder to be used up and not replacing it? Is there any sense in drawing such a distinction?

That we try to draw any distinction is traceable to the religious view, or the former religious view, that man must not interfere with the workings of Providence. The skills of the medical profession and drugmakers have made this view obsolete. Countless numbers of us owe our continued existence to these skills. Why is it always right to use medical skills to prolong life, and always wrong to cut it short, even for reasons of the highest humanity?

## (3) Opposing Views on Abortion

The following articles take diametrically opposed views on how the law should deal with abortions. What are the merits of each position? What are the valid objections? If you adopt one position rather than the other, what are your reasons?

Drinan, R. F., *The Inviolability of the Right to be Born*, 17 West. Res. L. Rev. 465 (1965)*

Every discussion of abortion must, in the final analysis, begin and end with a definition of what one thinks of a human embryo or fetus. If one has, by the application of several principles, come to the conviction that a fetus, viable or not, can be extinguished for the benefit of its mother or its own welfare, rational debate on changing or "liberalizing" existing laws forbidding abortion is not really possible or necessary. For if a person argues from the premise that a human fetus may have its existence terminated for any valid reason, then the only point about which to argue is the validity of the reasons asserted to be sufficient to justify the voluntary extinction of a human fetus. These reasons can have only three sources: (1) the welfare of the fetus; (2) the health or happiness of the mother; or (3) the overall future of the family. . . .

III. WHY THE LAW SHOULD HAVE SANCTIONS AGAINST THE ABORTION OF A NON-VIABLE FETUS

When one has conceded the principle that the life and rights of a non-viable fetus may be subordinated to the desires or rights of its mother or parents, one must then justify this hierarchy of rights by recourse to one or more of three reasons: (1) the welfare of the fetus; (2) the health or happiness of the mother; or (3) the over-all future of the family into which the unwanted child would be born. It may be helpful therefore to analyze each of these three reasons in the light of the justification for abortion drawn from these sources.

A. Future Welfare of the Fetus

One of the reasons regularly advanced to justify abortion is the damage or disability suffered by a fetus because of the sickness of the mother or because of some pre-natal disease contracted by the fetus itself. The assumption is, of course, that it is better to terminate the life of a future person if it is certain (or highly probable?) that he will be seriously deformed, physically or mentally. The proponents of this position do not seem to limit their advocacy of this measure to only those infants who would be forever pitiable, "sub-human" creatures incapable in any way of developing into a fully human person. The thrust of the argument of those who recommend the elimination of defective embryos reaches all future children whose development may have been harmed by the mother taking a drug like thalidomide, contracting German measles, or suffering any other of the known medical conditions which can adversely affect a fetus.

No one can deny the laudable humanitarian intentions of those who seek, by the elimination of anti-abortion legislation, to prevent the birth of those persons who, because of serious pre-natal injuries, cannot enjoy a normal life. At the same time, however, to concede that the life of the fetus, disabled through no fault of its own or of its mother, may be extinguished because it might not attain complete physical or intellectual development is to concede either (1) that the non-viable

* Reprinted by permission from *Abortion and the Law*, ed., David T. Smith (Cleveland: The Press of Case Western Reserve University, 1967). Copyright © 1965, 1967 by Western Reserve University.

fetus is really *not* the repository of any inviolable rights or (2) that the strong and dominant members of society may extinguish or terminate the life of those individuals whose physical or mental development may, in the judgment of society, be so substantially arrested that they cannot attain a life worth living.

Clearly no advocate of easier abortion laws will concede the second of these alternatives. He will resist and reject any imputation that by permitting abortion he is by implication permitting infanticide, euthanasia, "mercy-murder," or anything else in the "parade of the horribles" not unknown in the rhetoric of the defenders of existing laws forbidding abortion. But can one logically and realistically claim that a defective non-viable fetus may be destroyed without also conceding the validity of the principle that, at least in some extreme cases, the taking of a life by society may be justified by the convenience or greater over-all happiness of the society which takes the life of an innocent but unwanted and troublesome person?

It is submitted that it is illogical and intellectually dishonest for anyone to advocate as morally permissible the destruction of a defective, non-viable fetus but to deny that this concession is not a fundamental compromise with what is surely one of the moral-legal absolutes of Anglo-American law—the principle that the life of an innocent human being may not be taken away simply because in the judgment of society, non-life for this particular individual would be better than life.

It is intellectually dishonest to maintain that a defective, non-viable fetus may be destroyed unless one is also prepared to admit that society has the right to decide that for certain individuals, who have contracted physical and/or mental disabilities, non-existence is better than existence. The advocate of abortion who bases his position on the ground that this is best for the fetus would no doubt shrink from this extension of the principle by which he justifies abortion; he would retreat to the familiar ground that the non-viable fetus is not even *medically* a person and, hence, does not possess the same right to survive enjoyed by a human being who has lived outside the body of its mother. But does this distinction really make a difference? Is there any real moral or ethical difference between pre-natal and post-natal life? And is it not possible that medical discoveries will show more and more that fetal life is different from post-natal life only in degree and not in kind? Furthermore, if medical science makes it possible for a fetus to be viable at a time much earlier than the present moment of viability, will the advocates of the abortion of the defective fetus eliminate the distinction that only the non-viable fetus may be aborted?

Abortion performed for the asserted future welfare and happiness of a defective fetus cannot be justified morally or ethically except by the use of a principle which, however attenuated, leads logically to the validation of the termination by society of the life of an innocent but unwanted person. If one does not shrink from that consequence, the discussion has to be extended to a much broader base. But, it is submitted, it is intellectual dishonesty for anyone to advocate the destruction of a defective non-viable fetus without being prepared to accept the far-reaching consequences of the principle which justifies the termination of pre-natal life.

B. Health or Happiness of the Mother

*(1) A Mother's Health and Abortion.* As previously noted, all states permit a therapeutic abortion in order to save the life of the mother. Although there is no meaningful decisional law on this matter, it is clear that this policy allows a physician

to make the indisputably moral judgment that the life of the mother is to be preferred over the life of her unborn child. It could be argued that, since the law permits physicians to act upon their own moral judgments when a mother's life is at stake, the law should logically permit physicians to make similar moral judgments when the mother's future health, rather than her survival, is in question. If this line of reasoning is correct, it may be that those who oppose the legalization of abortion must urge that the right of physicians to perform an abortion to save the life of a mother be either abrogated or logically extended to a granting of permission to perform an abortion in order to save the health of the mother. On the assumption which permeates the case of those seeking the legalization of abortion—that society should concentrate on the quality, rather than the quantity, of life it preserves—there would seem to be no reason why a doctor should *not* be allowed to preserve the health of the mother by performing an abortion.

The medical hypothesis running through this line of argumentation is, of course, open to question. Assuming reasonably modern medical techniques, in how many instances is it likely that the birth of a child will permanently impair the *physical* health of a mother?

Some cases, of course, do exist where the continuation of a pregnancy may bring about a substantial risk, not to the mother's life, but rather, to her future physical health. If there is an inherent right in basic justice for a mother in this situation to request an abortion—and this case is probably the most appealing and compelling reason for a justifiable abortion—how should the law regulate the exercise of this right? The various proposals for changes in America's law regulating abortions silently suggest that the mother's right not to have her health impaired is paramount in this instance and that the state has no duty to speak for, or to protect, the fetus. However appealing such a solution may appear, its implications and consequences need examination.

Every married couple possesses a moral and a legal right to privacy from any undue interference from the state. This right, emphasized by the United States Supreme Court in *Griswold v. Connecticut*, [381 U.S. 479 (1965)] involving the Connecticut birth control statute, should be as broad and as inclusive as is consistent with the good of society. The right to have, or not to have, children and to determine the number of such children are matters in which the state, by general agreement, should not interfere. The welfare of children born to any marriage, however, is, by equally general agreement, a matter of grave concern for the state. Recent controversies over the advisability of statutes designed to curb the physical abuse or the battering of children by mentally upset or emotionally disturbed parents indicate that society feels a deep responsibility to protect children even at the expense of restricting the right to privacy enjoyed by married couples.

For at least a century and a half, this same concern of society and the law for children too young to speak for themselves has been extended to the unborn child by Anglo-American law. The law has taken the position that a married couple may refrain from having children or may restrict the number of their children but that a child, once conceived, has rights which its parents may not extinguish, even if the parents seek only to prevent a permanent impairment of the physical health of the mother.

Once again, the advocates of the right of a mother to an abortion, when confronted with the interest of the state in the child, born or unborn, will take refuge in the medically questionable and logically indefensible position that the unborn child is so different from a child after birth that the state has no right to interfere with a mother's desire to extinguish the life of her unborn child. It appears, however, that if Anglo-American law is to retreat from its present position of extending some, not total, protection to the fetus, it must logically say that the right to marital privacy precludes state interference with an abortion or that the non-viable fetus is not yet sufficiently a human being to merit the protection of the law.

The advocates of the abolition of anti-abortion laws will no doubt urge, as one of the principal arguments, the right to marital privacy as that right is explained in the *Griswold* decision. It is submitted, however, that even the broadest dicta in *Griswold*, and even the most sweeping language in other judicial decisions on the right to marital privacy, do not justify the exclusion of the interest of the state *after* a child has been conceived but not yet delivered. It may be, of course, that courts in the future will extend the right of marital privacy to exclude state interference with an abortion decided upon by a couple. But such a decision would be entirely different from existing decisional law and would, at least logically, have to reject the underlying assumption of present laws forbidding abortion which is, of course, that a non-viable fetus has an inherent and inviolable right to be born even if it is physically or mentally defective and even if its birth results in the impairment of the physical health of its mother.

*(2)  A Mother's Mental Health or Happiness and Abortion.*   The various proposals designed to liberalize America's abortion laws, including that of the American Law Institute (ALI), do not attempt to restrict the right to have an abortion to women who might otherwise have an impairment of their *physical* health. Those who would ease existing abortion laws recognize the fact that physical and mental health are so interdependent that it would be unrealistic to state that an abortion is allowable only for threatened damage to *either* the physical *or* mental health of the mother.

In evaluating the meaning and scope of mental health, however, many problems arise. The legislative history of the section on abortion of the Model Penal Code of the ALI suggests that the term "mental health" is not meant to be used in the proposed law in a narrow or technical sense but rather in a comprehensive way which would permit two physicians to authorize an abortion if in their judgment an operation of this nature would be best for the long-range happiness of the mother. Hence, the term "mental health" of the mother is not intended to be restricted to cases where there is a diagnosis that severe mental depression or some similar psychiatric phenomenon will follow childbirth.

Therefore, in view of the broad authorization which would result if the mental health of the mother became a norm for judging the advisability of abortions, it may be that the married and unmarried mother should be treated differently.

*(3)  Mental Health of Unwed Mothers.*   There is not much scientifically compiled information available on the number and nature of unwed mothers in America. Even less is known about those unwed mothers who terminate their pregnancy by an abortion. As a result, any writer moves into a sea of ambiguities when he attempts to analyze the factors involved in reaching a prudential judgment on the question of whether more relaxed abortion laws would promote the mental health of unwed mothers. Among the many factors which should be weighed in coming to a decision

regarding the basic legal-moral policy which America should adopt with respect to the availability of abortion for unwed mothers are the following.

*(a) Promiscuity Among Single Persons.* To what extent would more relaxed abortion laws promote promiscuity among single persons?

*(b) Adoption of Children of Unwed Mothers.* Should law and society give greater consideration to childless couples (one out of ten) who seek an adoptable child? If so, should the nation's public policy tend to encourage unwed mothers *not* to destroy their unborn child but to arrange that the child be born and placed for adoption?

*(c) Guilt Feelings of the Unwed Mother.* Who is to assess the nature and the consequences of the guilt which, according to reliable and virtually universal reports, comes to an unwed mother who resolves her problem by abortion? If accurate psychiatric testimony showed that the vast majority of unwed mothers who abort their child experience guilt that may have adverse consequences in their lives and their future marriages, would society be morally obliged to counsel unwed mothers about the likelihood of guilt before an easy method of abortion were made available to them? If, in other words, the mental health of the mother is to be the norm by which the advisability of an abortion is to be judged, then the assessment of an unwed mother's prospective mental health following an abortion must include the most careful and comprehensive evaluation of the impact which a feeling of guilt may have on her life.

*(d) "Happiness" of the Unwed Mother.* Since the term "mental health" in the Model Penal Code of the American Law Institute actually translates into "happiness," how and by whom is this broad norm to be interpreted and applied, not merely to the present predicament of the unwed mother but, more importantly, to her entire future life?

Some may object to the relevance of some or all of these factors and urge that the desire of the unwed mother for an abortion should be controlling. As much as one must be sympathetic to this apparently simple solution to a most difficult problem, it should never be forgotten that in modern society the unwed mother is in a position of shame, humiliation, and anguish which is possibly worse than any other human predicament. One may feel that society's attitude of disdain towards the unwed mother is one of hypocrisy, but the fact remains that the pressures and problems confronted by an unwed mother are such that it is not likely that she will be in a position to make rational decisions substantially uninfluenced by fear or panic. Society, therefore, has a very special and unique duty to furnish the most careful counselling to unwed mothers before it allows them to employ a legally approved method of abortion.

The various proposals to modify or repeal anti-abortion laws in America do not distinguish between married and unmarried mothers with respect to the reasons and the procedures by which an abortion would be sanctioned. In view of the very different problems faced by unwed mothers, it is submitted that any new law regulating abortion should take these factors into consideration. . . .

## V. CONCLUSION

It is submitted that no logically defensible or rational change of a substantial nature can take place in America's abortion laws unless the proponents of less strict sanctions against abortion confront and resolve the issue underlying all the other issues: what or whose moral values should the law endorse and enforce?

America's laws against abortion derive in large part from the concepts of the sacredness and the inviolability of every human being. This concept of the non-violability of the human person clearly has many of its most profound roots in the Judeo-Christian religious tradition. That tradition, in fact, is probably the principal source of Anglo-American criminal law. Not all of the elements of that religious tradition are, of course, incorporated or embodied in the criminal laws of England and America; but the essence or the most fundamental principles of that tradition *are* an inherent part of Anglo-American criminal law. And any change of a substantial kind in America's abortion laws would be a notable departure from that body of Anglo-American law which regulates conduct deemed to constitute a crime against society.

No one can reasonably insist that *all* of the actions now penalized by law should remain as they are. On the other hand, no one, presumably, desires to scuttle the entire fabric of Anglo-American criminal law. But, it is submitted, no one can take a position (allegedly between these two extremes) which advocates abortion without inevitably sanctioning a basic compromise of principle—a compromise which could undermine the very foundations of Anglo-American criminal jurisprudence.

The integrity, the untouchableness, the inviolability of every human life by any other human being has been the cardinal principle and the centerpiece of the legal institutions of the English-speaking world and, to a large extent, of every system of law devised by man. However convenient, convincing, or compelling the arguments in favor of abortion may be, the fact remains that the taking of a life, even though it is unborn, cuts out the very heart of the principle that *no one's* life, however unwanted and useless it may be, may be terminated in order to promote the health or happiness of another human being. If the advocates of legalized abortion desire to have an intellectually honest debate about the fundamental change they seek in the moral and legal standards of American life, they should not fall back on the error of fact that a fetus is not a human being. They should, rather, face the fact that they are stating that the rights of one or more human beings to health or happiness may in some circumstances become so important that they take precedence over the very right to exist of another human being.

The inescapable moral issues in the emerging struggle over the wisdom and fairness of America's abortion laws deserve to be discussed and dissected and eventually resolved. It will be a tragedy beyond description for America if the question of legislation on abortion is resolved on sentiment, utilitarianism, or expediency rather than on the basic ethical issue involved—the immorality of the destruction of any innocent human being carried out by other human beings for their own benefit.

## Williams, G., *Euthanasia and Abortion*, 38 Univ. Colo. L. Rev. 187 (1966)*

### ABORTION

All Christian countries started with a prohibition of abortion, at least for the period after "quickening." Nearly all permit some exceptions, at least for saving the life of the woman. The most liberal countries in Western Europe are the Scandi-

* Reprinted with permission of the *University of Colorado Law Review*.

navians, which allow pregnancy to be medically terminated not only on grounds of health (the therapeutic indication), but also where the child is likely to be defective (the eugenic indication) and where the pregnancy was the result of a rape or other criminal act (the so-called moral indication). In the United States, it is generally only permissible to operate to save the life of the woman; but "life" may be broadly interpreted to include health, and in some states the health ground is explicitly sanctioned. In Colorado the statute allows abortion to save the life of the woman or to prevent serious and permanent bodily injury to her.

The first statutes were passed at a time when termination of pregnancy was highly dangerous, even in skilled hands. It is now a routine operation, and majority public opinion would clearly support a somewhat wider measure of discretion being given to the medical profession. Take the case of rape. It is possible that *any* woman might be dragged into a car, driven off, raped, and possibly infected with venereal disease. If she becomes pregnant, is she to be forced to bear a child who will be a perpetual reminder of this terrible episode, a child that may itself be affected by congenital syphilis? Such a woman will inevitably demand an abortion. She may previously have had a general notion that abortion is somehow wrong, but when faced with this crisis she will set out to get one. If refused by her doctor, she may go to an illegal abortionist, well knowing that in doing so she is taking her life in her hands. A common method is for the illegal abortionist to bend a wire clothes-hanger and use that on the woman without an anaesthetic—a highly unpleasant and dangerous operation. If she is wise and has the money, she will flee (as many do) to Tijuana, Mexico, to San Juan, Puerto Rico, or to Tokyo, and have the job properly performed in a hospital.

Another illustration is the case of a criminal attack on a mentally defective girl, who must give birth to the child even though she is in no condition to rear it. Even more compelling is the case of a girl of thirteen who is seduced and becomes pregnant. She is well below the legal age of consent, since she is deemed not fully to understand the nature of the sexual act; she is also below the legal age of marriage. Yet the law says that if she becomes pregnant she must go through with it. The mere fact of her youth is no ground for termination, since young mothers can successfully be brought to term. The fact that she was made pregnant by her own father, as sometimes happens, makes no difference at all.

Marriages forced by pregnancy are often unhappy. In the United States, one girl in eight is married before she is eighteen; two out of five of these girls are pregnant before marriage, and over half of such marriages end in divorce within eighteen months. Much unhappiness caused by these "shotgun weddings" could be avoided if a girl who does not want to force a marriage were allowed to have an abortion instead. A marriage entered into under duress of public opinion is a travesty of what marriage should be.

Consider cases of the "thalidomide" type, where the woman has taken some drug during pregnancy, or has suffered some disease during pregnancy, or is carrying a genetic defect, and it is likely that the child will be born deformed or feeble-minded. It has been estimated that more than 100,000 children are born each year in this country with crippling hereditary defects; these defects cannot always be foreseen, but sometimes may be. However, the statute again makes no provision for termination. Many parents arrange bravely to rear a defective child; but would it not be far better if the child could be prevented from developing?

The problem is sometimes passed off by saying that abortions can be obtained in such cases on the recommendation of a psychiatrist. This is not always so, and psychiatrists resent the pressure brought to bear on them, since they feel it to be unfair that society should be enabled to maintain a two-faced attitude towards the moral problem of abortion by straining their professional consciences. Moreover, the cost of a psychiatric opinion is beyond the reach of many women. . . .

The deficiencies of the law have led to movements for reform. In Britain the Abortion Law Reform Association was founded in 1936, and proposes legislation similar to that in Sweden where, as mentioned earlier, medical abortion is allowed on grounds of health (the therapeutic indication), sexual offense (the moral indication), and foreseen defect of the child (the eugenic indication). The American Law Institute has recommended a similar solution in the Model Penal Code. The first national pressure group was formed in America this year under the name of the Association for Humane Abortion. California has had a Citizens' Committee for Humane Abortion Laws since 1962, and they have unsuccessfully backed a bill on the subject.

Even the legislation proposed by these bodies, though certainly better than none, would fail to provide for many deficiencies in the present law. There is the case where the family is unsuitable for bringing up a child. If the woman is neurotic, a psychiatrist may be able to say that her condition would be worsened by continuing with the pregnancy, and she may be able to secure a legal termination. But if she is already psychotic, and thoroughly unsuitable as the mother of a child, the psychiatrist will often find it quite impossible to affirm that her mental state will be rendered any worse by carrying the child to term. The more unsuitable the woman is to be a mother, the more difficult it becomes legally to terminate her pregnancy.

The unsuitability of the family may arise purely from social factors. A social worker frequently sees a "problem family" building up. The mother is in good health, but she is failing to cope with her existing three or four children, who are undernourished and out of control; the husband is on probation and in debt, and now further criminal charges are pending against him. The mother is pregnant. Abortion cannot be justified on health grounds, but new arrivals in the family will increase the probability that all the children will be neglected and later become delinquent. The social worker cannot take the only step that is likely to halt the worsening position of the family, namely arranging for the mother to have her pregnancy terminated.

Another social situation, by no means uncommon, is where a married woman has an illegitimate pregnancy, the result perhaps of a single indiscretion occurring when she had had too much to drink. There is no provision for abortion even though it may be quite clear that abortion is the only way to prevent the break-up of the marriage.

In short, in the present state of the law there is no provision allowing medical practitioners to do what they consider most advisable for their patients, and on a narrow interpretation it prevents them from giving effect to their ordinary human sympathies. The best that can be said is that prosecutors rarely bring charges against medical men who terminate pregnancies openly, without subterfuge, and in accordance with the ordinary procedures of the profession. Nevertheless, many doctors still are too apprehensive of the law to perform the operation. Most hospitals have set up abortion committees whose chief purpose is to put a damper on the operation. Some, it is said, even have a quota for abortions. Only 9,000 therapeutic abortions a year are performed in the United States—a ratio of one to perhaps a hundred illegal abortions.

The restrictions placed upon legal abortion have given this country what seems to be the largest problem of illegal abortion in the world. There is in all countries a widespread demand for abortion as a means of family limitation where all other methods have failed, and the more severe the law the greater the number of illegal abortions. The most that a penal law can do is to ensure that the operations are not performed by the only people who are competent to do it, medical practitioners. Dr. Nigel Walker summarizes the position by saying that "the criminal law not only fails to achieve the wider objective of discouraging abortion in general, but actually generates the only kind of abortion which can in practice be prosecuted—*viz.*, unskilled and therefore dangerous abortions. . . .

Some illegal abortionists perform the operation competently and safely, but the great majority are incompetent, some appallingly so. This appears clearly enough from a study of the American problem by Bates and Zawadsky, based on personal inquiries and court records. The authors quote an estimate of 5,000 deaths a year from criminal abortion, but since the practice of filing false death certificates is common, they think that the actual number of deaths may be twice that figure. Apart from deaths, it is estimated that 350,000 women a year suffer post-operative complications. Once more, it is not necessary to accept the full figure for even if the actual number is only a tenth of this, it is evident there is an immense amount of avoidable human suffering.

The authors' account of the bungling methods of the abortionists is grim. Although many abortionists operate on referral from physicians and drug-store keepers (who take a share of the fees), an enormous amount of malpractice goes on. The woman who goes to an abortionist can expect to pay in fees all the money she takes with her. "Not one of the court cases concerned a medical man or amateur type who consistently displayed any real kindness, understanding, patience or delicacy in handling their patients." Generally no anaesthetic was given. "There is no assurance of competence or even reasonable care. Just because the abortionist is a *bona fide* physician does not mean anything. Very frequently the abortionist merely poses as a physician, and actually has less knowledge than a butcher." The general practitioner who is so moved by the entreaties of a woman patient that he decides to refer her to an illegal operator is not likely to know of a good one. "He is more likely to have heard of the inept operator whose patients have to be saved by legitimate medical treatment."

While the operation, properly performed, confines the patient for three days or less in the hospital, the subject of unskilled attention will probably be in the hospital for upwards of two weeks after the operation, and sometimes becomes paralyzed for life or otherwise gravely impaired in health. Most of the women who seek these illegal abortions are married, and have already had a family.

The law has other ill effects. There is still much cruelty to children, and this cruelty, when intentional, is nearly always directed toward unwanted children. Mentally abnormal women often produce many children, for whom they are wholly unsuited to be mothers. Bad upbringing is a prime cause of delinquency in boys and of prostitution in girls. When a family is impoverished, an addition to its numbers will work hardship on all. A woman deserted by her husband cannot have a legal abortion. Even a dying woman cannot have one if the pregnancy will not alter the course of the disease. Thus our refusal to permit medical abortions where a pregnancy is unwanted can be seen as one of the reasons for many social ills.

If it is asked why the evils of the present situation can continue without public recognition, the answer, at least until recently, was the conspiracy of silence surrounding the whole subject of abortion, generally regarded as too shameful for discussion. The problem of abortion is affected, like all other sexual and reproductive matters, by the great gulf between public postures and private thoughts and conduct. There is the fear (anachronistic though it may be in these days of birth control) that the repeal of the abortion law would result in sexual license. There is an equally anachronistic anxiety that the human race may die out, when in fact the threat is one of overpopulation.

As with euthanasia, the immediate moral issue is not whether one thinks it right to procure an abortion in specified circumstances. The issue is whether a doctor should be sent to prison for performing an operation that he believes to be best for his patient. Since not all sins are crimes, it is not enough to say that abortion is sinful. Social, secular reasons must be found for making it a crime, and these reasons ought to be honestly weighed. Too often, allegedly social arguments are merely the outworks of a religious position.

As an illustration, consider the following argument which is sometimes advanced: Take any well-known genius of poor physical constitution, such as Beethoven, and point out that if abortion had been allowed the world might have lost a Beethoven. The argument is absurd, because it logically implies that a married woman should spend her whole time trying to achieve another conception, in case this time she is missing a Beethoven. We cannot tell in advance who the Beethovens are. One of the tragedies when a defective child is born (perhaps after the mother has had German measles) is that the cost and labor of rearing it are so great that the couple are prevented from having the normal child they want. This normal child might have been a Beethoven.

Those who, on religious grounds, oppose any change in the law generally offer as a complete solution of the problem the possibility of having an unwanted child adopted. But not all children can be adopted. There is often no prospect of arranging an adoption for racially mixed children, or those who will be born crippled or mentally defective. In any case many women do not want to part with their child after it is born. Despite the views of theologians, popular opinion sees a great difference between an embryonic mass of protoplasm and a new-born baby. A woman may readily procure an abortion when she feels that she cannot bring up a child, and yet find parting with the child when it is born too painful to be accepted. . . .

Let us look at the elements in the argument separately. It is said that, as a biological fact, life begins with the fertilized ovum. But in one sense "life" began in the prehistoric slime and has been continuous since. The question is not when life begins but when human personality begins. This is where the phrase "the unborn child" subtly begs the question. The early foetus cannot realistically be called a child, and if it is not a child it is not an unborn child. It is, if some phrase is needed, a child-to-be.

The phrase "unborn child" can be used, without offense to common sense, in respect of the viable foetus, that is after about the seventh month of pregnancy, when the foetus is capable of surviving apart from the mother. But the further one goes back in the development of the foetus, the more questionable its application becomes. It is an abuse of words to call the fertilized ovum, the zygote, which is a microscopic speck of jelly, a child or a human being. By no permissible stretch of language can it be said to be a human being. The notion of a human being connotes a human intelligence and a defined bodily structure; even under the microscope the zygote offers to the eye no single characteristic of a human being. When a baby has been born, we will call it a human being notwithstanding certain defects or any accidents that may befall it. But to describe a single cell as a human being is absurd.

One can easily fall into fallacy when arguing on this subject. "Tom Smith's body is composed of cells having a unique set of chromosomes. (Unique, that is, unless he happens to have an identical twin.) The development of this body of Tom Smith can be traced back to a zygote. Therefore, the zygote is Tom Smith." The conclusion does not follow because the last sentence is imperfectly expressed. The zygote is the beginning of what *will be* Tom Smith. It is not at present Tom Smith. . . .

Opponents of the above approach claim that it contradicts the "biological facts." Biologists, we are told, have discovered that development is continuous from conception, and, therefore, it is unscientific to draw some arbitrary line after which human personality is to be deemed to begin.

This objection involves a philosophical error. What we are concerned with in the present discussion is a matter of naming, and naming is not a scientific activity. It is an activity that is always subordinate to others. The biologist can and must name for the purpose of communicating the results of his researches. In the same way, the lawyer names for legal purposes, and the moralist names for moral purposes. The scientific status of the biologist gives him no special warrant to name in a moral context. When considering the moral rule that human beings must not be killed, it becomes necessary to define "human beings" for the purpose of the rule. Since the definition will settle the limits of the rule, it is distinctively the task of the moralist, not of the biologist. As so often with moral questions, a satisfactory definition involves drawing a rather arbitrary line. The fact that it is rather arbitrary in the precise position at which it is drawn is no objection, because this is always the case. To take an analogy, most people would agree that we ought not to be cruel to animals. But to distinguish between immoral cruelty and the necessary use of animals for human purposes involves drawing a line on which there may be much dispute. What about battery hens, and broiler calves, and the castration of cats, and the docking of dogs' tails? These are our present practices, at least in some countries, but some people object strongly to the first two of them, and some object to all of them. The moral line has to be drawn somewhere, even though we may admit that drawing it anywhere involves fine and almost indefensible distinctions.

Further, to assert that human development is continuous from conception contains a *suggestio falsi*, because conception does not represent the beginning of development. Development is continuous even before conception. Both sperm and ovum were living cells before they met. The so-called moment of conception, if by that is meant the fusion of the gametes, is not in fact a moment but a process somewhat extended in time. The latest account of conception appears to be as follows. The sperm meets and joins with the ovum. Two structures called asters appear, and a spindle forms between them. The chromosomes from the egg nucleus and the sperm collect around the equator of the spindle before dividing longitudinally into halves which move towards the asters, forming two daughter nuclei. Finally the cytoplasm of the egg cell divides, and two new cells result. If one is looking for a "moment of conception" it is not at all obvious which "moment" is to be selected. It is so artificial as to be ridiculous to find anything in this process as the emergence of a human being, in the sense that immediately after it has taken place you actually have a human being.

The truth surely is that human beings are part of the continuum of nature. A man's commencement is no more a perfectly fixed and definite point of time than his death. Philosophically speaking, our conception of human personality, like our conception of every other kind of unity, is something that we impress upon nature rather than something that is found in nature. All unity is subjective; it exists only to the extent that we choose to perceive it. There is, indeed, an underlying reality, but our conceptual unities have sharp edges nonexistent in nature. These sharp edges are the products of our imagining and are always in a sense arbitrary.

It is natural that we should feel affectionate and protective toward infants, and right that this feeling should be translated into morality and law. However, experience and rational argument support the view that it is a mistake to commence the legal protection too soon in prenatal development. We have been given no revelation as to the beginning of human personality (and certainly there is nothing in the Bible on the subject); thus, we are entitled to fix it at the point of time demanded by human needs.

## STATUTORY ALTERATION OF ABORTION LAWS

The two preceding articles present opposing academic points of view. Legislators, too, are giving active consideration to the area. One state, Colorado, enacted in 1967 a law permitting abortion on broader grounds than that of necessity to preserve the physical well-being of the mother. The statute provides as follows:

## Colo. Rev. Stat., 40–2–50 to 40–2–53

*40-2-50. Definitions.*   (1) As used in sections 40-2-50 to 40-2-53:

(2) "Pregnancy" means the implantation of an embryo in the uterus.

(3) "Accredited hospital" means one licensed by the Colorado state department of public health and accredited by the Joint Commission on Accreditation of Hospitals.

(4) (a) (i) "Justified medical termination" means the intentional ending of the pregnancy of a woman at the request of said woman or if said woman is under the age of eighteen years, then at the request of said woman and her then living parent or guardian, or if the woman is married and living with her husband at the request of said woman and her husband, by a licensed physician using accepted medical procedures in a fully accredited hospital upon written certification by all of the members of a special hospital board that:

(ii) Continuation of the pregnancy, in their opinion, is likely to result in: The death of the woman; or the serious permanent impairment of the physical health of the woman; or the serious permanent impairment of the mental health of the woman as confirmed in writing under the signature of a licensed doctor of medicine specializing in psychiatry; or the birth of a child with grave and permanent physical deformity or mental retardation; or

(iii) Less than sixteen weeks of gestation have passed and that the pregnancy resulted from rape, as defined in section 40-2-25 (1) (a), (1) (c), (1) (d) and (1) (e), or rape as defined in 40-2-25 (1) (a), (1) (b), or (1) (j) if the female person has not reached her sixteenth birthday at the time of said rape; or incest, as defined in section 40-9-4, and that the district attorney of the judicial district in which the alleged rape or incest has occurred has informed the committee in writing under his signature, that there is probable cause to believe that the alleged violation did occur.

(5) "Special hospital board" means a committee of three licensed physicians who are members of the staff of the hospital where the proposed termination would be performed if certified in accordance with sections 40-2-50 to 40-2-53 and who meet regularly or on call for the purpose of determining the question of medical justification in each individual case, and which maintains a written record, signed by each member, of the proceedings and deliberations of such board.

*40-2-51. Criminal Abortion.* (1) Any person who intentionally ends or causes to be ended the pregnancy of a woman by any means other than by justified medical termination of the pregnancy or live birth is guilty of a felony, punishable by imprisonment in the state penitentiary for not less than three years nor more than ten years and by a fine in a sum not exceeding two thousand dollars.

(2) If any woman shall die as the result of the intentional ending of her pregnancy by any means other than by justified medical termination of the pregnancy or live birth, the person responsible is guilty of murder and shall be punished accordingly.

*40-2-52. Pretended Criminal Abortion.* (1) Any person who intentionally pretends to end the real or apparent pregnancy of a woman by any means other than by justified medical termination of the pregnancy or live birth is guilty of a felony, punishable by imprisonment in the state penitentiary for not less than one year nor more than three years and by a fine in a sum not exceeding one thousand dollars.

(2) If any woman shall die as the result of the intentional pretended ending of her real or apparent pregnancy by any means other than by justified medical termination of the pregnancy or live birth, the person so pretending to end the real or apparent pregnancy is guilty of murder and shall be punished accordingly.

*40-2-53. Failure to Comply.* Nothing in sections 40-2-50 to 40-2-53 shall require a hospital to admit any patient under the provisions of sections 40-2-50 to 40-2-53 for the purposes of performing an abortion, nor shall any hospital be required to appoint a special hospital board as defined in section 40-2-50. A person who is a member of or associated with the staff of a hospital or any employee of a hospital in which a justified medical termination has been authorized and who shall state in writing an objection to such termination on moral or religious grounds shall not be required to participate in the medical procedures which will result in the termination of a pregnancy and the refusal of any such person to participate shall not form the basis for any disciplinary or other recriminatory action against such person.

What safeguards does the statute contain? What abuses does it aim to prevent? Does the statute accomplish the objective advocated by reform movements? For those who oppose abortions, what basic issue is ignored?

## (4) Moral Basis for Criminal Law

According to the American Law Institute [Comment, A.L.I., *Model Penal Code* §207.11 (Tentative Draft No. 9, 1959)], moral and religious rules can control conduct in areas that are not open to legal control. Why should this be so?

... (C) The criminal law in this area cannot undertake or pretend to draw the line where religion or morals would draw it. Moral demands on human behavior can be higher than those of the criminal law precisely because violations of those higher standards do not carry the grave consequence of penal offenses. Moreover, moral standards in this area are in a state of flux, with wide disagreement among honest and responsible people. The range of opinion among reasonable men runs from deep religious conviction that any destruction of incipient human life, even to save the life of the mother, is murder, to the equally fervent belief that the failure to limit procreation is itself unconscionable and immoral if offspring are destined to be idiots, or bastards, or undernourished, maleducated rebels against society. For many people sexual intercourse divorced from the end of procreation is a sin; for multitudes of others it is one of the legitimate joys of living. Those who think in utilitarian terms on these matters can differ among themselves as widely as moralists. Voluntary limitation of population can be seen as national suicide in a world-wide competition for numerical superiority, while to others uncontrolled procreation appears equally suicidal as tending to aggravate the pressure of population on limited natural resources and so driving nations to mutually destructive wars. To use the criminal law against a substantial body of decent opinion, even if it be minority opinion, is contrary to our basic traditions. Accordingly, here as elsewhere, criminal punishment must be reserved for behavior that falls below standards generally agreed to by substantially the entire community.

## (5) Insanity—Conflict in Legal Definition

In the following extract, the psychiatrist-authors take sharp issue with the M'Naghten Rule, and discuss the *Durham* and *Currens* cases. They go on to express their own preference for a test in which criminal responsibility rests on whether "the accused was suffering from disease of the mind or mental retardation to such a degree that he ought not to be held responsible."

Which of the tests suggested in the text and the article seems most beneficial to the accused? To society?

## Ebaugh, F., and Macdonald, J., The Medicolegal Dilemma—An Interment of Truth, *J.A.M.A.*, 184:131 (1963)*

> *He walks with the vacant eye of the waking dreamer. And the voices he hears are not of men, but the quick, incandescent shapes that inhabit the forests of the mind, and the chambers of Poe. . . . And sometimes, at a secret, frantic call, he becomes as they.*
> Anon.

Thus runs a classical description of psychosis. Would that the nature of legal insanity be equally clear-cut in revealing itself against the backdrop of modern civilization in which the members are highly interdependent. The tests of criminal responsibility in the majority of the states are derived from the English M'Naghten Rules. Was the accused laboring under such a defect of reason from disease of the mind that (1) he did not know the nature and quality of the act he was doing or (2) did not know that it was wrong? These rules have not been rendered obsolete by the remarkable strides in psychiatric knowledge since their introduction in 1843. They were untenable even by the psychological knowledge of that day.

Indeed, these rules represented a backward step in the laws of England. Forty-three years earlier, Erskine, who defended Hadfield on the charge of attempting to assassinate King George III, successfully advanced the theory that a man could know right from wrong, could understand the nature of the act he was about to commit, could manifest a clear design and foresight and cunning in planning and executing it, but if his mental condition produced or was the cause of the criminal act he should not legally be held responsible for it. . . .

*The Aim of the Insanity Trial Is to Determine Criminal Responsibility and the Psychiatrist Is Required to Express His Opinion on This Issue.* The question is often raised why lay jurors should be required to determine legal sanity or legal insanity, especially when there is disagreement among psychiatric witnesses. It has even been suggested that the issue of legal sanity should be determined by a panel of psychiatrists. It is not generally recognized that criminal responsibility is not a medical concept, but a moral concept.

Some have insisted that it is a philosophical concept, raising issues of free will and determinism, but no one has denied that it depends for its application on public opinion about what is just and moral. Should the psychiatrist be requested to express a moral opinion? There is general agreement that he should not be required to express an opinion in this field which is foreign to his special training and experience.

Yet the law makes this demand upon the psychiatrist and does so by cloaking a moral question with a pseudopsychiatric yardstick of criminal responsibility. The law has created fictional psychiatric entities and has enshrouded them in the M'Naghten Rules and their variants. The moral issue should be put to the jury untrammelled by pseudopsychiatric entities which serve only to cloud the issue and bring disrepute upon psychiatrists who, rightly or wrongly, discharge their public responsibilities by participating in a legal distortion of the truth of the issue.

The real issue which faces the jury is—does the accused suffer from mental disease or mental retardation to such a degree that he ought not to be held responsible for his illegal act? The psychiatrist should be required to testify regarding the

* Reprinted with permission of the *Journal of the American Medical Association* and the authors.

presence or absence of mental disease or mental retardation. He may or may not be able to speak with certainty upon the effects of any such disease or retardation upon self-control. As the M'Naghten Rules stand, in some cases which should clearly lead to a finding of insanity, the psychiatrist must either answer the test questions truthfully and acquiesce in the possible subversion of justice, or distort the meaning of the tests to permit the satisfaction of justice.

*The Truth Involves the Mental State of the Accused at the Time of the Forbidden Act.* The trial is a search for truth, but the court, with its focus on the "right-wrong test," may not permit excursions into the origins of the act. If the trial is a search for truth, the truth—or the best available approximation to the truth—should indeed be presented. "Ay, there's the rub." Whatever the skill of the psychiatrist witness, can he meaningfully present his findings?

Even though the psychiatrist may have a clear understanding of the psychological origins of the illegal act, it may be beyond his skill to convey this information to the jury. The explanation of criminal behavior is usually sought in such obvious conscious motivations as lust, greed, envy, revenge, and anger. Often, indeed, there is evidence of such factors but, even when present, they do not always provide an adequate explanation of the crime. The accused himself may seek to explain his behavior in like manner, yet the mainsprings of human conduct are so complex as to cast doubt on such explanations.

As early as 1864, Maudsley wrote: "The fundamental defect in the legal test of responsibility is that it is founded upon the consciousness of the individual. . . ." ". . . the most important part of our mental operations takes place unconsciously." When the expert psychiatric witness attempts to explain criminal behavior in terms of unconscious motivations, he ventures into territory which is often beyond the knowledge of judge, attorneys, jurors, and the accused himself. The body of psychiatric knowledge is so complex that it cannot be readily conveyed to laymen. . . .

## RECENT TESTS OF CRIMINAL RESPONSIBILITY

Legislative and judicial bodies across the nation have been struggling with the problem of selecting a suitable replacement for the outmoded M'Naghten Rules. In 1954, the United States Court of Appeals for the District of Columbia introduced the controversial Durham Rule, which is substantially similar to the New Hampshire Rule of 1870. The rule of Durham is as follows: "An accused is not criminally responsible if his unlawful act is the product of mental disease or defect." Although widely hailed by psychiatrists because it leaves them free to speak in a psychiatric frame of reference, the rule has been criticized sharply.

"How can a crime be the product of a mental illness?" Savage asks. "Crimes are committed by people not by mental illnesses. It is as though the mental illness were some daemon residing within the head which mediated some behavior and not others." Roche comments, "The psychiatrist can do no more than say that a causal connection invariably exists, for no other reason than, in his experience and within his psychological model, he has never encountered a case where outward behavior was unrelated to inward mental life."

The Currens Rule (1961) eliminates the troublesome "product" clause of the Durham Rule. Under Currens, the jury "must be satisfied that at the time of committing the prohibited act the defendant as a result of mental disease or defect, lacked substantial capacity to conform his conduct to the requirements of the law which he is alleged to have violated." The Currens Rule probably will lead to a great increase of verdicts of not guilty by reason of insanity. This has already occurred under the Durham Rule. In February, 1961, 25% of the persons tried for criminal offenses in the District Court for the District of Columbia were found not guilty by reason of insanity, as compared with less than 1% prior to the Durham decision.

Diamond has considered the consequences if Currens becomes the law of the land. Very large numbers of defendants, accused of crimes both great and small, in his opinion, will be acquitted on the ground of insanity and will be sent to mental hospitals. "A considerable proportion of our potential prison population will then be sent to hospitals, staffed and administered by psychiatrists ill equipped by temperament or training either to treat these borderline and character disorders, or to maintain the necessary security precautions that society demands. Modern trends in public and private mental hospitals are definitely toward the open-door hospital with voluntary admission of patients. It would not be easy and certainly not at all acceptable to the psychiatric profession and to the public to reverse this trend and return to the maximum security state hospital of the past in order to accommodate the new patients to be committed under Currens."

Diamond further points out that liberalization of the rules of criminal responsibility may inadvertently subvert the basic principles of humanitarian penal reform. Large numbers of offenders can, under the laws, be labeled as insane, then confined for indeterminate periods, up to life, in institutions called mental hospitals, which are really prisons in disguise, with only a pretense of treatment and with gross disregard of civil liberties and due process. In his opinion, the development of the legal doctrine of limited or diminished responsibility may accomplish more than would the adoption of Durham or Currens or any other rule that enforces the sane-insane dichotomy. . . .

The defects of the M'Naghten Rules are so great as to demand their abrogation. We recommend the adoption of a rule which puts the issue clearly to the jury—a rule which was recommended by the Royal Commission on Capital Punishment— "The jury should determine whether at the time of the act, the accused was suffering from disease of the mind or mental retardation to such a degree that he ought not to be held responsible."

The introduction of this rule, together with provision for a simultaneous plea of diminished or partial responsibility would, it is believed, resolve many of the present problems to the satisfaction of society and with justice to the accused offender.

## THE PSYCHIATRIST IN THE CRIMINAL COURTS

There is growing public dissatisfaction with the administration of our insanity laws and the psychiatrist has been selected as the scapegoat.

The public is critical of psychiatric disagreement on the witness stand and even fellow physicians share this viewpoint. Yet it is not unusual for internists and surgeons to disagree on the witness stand and no voice is raised in protest. Lawyers have joined in the chorus of criticism, although such criticism seems strange, coming as it does from a profession which is dependent upon disagreement for its livelihood. Is it surprising that psychiatrists differ when they are required to express an opinion within the framework of a legal test which bears little relationship to the practice of psychiatry? If a medical, rather than a moral, opinion were sought, and if all pertinent information was made available to the psychiatrists, whether appointed by the prosecution or defense, the battle of experts would be much less frequent.

The public is critical of psychiatrists when a defendant who has committed a brutal crime is acquitted on the ground of insanity. Herein lies a paradox. Although the community is angered by the number of defendants so acquitted, juries continue to return this verdict with surprising frequency. What is the explanation? We are reminded of the reaction of an elderly English woman to a play in a London theatre. Acting in the part of Queen Cleopatra, Sarah Bernhardt stabbed the slave who bore to her the ill tidings of Mark Antony's defeat at Actium; she stormed, raved, wrecked some of the scenery in her frenzy, and finally, as the curtain fell, dropped in a shuddering convulsive heap. As the applause died, the elderly English lady was heard to say to her companion, "How different, how very different from the home life of our own dear Queen."

In like manner, jurors, as they listen to testimony regarding a defendant's childhood and adolescence, say to themselves, how different, how very different from our own lives. The consequence of the charitable response of juries to stories of hardship and parental brutality is that an increasing number of persons who are not psychotic are being acquitted by reason of insanity. The public, in its anxiety over the incidence of major crimes, finds fault with these decisions and blames the medical profession. Such blame, often based upon inadequate or misleading newspaper summaries of the evidence, is surely unjustified.

The public is critical because it believes that those defendants who have been committed to a mental hospital following acquittal by reason of insanity are quickly released. Hospital administrators are very sensitive to the danger of being criticized if they release, as cured, a person who has committed a criminal act. If such a person, after release, commits another criminal act, there will be a public outcry; hospital administrators are therefore probably too conservative in their releasing practices rather than too liberal. Nevertheless, there are well-documented cases in which potentially dangerous persons have been released with tragic consequences to the community. Herein the law may be at fault rather than the psychiatrists. For example, so long as the test for release in Colorado is the M'Naghten Rules, such cases are bound to occur. The test for release in all jurisdictions should be "freedom from such abnormal condition as would make the individual dangerous to himself or the community in the reasonably foreseeable future."

The public image of the psychiatrist has been damaged by his appearance on the witness stand, where he is not rarely subjected to unjustified ridicule and personal humiliation by overbearing attorneys. In these cases, the attorneys have paraphrased the admonition of the great Roman lawyer, Cicero, "When you have no basis for argument abuse the plaintiff" to read "abuse the psychiatrist." The ethical psychiatrist who attempts to present his testimony fairly and adequately may be hampered by the skillful, if unscrupulous, methods of interrogation employed by prosecuting or defense attorneys. The consequence of such abuse should not be attributed to the psychiatric witness.

## PROGRAM FOR CHANGE

A substantial change in the word and spirit of the law on criminal responsibility is overdue. The M'Naghten Rules should be abrogated. The moral question which underlies determination of criminal responsibility should be stated clearly and frankly to the jury by asking them whether the accused was suffering from mental disease or mental retardation to such a degree that he ought not be held responsible. A plea of diminished responsibility should be required in conjunction with a plea of insanity and the jury should be told what the consequence of their verdict will be.

Society should recognize that harsh, punitive measures have never provided protection from criminal behavior. It has been well said that society has the criminals it deserves. Greater attention should be focused on the prevention of crime and the rehabilitation of persons who have committed illegal acts, regardless of whether they are confined in penitentiaries or mental hospitals.

The contributions of psychiatry to the administration of justice will be enhanced by the appointment by the court of neutral experts to examine defendants who plead insanity. Psychiatrists should have free communication with one another and free access to all available information to achieve a maximally valid, dynamic understanding of the defendant.

Courses in psychiatry and law, with particular emphasis on the dynamics of human behavior, should be taught in all law schools. Such instruction has been found valuable in orienting attorneys to the contributions psychiatry can and should make to the courts and in improving communication between the professions.

In some states, the laws should be revised to prevent the release of potentially dangerous persons who have been acquitted by reason of insanity at the time of the offense. There should be "freedom from such abnormal conditions as would make the individual dangerous to himself or the community in the reasonably foreseeable future."

It is believed that implementation of these recommendations would do much to provide both greater protection for society and greater justice for the mentally abnormal offender and yet would not overwhelm our mental hospitals with large numbers of criminal offenders. Such a program will obviously require extensive revisions in laws and court procedures. Much of this is a housecleaning task which must be laid in the lap of the legal profession. No one else is qualified to do the job and no one else holds a greater stake in this reform. The determination of truth, the protection of individual rights of both the accused and the victim, and the facilitation of an effective social organization are charged to the law and to the courts. Psychiatry can help, if talents, training, and experience are effectively used in consulting capacities. The psychiatrist has no place in court as a contestant. His sole, primary, and permanent realm is the practice of medicine, with a specialty in the treatment of the mentally ill. Under present court and commitment procedures, he is unable to play his role in a maximal way for the welfare of the patient and the larger society. Public ire is justified. It should not, however, be directed at the psychiatrist or the jurist, but at the laws themselves. Some of these laws are so archaic that they are dangerous. The problem is crucial and the changes must be sweeping and immediate.

## (6) M'Naghten Rule in Actual Practice

The difficulties in applying the M'Naghten rule are graphically illustrated in the following example. In what respects does the situation described support or refute those who criticize the M'Naghten formulation?

## Roche, P., *The Criminal Mind,* 92 (New York: Farrar, Straus & Cudahy, Inc., 1958)*

COMMONWEALTH v. JAMES ERNEST MONROE

Let us take a trial run with M'Naghten in the following case. James Ernest Monroe, a middle-aged, married postal employee was observed to undergo a change in personality marked by moodiness and withdrawal. Those about him offered the following observations of his change of personality which became visible in the year preceding his offense. The defendant would take turns between moments of agitation and unresponsive remoteness to others when he wore an expression of inner preoccupation and absorption. At times his responses were either inadequate or far afield. When his mother received insulin injections he would run out of the room. During the mother's illness, and at the passing mention of it, he would spontaneously burst into crying spells which at times were seemingly intractable. Once during a thunderstorm the defendant rushed out of the house and remained secluded for a long time.

One day he proceeded in the direction of the river without announced purpose. Near his intended destination he stepped into a small real estate office occupied by two women to whom he was a complete stranger. Without uttering a word he drew a gun from his pocket and leveled it in the direction of the women. One promptly emptied a cash box within his reach and again without a word he automatically withdrew the contents of the box—some fifty dollars. We do not know what the terror of the women meant to him beyond the fact that no threat was verbally communicated. Again without hint of motivation he fired at random and walked out of the office; upon observing someone coming at him, he broke into a run, but was caught. After a momentary struggle he meekly surrendered, was arrested and placed in prison.

The question is why did he kill one strange woman and wound another? The first answer implying purpose was supplied by the prosecution. He did so in order to carry out an armed robbery in "cold blood" because he needed money and this raised his crime to first degree homicide. Much evidence was introduced to sustain this answer. His actions spoke for his intentions. His crime was dramatically repeated in fantasy step by step in the evidence and the Commonwealth concluded its case. The defense conceded that the prosecution had narrated the evidence correctly. The defendant had not denied it. It was clear that the issue of the defendant's liability to the penalty of execution did not turn on the question of his having carried out the killing. The issue was not the outside events; it was centered on something inside the accused. This called for experts on inside problems; on the inner movements of wills. The shift of interest moved to psychiatry. The prosecution engaged two reputable psychiatrists. The defense did likewise and balanced the opposing teams. The psychiatrists came to the trial with their medical data which among them had more or less a rough correspondence despite the fact that the contending experts had examined the accused separately and at different times. They could not have rendered opinions on the same facts, since the same facts could have been secured only if all the experts sampled them together. This would be scarcely permitted by either side. When the experts appeared for testimony those for the defense could only assume that the prosecution experts had the same data, and vice versa.

In his contact with the defense psychiatrists the accused communicated little of an outward pathological nature beyond the existence of a depression of mood, fantasies of suicide both before and after the offense and only a hint of mystical hallucinatory promptings from his deceased mother who had died in a mental hospital a short time before the visible onset of his personality change.

By necessity the law was concerned for the outside events which purported to explain purposeful causality, but the defense had erected an exculpatory plea of insanity which implied an answer of deterministic necessity. This answer was to the effect that the accused was acting out an old score in the present against a surrogate of his deceased mother, all within the frame of a fantasy of rejoining her in suicide. We don't know what was the momentary transaction between him and the woman victim that completed the connection which released the destructive impulse. The testimony of the defense experts implied that the accused actions were carried out by deterministic necessity on the basis of past experiences and that they were carried out in an individual who was undergoing a process regarded as a mental disease of clinical dimensions.

Each psychiatrist would be expected to make answers inferred from a communication coming from within the accused. Four psychiatrists paired in opposing sides drew their inferences. I think it is proper to say that with their inferences drawn from their examinations each in a private capacity would have been moved to accept the accused as a patient in need of psychiatric help. There was something wrong with him which could be inferred at least from his apparently unmotivated behavior with two strange women. Even the taking of the money proffered by the victim did not fit into a standard technique of armed robbery. He expressed regret for what had taken place but could offer no common sense explanation for it. The psychiatrists took oaths to tell the "truth" which the jury would presently know from the inferences of the opposing witnesses. The defense presented to his experts a lengthy hypothetical question which chronicled the prior personality change as observed by others, the events leading up to the killing and finally posed to the experts a question of the mental condition of the accused at the time of the offense. The experts were already convinced that the accused presented a picture of a person within whom there had been a psychotic process unitary with the killing. Having so convinced themselves, they were ready with their answers. They answered that the accused was mentally ill. The right and wrong rule was then put to them. At the time of the killing, did the accused "know the nature and quality of the act that he was doing, or if he did know it, . . . did he know what he was doing was wrong?" Now the accused knew what he had done and he knew it was wrong insofar as he could convey his "knowing" in words in answer to these same questions put to him. Here the psychiatrists were faced with a problem—how to answer the questions from words of the accused and at the same time come to grips with the facts of his mental illness. In the opinion of the two psychiatrists here was a psychotic person who "knew" what he did and that it was wrong. The only way out of this was for the psychiatrists to convince themselves that inside the accused a psychotic process must in some occult way effect the cognitive faculties to set apart the accused from non-psychotic killers. In words, the accused had knowledge; what about his actions?

His actions had equivocal significance. He grabbed money, yet had some. He shot at random at strange women killing one and wounding another, but there was no evidence of a move or threat to tie to the shooting; he ran out as if in a design of escape. His manner of resignation and distance from the examiners spoke for no effort to rationalize in words his deed even delusionally. On the stand the psychiatrists sensed that to testify to the words of the accused would push his psychosis out of reach. The tie between psychosis and his knowledge had to be rearranged to reconcile their data of observation with the requirements of the law. The defense psychiatrists answered the question; the accused did not have the requisite knowledge and on cross-examination they defended their answers with their inferences of the existence of a mental disease in the accused.

The two experts for the prosecution were duly qualified and sworn. They related their examinations of the accused and both came to the identical conclusion that he suffered with no mental illness; one expert volunteered his opinion that the accused was faking mental illness in order to escape justice. This opinion was explicit that the accused, an untutored person, had either come upon a facile compliance with instruction or had found hitherto untapped native sources of intuitive dissembling. Both the experts declared flatly that the accused had requisite knowledge. Their answers made sense to the jury. The accused was found guilty and condemned to die in the electric chair. A short time after conviction he was found in his prison cell hanging dead by his own hand. His passing denied us further knowledge of how much he really knew.

Jerome Hall has admonished that psychiatrists should be on "tap and not on top." In afterthought the psychiatrists who took part in this case might well ponder their contribution to social order. Was it psychiatry and was it scientific? Is being on *tap* really being *used* to move a public moral issue which had no necessary connection with scientific inquiry?

## (7)  The Deterrence Function in Narcotics Regulation

In a joint study of the American Bar Association and the American Medical Association, the effectiveness of heavy penalties for narcotics users as a device for the control of traffic in narcotics is analyzed. Are the author's conclusions supported by your own studies in the field of narcotics?

### Drug Addiction: Crime or Disease? Interim and Final Reports of the Joint Committee of the American Bar Association and the American Medical Association on Narcotic Drugs (1961)

APPENDIX A. ROSCOWE, M., SOME BASIC PROBLEMS IN DRUG ADDICTION AND SUGGESTIONS FOR RESEARCH

1. Introduction—Severity of Punishment as Deterrence to Drug Addiction

In 1914 Congress, with the passage of the Harrison Act, embarked upon a policy of prohibiting legal access to narcotic drugs on the part of those addicted to such drugs. This prohibitory policy has been strengthened by subsequent legislation. It has been implemented with considerable vigor by the Narcotics Bureau of the Treasury Department and by other state and local enforcement agencies throughout the country, acting under the authority of state and local statutes. Despite this effort, a Senate Committee recently came to the conclusion that, "The United States has more narcotic addicts, both in total numbers and population-wise, than any other country of the Western World."

Such a finding, that we have more drug addicts than any other Western country, despite forty years of enforcement of prohibitory laws, raises doubts concerning the wisdom of the prohibitory approach to problems of drug addiction. It would seem to require a re-examination of our narcotics policy. Nevertheless, the two Congressional Committees which recently conducted nationwide inquiries into problems of drug addiction and the drug traffic appeared to be oblivious to doubts concerning the wisdom of the current policy toward narcotic drugs. Both Committees took the basic position that even stronger prohibitions were required if our narcotic addiction problems were to be satisfactorily controlled.

Three basic concepts run through the recommendations of both Congressional Committees: (1) more stringent narcotic law enforcement; (2) severer penalties for offenders against the narcotic laws; (3) the permanent isolation of incurable drug addicts. The thinking of the Committees is contained in the following extracts from their reports:

Effective control of the vicious narcotic traffic requires not only vigorous enforcement, but also certainty of punishment. Conclusive evidence was presented during your sub-committee's investigation that the imposition of heavier penalties was the strongest deterrent to narcotic addiction and narcotic traffic. . . .

Unless immediate action is taken to prohibit probation or suspension of sentence, it is the sub-committee's considered opinion that the first offender peddler problem will become eventually worse and eventually lead to the large scale recruiting of our youth by the upper echelon of traffickers. . . .

Some testimony received by the sub-committee that . . . a distinction should be made between the non-addict trafficker and the addict trafficker, with the latter group being dealt with less severely. It is the view of your sub-committee that the addict trafficker is just as vicious a person as the non-addict trafficker. . . .

It is urged . . . that the minimum and maximum penalties applicable to conviction for violations of the narcotic laws be increased on both the federal and state levels.

Criminal laws and procedures are insufficient to insure the apprehension and punishment of narcotics offenders. . . .

Penalties for narcotic violations are neither commensurate with the seriousness of the crime nor sufficient to remove the profits. . . .

The minimum and maximum penalties be increased for all violations of the narcotics law, with greatly increased penalties for sales to juveniles. . . .

The Committee has found that whenever and wherever penalties are severe and strictly enforced drug addiction and narcotic trafficking have decreased proportionately. . . .

That habitual narcotic addicts be committed to "an indeterminable quarantine type of confinement on a suitable narcotics farm. . . .

The Report to the President of the Inter-Departmental Committee On Narcotics also stresses the vital importance of severe punishment as a basic means of controlling drug addiction and the drug problem.

The Committee has arrived at the conclusion that there is need for a continuation of the policy of punishment of a severe character as a deterrent to narcotic law violations. It therefore recommends an increase of maximum sentences for first as well as subsequent offenses. With respect to the mandatory minimum features of such penalties and prohibitions of suspended sentences or probation, the Committee fully recognizes the objections in principle. It feels however that in order to define the gravity of this class of crime and the assured penalty to follow, these features of the law must be regarded as essential elements of the desired deterrents, although some difference of opinion still exists regarding their application to first offenses of certain types.

These predilections for stringent law enforcement and severer penalties as answers to the problems of drug addiction reflect the philosophy and the teachings of the Bureau of Narcotics. For years the Bureau has supported the doctrine that if penalties for narcotic drug violations were severe enough and if they could be enforced strictly enough, drug addiction and the drug traffic would largely disappear from the American scene. This approach to problems of narcotics has resulted in spectacular modifications of our narcotic drug laws on both the state and federal level.

The 84th Congress passed legislation which provided that whoever "receives, conceals, buys, or sells" heroin, etc., shall be punished by 5 to 10 years imprisonment for a first offense. The giving, selling, or furnishing of heroin to a person under 18 years of age was made punishable by sentences of 10 years to life or the death sentence if directed by the jury. Legal provisions permitting suspended sentence and probation for violations of the drug laws were struck from the federal statutes.

The states have followed the lead of the Federal Government in strengthening penalties for violations of the drug laws. In California, unlawful possession of narcotics was formerly punishable by a maximum of 6 years in the State prison. A 1953 amendment increased the maximum to 10 years and to 20 years for a second offense. In Illinois, illicit possession of a narcotic drug used to be punished by a maximum of one year in the County jail. It is now punishable by 2 to 10 years in the penitentiary for a first offense, and 5 years to life for subsequent offenses. In Michigan, unlawful possession of narcotic drugs was punishable by a maximum of 4 years imprisonment. At present, such possession is punishable by a maximum of 10 years for a first offense, 20 years for a second offense, and 29 to 40 years for a third offense. In Ohio, unlawful possession of drugs was punishable by a maximum of 5 years imprisonment. Today, the penalties for unlawful possession as a first offense are 2 to 15 years, for a second offense, 5 to 20 years, and for a third offense, 10 to 30 years.

Stringent law enforcement has its place in any system of controlling narcotic drugs. However, it is by no means the complete answer to American problems of drug addiction. In the first place it is doubtful whether drug addicts can be deterred from using drugs by threats of jail or prison sentences. The belief that fear of punishment is a vital factor in deterring an addict from using drugs rests upon a superficial view of the drug addiction process and the nature of drug addiction. This will be apparent from the discussion of the nature and mechanics of drug addiction (see *infra*). It is also doubtful whether it will be possible to incarcerate indefinitely relapsing, uncured drug addicts as recommended by the Senate Committee. The Committee urged this step because of the fear that incurable drug addicts carry the contagion of drug addiction to others. In order to prevent such contagion, incurable drug addicts must be permanently incarcerated and permanently isolated from the community. There are thousands of men and women in this country who are confirmed drug addicts and who are incurable by present methods and techniques. If the Senate Committee recommendation is to be acted upon, places of detention will have to be set up for these thousands of men and women, by Congress and state legislatures. There is little likelihood that federal and state legislation will provide new places of detention for large numbers of confirmed drug addicts. Men and women may jam our prisons and penitentiaries for alleged violations of the drug laws. But it is not likely that in the foreseeable future there will be any wholesale round-up of chronic and incurable drug addicts for more or less permanent isolation.

Since all confirmed addicts cannot be incarcerated, permanently, there will always be addicts at liberty to serve as customers for an illicit drug traffic. Even where drug addicts are sentenced to penal or correctional institutions, they eventually come out. They may be off the drug when in the institution but they usually relapse to the use of drugs shortly after they are released from institutional confinement. Severe penalties and strict enforcement may deter or discourage some drug peddlers. But there will always be others attracted by the lure of the large profits to be made in the drug traffic. The very severity of law enforcement tends to increase the price of drugs on the illicit market and the profits to be made therefrom. The lure of profits and the risks of the traffic simply challenge the ingenuity of the underworld peddlers to find new channels of distribution and new customers, so that profits can be maintained despite the risks involved. So long as a nonaddict peddler is willing to take the risk of serving as a wholesaler of drugs, he can always find addict pushers or peddlers to handle the retail aspects of the business in return for a supply of the drugs for themselves.* Thus, it is the belief of the author of this report that no matter how severe law enforcement may be, the drug traffic cannot be eliminated under present prohibitory repressive statutes.

Moreover, even if it were [theoretically] possible to eliminate the drug traffic through strict and uniform enforcement of narcotic laws, this objective is practically unrealizable. In the first place, inefficiency in law enforcement is endemic in this country. The causes are many and varied. Among such causes are inadequate recruiting and training of police officials, lack of specialized expert direction of police departments, political selection of police chiefs and district attorneys, part time and amateur administration in district attorney's offices and courts, political selection of judges, lack of coordination between law enforcement agencies, lack of State supervision of local law enforcement, conflicts between uncoordinated law enforcement agencies, inadequacies in the law of arrest, search and seizure, and other branches of procedural law, etc.

Any particular community can overcome the factors contributing to inefficient law enforcement and stage a concerted drive against drug addicts and drug peddlers. Such a drive can result in imprisoning many individuals. But it will also

---

* It should be noted that on occasion, law enforcement agencies themselves may act as suppliers of drugs to addicts. The greater the pressure upon law enforcement agencies, the greater the necessity of producing arrests in drug cases. Arrests in drug cases cannot be made without information. Stool pigeons or informers are vital suppliers of information. Nobody is better equipped to provide information concerning violations of the narcotic drug laws than the narcotic addict himself. One pays off the stool pigeon in money, in winking at his illegal activity, and in the case of the addict, sometimes in seeing that he obtains his drugs. Thus it has been alleged that the law enforcement agencies that are engaged in enforcing the narcotic laws may themselves see that drugs are supplied to addicts.

bring about an exodus of drug addicts and drug peddlers to communities where the "heat" is not on, and where law enforcement is a little more lax and lenient. So long as our law enforcement agencies consist of thousands of independent units, there will always be communities where the enforcement of the drug laws will be viewed with relative indifference and where drug addicts and drug peddlers can wait out a flurry of law enforcement in their own communities.

Strict law enforcement and severe penalties are therefore not the easy answers to problems of drug addiction. We must look elsewhere for a rational drug control program for this country. Any such program must be based on a thorough understanding of the phenomenon that we are seeking to control. Failure to understand the nature of the phenomenon of drug addiction and the practical problems involved in controlling it are responsible for the fact that drug addiction has such serious consequences in this country.

# CASES

The following cases raise questions of social justice running throughout the criminal law. What are the questions posed here that challenge individual personal philosophical beliefs?

## The Queen v. Dudley and Stephens, (1884) 14 Q.B. 273

Indictment for the murder of Richard Parker on the high seas within the jurisdiction of the Admiralty.

At the trial before Huddleston, B., at the Devon and Cornwall Winter Assizes, November 7, 1884, the jury, at the suggestion of the learned judge, found the facts of the case in a special verdict which stated "that on July 5, 1884, the prisoners, Thomas Dudley and Edward Stephens, with one Brooks, all able-bodied English seamen, and the deceased also an English boy, between seventeen and eighteen years of age, the crew of an English yacht, a registered English vessel, were cast away in a storm on the high seas 1,600 miles from the Cape of Good Hope, and were compelled to put into an open boat belonging to the said yacht. That in this boat they had no supply of water and no supply of food, except two 1 lb. tins of turnips, and for three days they had nothing else to subsist upon. That on the fourth day they caught a small turtle, upon which they subsisted for a few days, and this was the only food they had up to the twentieth day when the act now in question was committed. That on the twelfth day the remains of the turtle were entirely consumed, and for the next eight days they had nothing to eat. That they had no fresh water, except such rain as they from time to time caught in their oilskin capes. That the boat was drifting on the ocean, and was probably more than 1,000 miles away from land. That on the eighteenth day, when they had been seven days without food and five without water, the prisoners spoke to Brooks as to what should be done if no succour came, and suggested that some one should be sacrificed to save the rest, but Brooks dissented, and the boy, to whom they were understood to refer, was not consulted. That on the 24th of July, the day before the act now in question, the prisoner Dudley proposed to Stephens and Brooks that lots should be cast who should be put to death to save the rest, but Brooks refused to consent, and it was not put to the boy, and in point of fact there was no drawing of lots. That on that day the prisoners spoke of their having families, and suggested it would be better to kill the boy that their lives should be saved, and Dudley proposed that if there was no vessel in sight by the morrow morning the boy should be killed. That next day, the 25th of July, no vessel appearing, Dudley told Brooks that he had better go and have a sleep, and made signs to Stephens and Brooks that the boy had better be killed. The prisoner Stephens agreed to the act, but Brooks dissented from it. That the boy was then lying at the bottom of the boat quite helpless, and extremely weakened by famine and by drinking sea water, and unable to make any resistance, nor did he ever assent to his being killed. The prisoner Dudley offered a prayer asking forgiveness for them all if either of them should be tempted to commit a rash act, and that their souls might be saved. That Dudley, with the assent of Stephens, went to the boy, and telling him that his time was come, put a knife into his throat and killed him then and there; that the three men fed upon the body and blood of the boy for four days; that on the fourth day after the act had been committed the boat was picked up by a passing vessel, and the prisoners were rescued, still alive, but in the lowest state of prostration. That they were carried to the port of Falmouth, and committed for trial at Exeter. That if the men had not fed upon the body of the boy they would probably not have survived to be so picked up and rescued, but would within the four days have died of famine. That the boy, being in a much weaker condition, was likely to have died before them. That at the time of the act in question there was no sail in sight, nor any reasonable prospect of relief. That under these circumstances there appeared to the prisoners every probability that unless they then fed or very soon fed upon the boy or one of themselves they would die of starvation. That there was no appreciable chance of saving life except by killing some one for the others to eat. That assuming any necessity to kill anybody, there was no greater necessity for killing the boy than any of the other three men." But whether upon the whole matter by the jurors found the killing of Richard Parker by Dudley and Stephens be felony and murder the jurors are ignorant, and pray the advice of the court thereupon, and if upon the whole matter the Court shall be of opinion that the killing of Richard Parker be felony and murder, then the jurors say that Dudley and Stephens were each guilty of felony and murder as alleged in the indictment.

Lord Coleridge, C.J.:

There remains to be considered the real question in the case—whether killing under the circumstances set forth in the verdict be or be not murder.

Is there . . . any authority for the proposition which has been presented to us? Decided cases there are none. . . . The American case cited by my Brother Stephen in his Digest, from Wharton on Homicide, in which it was decided, correctly indeed, that sailors had no right to throw passengers overboard to save themselves, but on the somewhat strange ground that the proper mode of determining who was to be sacrificed was to vote upon the subject by ballot, can hardly, as my Brother Stephen says, be an authority satisfactory to a court in this country.

. . . We are dealing with a case of private homicide, not one imposed upon men in the service of their Sovereign and in the defence of their country. Now it is admitted that the deliberate killing of this unoffending and unresisting boy was clearly murder, unless the killing can be justified by some well-recognized excuse admitted by the law. It is further admitted that there was in this case no such excuse, unless the killing was justified by what has been called "necessity." But the temptation to the act which existed here was not what the law has ever called necessity. Nor is this to be regretted. Though law and morality are not the same, and many things may be immoral which are not necessarily illegal, yet the absolute divorce of law from morality would be of fatal consequence; and such divorce would follow if the temptation to murder in this case were to be held by law an absolute defence of it. It is not so. To preserve one's life is generally speaking a duty, but it may be the plainest and the highest duty to sacrifice it. War is full of instances in which it is a man's duty not to live, but to die. The duty, in case of shipwreck, of a captain to his crew, of the crew to the passengers, of soldiers to women and children, as in the noble case of the *Birkenhead*; these duties impose on men the moral necessity, not of the preservation, but of the sacrifice of their lives for others, from which in no country, least of all, it is to be hoped, in England, will men ever shrink, as indeed, they have not shrunk. It is not correct, therefore, to say that there is any absolute or unqualified necessity to preserve one's life. . . . It is not needful to point out the awful danger of admitting the principle which has been contended for. Who is to be the judge of this sort of necessity? By what measure is the comparative value of lives to be measured? Is it to be strength, or intellect, or what? It is plain that the principle leaves to him who is to profit by it to determine the necessity which will justify him in deliberately taking another's life to save his own. In this case the weakest, the youngest, the most unresisting, was chosen. Was it more necessary to kill him than one of the grown men? The answer must be "No"—

> So spake the Fiend, and with necessity,
> The tyrant's plea, excused his devilish deeds.

It is not suggested that in this particular case the deeds were "devilish," but it is quite plain that such a principle once admitted might be made the legal cloak for unbridled passion and atrocious crime. There is no safe path for judges to tread but to ascertain the law to the best of their ability and to declare it according to their judgment; and if in any case the law appears to be too severe on individuals, to leave it to the Sovereign to exercise that prerogative of mercy which the Constitution has intrusted to the hands fittest to dispense it.

It must not be supposed that in refusing to admit temptation to be an excuse for crime it is forgotten how terrible the temptation was; how awful the suffering; how hard in such trials to keep the judgment straight and the conduct pure. We are often compelled to set up standards we cannot reach ourselves, and to lay down rules which we could not ourselves satisfy. But a man has no right to declare temptation to be an excuse, though he might himself have yielded to it, nor allow compassion for the criminal to change or weaken in any manner the legal definition of the crime. It is therefore our duty to declare that the prisoners' act in this case was wilful murder, that the facts as stated in the verdict are no legal justification of the homicide; and to say that in our unanimous opinion the prisoners are upon this special verdict guilty of murder.*

The court then proceeded to pass sentence of death upon the prisoners.†

---

* My brother Grove has furnished me with the following suggestion, too late to be embodied in the judgment but well worth preserving: "If the two accused men were justified in killing Parker, then if not rescued in time, two of the three survivors would be justified in killing the third, and of the two who remained the stronger would be justified in killing the weaker, so that three men might be justifiably killed to give the fourth a chance of surviving."

† This sentence was afterwards commuted by the Crown to six months' imprisonment.

ANALYSIS

1. The facts in this case illustrate one form of behavioral reaction that occurs when human beings are under stress and when moral values become nonexistent. What arguments can you set forth to condone this action?

2. It was probable that the boy would have been the first to die. Why then was this conduct not justifiable in terms of the survival of the fittest? What was the reasoning of the court that denied this position? Do you agree with it?

3. Had the men been executed, which of the four purposes served by sanctions in the criminal law would have been fulfilled? Viewing execution as a socially desirable outcome, what might some of the benefits have been?

## The King v. Bourne, (1939) 1 K.B. 687

The evidence called on behalf of the Crown proved that on June 14, 1938, the defendant performed an operation on the girl in question at St. Mary's Hospital, and thereby procured her miscarriage. The following facts were also proved: On April 27, 1938, the girl, who was then under the age of fifteen, had been raped with great violence in circumstances which would have been most terrifying to any woman, let alone a child of fourteen, by a man who was in due course convicted of the crime. In consequence of the rape the girl became pregnant. Her case was brought to the attention of the defendant, who after examination of the girl, performed the operation with the consent of her parents.

The defence put forward was that, in the circumstances of the case, the operation was not unlawful. The defendant was called as a witness on his own behalf and stated that, . . . he [would not] have performed the operation if he had found that the girl was either feeble-minded or had what he called a "prostitute mind," since in such cases pregnancy and child-birth would not be likely to affect a girl injuriously. He satisfied himself that she was a normal girl in every respect, though she was somewhat more mature than most girls of her age. In his opinion the continuance of the pregnancy would probably cause serious injury to the girl, injury so serious as to justify the removal of the pregnancy at a time when the operation could be performed without any risk to the girl and under favorable conditions.

The evidence of the defendant was supported and confirmed by Lord Horder, and also by Dr. J. R. Rees, a specialist in medical psychology. Dr. Rees expressed the view that, if the girl gave birth to a child, the consequence was likely to be that she would become a mental wreck.

MacNaghten, J., in summing-up the case to the jury, said: Members of the jury, now that you have heard all the evidence and the speeches of counsel, it becomes my duty to sum-up the case to you and to give you the necessary directions in law, and then it will be for you to consider the facts in relation to the law as laid down by me, and, after consideration, to deliver your verdict. In a trial by jury it is for the judge to give directions to the jury upon matters of law, and it is for the jury to determine the facts; the jury, and the jury alone, are the judges of the facts in the case.

The charge against Mr. Bourne is made under s. 58 of the Offences Against the Person Act, 1861, that he unlawfully procured the miscarriage of the girl who was the first witness in the case. It is a very grave crime, and judging by the cases that come before the Court it is a crime by no means uncommon. This is the second case at the present session of this Court where a charge has been preferred of an offence against this section, and I only mention the other case to show you how different the case now before you is from the type of case which usually comes before a criminal court. In that other case a woman without any medical skill or medical qualifications did what is alleged against Mr. Bourne here; she unlawfully used an instrument for the purpose of procuring the miscarriage of a pregnant girl; she did it for money; £2 5s. was her fee; a pound was paid on making the appointment, and she came from a distance to a place in London to perform the operation. She used her instrument, and, within an interval of time measured not by minutes but by seconds, the victim of her malpractice was dead on the floor. That is the class of case which usually comes before the Court.

The case here is very different. A man of the highest skill, openly, in one of our great hospitals, performs the operation. Whether it was legal or illegal you will have to determine, but he performs the operation as an act of charity, without fee or reward, and unquestionably believing that he was doing the right thing, and that he ought, in the performance of his duty as a member of a profession devoted to the alleviation of human suffering, to do it. That is the case you have to try to-day.

It is, I think, a case, of first instance, first impression. The matter has never, so far as I know, arisen before for a jury to determine in circumstances such as these, and there was, even amongst learned counsel, some doubt as to the proper direction to the jury in such a case as this. . . .

In this case, therefore, my direction to you in law is this—that the burden rests on the Crown to satisfy you beyond reasonable doubt that the defendant did not procure the miscarriage of the girl in good faith for the purpose only of preserving her life. If the Crown fails to satisfy you of that, the defendant is entitled by the law of this land to a verdict of acquittal. If, on the other hand, you are satisfied that what the defendant did was not done by him in good faith for the purpose only of preserving the life of the girl, it is your duty to find him guilty. It is said, and I think said rightly, that this is a case of great importance to the public and, more especially, to the medical profession; but you will observe that it has nothing to do with the ordinary case of procuring abortion to which I have already referred. In those cases the operation is performed by a person of no skill, with no medical qualifications, and there is no pretence that it is done for the preservation of the mother's life. Cases of that sort are in no way affected by the consideration of the question which is put before you to-day.

What then is the meaning to be given to the words "for the purpose of preserving the life of the mother." There has been much discussion in this case as to the difference between danger to life and danger to health. It may be that you are more fortunate than I am, but I confess that I have found it difficult to understand what the discussion really meant, since life depends upon health, and it may be that health is so gravely impaired that death results. A question was asked by the learned Attorney-General in the course of his cross-examination of Mr. Bourne. "I suggest to you, Mr. Bourne," said the Attorney-General, "that there is a perfectly clear line —there may be border-line cases—there is a clear line of distinction between danger to health and danger to life." The answer of Mr. Bourne was: "I cannot agree without qualifying it; I cannot say just yes or no. I can say there is a large group whose health may be damaged, but whose life almost certainly will not be sacrificed. There is another group at the other end whose life will be definitely in very great danger." And then he adds: "There is a large body of material between those two extremes in which it is not really possible to say how far life will be in danger, but we find, of course, that the health is depressed to such an extent that life is shortened, such as in cardiac cases, so that you may say their life is in danger, because death might occur within measurable distance of the time of their labour." If that view commends itself to you, you will not accept the suggestion that there is a clear line of distinction between danger to health and danger to life. Mr. Oliver wanted you to give what he called a wide and liberal meaning to the words "for the purpose of preserving the life of the mother." I should prefer the word "reasonable" to the words "wide and liberal." I think you should take a reasonable view of those words.

It is not contended that those words mean merely for the purpose of saving the mother from instant death. There are cases, we are told, where it is reasonably certain that a pregnant woman will not be able to deliver the child which is in her womb and survive. In such a case where the doctor anticipates, basing his opinion upon the experience of the profession, that the child cannot be delivered without the death of the mother, it is obvious that the sooner the operation is performed the better. The law does not require the doctor to wait until the unfortunate woman is in peril of immediate death. In such a case he is not only entitled, but it is his duty to perform the operation with a view to saving her life.

Here let me diverge for one moment to touch upon a matter that has been mentioned to you, the various views which are held with regard to this operation. Apparently there is a great difference of opinion even in the medical profession itself. Some there may be, for all I know, who hold the view that the fact that a woman desires the operation to be performed is a sufficient justification for it. Well, that is not the law: the desire of a woman to be relieved of her pregnancy is no justification at all for performing the operation. On the other hand there are people who, from what are said to be religious reasons, object to the operation being performed under any circumstances. That is not the law either. On the contrary, a person who holds such an opinion ought not to be an obstetrical surgeon, for if a case arose where the life of the woman could be saved by performing the operation and the doctor refused to perform it because of his religious opinions and the woman died, he would be in grave peril of being brought before this Court on a charge of manslaughter by negligence. He would have no better defence than a person who, again for some religious reason, refused to call in a doctor to attend his sick child, where a doctor could have been called in and the life of the child could have been saved. If the father, for a so-called religious reason, refused to call in a doctor, he also is answerable to the criminal law for the death of his child. I mention these two extreme views merely to show that the law lies between them. It permits the termination of pregnancy for the purpose of preserving the life of the mother.

As I have said, I think those words ought to be construed in a reasonable sense, and, if the doctor is of opinion, on reasonable grounds and with adequate knowledge, that the probable consequence of the continuance of the pregnancy will be to make the woman a physical or mental wreck, the jury are quite entitled to take the view that the doctor who, under those circumstances and in that honest belief, operates, is operating for the purpose of preserving the life of the mother.

These general considerations have to be applied to the particular facts of this case; the verdict of the jury must depend on the facts of the case proved before them. The girl in this case was under the age of fifteen, for she has attained that age within the last ten days. It is no doubt very undesirable that a young girl should be delivered of a child. Parliament has recently raised the age of marriage for a girl from twelve to sixteen, presumably on the view that a girl under the age of sixteen ought not to marry and have a child. The medical evidence given here confirms that view; the pelvic bones are not set until a girl is eighteen, and it is an observation that appeals to one's common sense that it must be injurious to a girl that she should go through the state of pregnancy and finally of labour when she is of tender years. Then, too, you must consider the evidence about the effect of rape, especially on a child, as this girl was. Here you have the evidence of Dr. Rees, a gentleman of eminence in the profession, that from his experience the mental effect produced by pregnancy brought about by the terrible rape which Dr. Gorsky described to you, must be the most prejudicial. You are the judges of the facts and it is for you to say what weight should be given to the testimony of the witnesses; but no doubt you will think it is only common sense that a girl who for nine months has to carry in her body the reminder of the dreadful scene and then go through the pangs of childbirth must suffer great mental anguish, unless indeed she be feeble-minded or belongs to the class described as "the prostitute class," a Dolores "marked cross from the womb and perverse." You will remember that the defendant said that if he had found that this girl was feeble-minded or had what he called a "prostitute mind" he would not have performed the operation, because in such a case the pregnancy would not have affected her mind. But in the case of a normal, decent girl brought up in a normal, decent way you may well think that Dr. Rees was not overstating the effect of the continuance of the pregnancy when he said that it would be likely to make her a mental wreck, with all the disastrous consequences that would follow from that.

I do not think it is necessary for me to recapitulate the evidence that has been given before you as to the reasons why Mr. Bourne in this case thought it right to perform the operation. You remember his evidence. The learned Attorney-General accepts his evidence as a frank statement of what actually passed through his mind. In view of the age and character of the girl and the fact that she had been raped with great violence, he thought that the operation ought to be performed. As I told you yesterday, and I tell you to-day, the question that you have got to determine is not are you satisfied that he performed the operation in good faith for the purpose of preserving the life of the girl. The question is, has the Crown proved the negative of that? If the Crown has satisfied you beyond reasonable doubt—if there is a doubt, by our law the accused person is always entitled to be acquitted—if the Crown has satisfied you beyond reasonable doubt that he did not do this act in good faith for the purpose of preserving the life of the girl, then he is guilty of the offence with which he is charged. If the Crown have failed to satisfy you of that, then by the law of England he is entitled to a verdict of acquittal. The case is a grave case, and no doubt raises matters of grave concern both to the medical profession and to the public. As I said at the beginning of my summing-up, it does not touch the case of the professional abortionist. As far as the members of the medical profession themselves are concerned—and they alone could properly perform such an operation—we may hope and expect that none of them would ever lend themselves to the malpractices of professional abortionists, and in cases of this sort, as Mr. Bourne said, no doctor would venture to operate except after consulting some other member of the profession of high standing.

You will give the matter your careful consideration, and if you come to the conclusion that the Crown has discharged the burden that rests upon it, your verdict should be guilty. If you are not satisfied of that, then your verdict should be not guilty.

Verdict Not Guilty.

## ANALYSIS

1. Does this decision point the way for what today might be considered by some to be a justifiable position to take, both medically and legally, regarding abortion?

2. The point was made that there is a clear distinction between danger to health and danger to life. The surgeon's judgment was that the mental health of the girl would have been impaired had she been allowed to give birth to the child. Can you bring any scientific medical evidence to bear in supporting this position? Can mental trauma be accurately predicted?

3. In similar factual situations do you think this decision should be used as precedent? If you agree, why? If not, why not?

## CASES FOR FURTHER ANALYSIS

### *State v. Ehlers,* 98 N.J.L. 236, 119 Atl. 15 (1922)

At trial for the shotgun killing of the defendant's wife and child, the jury found the defendant guilty of first-degree murder, and he was sentenced to death. On appeal, the defense contended that the prosecution had failed to establish that the murder was wilful, deliberate, or premeditated. Because there was no proof of motive and because of the usual contradictory testimony of mental and medical experts, pro and con, the defense also urged the court to conclude that the defendant was an epileptic, and that at the time of the killing he was suffering from a secret unobservable form of this disease called "petit mal" and not accountable for, because not conscious of, what he was doing. The court rejected both contentions, saying that proof of motive is not an essential element in murder in the first degree, and that the state has a deep interest and concern in the preservation of the life of each of its citizens and if it punishes one for attempting to take his own life it has infinitely more reasons for not permitting one to take the life of another. The jury verdict was upheld.

### *State v. Lewis,* 133 W.Va. 584, 57 S.E.2d 513 (1950)

This is a case where the court affirmed a murder conviction of a physician for causing a criminal abortion. The defendant, a practicing physician and surgeon, was jointly indicted with his nurse. He was tried separately and sentenced by the trial court to five to eighteen years in the penitentiary.

The evidence was in sharp conflict. The decedent's sister and young man friend testified that they went with Mildred Ferguson, the deceased, to the office of the physician to have an abortion performed. She appeared in normal health and good spirits and walked into the office without assistance. Shortly afterward, the nurse came to the sister and asked for the purse of the deceased containing $300. About three hours later, the sister and friend were notified that Mildred was in serious condition. She was taken to the hospital where she was in surgery for two hours. She failed to respond after surgery and several hours later she died. The conflicting testimony of the physician and his nurse was that Mildred Ferguson was admitted with the assistance of the nurse, that she was bent over holding her lower abdomen and said that she had been treated by another doctor to produce an abortion who had given her an injection and probed the inside of the uterus and told her that she was allright, that she decided to perform an abortion herself, and that she attempted to do so by using a long knitting needle or some apparatus. Examination by the defendant surgeon showed an elevated temperature and that the uterus was filled with blood and appeared to have been punctured. He denied that she was pregnant at the time or that he had performed an abortion on her.

The surgeon who assisted the defendant at the operation in the hospital testified for the state that during the operation it was found that the uterus was punctured, and that there was a hole in the ileum, an opening in the sigmoid region of the large intestine, and a hole in the omentum. The uterus was not greatly enlarged and the surgeon could not say whether she was or was not pregnant. Another physician who performed an autopsy said that she had been pregnant and that the uterine cavity had been scraped with a sharp instrument.

The statement of the physician who performed the operation, the girl's record at work that she was well and happy the day previous, together with that of her sister and friend, all refuted the testimony of the surgeon. The appellate court stated that the jury had resolved the factual issues against the defendant and that he had been fairly tried and justly convicted.

### Recommended Source Material

TEXTS

Gradwohl, R., *Legal Medicine*, 81 (St. Louis: C. V. Mosby Co., 1954).

Inbau, F., and Reid, J., *Criminal Interrogation and Confessions* (Baltimore: The Williams & Wilkins Co., 1967).

MacDonald, J., *Psychiatry and the Criminal* (Springfield, Ill.: Charles C Thomas, Publisher, 1957).

Paulsen, M., and Kadish, S., *Criminal Law and Its Processes*, 3–228 (Boston: Little, Brown & Co., 1962).

Shartel, B., and Plant, M., *The Law of Medical Practice*, 353–76 (Springfield, Ill.: Charles C Thomas, Publisher, 1959).

Stetler, C., and Moritz, A., *Doctor, Patient and the Law*, 93–99 (St. Louis: C. V. Mosby Co., 4th ed., 1962).


PERIODICALS

Borrillo, T., and Ebaugh, F., *Medical-Legal Liaison: A Need for Dialogue in the Criminal Law*, 37 U. Colo. L. Rev. 169 (1965).

Note, *Narcotics Regulation: A Study in Irresolution*, 34 Temp. L. Q. 310 (1961).

Packer, H., and Gampsell, R., *Therapeutic Abortion: A Problem in Law and Medicine*, 11 Stan. L. Rev. 417 (1959).

Silving, H., *Euthanasia: A Study of Comparative Criminal Law*, 103 U. Penn. L. Rev. 350 (1954).

# Part Five

Social Concern for Safety of Professional Practice—Board of Nursing, an Administrative Agency

# Chapter Ten

# Administrative Law

To this point in the book, we have concerned ourselves with the principles and processes the courts apply in resolving private disputes. We have seen the position of the state in private civil disputes to be that of a neutral arbiter, an impartial sovereign with no interest in any particular outcome. In the area of the criminal law, the state seeks to control conduct through the imposition of sanctions.

In this chapter, we turn to another role played by the state in the affairs of its citizens. Now we will see the state as an active participant, and regulator, a solver of social problems. We will see the state taking the initiative in creating the framework for affirmative action in an area of social concern and in assuming responsibility for its operation.

The vehicle of this form of state action is the administrative agency. In broad terms, an administrative agency can be defined as an entity established by a government (which can be federal, state, municipal, or other) with the responsibility and authority for dealing, on a governmental level, with a specifically defined area of social concern. These problems include social problems, industrial problems, professional problems; the array is endless. When such an entity (an agency, a bureau, a board, an authority, or a commission) is first created, it, of course, takes action where none was being taken before. Generally, this action will include prohibitions on activities that were previously unrestrained; it will mean restriction on conduct, where no restriction existed. This is really what is meant by government regulation. Order is produced from disorder; energies are channeled, and direction is provided. Inherent, too, in the idea of regulation is the need for sanctions. Not only are rules established, but penalties for noncompliance are imposed. With the imposition of penalties must go procedures for determining whether rules have been violated.

All these functions are performed by administrative agencies in the course of their work. We will study this area by analyzing the origins of the administrative process, the functions fulfilled, and the existing power it exercises in areas designated for legal control. We will also give consideration to the workings of a particular administrative body, the board of nurse examiners.

The Board of Tax Appeals, an administrative agency of the United States, adopted certain rules governing the qualifications of individuals who were entitled to represent others in tax matters pending before the Board. An applicant for the right to appear on behalf of others was required to make brief biographical statements, and to state whether he had ever been disbarred from the practice of law or had his right revoked to practice as a certified public accountant. The rules also provided that the administrative board had discretion to deny admission to any applicant. Mr. Goldsmith, a certified public accountant from New York, who had never been disbarred or had his accounting license revoked, filed such an application and then received notification that his application was denied on the ground that he had been discharged for improper conduct as an examiner of accounts in a state office, and of having been found by the Treasury Department to have given improper advice to clients. He immediately repaired to the courts, contending that he had been deprived due process of law by the Board's action because he had been given no opportunity to be heard with respect to the charges that led the Board to deny him admission to practice.

The Supreme Court of the United States said that, once he had shown that he basically complied with the Board's rules, his application should not have been rejected on the basis of charges of unfitness, without having given him the opportunity to respond to those charges. Although recognizing that the Board had discretion to deny admission to applicants, the Supreme Court said that this had to be construed "to mean the exercise of a discretion to be exercised after fair investigation, with such a notice, hearing and opportunity to answer for the applicant as would constitute due process." [*Goldsmith v. United States Board of Tax Appeals*, 270 U.S. 117 (1925).]

Today, the administrative process is an accepted fact of governmental life. Government agencies perform an endless variety of tasks, from setting conditions for government employment to managing hospitals, from regulating welfare to controlling the stock markets. Pervasive though it is, this feature of government is relatively new in our system, and before examining the legal limits on administrative action, we will give attention to the forces that lead to the birth and rapid growth of the administrative agency as a device for governing.

## History and Development of the Administrative Agency

In 1787, the Constitution established a tripartite government, that is, a government of three branches, the legislative branch, the judicial branch, and the executive branch. The legislative branch, the Congress, is charged with the responsibility of determining the need for statutory action and drawing up and enacting the necessary statutes to fulfill the need. The judicial branch, consisting of the court system, was established to provide a forum for the resolution of civil disputes, and to provide fair and just means for ascertaining criminal responsibility and meting out punishment. The third branch, the executive, conducts the day-to-day administrative operations of government, from foreign affairs through collection of revenues, from the defense of the country to the maintenance of public roads.

For the first century of our country's existence, and during the period when it expanded from a narrow strip of developed territory on the east coast to a vast land extending from ocean to ocean, the tripartite system of government adequately fulfilled the needs of the governed. In those days, the government's primary functions were to keep the peace within its borders, to furnish protection from outside attack, and to provide a framework within which international trade and westward expansion were both facilitated. These functions, though vital to our young country, did not require or necessitate a great amount of day-to-day work of governing, and were carried out in a manner relatively isolated from the everyday life of the people.

Moreover, there was a philosophical commitment to the notion that "the government governs best that governs least." To the late 1800's an independence of spirit, rooted in the philosophy of the westward-moving frontier, had kept government intervention in everyday affairs to a minimum. No man was thought entitled to help from the government; he succeeded or failed according to his own lights and according to his own abilities. Nothing but benefit, so the theory went, could come from the uninhibited operation of economic forces. It was no concern of the government if people—even large numbers of people—were disadvantaged through forces beyond their control. Employment conditions, gross abuse of the public by some banking interests, unfair trade practices, and many other social and economic problems went uncorrected and unexamined by government.

As the nineteenth century moved toward a close, however, American society was growing ever more complex. The industrialization process began the expansion that continues in the present day. The livery stable gave way to the locomotive, just as handcrafted goods began to be replaced by the fruits of mass production. Business empires were created in steel, in coal, in textiles, in railroads, and in lumber. Factories appeared, and with them they brought abominable working conditions; cities grew, and slums were born; affluence increased, and poverty became more painful and degrading.

The constantly increasing industrialization brought about increased interaction among commercial interests throughout the country. With the widening of horizons from narrow geographic areas to larger ones perhaps countrywide in scope went greater influence and power to the industrial leaders. At the same time, the growth of industry involved more and more people in one way or another. Tens of thousands felt new effects from the manner in which industry was conducted.

Industrialization was not the only force at work. A second significant phenomenon gradually developed throughout the nineteenth century and became increasingly important: an expanded political awareness and strength on the part of the vast mass of the population. The vote began to be an instrument working for social change. Control of, or at least influence on, the workings of government became a meaningful possibility to large groups. Furthered by increasing education, and disseminated by ever more effective communication systems, this movement began to see in increased governmental activity a hope and a possibility for control of some of the disruptive forces arising from the growing industrialization, which were radically altering traditional social and economic patterns. The federal government, through the Congress, began to turn its attention to these difficulties. Its willingness to do so was in no small part attributable to the increased political power of the populace as a whole, composed of people who felt the pressure of the newly emerging way of life most keenly.

A particular problem had grown out of the services provided by the railroads. Railroads in the 1880's were tremendously important to the continuing development of industry and business. Railroads themselves were big business, and there were numerous competing lines, as well as an enormous concentration of economic power centered in giant rail networks. Abuses were mounting, and large numbers of people found themselves at the mercy of the railroads in their commercial life. Discriminatory rates were common. Exhorbitant rates and fares were charged farmers faced with the absolute necessity of using the railroads to market their crops.

It had proved impossible for the individual states to regulate in any meaningful way the vast nationwide complex of railroads. Court actions directed to the abuses were ineffective because they were too complicated, too time-consuming, and too uncertain. In particular, individuals rarely had the resources or the motivation to take on the industrial giant in protracted lawsuits. Legislative attempts at solution had also failed. Action was needed, of a new and different kind, and the Congress of the United States, in a creative and imaginative move, established a new kind of government entity in 1886 by the creation of the Interstate Commerce Commission, whose purpose was to bring order to a chaotic industry, and to protect the public from abuses of economic power. This represented, for the first time in our history, "the deliberate organization of a governmental unit whose single concern was the well-being, in a broad public sense, of a vital and national industry." [Landis, J., *The Administrative Process*, 10 (New Haven: Yale University Press, 1938).]

The administrative agency, as we know it today, was born. The Interstate Commerce Commission was the first of a long series of commissions, or administrative agencies, created initially by the Congress and then in large numbers by the state legislatures to provide a governmental means for handling specific areas in need of public control. States began to establish commissions to regulate utility rates, telegraph and telephone operations, public carriers, and an infinite variety of other sections of life. Congress soon followed its own precedent and created additional agencies, such as the Federal Trade Commission, to correct various forms of business overreaching and dishonesty, and the Federal Reserve System to regulate banking, in 1914. In 1933, through the establishment of the Securities and Exchange Commission, a detailed and elaborate structure of regulation over the securities market was provided. Now, on the federal level, dozens of agencies exist covering many, many facets of society, each attempting to provide a governmental solution to a problem that formerly had been unregulated.

These agencies, generally speaking, provided governmental regulation and intervention in areas that had been left entirely to the private sector of our society. Prior to their formation, commercial life was subject only to the give and take of the marketplace; social problems, if any attempt at all was made to solve them, were handled only by a few private individuals who were willing to devote their energies and their resources to a solution. The great significance of the appearance of administrative agencies, therefore, was the fact that for the first time, the sleeping giant of government was stirred to action, with all the resources, powers, and sanctions available to it.

## Organization and Structure of Administrative Agencies

The initial step in the creation of an administrative agency is the perception by a legislative body of an area of social concern or difficulty that requires or can benefit by governmental action for its amelioration or cure. If the perception occurs on a federal level, naturally the Congress is the legislative body concerned. If an area of state concern is under discussion, it will be the legislature of the particular state that takes the necessary first step. The legislative body (let us refer to the Congress for simplicity) then considers what the true problems are and how regulation could best be accomplished. When the problem area is identified and the approach to its solution settled, the next and operative step is the enactment of legislation creating an agency. This statute, usually called an *enabling act*, defines the need for governmental action, establishes a general policy toward its solution, provides for the appointment of a board or commission, and grants to this board the necessary authority to carry on its duties.

Once the movement toward administrative agencies was under way, and Congress and state legislatures were of a mind to create agencies charged with the responsibility of regulating certain sectors of our economy in the public interest, questions immediately arose as to how such a body should be organized. Government functions had typically been performed by one of the existing branches of the tripartite form of government, i.e., legislative, judicial, executive, or by a loose coordination of them. However, the existing system was too inflexible to handle the new problems and, therefore, in administrative agencies the three functions are combined in single agencies, with the goal of providing a consistent, just, and effective regulation of an industry or social area.

Congress makes the fundamental policy decision about how to approach the solution and embodies this approach in the act. For example, the stock market crash of 1929 and the subsequent depression led to the legislative view that wild and speculative trading in securities had produced a problem so severe that the very foundations of the economy were in danger. Something had to be done, so the Congress decided that one of the ways to reduce speculation was to require buyers and sellers of certain types of securities to make full and complete disclosure of all the facts about a stock or bond that would interest a buyer. Legislation was enacted establishing the Securities and Exchange Commission, and this legislation imposed on all companies selling new stock requirements of full disclosure, and authorized the Commission to implement this disclosure by making appropriate rules. The statute thus represented a legislative approach, or overall direction for how to proceed, and, once having set this policy, did not deal directly with the specific means of implementation.

Within the policy principles and guidelines established by the enabling acts the details are left to the agency itself, and here lies the core of the effectiveness of the agency. This detailed regulation proceeds in two ways: first, through the exercise of the rule-making power, and second, through adjudication of matters within the authority of the agency. With overall direction and leadership, each of the executive, legislative, and judicial functions could be coordinated and utilized to achieve the long-range policy goals of the agency. In creating the administrative agency, the enabling acts brought into being unified structures which possessed great flexibility in responding to changing conditions or developing needs, and which provided a reservoir of expertise and sophistication in the characteristics of the activities within the sphere of the agency operations.

## Delegation of Legislative Power

The legislature, through the enabling act, effectively delegates to the agency the power to make rules and regulations. Delegation is essential if detailed regulations are to be adopted, for the simple reason that legislatures do not have time to consider all the details and all the problems of regulation. If left to them, the job would not get done. Moreover, one of the advantages of administrative regulation is that the problems will be dealt with by experts in the field, and that there will be consistency and long-term continuity in policy. Both these advantages are difficult to obtain through legislative action alone.

At the same time, the idea is deeply held that the democratic process works through elected officials, and that these representatives are directly accountable for the policy decisions they make. They and no one else, the feeling is, are elected to provide necessary governing, and consequently they cannot shunt their duties onto other tracks. As a result, a legal doctrine has grown up that declares invalid statutes that attempt to transfer too much of the legislative function away from the elected representatives, and vest that power solely in administrative officials. This doctrine is exemplified by *Levine v. O'Connell*, 275 App. Div. 217, 88 N.Y.S.2d 672 (1949), *aff'd*, 300 N.Y. 658, 91 N.E.2d 322 (1950). The New York State Liquor Authority had, pursuant to statutory authority to adopt rules "to foster and promote temperance, and provide for the orderly distribution of alcoholic beverages," enacted a rule in effect requiring minimum prices to be maintained. The New York court held the rule void, saying that under the statute, the Authority had no power to determine the important and delicate question whether price fixing of branded alcoholic beverages does tend to foster and promote temperance and provide for orderly distribution of liquor and that:

The Constitution of the State and the orderly processes of representative government require that the legislature should make such important decisions itself. Otherwise there is no method by which the people can locate responsibility for such fundamental determinations of public policy.

The touchstone of valid delegation is the setting by the legislature of fundamental standards for policy to be followed by the Board. If these standards are set forth in the enabling act, and a discernible framework created within which a board can carry out prescribed duties, there is no problem of illegal delegations.

## Rules and Their Functions

Rule-making has been defined as "the issuance of regulations or the making of determinations which are addressed to indicated but unnamed and unspecified persons or situations." [Fuchs, R., *Procedure in Administrative Rulemaking*, 52 Harv. L. Rev. 259, 265 (1938).]*

The fundamental objective of all administrative action is to fulfill a social need; the making of rules is the principal method used by agencies to attain the objective. Agency rules, like statutes, define standards, impose requirements, and often provide penalties for noncompliance.

They determine future conduct of all those to whom they apply. Thus it is that the administrative agency performs a legislative function, for the exercise of rule-making power consists of the very type of delineation of standards, selection of policy devices, setting boundaries for permissible conduct, and devising and determining standards engaged in by the legislatures themselves. Necessarily, in deciding what rules to adopt, a board will establish policies and choose between alternative methods of bringing order to an unregulated field. A constant flow of policy choices will be made by any organized body when it embarks upon the task of carrying out the legislative goals specified in the enabling act.

The effectiveness of agency rules stems from the fact that rules have the force of law. Penalties may be imposed for their violation, or some desirable privilege or license may be withheld unless rules are fully complied with. The power of administrative rules and regulations arises from the statutory authority given to the agency by the enabling act. When the legislature delegates power to make rules in certain areas, the resulting rules are tinged with the legislative power. To be sure, agency rules may operate only within the purposes and restrictions of the enabling act; nevertheless, in that area they have behind them the full power of the state.

Not only does an agency interpret and apply its rules, but it also interprets and applies the provisions of statutes. A clear example is a determination by a board that a physician has engaged in "unprofessional conduct," where a statute specifies that a medical license shall be revoked when it appears that a licensed doctor is guilty of conduct that is "unprofessional" in the view of the board.

## The Adjudication Process

The second basic way in which an administrative agency does it job is through the adjudication process. In engaging in adjudication, the agency is dealing, on a case-by-case basis, with questions that involve particular persons;

* Reprinted with permission of the *Harvard Law Review*.

it is deciding whether or not to take action affecting these people. The decision may be to grant, deny, or revoke a license; it may be whether to permit a factory, or railroad car, to continue running; it may be whether set standards have been violated. In adjudication, the agency interprets and applies its own rules, or the provisions of the enabling act.

The difference between the rule-making and adjudication functions has been described in these words [Dickinson, J., *Administrative Justice and the Supremacy of Law*, 21 (New York: Russell and Russell, 1959)]:

What distinguishes legislation from adjudication is that the former affects the rights of individuals in the abstract and must be applied in a further proceeding before the legal position of any particular individual will be definitely touched by it; while adjudication operates concretely upon individuals in their individual capacity.

The adjudication process refers to those activities of an agency that comprise the judicial side of agency operations. It generally deals with events that have taken place, and decides their legal effect upon the persons involved.

Administrative regulations, like laws passed by legislative bodies, require enforcement before they are effective: stating a rule does not mean that it will be obeyed. Before any rule can be enforced against an alleged violator, there must be some procedure for determining whether and how the mandate of the rule has been transgressed. The agency itself will make this determination, and in so doing engages in the judicial part of its task. In judicial parlance, it determines the guilt or innocence of the persons before it, who stand accused of violating administrative regulations or statutes enforced by the agency.

## Limitations on Agency Action in Rule-Making and Adjudication

The authority vested in an administrative body to make rules gives to it great power in its sphere. In regulated areas of life, deference must be paid to the agency by those subject to its rulings. Rights conferred or denied can involve tremendous sums of money, e.g., the award of airline routes, or oil and gas pipelines. They can permanently deprive persons of the ability to earn their livelihood in a field where preparation may have taken years of study, e.g., revocation of professional licenses. Rules setting new standards require heavy expenditures by industry, e.g., regulation of water and air pollution. They may involve preparation and submission of vast amounts of data, e.g., disclosure standards in securities issuance.

Our society does not permit power such as this to go unchecked and uncontrolled. Nearly all administrative actions in the rule-making and adjudication fields are subject to review in the courts. That is, a party aggrieved by administrative action has the right to go to court, asking that the action be set aside or changed. There are numerous requirements of considerable complexity that must be met before judicial review can be obtained; these will not be discussed here. The fundamental principle stands out: administrative actions are subject to court control, and therefore are subject to limitations and boundaries, beyond which they may not go.

There are two primary reasons why a court, reviewing a rule promulgated by an agency will invalidate that rule. These are, first, because the rule is beyond the scope of the authority granted to the rule-making body by the statute establishing that body and, second, because the rule, though seemingly within the scope of the authority granted by the statute, is not reasonably related to the matters to be regulated.

Every statute creating an agency will, as we have noted, establish policy guidelines and goals. The agency's job is to carry out these policies in the best way possible to achieve the legislative goals; that is its exclusive job. It is not entitled to impose any requirements over and above those it is specifically authorized to impose, regardless of how good or desirable or beneficial the agency believes those rules to be. An instance in which an agency overstepped its authority, with the result that a rule was held invalid upon court review, is *Morrill v. Jones*, 106 U.S. 466 (1883). There, a federal statute authorized the Secretary of the Treasury to admit duty free "animals, alive, specially imported, for breeding purposes, from beyond the seas," under regulations that he would prescribe.

The regulation as imposed by the Secretary required the official, before admitting the animals duty free, to be "satisfied that the animals are of superior stock, adapted to improving the breed in the United States." The Supreme Court of the United States held this regulation invalid, as beyond the scope of the enabling act. The reasoning was that Congress, by the language of the statute, had permitted duty-free importation of breeding animals, without any limitation to animals of superior stock. Therefore, however desirable the Secretary of the Treasury felt such a limitation to be, and, indeed, however desirable such a limitation might intrinsically be, he could not impose such limitation in the absence of Congressional authority.

In reviewing the exercise of an agency's rule-making function, the court will not itself take into account the inherent desirability of a rule promulgated by an agency. To the Congress is reserved the right to make initial policy determinations; the agency is not permitted by the courts to go beyond the specific authority granted it, and any attempt by it to act in areas outside those delegated to it will necessarily fail.

The second requirement a rule must meet before it will be upheld in court is that the rules and regulations promulgated by the agency be *reasonably* designed to carry out the purpose of the statute. If a rule or requirement is arbitrary, or the result of capricious, unthinking, or vindictive action, a court will declare it void. To make this determination, the court will inquire what the rule if enforced would accomplish and weigh this against the need for that accomplishment, in view of the overall statutory purpose. If the achievement of the statutory purpose clearly does not necessitate a rule such as the rule in question, the court will strike it down.

Judicial disposition of a claim of unreasonableness is illustrated by *Sandstrom v. California Horse Racing Bd.*, 31 Cal.2d 402, 189 P.2d 17, 3 A.L.R.2d 90 (1948). There, the California Horse Racing Board was responsible for the supervision of horse racing where betting was allowed, and the enabling act gave the Board the power to prescribe rules and regulations as necessary in carrying out its duties. One of the regulations provided that the license of a horse trainer could be immediately revoked if any one of the chemical analyses routinely carried out on racing horses revealed the presence of a narcotic or stimulating drug. No misconduct on the part of the trainer himself was required, and no defense based upon ignorance of the drug source was permitted the trainer. Pursuant to this regulation, trainer Sandstrom's license was revoked because the urine of one of his horses had inexplicably been found to contain a caffeine-type alkaloid. He contended before the California Supreme Court that the rule was arbitrary and unreasonable, because it imposed upon him absolute responsibility, without regard to his personal guilt. The Court found that the wagering public was entitled to the fullest possible protection against doped horses and fixed horse races, and that the Board had acted reasonably in promulgating a rule that fixed full responsibility on the person best equipped to prevent the illegal doping of horses. Therefore, the six-month suspension of the trainer's license was upheld.

## Board of Nursing as an Administrative Agency

When the Board of Nursing is viewed as an administrative agency, an analysis of the source of its legal authority and knowledge of the restrictions on and reasons for its mode of operation give it an added meaning. As a branch of state government it, together with many other state administrative agencies, exercises specialized executive, legislative, and judicial functions within a clearly defined area of activity. The Board of Nursing within this context no longer, then, appears to be a separate legal entity dealing with certain functions pertaining to nursing, but in its organizational structure and powers it belongs to the vastly influential administrative branch of the government. Its concerns, in common with other administrative agencies, are broadly societal in nature.

A governmental agency to control the preparation and licensing of its practitioners is not unique to nursing. The first state administrative agency dealing with nursing was created in 1903, but it was preceded by similar agencies controlling the practice of law and medicine. In each of these three fields the aim was to secure for society the services of a highly skilled group of professional practitioners and to protect society from the unprepared and the incompetent, and from the failures of those qualified.

NEED FOR LEGISLATIVE CONTROL

In the early 1900's, professional education was of an apprenticeship type, highly individualized in form. Under this system the student learned by doing with little or no formal education required of him. As the disciplines of law and medicine saw the inadequacies of this type of education, they gradually evolved systems for the regulation of the preparation of practitioners within institutions of higher learning. In the meantime the preparation of nurses had become the responsibility of the hospitals of the country.

Hospitals were developing rapidly, not only in this country but abroad, and nursing was caught in the stream of this development. Since individual freedom was the existing political philosophy, it came about naturally that any hospital, without regard for its resources, could operate its own school of nursing if it chose to do so. This system allowed for both strengths and abuses, for there were no common standards for judging competency for nursing practice. The products of these schools were known as "trained nurses," many of whom were excellent practitioners who contributed much to the present-day favorable image of the nurse. Others, not so fortunate or so able, had little to offer in proficiency in the care of the sick. The gap in competence was wide and a public disservice was evident. What was to be done?

The early history of national nursing organizations reports numerous discussions of the need for standards for schools of nursing and the need to establish minimum requirements for both the school and for the preparation of its graduates. Although voluntary controls were advised, the idea was not favorably received. With the decision at that time to seek legal control, each state constituent of the American Nurses' Association adopted as one of its expressed purposes the enactment of a regulatory law to control the practice of nursing. While record does not explicitly show it, it is safe to assume that the far-seeing leaders who defended the proposed nurse practice act in each state saw its passage as a means of service to society by the improvement of patient care. It is of interest to speculate whether they foresaw the creation of an administrative body with all the powers and responsibilities of a tripartite form of government.

ORGANIZATION AND FUNCTION

In their organization and functioning, administrative agencies, nursing and otherwise, follow a similar pattern of providing governmental regulation of some area hitherto left to some informal individual or private group management. In the initial formation of the agency for nursing, there was first identified an area that needed governmental action, because of the interest of society in the health, safety, and welfare of its citizens. The next step was for the legislature to consider how best nursing could be controlled to insure competency from its practitioners. The method adopted was to pass a statute, an enabling act, stating the purpose to be accomplished, defining the general areas of control, and providing for the appointment of a board or commission to put into effect the provisions of the act; in this act wide authority is granted to the board to achieve the purposes sought within the limits of the area being controlled. Following the first enabling act regulating the practice of nursing in 1903, within a span of twenty years all the then existing states had secured similar legislative measures.

Present-day characteristics of enabling acts for nursing are patterned after the Model Act, as approved by the Committee on Legislation of the American Nurses' Association in 1964 (see Appendix V). In common with similar acts for administrative agencies in general, the initial portion deals with the major areas to be covered in the act and the purpose, which clearly states the need for and the intent of the law. Some states in drafting their legislation have chosen to first make a statement of public policy as was done in Colorado, 1963 C.R.S. 97–1–1:

Policy—It is hereby declared to be the policy of this state that professional nursing is a learned profession and that, in order to safeguard the life and health of the people of this state, it is necessary that a proper regulatory authority be established and adequately provided for. Any person who practices professional nursing without qualifying for proper registration and without submitting to the regulations herein provided endangers the public health thereby.

Having set forth the purposes, the next step in the enabling act is to define the terms to be used throughout the remainder of the statute. In an area, such as nursing, where licensing is a primary function, the definition of the practice to be controlled has wide legal implications. In its wording it should be broad enough to encompass the scope of the particular level of nursing practice being defined and should delineate the areas of practice to be excluded. A second requirement is that the wording permit flexibility and allow for changes in practice that are bound to occur, and permit enlightened legal interpretation in relation to these changes. The wording of the definition of professional nursing as proposed in the Model Act allows for change, and thus is highly desirable. Illustrative of broad terminology are the phrases: "maintenance of health or prevention of illness of others, . . . supervision and teaching of other personnel . . . specialized judgment and skill and based on knowledge and application of the principles of biological, physical and social science." It is the responsibility of the profession to continually develop and refine the statements of functions and standards needed for legal interpretation and judicial decisions.

The enabling act then makes the necessary legal provision for creating a commission or board charged with responsibility for the implementation of the law. Within the statute, provision is made for the nomination and appointment of members of the board. Underlying the provisions of the law, there must be recognized the responsibility of the profession to participate actively in the nomination of candidates whose qualifications are based on education, experience, and ability to contribute to the work of the agency. The value of a board composed of nurses is indisputable. It has long been acknowledged that the public has granted to each profession the right to determine the scope and standards of its practice, on the assumption that the profession is best qualified to function in the highly specialized fields of accreditation, evaluation of individual qualifications, and examination. Administrative agencies created to regulate an industry have often followed the principle that the commission should be made up of experts drawn from the field under control, for the art of regulating an industry requires a knowledge of the details of its operation and ability to shift requirements as the condition of the industry indicates. In this way, an agency is able to exercise invaluable expertise, which enables it to regulate more effectively.

Uniquely characteristic of an administrative agency is the authority that is granted in the enabling act to exercise the three major functions of government within a clearly defined area. In common with other regulatory commissions, professional boards have these powers. Each of these functions deserves discussion in some detail if the nurse is to understand the purpose, the program, and the activities of the board of nursing as an example of an administrative agency.

EXECUTIVE FUNCTIONS

Because the members of professional boards do not usually serve in a full-time capacity, the day-to-day functioning of the agency is carried on by professional staff. The contribution of well-qualified nurse staff can be creative and dynamic and can well set the pace for the vitality of board action. Its primary function is to implement board policy, and in addition to its interaction with the board, staff members concern themselves with general administration of the agency. Even though the agency may be organized to control an independent activity, it has many interdependent relationships with other state departments for its effective functioning. It is subject to policies of the executive department for budget and regulations for fiscal control, and it calls upon the civil service commission to secure qualified professional and secretarial staff. The office of the attorney general counsels on rules and interpretation of the law, and issues legal opinions on request. Both board and staff participate in a continuing assessment of the enabling act and its strengths and pinpoints areas where it may be obsolete or ambiguous. When social and professional developments indicate that changes are necessary, the need is brought to the attention of the official state organization for nurses who are responsible to stimulate legislative action.

Often when agencies were created, they were not subject to external controls over the actual conduct of their programs; these were determined by the agencies themselves within the limits of the legislative enactment. In some jurisdictions, however, there seems to be increasing emphasis on various devices of overseeing by other branches of government to insure that administrative authority is properly exercised. For example, in some states rules cannot be changed, no matter how minor they may be, without a review by the attorney general, an open hearing, or both. In others, detailed reports of program and accomplishments are required by the governor's office to seek more efficient ways of bringing about operational changes. In the main, these types of control work for the ultimate good of the agency operations.

RULE-MAKING FUNCTION

The promulgation of rules and regulations to supplement the statutes has been a normal and necessary feature of the administrative agency for many years. Authority is granted in the enabling act to make rules needed to carry out the legislative intent of the act, but no power is given to change the act or to go beyond it.

In the nursing practice act in every jurisdiction, a provision similar to the following from Section III, c, 1, of the Model Act (Appendix VII) is found:

The board is authorized to: 1. adopt and, from time to time, revise such rules and regulations not inconsistent with the law, as may be necessary to enable it to carry into effect the provisions of this act.

Rules and regulations, no less than statutes, establish patterns of conduct to which those affected must conform or be subject to the imposition of sanctions. These rules are valid and binding as a statute and have the force of law if they fall within the granted power, follow proper procedure, and are reasonable. In the wise exercise of rule-making power there are two phases to consider, each discreet and necessary to the effectiveness of the rule as a whole: first, the substance or content of the rule and, second, the process by which the content of the rule is developed and implemented.

The rule-making power of the board of nursing may be exercised within the two major purposes for which it is created: to license practitioners of nursing and to establish standards for educational programs preparing for nursing practice. The boards may, in turn, prescribe penalties for violations of applicable statutes in either of these areas or for nonconformance to rules pertaining thereto.

The substance of a rule may be quantitative or qualitative. It may be designed to allow for flexibility and individual institutional variation or it may be so restrictive that it serves as a straitjacket. At the other extreme, it can be so general that it would be illusory, easily met, and really no rule at all. In fact, under the guise of a general rule of this type, poor practice might be condoned. The substance of a rule must be reasonable; for example, if an additional area of clinical competence is to be required for all candidates admitted to the licensing examination, a reasonable time must be allowed to permit the student to receive the necessary preparation in the new area. One date might give so little time that it would work a hardship on those affected, and a delayed date might defer action and deny individual students the opportunity of this curriculum offering.

At times the substance of the rule may be derived by seeking the meaning of the statute. For example, the definition of professional nursing is stated in broad and general terms. When a question of legal authority is brought before the board regarding a particular nursing task, the board may decide that this task is within the scope of nursing, that there is ample authority in the law to permit the nursing profession to assume responsibility for the task, but that certain prerequisites of knowledge and supervised practice must be met prior to independent performance of the task.

At times, a similar inquiry might call for a legal interpretation of the meaning of the law regarding nursing practice and a reconciliation must be sought for what might appear to be a conflict between two existing statutes, such as, for example, those governing medical and nursing practice. In this instance, it would be necessary to ask for a legal opinion from the state attorney general. Since legal opinions will govern action until set aside by the courts, they should be sought with great care, and with due consideration of the professional and practical implications of the response. In the process of preparing a request for a legal opinion the board should first, with the help of professional staff, explore the factual background in the area of nursing practice related to the inquiry, what current practice is in this and similar localities, what the societal considerations are in terms of delivery of safe nursing care, and the legal implications for the enforcement of the decision whether it be positive or negative. For example, suppose the basic question concerns the legal responsibility of the nurse working in a health service where a system of standing medical orders is in force. To present the question against the background of current nursing practice, the inquiry to the attorney general might indicate changing health care plans and why continuing medical supervision is not always possible, and then indicate the functions of the nurse working in this type of service, and the tasks she undertakes based on her independent evaluation of the situation. From this background the inquiry poses the specific questions and seeks a response that will deal with the setting in which nursing care is given. The response should enable the board to establish rules within the boundaries of the opinion that will guide the nurse in rendering safe patient care. There follows an extract from a legal opinion sent by the attorney general of the state of Montana to the Board of Nursing, which illustrates a ruling on a procedure based upon consideration of the environmental setting for nursing practice [26 Op. Mont. Att'y Gen. No. 89 (Nov. 9, 1956)]:

Certainly venipuncture is an "application of principles of physical science," and although such treatment can be inherently dangerous in the absence of a trained and skilled administrator, by the very term "professional nurse" the requisite training and skill are implied. Further, it is perhaps not part of the nurses' traditional independent functions but more properly part of the nurses' role in the doctor–nurse team. The professional nurse of today must perform, either by herself or as a member of that doctor–nurse team, duties as complex as medicine itself. Professional nursing, as such, cannot be confined to certain traditional duties, if such was the past history of the profession then her duties would have progressed only to the dignity of a paid companion . . . .

It is therefore my opinion that a venipuncture . . . by a professional nurse, upon order of a doctor of medicine, is a professional nursing service and not the practice of medicine.

The opinion, dated 1956, deals with what is now accepted as current practice. Any such opinion requires the board to consider rules necessary to implement the opinion, in order to safeguard nursing practice. For example, what would the board require as "requisite training and skill"? Might the board ask itself or an appropriate committee of the professional organization to identify nursing responsibility inherent in the terms used in the opinion "traditional independent functions" and "role in doctor–nurse team"?

To this point we have examined sources of content for the substantive portion of the rule-making process carried on by an administrative agency, and particularly the board of nursing. Now we turn to another phase of rule making, which includes not only the content of the rule, but also the method of its preparation, adoption, and consideration by those who will be affected by the proposed rule.

Whether it is required by statute or voluntarily done, a principle that administrative agencies follow—boards of nursing in particular—is to secure participation in the rule-making process of those who are in a position to be affected by the proposed rule or those who might be farseeing and alert to the overall implications of the rule. Three procedural steps used by administrative agencies in general are directly applicable to the procedure that could be used by boards of nursing.

*First*, consultationand conferences with those interested and qualified can affect the formulation of the rules. This is a valuable method and is used as a technique of rule-making where groups concerned are organized and vocal. Independent work of outside groups may be to the point that agencies or individuals actually propose the rules by tentative construction, or by suggestions or comments. At times the consultant group is chosen in terms of its special ability to contribute to a particular area of rule-making; for example, if criteria were being developed for the accreditation of a clinical area for teaching psychiatric nursing, consultants chosen might be nurse clinicians in this area and nursing service representatives. If a major rule revision project is authorized, for example, the accreditation policies for schools of nursing on a statewide basis, an advisory committee might be chosen to spearhead the initial work with broad representation from all interests concerned.

A difficult phase of the consultant and conference method is working effectively with numerous individuals or groups who are unorganized, such as the consumer public, particularly when the rules under consideration are technical and in a highly specialized field. The value of such a group is its contribution to the promotion of public acceptance of the rule rather than addition to its content.

*Second* is the step of antecedent publicity, in which the tentative rules are published, and provision is made for oral or written comment, either individually or by some organized group, with sufficient time allowed for the consideration of all relevant issues. The purpose here is to insure that all those affected will know of the proposed rules and will have a chance to submit their views. Consequently, nonobjection can be equated with acquiescence.

*Third* is the public hearing which is publicly announced and at which any interested parties are permitted to attend and to testify.

These three steps in the rule-making process are wise safeguards for the administrative agency to follow; counsel in the development of the rule and discussion to inform the public before adoption of the rule will create a favorable climate for the implementation of the rule. In fact, promulgation of rules has many characteristics in common with the legislative process itself; the need for the legislation is identified and a draft of the proposed law is prepared and introduced publicly. Preliminary to its passage hearings are held, individual legislators are available to discuss the measure, and when it has finally run the gamut of public scrutiny, it is passed into law and published. The rule-making power granted to a board of nursing is a delegated legislative function that should follow a similar plan to the end that all concerned will have a voice in and a full knowledge of the rule adopted.

A final safeguard for the public in the total rule-making process of an administrative agency is that of judicial review. Just as a law passed by the legislature can be challenged as to its constitutionality or for numerous other reasons, and on review by the courts may be set aside, so may the rules of an administrative agency be questioned. When this is done the concern of the court is twofold. First, the court determines whether the rule fell within the powers granted to the agency. If the rule exceeded the authorization of the enabling act, no matter how desirable it might be for the social good, it would not be upheld by the court. For example, if the board of nursing passed a ruling that all hospitals in the particular state were required to have at least one registered nurse on duty at all times during the twenty-four-hour period, it is doubtful that authority could be found in the enabling act for such a ruling. The board has no jurisdiction over staffing problems in hospitals; its concern would be only for the proper licensing of the nurses who were staffing the hospital. A second point upon which the courts might question a rule is whether it could be shown to be unreasonable or capricious. If, for example, the board in its zeal to raise standards of education in a certain state made a rule requiring faculty to have academic preparation beyond that necessary to achieve the objectives of the program offered, it might be set aside by the court.

JUDICIAL FUNCTION

The administrative agency granted legislative or rule-making power also has the power to impose sanctions on those individuals or agencies who violate the rules. For example, the board of nursing that is granted the power to accredit schools of nursing is also authorized to deny or withdraw accreditation from educational programs for failure to meet prescribed standards. Within its licensing powers it may deny, revoke, or suspend a license. The process of adjudication requires certain procedural safeguards that are in common usage both in the courts and in the hearings of administrative agencies. The first safeguard is that one may not be denied life, liberty, or property without due process of law, which has been interpreted by the courts to mean that the one charged must be served with a notice of the time and place of the hearing together with the charges against her.

When a nurse is charged with grounds for disciplinary action, generally state statutes require that a notice be served upon her a prescribed period in advance of the hearing, giving the charges and the time and place of the hearing. The statutes also fix standards for preparation and conduct of the hearing by the board of nursing, following prescribed rules of procedure. Every detail should be as carefully considered as it would be in a courtroom setting. The party charged may be represented by counsel if she chooses, and witnesses may be called and cross-examined under oath. Sometimes exhibits are presented as direct evidence. At the close of the hearing the board is faced with the task of making a decision, which can be fraught with legal difficulties unless the board is cognizant of the importance of precise legal detail in this process. The statute may have stated the grounds for disciplinary action in such general terms as "incompetence" or "unprofessional conduct." The body of experts must then determine the meaning of these terms as reflected in this particular conduct. They must guard against a decision based on unsupported inferences from the facts; rather, they must express conclusions in specific terms. Disciplinary action against a professional nurse is a serious imposition of a sanction; it affects her reputation and interferes with her opportunities to earn a livelihood, and she has a right to know in specific terms the reason for the withdrawal of the license.

A hearing for the withdrawal of the accreditation of a school of nursing follows the same legal procedure: the board is charged with the exercise of great care in proof of the facts necessary to establish a violation. The statute may authorize withdrawal of accreditation if prescribed standards are not met. The way in which the board implements these general criteria may mean the difference between arbitrariness and the exercise of power with wise discretion. The withdrawal of the accreditation of a school of nursing is a very serious decision; it denies students in that school the privilege of qualifying for admission to the licensing examination, it adversely affects the reputation of the school, and hinders its future recruitment; it restricts the supply of nurses needed to fill the public's need for patient care. A *reasoned decision*, therefore, is an essential part of the administrative body's action. Schwartz views its importance as follows [Schwartz, B., *An Introduction to Administrative Law*, 157 (New York: Oceana Publications, 1958)]:

> . . . For the obligation to give a reasoned decision is a substantial check upon the misuse of power. The giving of reasons serves both to convince those subject to decisions that they are not arbitrary and to insure that they are not, in fact, arbitrary. The need publicly to articulate the reasoning process upon which a decision is based, more than anything else, requires the magistrate (judicial or administrative) to work out in his own mind all the factors which are present in a case. A decision supported by specific findings and reasons is much less likely to rest on caprice or careless consideration. . . .

JUDICIAL REVIEW BY THE COURTS

Once the administrative agency has performed its judicial function in a particular case, the decision is not necessarily final. The injured party may then seek the assistance of the court through judicial review of the proceedings of the hearing. Through this process the courts and not the administrative agency are the final arbiter in dispensing justice. Judicial review of an administrative decision may be provided for in the enabling act. Even in those instances in which the law is silent, the right of review is generally not denied. When a review is requested, the records of the hearing held before the administrative agency may be made available to the court. In the review the questions to which the court may seek answers are those concerning the exercise of authority by the agency, whether it exceeded its legal authority, whether the evidence supported the decision, and whether there were procedural errors that invalidated the hearing.

In the instance of *Colorado State Bd. of Nurse Examiners v. Hohu*, 129 Colo. 195, 268 P.2d 401 (1954), the action taken by the board to revoke the license of Margaret Hohu was reversed by court action, which held that the evidence was insufficient to sustain the findings. The charges, as submitted by a physician to the board, stated that the nurse's delay in admitting an obstetrical patient, insufficient supervision of the progress of labor after admission, and failure to call the physician in time resulted in a precipitous delivery and laceration. The board notified the defendant of the time and place of the hearing and called upon her "to show cause why her license to practice professional nursing should not be revoked on cause of unprofessional conduct and gross incompetence," appending the copy of the letter from the physician as the basis for the charges.

A hearing was held at which only four of the five board members were present, all of whom voted to revoke the license. The statute required unanimous action for license revocation, and the absent board member voted for revocation after reading the transcript.

Upon review of the board's action, the court held the revocation to be void and ineffective on two grounds. First, the court said that the accused nurse was entitled to a full and fair hearing and that she had not received such a hearing when one of the board members whose vote was given had not been in attendance.

Second, though the court recognized that the board had the power to determine what constituted "gross incompetency, dishonesty, intemperance, immorality, unprofessional conduct, or any habit rendering the nurse unfit or unsafe to care for the sick," it found that the evidence failed to support the charges of the doctor and failed to show any other grounds for revocation, and that therefore the board in revoking her license had abused its discretionary powers and acted arbitrarily.

SUMMARY

The administrative agency exercises a valuable function by its efforts to insure to the public the safest possible nursing care. Its rules have the force of law in restricting conduct. Licensing is a preventive device: if anyone at all were allowed to care for the sick, and punishment followed only after harm was done, little public safety would be afforded. It may be a somewhat burdensome form of control for everyone engaged in an activity to be licensed for the few who act improperly to be controlled, but it serves a valuable social purpose.

## NOTES

### (1) Social Change and Change in the Administrative Agency

In this history of the development of the administrative agency in general, note the elements in common with the need for the creation and functioning of the board of nursing as an administrative agency. The writers of the following passage note that human relations within society and the expansion of the arts and sciences were factors that contributed to the development of this form of government. In a projection for the future, these two forces closely related to the practice of nursing might lead to changes in the administrative agency controlling the practice of nursing. If so, what changes are imminent now? What do you see for the future?

**Gellhorn, W., and Byse, C., *Administrative Law, Cases and Comments*, 2 (Brooklyn: The Foundation Press, Inc., 4th ed., 1960)** *

In the Federal realm, as is well known, the administrative process may be traced in an unbroken line from 1789, the first year of government under the Constitution of the United States. Commencing in that year with the administration of customs laws, the regulation of ocean-going vessels and the coasting trade, and the payment of veterans' pensions, Congress provided the statutory foundation for the considerable body of agencies which now administer the public laws. The circumstance that the national legislature has through so many generations, from the customs law of 1789 to the Federal Aviation Act of 1958, seen wisdom in the administrative process suggests that bureaucracy may after all have its admissible virtues.

The striking fact is that new agencies have been created or old ones expanded not to satisfy an abstract governmental theory, but to cope with problems of recognized public concern. It was the growth of steam navigation, rather than a predisposition toward administrative agencies, which gave rise in 1838 to "An Act to provide for the better security of the lives of passengers on board of vessels propelled in whole or in part by steam," and so commenced the process of steamboat inspection which continues until the present day in the United States Coast Guard. No different in essence were the considerations that exactly a century later led to the creation of the Civil Aeronautics Authority to coordinate regulation of the air transportation industry. If human relationships within society had remained unchanged, if the Nation's territorial limitations had been unexpanded, if the arts and sciences had not progressed with the years, the machinery of government might similarly have remained undeveloped. Instead, in the span of a century and a half, new rights and duties among men have emerged, and the Government has responded to demands for their adjustment, their execution, and their protection.

It is of course plain that precisely similar considerations did not lead to the utilization of the administrative device in all the various situations in which it is to be found today. True, in each instance prescriptions by the legislature or decisions in individual cases by the judiciary were deemed to be comparatively inadequate mechanisms for dealing with governmental problems. But the reasons for the inadequacy were not always the same, nor did they by any means reflect discredit on Congress or the courts. In some cases decision to create an agency outside the courts was influenced by desire to avoid referring to the judiciary myriad controversies which would interfere with existing duties. In some instances, decision to transfer subordinate legislative authority to administrative agencies was influenced by the need of relieving Congress from details so that its essential policy-making work might go forward. In yet other cases, the choice of the administrative agency was essential to the effectuation of a preventive program, necessitating constant supervision and inspection for which neither judicial nor legislative organization is adapted.

Illustration may be found in the possible choices of methods for the granting of a privilege or license or the fixing of prices or wages. The granting of licenses is an individual and private act and, at the same time, a step in the effectuation of a general policy. To fix a price or wage is to prescribe future conduct. The legislature may formulate policy and, indeed, this is its traditional function; but its attention to the specific is necessarily spasmodic because it does not remain constantly in session, nor is its machinery most suitable for the finding of facts which are necessary to the issuance of licenses or the fixing of prices or wages. Hence, while these functions might, without disregard of constitutional divisions of power, be performed by the legislature itself, practical considerations argue that they be undertaken elsewhere. Nor are these functions readily susceptible of initial judicial treatment; the judicial function is traditionally to weigh the merits of particular controversies, but not to engage in a consistent determination of policy or to maintain steady contact with a general and continuing problem. Accordingly, a body which could combine both functions—ascertainment of facts and the establishment of a continuous and uniform policy the development of which is not dependent upon the largely accidental emergence of litigated cases—would be logically chosen to perform functions of this nature. So it is that administrative agencies have been devised to concentrate their attention upon phases of work somewhat alien to the basic functions of courts and legislatures, and from their concentration have developed the special knowledge and special skills which characterize the administrative process at its best.

## (2) Philosophy of Professional Licensure

Professional, and other, licensing imposes a limitation on the public: no one can engage in the activity for which a license is required unless he has met the prescribed standards and in fact procured the license. He is subject to fine, perhaps even imprisonment, for violating this prohibition. A licensing requirement, therefore, is a restriction on every citizen's personal freedom. What justifies such a restriction? Why is it imposed in any given case? What are the goals society attempts to reach in imposing licensing requirements? Some of the answers are suggested in the following excerpts from an address delivered by Justin Miller, the Dean of the School of Law, Duke University, at a 1934 Congress on Medical Education, Licensure, and Hospitals. Dean Miller's address was entitled *The Philosophy of Professional Licensure*:

... My purpose is to consider rather broadly the underlying philosophy of licensure. My belief is that agreement upon a few fundamentals will make the other problems much more simple in their solution and that failure to understand and agree upon fundamentals is the main cause of our present professional difficulties. I shall adopt for my definition of philosophy that one which reads, "In more general application and usually with 'the' or 'a' philosophy denotes a systematic body of general conceptions ordinarily with the implication of their practical application."

All who associate with the so-called academic group are familiar with the discussions which take place, from time to time, regarding the true purpose and function of honor societies or fraternities such as Phi Beta Kappa. Occasionally, in some schools an effort is made to spur such organizations into activities such as dinners, discussions, debates, et cetera. Usually such societies remain dormant, except for those periodic occasions when they revive long enough to elect new members and replenish their exchequers. One, who is elected to membership, quickly finds, if he was not already aware of the fact, that the awarding of the key means little more than a recognition of achievement, similar to the placing of a laurel wreath on the victor's brow or pinning a medal on his breast. Nothing remains for him to do in connection therewith except proudly, but unostentatiously, to display the medal through his remaining years.

In sharp contrast, is the licensing of one to practice a profession. It is true that licensure does involve some recognition of achievement, but it is a minimum of achievement which is stressed in this case; a minimum which is deemed adequate to guarantee a safe performance within the field of practice. Here we have, as it were, the opening of the door of achievement. It is the possibility of achievement in the future, rather than recognition of achievement already accomplished, which is emphasized in the concept of licensure. For indeed one of the essential elements in the definition of the word license and of its derivatives, of which licensure is one, is *action*, "authority or liberty given to do, or forbear any *act*; permission to *do* something; a formal permission from the proper authorities to *perform* certain *acts* or to *carry on* a certain business which without such permission would be illegal; ... as a *license* to *preach*, to *practice* medicine, to *sell* gunpowder or intoxicating liquors." ...

However, we must inquire further to discover those characteristics of the philosophy of professional licensure which distinguish it from business or other licensure. In pursuing this inquiry we may give thought to the effect of each of the following considerations: (1) the nature of the authority which licenses or authorizes action, (2) the purpose sought to be accomplished by the licensing authority, (3) the nature of the act to be performed, (4) the character, training, and skill required for the proper performance of the act.

Numerically considered most licenses are granted by governmental agencies, federal, state or local. Usually this power is exercised by boards, commissions, or agents appointed for that purpose, and in many instances is administered on a fee, or percentage, or a tax collection basis, sometimes, frankly, to the highest bidder. The familiar example of the so-called *sale* of concessions at public fairs and markets well illustrates this situation at its lowest point.

The more closely we approach the professional groups, however, the less important becomes the tax or fee element, until finally it is reduced to a minimum, the amount charged being, usually, only enough, or even less than enough, to carry the cost of administration. On the other hand, the more important become the qualifications of examining boards and the rules and regulations regarding the prerequisites for eligibility to take examinations as well as the nature of the examinations themselves. Thus without attempt to arrange them in proper relation, it is easy to see an ascending order in the qualifications of examiners, and in the rules of licensure, for example, in the following: plumbers, barbers, civil service employees, nurses.

Finally, when we reach the professional group, we find a situation in which only the members of each group are qualified to set standards and give examinations. Here then, though the government is the final arbiter of matters of general policy, it, actually, delegates authority to members of each professional group to set up standards and administer rules regarding licensure. Sometimes this takes form through an administrative body such as a board of examiners. Sometimes it consists in recognizing the degree of an "approved" school; approval being given directly by the legislature to particular schools, or generally to a list prepared by a professional association. Sometimes it even goes so far as to transfer to an organized professional group power to set up an examining board, establish standards and generally control the whole matter of licensure. Whatever may be the local variation, in each case it appears clearly enough that there exists as regards professional licensure, a definite recognition of the propriety and necessity of control thereof by each professional group for itself.

It is only natural that some members of the professions should assume from these facts that the right of self-determination and self-perpetuation is inherent in professional life. ...

It is said that in former ages the general level of intelligence was so low that lay people were actually at the mercy of members of the learned professions. Today, though the general level of intelligence has moved up appreciably, the content of knowledge in the professions has, perhaps, increased even more greatly. It is a matter of necessity, therefore, not of choice, that the control of licensure is delegated to members of each profession. No one else knows enough about the science and the art involved in each case, to insure to those outside the profession, the benefits thereof, on the one hand, and the protection from spoliation on the other. Normally this delegation of authority indicates a confession of inability, adequately to determine the qualifications of desirable new members of the various professions and faith that the leaders of the professions will establish and maintain such standards as will insure the benefits thereof and prevent the spoliation which might otherwise occur.

This attitude of the people and of the governmental officials who represent them will no doubt continue only so long as their faith in the capacity and honesty of the members of the various professions shall continue. It is well to note in this connection that the attitude of lay people and the extent of delegation of governmental control over licensure have varied considerably in the past, with reference to different professions, and may very well do so in the future. . . .

One way of testing the nature and extent of that obligation is to consider the difference between a profession and a business. In business transactions each participant is assumed to be equally well informed and equally able to hold his own in the give and take of trade and barter. The well-known maxim of the law warns: "Let the buyer beware." On the other hand, the member of a profession is assumed to be better informed than the client or patient whom he serves, and stands in the position of champion or protector.

The very nature of professional service requires the existence of a relationship of trust and confidence. In order that he may be best served, a person must break down the barriers of reserve which otherwise serve to protect him, and deliberately reveal to his professional adviser secrets of physical or mental disability or secrets of business, of the most intimate nature. The situation which makes possible the most beneficent service from a highly skilled, trustworthy professional, therefore, is one which makes equally possible his spoliation, if the one in whom confidence is placed happens to be a charlatan or a shyster.

The very words used in describing those who seek service from professional men is evidence of the nature of this fiduciary relationship. The word "client," which means "one who consults a legal adviser in order to obtain his professional advice or assistance or submits his cause to his management," comes directly from the Latin where it meant in Roman society "one of a class of dependents—directly bound to their patrician patrons, whose duty, in turn, it was to protect them." The word "patient" comes from a Latin verb meaning "to suffer," and, in present-day usage, means one under medical or surgical treatment or one under care, supervision, or discipline.

Obviously a professional man cannot treat such a relationship in a casual way and the methods of licensure must be such as to insure the constant recruiting of men who are adequately trained to render skilled service and alert to accept the responsibility of protecting those whom they serve, against spoliation. . . .

So far as licensure is concerned it should insist that professional and preprofessional education measure up to standards set by competent members of the professions. In view of the present large supply of professional men, there is no possible excuse for continued failure to do this. And there are plenty of members of each profession thoroughly competent to set such standards and to establish methods of examination which discover compliance therewith. This is the essential point in the relationship between education and licensure. . . .

In other words, it is quite possible for us in the educational group to discover for those in the licensure group, not merely ability of the type which has been tested in the past, but to answer almost any question which you care to ask concerning these neophytes who are in our care. With the backing which well-regulated licensure gives, we can establish such standards of education as licensure requires. Moreover, it is the right of those who administer licensure, to inquire of us and to require of us whenever and whatever their good judgment tells them the occasion demands. The important question is, whether those of us in whose hands now rests the destiny of the professions, are really interested in the underlying philosophy of licensure, and willing to establish the necessary procedures for properly determining, by adequate training and selection, those who are to follow us.

## (3) Justification for Revocation of a Professional License

The revocation of a license to practice a profession denies the individual the right to earn a livelihood. A Note in the *Oklahoma Law Review* discusses a number of cases in which the courts were faced with the issue of fitting the punishment with the crime. Questions a board of nursing might have to face include: whether shoplifting, passing fraudulent checks, or evading one's income tax have bearing on the ability of the nurse to practice her profession.

**Burleson, D., *Constitutional Law: Licenses: Revocation for Felony Without Regard to Nature of Crime,* 10 Okla. L. Rev. 443 (1957)** *

We must begin with the basic premise that the right to pursue a gainful profession is now incorporated into our Constitution under the concepts of "liberty" and "property," which we may not be deprived of without due process of law by virtue of the fifth and fourteenth amendments. The early cases treated the right to pursue a lawful vocation as a "property" right. Later cases have tended to treat it as an essential element of "liberty" insured by the Constitution. But, this right must be balanced against the duty of the state, under its "police power," to protect public health, safety, morals, and general welfare. However, a state cannot, under the guise of protecting the public, arbitrarily interfere with private business or prohibit lawful occupations, or impose unreasonable, unnecessary restrictions upon them.

Substantive due process is satisfied if the objective of the legislation is valid, reasonable means to accomplish it are outlined in a standard which is not objectionable for vagueness, and the legislation is applied consonant with the purpose for which enacted. The cases applying this concept to professional qualifications have a curious evolution. In *Cummings v. Missouri*, the Constitution of Missouri provided that before one could pursue the occupations of priest, minister, lawyer, teacher, or office holder, he must take an oath that he had never given aid to the enemies of the state, left the state to evade the draft, nor expressed the desire that the enemies of the United States would prevail over it. Cummings was convicted of performing the ritual of a priest without having taken such an oath. On review, the United States Supreme Court conceded the state's power to determine the qualifications which its citizens must attain before pursuing their callings within a jurisdiction, if related to fitness or capacity for a particular pursuit or profession. But it saw no connection between the fact that Mr. Cummings had allegedly evaded the draft and his fitness to teach the doctrines or administer the sacraments of his church.

In contrast, in *Hawker v. New York*, the petitioner, who had been convicted of the felony of abortion, was successfully prosecuted for violating a state statute punishing the practice of medicine by any person after conviction of a felony. Here, it is to be noted that the crime for which the physician was convicted does indicate qualities which could make him unfit to practice medicine. But, *Dent v. West Virginia* declared that the nature and the extent of the qualifications required depend primarily upon the judgment of the state as to their necessity; if they are appropriate to the calling or profession, and attainable by reasonable study or application, no objection to their validity can be raised because of their stringency or difficulty. Only when they have no relation to such calling or profession do they invalidly deprive one of his right to pursue a lawful vocation. . . .

The majority of the United States Supreme Court discusses voluminously procedural due process, and finds its requirements have been met, but the petitioner's argument, that substantive due process was violated by the revocation for an offense which in no way reflected on his fitness to pursue his profession, was hardly noticed. To this opinion Justice Frankfurter dissented strongly:

> Reliance on the good faith of a State Agency entrusted with the enforcement of appropriate standards for the practice of medicine is not in itself an investiture of arbitrary power offensive to due process. . . . So far as concerns the power to grant or revoke a medical license, that means that the exercise of the authority must have some rational relation to the qualification required of a practitioner in that profession.
>
> It is one thing thus to recognize the freedom which the Constitution wisely leaves to the States in regulating the professions. It is quite another thing, however, to sanction a State's deprivation or partial destruction of a man's professional life on grounds having no possible relation to fitness, intellectual or moral, to pursue his profession. Implicit in the grant of discretion to a State's medical board is the qualification that it must not exercise its supervisory powers on arbitrary, whimsical or irrational considerations. A license cannot be revoked because a man is redheaded or because he was divorced, except for a calling, if such there be, for which redheadedness or an unbroken marriage may have some rational bearing. If a State licensing agency lays bare its arbitrary action, or if the State law explicitly allows it to act arbitrarily, that is precisely the kind of State action which the Due Process Clause forbids.

## (4) Do Changing Roles Necessitate Changing Statutory Definitions of Practice?

The article that follows is not a dream for the future but a report of the actual changes in practice in office and ambulatory patient care. What are the legal implications for the nurse who works in either of these settings? Does the definition for practice as it appears in the Model Nurse Practice Act [see Appendix VII, Section II, b, 1] give her the necessary authority for this expanded role? Legal opinion and consideration by the professional organization in nursing, particularly the Nurse Practice Committee, would enter into this decision. What legal principles would have bearing on this role for the future, which offers a challenge to the nurse and a needed service to society?

## Connelly, J., Stoeckle, J., Lepper, E., and Farrisey, R., The Physician and the Nurse—Their Interprofessional Work in Office and Hospital Ambulatory Settings, *New Eng. J. Med.,* 275:765 (1966)*

There are not enough doctors now nor will there be enough in the future, according to present standards, to care for the health needs of the country. One obvious way to make the most of the physician's unique skills is to transfer some of his less demanding functions to other professionally trained people. This delegation of clinical work or "Task Allocation" is already widespread in the hospital, but only recently has purposeful consideration been given to the ways in which nurses can promote better care of the ambulatory patient by assuming a new role. The effectiveness of a planned program of task allocation and its acceptance by patients and by the professions are the subjects of this report.

RATIONALE

Although the nurse is the professional person most able to assume some of the physician's traditional role in the home and in the office, in this country her customary role in ambulatory medicine is usually as a visiting and public-health nurse or a doctor's office aide. As a home visiting or public-health nurse, her practice is centered about a geographical district and a large number of medical practices and is divorced from close collaboration with doctors. As an office aide, she has greater opportunity for collaborative work but usually performs minor technical duties and manages the administrative aspects of the doctor's practice.

In a few cases, however, she has had a greater role. Cartwright and Scott analyzed the work done by nurses attached to general practitioners in England, where both the doctor and the nurse saw the patient at each consultation. The nurse was engaged in preparation of patients for the physician consultation, in answering questions after the visit and in "therapeutic listening." In fact, "therapeutic listening" was her chief function in 1 out of 5 office consultations, in half the home visits, and in 13 percent of the well-child sessions. With such help from the nurse, the physician was able to devote more of his time to the history and physical examination and to making arrangements for further care. Despite this more direct patient-nurse interaction, the nurse's work was still conceived by the physicians as an aid to them.

In Sweden Richards reports that the shortage of doctors has caused 1 doctor to be responsible for 12,000 patients. Three highly trained, experienced senior

* Reprinted with permission of the *New England Journal of Medicine* and the authors.

nurses have been assigned to each practitioner. In many cases patients first sought help through the nurse, so that some of the patients' problems were met without their having to see the doctor. In some districts nurses were empowered to admit patients directly to the hospital as in cases of possible appendicitis. The Swedish nurse, with the right to "lay on hands," diagnose and treat patients, is a colleague practitioner responsible to the physician.

Greater support is found in this country for a different approach to inter-professional care by the pediatrician and the nurse in community-based well-child conferences and in hospital outpatient clinics. In these situations, after consultation with the doctor, the nurse undertakes preventive and supervisory care of ambulatory patients. Broad mandate is given to promote preventive care in communicable disease and nutrition, to analyze family interaction, to detect physical, mental and emotional handicaps and to work in accident prevention and family planning.

Psychosocial care is an explicit objective of the conferences. This objective is based on the knowledge that about a third of the children and adults seeking medical treatment have functional or emotional disturbances and that emotional and attitudinal factors seriously complicate the illnesses of another third. Yet, in the usual well-child conference, there is insufficient time for "therapeutic listening" and for the psychologic work of the doctor. In fact, the medical staff is so over-whelmed by numbers of children and mothers that their focus is exclusively on physical health. The conferences often become "shot" clinics.

In the community-based well-child conference the doctor meets jointly with the nurse and parents, examines the child at four weeks, six and twelve months and then yearly through six years of age. The nurse sees the child monthly through the first year and at six-month intervals thereafter. The content of the nurse's visit with the child and mother includes an interval developmental history and inquiry about the child's social and emotional adjustment. Her other duties include follow-up phenylketonuria testing, hearing and vision testing and accident-prevention education. Although the physician sees the child less frequently, when he does see him, he is able to spend the time to go over both the physical and psychologic care, starting with the nurse's notes. So that this professional arrangement will not result in depersonalization of the patient-physician relation, the doctor maintains a comprehensive interest in the patient at the time of his own consultations and is available to the nurse for advice or for consultation with the patient whenever necessary.

At the Children's Clinic of the Massachusetts General Hospital, nurse well-child conferences, using a similar format, have been in existence since 1963. Physical examination of the child by the nurse is presently limited to inspection, but it is our impression that it could also include a screening physical examination, particularly for abnormal heart and lung sounds, abdominal masses and signs of congenital dysplasia of the hip.

In the Adolescent Weight-Control Clinic children have been treated by a nurse after the physician's initial interview and examination. The children visit the nurse weekly. She weighs the patient, goes over prescribed exercises, emphasizes proper mental attitude and gives encouragement and practical suggestions. Group exercises and discussion follow the individual conferences. The physician-in-charge sees the children at three-month intervals, or sooner if necessary, and is always kept informed of their status.

Similar physician-nursing practice has been organized with adult patients in the General Medical Clinic. The care of medical patients with chronic disease had three objectives: maintenance of patient participation in medical treatment over long periods; prevention and early recognition of complications of the disease or its treatment; and management of the ordinary emotional adjustment problems. As presently organized, the nurse has scheduled consultations with patients and, when necessary, initiates limited physical and laboratory examinations. The operation of this clinic is similar to that of the Child Health Conference in that patients are constantly in contact with the nurse and periodically with the physician. Such nursing-medical practice has been extended to special clinics concerned with long-term anticoagulation, diabetes, tuberculosis, alcoholism and occupational health.

In the United States expanded roles for the nurse are being used in other clinics. Within the framework of a prepaid medical group practice, Ford, Milvoy and Silver are exploring the roles of physician and nurse in prenatal and well-baby care in much the same way as the Massachusetts General Hospital Clinics. In Memphis, Tennessee, adult diabetic patients make scheduled visits to a community-based visiting nurse instead of hospital outpatient attendance. At a rheumatic fever follow-up clinic in New York City, the nurse rather than doctor is the patient's major contact at clinic visits. Ambulatory treatment by nurses is also carried on at the University of Kansas, where a nurse, under the supervision of a physician, treats patients with chronic degenerative disease and psychosomatic disorders. Green's outpatient program at the University of Indiana for handicapped children employs a highly trained public-health nurse as a health educator to help parents understand and cope with their child's illness. Industrial, rural, military and college-health medical practices have also broadened the scope of the nurse's duties, but long-term therapeutic work with ambulatory patients in these situations has not been a feature.

## EFFECTIVENESS AND ACCEPTANCE

In evaluating the nurse role change in community-based well-child care projects, Siegel and Bryson reported that nurses generally favored an expanded role for their discipline, but the majority of physicians were opposed. Both groups expressed similar concerns about the acceptance of the new practice by families and referral sources, ability of the nurses to perform responsibilities traditionally thought of as the physician's and the nurse's need for additional education, training and experience. Although the nurse did indeed have less factual knowledge than the physician when tested, in the clinical care of the children she became more involved with health education in relation to behavior of the child. The orientation of the nurse toward behavior was either through personal interest or previous training or because her medical knowledge was less comprehensive.

Although the clinic-based nurse-care projects have not yet been systematically evaluated, observation indicates that patient acceptance of them is high as is substantiated by good attendance records and by a negligible number of dropouts. Nurses have noted that patients feel more freedom to express personal concerns not considered important enough to address to the doctor. Many of these concerns have a direct relation to the patient's medical problem. So far, most of these experiences have been with patients from lower-class or lower-middle-class background.

Application of such a practice to a wider social class of patients and its adoption by a larger group of nurses and doctors may reveal different results.

PROBLEMS

For a transition in clinical practice from total care by the physician to care by other professions to occur without loss in quality, several problems must be solved. In the first place, hospital administrators and nursing leaders must be able to free nurses from the administrative or managerial work that often makes up a major part of their job. With assurance that the administrative tasks will be passed on to competent personnel, this change within nursing is also desired by many nurses. A study of nurses in several Boston hospital outpatient clinics suggests that most nurses would like to work with patients, even though they have successfully adapted to administrative work. . . .

Adoption of professional change may also be limited by patients, for patients do care who treats them. In institutions the patients often accept nurses as a preferred and initial source of help. This acceptance may be related to social class, to the nature of the patient's problems and the decisions to be made or to reliance on whatever practice arrangements the institution sets up. As nursing-medical practice is more widely adopted, limitations on the acceptance of the nurses' expertise may disappear.

In the final analysis, the individual physician must be willing to work co-operatively with the nurse in an expanded therapeutic role. The doctor may continue to regard himself as the first source of aid and to retain the responsibility of deciding what, if any, treatment needs to be started. Yet little doubt remains that nurses can often carry out such treatment and follow its effect. Among the reasons preventing the transfer of the physician's functions to others, Levy has identified the traditional concern about maintaining medical responsibility for the patient. To the doctor, any transfer of functions may mean that responsibility is also being surrendered. Neither surrender nor delegation of function may be easy unless medical responsibility is viewed as a shared task. . . .

PROSPECTS

Proposals to divide some of the therapeutic and medical work of the doctor further is likely to arouse discussion. This is certainly needed. The solutions envisioned are not detailed enough, nor the current projects sufficiently evaluated, to guarantee the best possible care. If task and role allocation are widely adopted, how can such a change be viewed? The "doctor's job" changes, not completely of course, but at least it changes for some patients and at some stages of their illness or their career as patients. Task allocation requires planning among the professions, not an executive decision. And so the reorganized work of the doctor is no longer his "job" alone but interprofessional care, which requires clinical leadership.

From an industrial model, task allocation may be viewed as decentralized decision making. Some may also see a depersonalization of care and an over-organization of treatment roles of professionals themselves. Yet these changes in clinical work may also be viewed as an opportunity for more effective education and support of the patient and for better control of medical treatment.

## (5) Peripheral Boundaries for the Professional Nurse

Rapidly shifting functions in the practice of medicine and the practice of nursing comes at a time when patient care is becoming increasingly complex. Doctor Joseph Sadusk, Jr., discusses the legal problems implicit in some of these changes. He points to the need for the legal expert to guide the nurse, to which we might add that it should be a type of guidance that permits her to integrate the necessary knowledge of law into her daily practice and also guides her in knowing when to assume a function and when to guard against accepting responsibility for a task for which she is not prepared.

### Sadusk, J. F., Jr., Legal Implications of Changing Patterns of Practice, *J.A.M.A.*, 190: 1135 (1964)*

The complexity of modern medical care and, more directly, the shortage of highly trained personnel present a need for increased interdependence of nurse and physician. Whereas a poor delineation of duties between physician and nurse has emerged, a clearer delineation between the professional nurse and the practical nurse is evident. It seems likely, therefore, that some of the physician's present obligations to his patient will be passed to the professional nurse, who in turn will pass along some of her tasks to the practical nurse. Indeed, such changes are already taking place. For example, the professional nurse has transferred many of her traditional bedside-care duties to the practical nurse; and the physician has transmitted responsibility to the professional nurse for starting intravenous solutions.

The legal implications of these changes in duties are important, as it is basic in the law that increased authority necessarily carries with it increased responsibility. This responsibility cannot be averted. Defining the type and degree of these changes will be difficult, perhaps even traumatic, should court action in malpractice trials involving the nurse and physician determine the groundwork for clarification. . . .

#### PROBLEMS OF NURSE AND PHYSICIAN

Whereas practically all states have defined the practice of nursing through nursing practice acts, only a relatively few states require licensure of nurses. It would therefore seem logical that if nurses are given new and more technical professional duties, licensure will have to be made mandatory to ensure that nurses are professionally qualified. This thought may be anathema to some nurses; experience indicates, however, that legislative bodies and the courts will require a definition of what a nurse may and may not do, if and when injury results to the patient as the nurse is performing such professional acts.

Modification of nursing practice acts may be more difficult than has been assumed. Physicians may be loathe to dispense with some of their authority and responsibility; furthermore, consideration must be given to the patient's reaction to

* Reprinted with permission of the *Journal of the American Medical Association* and the author.

these changes. Will the patient be willing to permit the physician to pass along to the nurse certain matters of professional care requiring precise judgment? Will he be more likely to jointly sue the nurse, the hospital, and the physician when things go wrong?

Another problem is that of training. Careful selection of students by the deans of nursing schools and modification of curricula will be necessary. Can enough persons be found for more highly professional careers? Should candidates apply to medical schools if they wish to do such professional work? In the responsibility for administration of intravenous solutions, for example, it is one thing for the nurse to begin therapy with simple saline or glucose solution, but it is another matter when she is asked to add potent and toxic medications to the flask. If the nurse is made responsible for review and interpretation of laboratory data, will she be asked to specify the exact dose of these agents? Will she be asked to specify how much potassium is to be added to the solution? It is doubtful that the legislatures and courts will accept a proposal for nurses to undertake such highly technical matters, as they involve decisions necessitating judgment through knowledge that cannot be acquired in three or four years of a nursing school.

In the administration of stat doses of insulin to a patient who is coming out of diabetic coma, as another example, the physician generally evaluates the blood sugar and checks the diabetic patient's urine at hourly intervals and then, based on results of these tests and *his long clinical experience*, he determines the precise dose of insulin required. Is this judgment one which the nurse of the future will assume? It is dubious that the courts will accept this, particularly if errors are made and patients are harmed.

Until now, the hazard to malpractice has been relatively mild for the nurse. It is unusual for her to be named as the sole defendant in a lawsuit for malpractice. In general, she has come under the protective umbrella of the doctor or hospital and is usually sued as a co-defendant along with physician or hospital, or both. Her main difficulties resulted from circumstances involving retention of foreign bodies, such as sponges; burns from hot water bottles, lamps, or hot soaks; falls from tables or beds; errors in administration of medications; defects in equipment; and abandonment of patients.

FUTURE HAZARDS

More than 500 years ago, a learned British Justice said, "If a surgeon does so well as he can and employs all of his diligence to the cure, it is not right that he should be held culpable." The law has not improved much on this simple and basic definition, although a more sophisticated explanation is now made. The law requires a nurse—or physician—to possess that degree of skill and competence commonly possessed by other nurses—and physicians—in the same locality and to utilize that skill and knowledge as other reputable nurses—and physicians—in the same community would have done under similar circumstances. Failure to do this constitutes malpractice on the part of the nurse—or physician. Consequently, the nurse is going to be subject to an increased malpractice hazard by virtue of her entry into new duties necessitating a higher degree of skill and knowledge than she may now possess. During the period of change of duties—and perhaps even beyond—the physician is going to be subject to an increased risk of malpractice, since he will be delegating these duties and the courts may consider that such procedures are matters of medical rather than nursing practice. In much the same manner, the nurse may be considered responsible by the courts when she delegates some duties to the practical nurse. Indeed, this risk will be considerable because of the professional nurse's responsibility for supervision of not only the practical nurse but also the graduate nurse, the student nurse, and other ward personnel. . . .

The nurse of the future, as she assumes her increased professional status and authority for independent action, will necessarily be given increasing legal responsibility. As these new responsibilities unfold, she will need guidance by the legal expert. Her new duties will need to be defined in the nursing practice act, and state— or national—licensure will doubtless be made mandatory. It is most important that these things be done, as attempts to set a standard of practice at local—or hospital— levels could well lead to a series of medical malpractice court decisions to define the matter.

## (6) Continuing Responsibility for Redefining Nursing Practice

The following article by Richard M. Schmidt, Jr., writing as legal counsel for the Colorado Nurses' Association, discusses the importance of a profession's assuming the responsibility for defining its areas of practice. When rapid changes in nursing are taking place, Mr. Schmidt's article sounds a prophetic note in urging the profession of nursing to continually seek the answer to the question of "what is nursing?" Once defined, the nursing profession should then knowingly accept all functions within the definition and guard against losing such functions by default.

### Schmidt, R., The Definition of Nursing, *Colo. Nurse,* (Nov., 1958)*

It should be understood that the Colorado Nurse Practice Act, as all other nurse practice acts containing statutory definitions, does not contain a statement of specific functions but merely defines the broad area of control. The nurse practice act merely stands as an aid to identification as it were. The scope of professional nursing is ever changing and is not static and therefore the nursing practice definition contained in the law must be sufficiently elastic to encompass future changes.

It is therefore necessary to the profession itself to undertake studies of functions, standards and qualifications and as you all know, this is part of the program of the American Nurses' Association and its affiliated state groups. If a court test comes of a specific situation and the court is called upon to determine whether or not the item in question is a function of the professional nurse and should be wholly related to her activities and not to some other field, the court would call upon experts in the field to give evidence as to the identification of this function. The American Nurses' Association statement of functions has undertaken to recognize seven areas

* Reprinted with permission of the Colorado Nurses' Association.

of control for professional nursing. These should be studied and should be adapted and evaluated to the local situation. These areas of control as set down in the functions, standards and qualifications program of the ANA are based upon the recognized patterns that have evolved over the years by professional nurses and also upon the study of the various judicial interpretations of professional nursing standards. Therefore, as recognized by Lesnik and Anderson, "Thus, an examination of the reported cases reveals legal recognition that among the professional nurses supervisory functions are the necessity to determine the physician's attendance; the adaptation of the patient to a procedure, treatment or technic, as, for example, where liability was imposed for a nurse's failure to discontinue injection of saline solution after evidence of adverse effect upon an unconscious patient; the evaluation of a patient's response post-operatively, to determine need for sedation, and his response to hospital or medical routine and capacity for self-help as, for example, the patient's position for insertion of a drainage tube, or the ability of a patient to get out of bed and wash himself."

Therefore, the only possible method is an evolvement of a complete program of functions, standards and qualifications and this must come from the profession itself. I cannot over-emphasize the importance of this program being undertaken and kept constantly in motion and pushed with all convenient speed. Earlier in this letter I mentioned the fact that at least two cases from the Colorado Supreme Court within the last year had concerned judicial interpretation of the practice of law. One of these cases is a signpost of warning for all professions. In this particular case the Supreme Court of Colorado undertook to discuss whether or not certain functions involving real estate constituted the practice of law and unequivocally set forth the proposition that indeed the drafting of these particular instruments was the practice of law, but the Court went on to state that these particular acts, even though they constituted the practice of law, had been done for such a long period of time by real estate brokers and other non-professional groups, that they were now reluctant to stop them from this practice. In other words, this exclusive function of a profession was lost by default.

I believe that professional nursing stands in danger of losing identification of certain functions as being within its exclusive field and may, by default, see these particular areas of control turned over to other less highly trained, and even in instances, completely untrained, persons. The answer to this, I believe to be two-fold, first the individual professional nurse must carry out her duties and functions with all of the skill available to her by virtue of her training and experience and in so doing bring about a general public recognition of her functions and create in the public an awareness of the seriousness of these particular functions and of the need for a highly skilled and educated person to carry them out. Secondly, I believe that it behooves the profession to so define and create its own functions, standards and qualifications so that they obtain not only public recognition but that the licensing bodies of the professional nurses throughout the country may exercise all of the rights available to them under the law to prevent others from infringing upon these areas. It should be kept in mind that this is not done through selfish desires to exclude others from the field and keep this unto a small group for their own gain but is done so because of recognition of the need for skilled and trained personnel to carry out these difficult functions. If others wish to undertake the practice in this area then they are cordially invited to go through the necessary training and preparation so that they are qualified to do so. It is not the professional nurse who suffers the most when untrained and unqualified people undertake care beyond their means, but it is the patient and the public who suffer from this unskilled help. This too, as part of a public relations program must be carried on by the professional nurse. She does this first of all through her own activities, for she is her own best or worst public relations agent as the case may be. Secondly, those of the general public who do not come into contact frequently with professional nurses and other persons who serve in the field of health care must be kept aware of the functions of the professional nurse and the need for said functions by a public education program which can be carried on by the nurses' own organization as well as by individual nurses themselves.

This then, I believe to be the problem as I see it and also the solution. There will never be a final answer to the problem for just as the problem is ever changing so are the solutions. It should be kept in mind that nursing as a profession is relatively young and when we look to the professions that have been recognized for many years longer than nursing, we see that even there, you cannot set down, one, two, three, the statements, "this constitutes the practice of medicine" or, "this constitutes the practice of law," then you realize that it is an ever continuing problem, but one that must be faced squarely and constantly.

## (7) Interaction of Direct and Indirect Professional Controls

In the practice of professional nursing, two regulatory forces are brought to bear on the individual practitioner, the direct control of the administrative agency with its power over preparation and licensure, and the indirect control of the professional organization which, although voluntary in its power of action, can and does exercise a direct influence on the quality of nursing service being provided by the individual nurse.

In this chapter, detailed consideration has been given to the authority and restrictions which operate on the administrative agency. Here will be briefly examined some of the forces exerted by the professional organization that augment and contribute to the effective functioning of the administrative agency. Although it is true that their activities are and should be closely related, each performs its own unique functions that contribute to a total professional strength in rendering an essential public service.

The determination and implementation of standards of preparation and practice for the professional nurse are a primary concern for both the administrative body and the professional organization. The professional organization engages in continuous study of its practice to determine whether it is fulfilling the expectations of society as a whole. The organization is responsive to pressures of social change, particularly when the changes call for extended professional services that will influence the number and preparation of its practitioners or create a demand for new and more effective methods of utilization of nurse power.

A professional organization may choose, as one means of establishing and improving educational standards, to create and operate a national accrediting association free from any legal control either on the state or federal level. When other professions, as law and medicine, chose to accept candidates for licensure who were graduates from schools on the national roster rather than to operate an independent accrediting program on the state level, it became necessary to seek legislation to grant to the state administrative agency the required discretionary powers.

At present, the nursing profession has developed an active national accrediting association that exerts a powerful influence on the improvement of the preparation of practitioners. Thus far, however, this voluntary accreditation of educational programs has not replaced state accreditation by the administrative agency. Whether or not nursing will eventually follow the pattern of law and medicine depends upon a number of variables unique to nursing and also on a professional commitment that accreditation of schools of nursing on a state level has made an invaluable contribution but that a single unified accrediting body of a national nursing organization could reflect the strength of the total profession and be an even more powerful tool in the upgrading of educational standards than programs that inevitably vary from state to state. If the position is accepted, administrative bodies for nursing would need legislative authority for discretionary power to accept candidates for licensure who come from schools approved by the national professional accrediting body in lieu of present state-accredited lists.

The professional organization may assume a leadership role for all legislation of concern to its occupational field, and in general legislation affecting health, morals, and social welfare. In this capacity, it may either sponsor or support desirable legislation or actively oppose that which it believes would render a public disservice. In the development of its legislative program, the profession must be continually alert to changes in its practice and patterns of education, and undertake a continuing review of the statutory law to determine the potential need for revision. Changes in the law could be initiated by findings from research in such areas as the philosophy of licensure as a social process and its bearing on the control of practice, or a survey of the kinds of voluntary and legal designations used by varying professions to describe competencies of its practitioners together with any implications for nursing. If these and other studies were implemented, they could lead to greater improvements in the quality of care being offered to the public.

Still another way for a professional organization to extend its influence is for it to carry on a continuing program of public information that aims to develop a public confidence and support for its social commitment to a public service.

In these ways, among many others, it is apparent that the collaborative interaction of the professional organization and the administrative agency for the control of the occupation can be an important factor in the effectiveness of the profession's service to the public, and in the strength and character of the administrative activities. That the professions have a real obligation to foster and contribute to the work of the administrative agency was summed up, some years ago, in a discussion of the obligations of the legal profession:

In the long run, the public is going to be served in any particular field by those who serve it best, whether it be attorneys or laymen. What the public has given to us the exclusive right to do today, the public can take away from us tomorrow. . . . The public that gave us the exclusive right to practice law can take it away or modify it at any time; and in the long run, we are going to retain the exclusive right only so long as we serve the public better than anyone else. [Beardsley, J., *Lay Encroachments*, 14 J. Am. Jud. Soc'y 130 (1930).]

## (8) Administration Discretion

The establishment of criteria for professional licensing is a proper subject for administrative action. This has been consistently held by the courts. Illustrative is the case of *Douglas v. Noble*, 261 U.S. 165 (1923), where the United States Supreme Court held that it is a proper exercise of administrative discretion to determine the standards or qualifications that applicants should meet to be admitted to practice their profession. There, a dentist had failed his licensing examination but continued to practice dentistry. The Supreme Court of the United States upheld the examining board's action in enjoining his practice without a license against the dentist's contention that the board had exercised arbitrary power. The Court pointed out the two-step process that a professional examining board follows:

The first, what the knowledge and skill are which fit one to practice the profession. The second, whether the applicant possesses that knowledge and skill. The latter finding is necessarily an individual one. The former is ordinarily one of general application. Hence, it can be embodied in rules. The legislature itself may make this finding of the facts of general application, and, by embodying it in the statute, make it law. When it does so, the function of the examining board is limited to determining whether the applicant complies with the requirements so declared. But the legislature need not make this general finding. To determine the subjects of which one must have knowledge in order to be fit to practice dentistry; the extent of knowledge in each subject; the degree of skill requisite; and the procedure to be followed in conducting the examination—these are matters appropriately committed to an administrative board. . . . And a legislature may, consistently with the Federal Constitution, delegate to such board the function of determining these things, as well as the function of determining whether the applicant complies with the detailed standard of fitness. [261 U.S. at 169–70.]

# CASES

The following cases are illustrative of judicial review of the functioning of the administrative agency for nursing. In each instance the decision of the administrative body was reviewed by the courts. In Part I of the text, the hierarchy of the courts was discussed; to which level of the court system might the judicial functioning of the administrative agency be likened?

## Stefanik v. Nursing Education Committee, 70 R.I. 136, 37 A.2d 661 (1944)

Flynn, Chief Justice.

This is a petition for certiorari to quash the action of the respondent nursing education committee in recommending that the state's director of health revoke the petitioner's license to practice nursing and annul her registration. Pursuant to the writ the respondents have made a return to this court of all pertinent records, including a certified transcription of the evidence presented at the hearings held by the nursing education committee prior to its finding and recommendation.

The following facts, among others, appear from the petition and evidence: Respondent nursing education committee, hereinafter called the committee, existed and functioned by virtue of General Laws 1938, chapter 280. The other respondent was the director of health for the state and will be hereinafter called the director. Petitioner was a duly registered nurse and had practiced her profession for about sixteen years. During the period covered by the charges in question she served as a district nurse in the welfare department of the town of North Providence.

Upon receipt of complaints against petitioner, involving several charges of alleged unprofessional conduct, the committee, acting in accordance with § 2 of chap. 280, gave her written notice that a hearing would be held on April 14, 1943, to consider charges that she had been guilty of acts derogatory to the morals or standing of the profession of nursing and that she then would be given opportunity to show cause why her license to practice nursing should not be revoked and her registration annulled.

The petitioner accordingly appeared before the committee on April 14 and at the subsequent hearings upon these charges and was at all times represented by counsel. Witnesses appeared, including patients and several duly licensed and practicing physicians, and gave testimony in support of some or all of these charges. The petitioner herself also testified and introduced other witnesses who gave testimony tending to refute such charges. No physician testified in her favor.

During some, if not all, of the hearings, the director apparently sat as a member ex-officio of the committee as constituted by the statute; but he did not participate in the consideration or vote of the committee when it made its finding and recommendation. The remaining members of the committee, upon consideration of the charges and evidence, found that petitioner was guilty of acts derogatory to the morals or standing of the profession of nursing" and voted unanimously to recommend that her license to practice as a registered nurse be revoked as of July 10, 1943, for an indefinite period. The director, by a letter dated June 30, 1943, notified the petitioner that, in accordance with the committee's recommendation, he revoked her certificate to practice professional nursing and annulled her registration as of July 10, 1943, and called upon her to surrender her certificate as provided by the statute. That statute contains no express provision for a review of alleged errors of law in such a decision and the petitioner thereupon brought the present petition for certiorari.

The petitioner contends that: (1) The committee's finding is not supported by legally competent or sufficient evidence; (2) the committee did not examine the charges with an open mind, did not act impartially in passing upon them, and did not accord the petitioner a fair and impartial hearing; (3) the director had no authority under chap. 280, § 2, to revoke petitioner's license; (4) if the director had such authority petitioner was entitled to a second hearing before him; and that in any event he was prejudiced and disqualified because of his participation in the committee's hearings; (5) petitioner was prejudiced by the committee's action in permitting its legal adviser to act in the dual capacity of prosecutor and judge; (6) petitioner was prejudiced by its action in permitting counsel for complaining witness to direct the examination and cross-examination of witnesses without express permission of proper authorities; (7) the decision and ruling of the respondents deprive petitioner of due process of law in violation of her rights under the constitution of the United States; (8) section 2 of chap. 280 requires judicial or quasi judicial action by the committee which nevertheless acted arbitrarily.

Under the first of these contentions petitioner argues that the recommendation of the committee is illegal because it was not supported by "legally competent or sufficient evidence." This contention appears in part to be based on a misconception of the law governing certiorari. In such proceedings we do not consider the sufficiency of the evidence, that is, its preponderance. Once jurisdiction is established we examine the evidence, not to weigh it or pass upon its credibility, but merely to determine whether there is any legally competent evidence to support the finding and action in question.

In the instant case the committee clearly had jurisdiction. Our examination of the record discloses some legal evidence, particularly from persons who had received and paid for nursing services rendered by petitioner, which tends to support her claim that she was efficient and was not guilty of the charges as made. But there is also legal evidence from other persons, who were not in the category of paying patients, which shows that the petitioner, in several instances and at different times and places, called upon patients without the knowledge or consent of their doctors and without invitation from the patients; that on certain occasions she, in effect, told patients that the doctor's diagnosis was wrong, and gave her own diagnosis and instructions to be followed by the patient notwithstanding certain different treatments or prescriptions as ordered by the doctor; that she had voluntarily and officiously interfered in matters that concerned the private lives and affairs of patients and their families, which matters were entirely beyond the proper scope and ethics of her professional calling; that she, as a public nurse, had used unwarranted and unprofessional language in criticizing patients, members of their families and doctors, thus tending to promote friction between doctors and their patients.

The petitioner categorically denied most of this testimony. In some cases her explanation of the circumstances was far different from that of other witnesses, and in one case she admitted changing the doctor's prescription and direction, but attributed it to a misunderstanding. The doctor, however, gave testimony which showed that there was no reasonable basis for any such misunderstanding; and other doctors testified to certain instances within their own experience which would support a finding that petitioner was in the habit of dealing with certain patients in her own way, regardless of the doctors' diagnoses and directions.

For our purposes it is sufficient to point out that there was a sharp conflict upon the material evidence from which the committee under the law had to make its finding. The credibility of the witnesses and the sufficiency, or preponderance, of the evidence were matters for them to consider, but are not before us in this type of proceeding. We cannot say, from our examination of the record, that there was no legal evidence to support the committee's finding and recommendation.

The petitioner's second, fifth, sixth and eighth contentions as above mentioned allege different grounds for her general contention that the committee was biased and arbitrary and failed to give her a full and fair hearing under the law. We have examined the record and, in our opinion, none of these contentions has any foundation or justification in fact and therefore they are without merit.

Petitioner's third contention is that chap. 280 gives no express authority to the director to revoke a nurse's license and that this omission can properly be supplied only by the legislature and not by judicial construction. The director contends substantially that he has such authority by necessary implication from the express language in the statute. In our opinion, the director's argument is correct.

Section 2 of the statute expressly provides in part that the committee "shall refer to the director of public health any recommendation to revoke the certificate and annul the registration of any nurse for gross incompetency, dishonesty, or any habit or act derogatory to the morals or standing of the profession of nursing." It next provides for due notice and hearing on charges before the committee may make such a recommendation; and then proceeds immediately in the same paragraph to specify what shall be done by the nurse and the secretary of the committee "upon the revocation of any certificate."

By thus limiting the committee's authority to a mere *recommendation* to the director that a certificate *be revoked* and by immediately prescribing certain action by the nurse and secretary *upon the revocation* of any certificate, it seems clear to us that the director's authority to revoke, after such hearing and recommendation, is necessarily to be implied from the express terms of the statute. Otherwise this part of the section of the statute would be wholly ineffectual and without reasonable purpose.

Our conclusion as above stated is consistent with well-established rules of statutory construction and is further confirmed by a consideration of the history of this statute. When all pertinent chapters are read in sequence, having in mind the purpose and express language of this statute, the case is clearly and properly one for statutory construction by the court and does not require "judicial legislation," as contended by the petitioner.

The fourth contention is that, even if the director had such authority, he was nevertheless disqualified from exercising it because he had participated in the hearings of the committee; and further that before acting he was required to hold a second hearing at which the petitioner was entitled to be represented. The director is made a member ex officio of the committee by the express provision of the statute. Therefore he had the legal right to sit with the committee, whose authority was limited to a recommendation. Apart from his mere membership on the committee and presence at the hearings, the record discloses no claim or evidence to justify a finding of any personal or other disqualification of the director. . . .

Petitioner's seventh contention is to the effect that she was deprived of property rights in her license without due process of law, in violation of the fourteenth amendment of the constitution of the United States. We find nothing in the record which could reasonably justify such a contention.

A consideration of the record leads us to the conclusion that the hearings before the committee were conducted in accordance with the provisions of the statute and in a fair and impartial manner; that there was legal evidence to support the committee's finding and recommendation; that in making such finding and recommendation it did not act unreasonably and arbitrarily, as contended by the petitioner; and that the action of the director in the circumstances was not illegal and did not exceed his jurisdiction under the law.

The prayer of the petition for relief is denied.

ANALYSIS

1. What were the charges on which the committee had considered factual evidence as a basis for its decision?

2. What was the court's reply to the contention of the nurse that the committee's action was illegal because it was not supported by legally competent or sufficient evidence?

3. Where in the content of the case do you find the evidence to support the court's decision that the second, fifth, sixth, and eighth contentions of the defendant were without merit?

4. The decision was that the statute was clear in the area under discussion and that "judicial legislation" was not required. What does this mean? As a member of the legislative committee of your state nurses' association what principle in the construction of statutory law is brought out here that could be useful to you?

5. If you support the decision, state why. If you think it too harsh, what might have been your recommendation for disciplinary action?

## Hamlet Hospital and Training School for Nurses v. Joint Committee on Standardization, 234 N.C. 673, 68 S.E.2d 862 (1952)

Johnson, Justice.

The statutory machinery for licensing trained nurses and accrediting training schools for nurses in this State is codified in Chapter 90 of the General Statutes of North Carolina, G.S. § 90–158 through G.S. § 90–171.

G.S. § 90–158 sets up "The North Carolina Board of Nurse Examiners," composed of five members, consisting of three registered nurses to be elected by the North Carolina State Nurses' Association and one representative each from the State Medical Society and the State Hospital Association.

G.S. § 90–159 sets up a Joint Committee on Standardization, consisting of three members appointed from the State Nurses' Association and four members from the State Hospital Association. The statute directs that the Joint Committee on Standardization shall advise with the Board of Nurse Examiners in the adoption of regulations governing the education of nurses. The statute also provides that the Board of Nurse Examiners and the Joint Committee on Standardization shall "have power to establish standards and provide minimum requirements for the conduct of schools of nursing of which applicants for examination for nurse's licence . . . must be graduates before taking such examination." A related statute, G.S. § 90–162, also requires in effect that an applicant before being permitted to take the examination for licensure as a registered nurse shall have graduated from a school of nursing connected with a general hospital giving a three years course of practical and theoretical instruction, meeting the minimum requirements and standards for the conduct of schools of nursing set up and established by the Joint Committee on Standardization provided for in G.S. § 90–159.

The record in the instant case indicates that this joint accrediting agency had formulated regulations establishing certain minimum requirements and standards for the conduct of schools of nursing in this State. The regulations so promulgated contain a stipulation that if a school meets the minimum requirements for accreditation, it shall be accredited for a period of one year, with provision that "accreditation shall be renewed annually provided the school continues to meet the minimum requirements for approval."

It thus appears that under the regulations an accredited nursing school automatically goes off the approved list at the end of the year (30 June), unless the accrediting agency in the meantime takes affirmative action and renews the listing for another year,—and so on from year to year.

The plaintiff's school was on the list of accredited schools of nursing for the year ending 30 June, 1951. The record also shows that on 24 May, 1951, the Joint Committee on Standardization and The North Carolina Board of Nurse Examiners met in executive session for the purpose of accrediting schools of nursing for the succeeding year. At that meeting "a motion was . . . passed to the effect that Hamlet Hospital School of Nursing should not be accredited for the school year June 30, 1951–June 30, 1952." And by notice dated 29 May, 1951, the plaintiff was notified and directed by this joint accrediting agency to show cause before the joint boards in Raleigh on 11 June, 1951, why plaintiff's school of nursing should be listed on the accredited list for the year June 30, 1951 to June 30, 1952. The plaintiff appeared with witnesses before the joint boards at the appointed time and place and at the conclusion of the meeting "a motion was . . . passed to the effect that plaintiff's school of nursing should not be placed on the accredited list for the year June 30, 1951–June 30, 1952," and a directive to that effect was issued by the joint boards.

The plaintiff then instituted this action to compel accreditation. After the summons was issued and the complaint filed, the plaintiff obtained from Judge Clement on 21 June, 1951, a temporary order of injunction restraining the defendants from removing the plaintiff's school of nursing from the list of accredited schools in the State until the further order of the court.

After this order of injunction was issued, the plaintiff obviously realized that under the terms of the defendants' regulation for accrediting schools from year to year, the then current accreditation of its school would terminate by virtue of the rule itself on 30 June, 1951, thus rendering the preliminary order of injunction, which merely restrained the removal of plaintiff's school of nursing from the accredited list, insufficient to compel the defendants to place the school on the accredited list for the next year, so as to preserve the *status quo* pending final determination of the case. Accordingly, the plaintiff on 25 June, 1951, sought and obtained from Judge Clement an order requiring the defendants to appear before Judge Phillips in Rockingham on 30 June, 1951, and show cause "why an interim mandamus should not be entered . . . commanding them to continue the nursing school of plaintiff on the accredited list . . . until the final determination of this cause."

When the plaintiff's motion for this affirmative, interim relief came on for hearing, the defendants entered a special appearance and by motion to dismiss challenged the power of the court to hear the matter or issue any form of mandamus. The defendants also interposed a demurrer alleging that the complaint failed to state facts sufficient to constitute a cause of action. At the hearing on 30 June, 1951, Judge Phillips overruled the defendants' demurrer and motion to dismiss, and allowed the plaintiff's motion for what is inexactly denominated an "interim mandamus," requiring the defendants to continue the plaintiff's school on the accredited list until the final determination of the cause.

Thus the instant appeal challenges the action of the court below in (1) overruling the demurrer to the complaint, (2) disallowing the defendants' motion to dismiss, and (3) allowing the plaintiff's motion for interim writ compelling the defendants to keep plaintiff's school on the accredited list pending trial of the cause on its merits. . . .

These in substance are the pertinent facts alleged in the complaint:

1. The plaintiff, non-profit corporation, has operated a hospital and training school for nurses in the Town of Hamlet since 1915. This school is the only training school for nurses between Charlotte and Lumberton, North Carolina, and between Raleigh, North Carolina, and Columbia, South Carolina. It serves the areas referred to for those desiring training in nursing. Its graduates are well-trained, well-qualified graduate nurses. They have maintained a creditable average in passing the State Board of Nurse Examiners.

2. In January, 1951, an inspector of the Joint Committee on Standardization inspected plaintiff's school and made certain criticisms and recommendations. The plaintiff has met these criticisms and recommendations, and the corrections suggested have been made.

3. On or about 1 June, 1951, plaintiff received notice from The North Carolina Board of Nurse Examiners and the Joint Committee on Standardization to show cause before these boards in Raleigh on 11 June, 1951, why the Hamlet Hospital School of Nursing should be listed on the accredited list of schools of professional nursing in North Carolina for the year ending 30 June, 1952. Attached to the notice was a memorandum advising the plaintiff that, because of certain deficiencies and criticisms listed, its "school of nursing fails to meet the minimum requirements and

standards prescribed by the Joint Committee on Standardization and approved by the North Carolina Board of Nurse Examiners, as set forth in the 'Regulations for Schools of Nursing in North Carolina 1948' as amended." Attached to the complaint is a copy of this list of deficiencies and criticisms pointed out by the joint accrediting boards as constituting the particulars in which the plaintiff's school of nursing failed to qualify for accreditation. These deficiencies and criticisms may be summarized as follows:

*Records.* The Board's memorandum of deficiencies points to and quotes from its regulations requiring that "a good system of record be . . . maintained,"—so as to furnish a continuous history of each student's education and practice, indicating "the student's efficiency in work, attendance, and rating in her classes; lectures and demonstrations; the time she has spent in each department (day and night); absence from duty; sickness; and vacation." Here, the memorandum charges violations in these particulars: (a) "No record of required clinical instruction for students"; (b) senior students' final records showed substantially more class hours than shown in class roll book, thus reflecting violation of rule requiring accuracy of records; and (c) records "showed that an entire new curriculum was not started for the pre-clinical class admitted September 20, 1950, but that they began anatomy and physiology classes with the June 20, 1950 group," in violation of regulation requiring that "a new curriculum shall be started with each new class."

*Personnel Practices for Students.* Here, the memorandum of the Board charges: (a) that "student nurses on night duty were working eight hours per night plus class hours during the day," in apparent violation of the regulation limiting time on duty, including clinical practice and class hours, to 48 hours per week; (b) that the student residence was without adequate graduate supervision, furnishings, and bath facilities (as shown by annual report), with no provision for "a reception room where the nurses could entertain their friends,"—in violation of regulations providing that nurses shall have "comfortable living quarters with provision for rest and recreation," and that "there shall be a reception room where nurses can entertain their friends."

*Clinical Facilities.* Here the memorandum of the Board charges: (a) failure of the affiliated hospital to maintain the required daily average of twenty patients in medicine and ten each in the pediatric and obstetric departments; (b) "Hospital equipment appeared inadequate for students to practice good patient care," for that there were only "two thermometers for 20 patients," and "one bed pan sterilizer for entire hospital and that not in use," and "majority of patients did not have individual equipment," (no regulation cited as prescribing specific standards as to required articles of equipment or use thereof); (c) failure to maintain separate nutrition and cookery laboratory for teaching course, in violation of specific regulation to that effect.

*Library Facilities.* The memorandum quotes the regulation requiring maintenance of a reference library of "at least one hundred well selected reference books," including "new editions and no duplications." Here, it is charged that the annual report lists only 75 books, and that the survey "showed that majority were out of date and there was no reference book on nutrition or dietetics."

*Student Supervision.* The memorandum charges violation of the following regulation: "Head nurses and floor duty nurses shall be employed as needed in order that the nursing service of the hospital may go on without interruption, and that student nurses may be properly taught and supervised throughout the twenty-four hour period." Here, the particular violations charged are: (a) "only one full time instructor, and she does not supervise the students during their pre-clinical nor subsequent practice on the wards"; (b) "the instructor in the nursing arts course is in charge of the third floor which is the medical-surgical service." This "does not give her time to teach and supervise the students properly"; (c) sixteen registered nurses were listed as employed on the annual report; whereas there were only twelve the day of the visit, and one of these was working in the office.

4. "On 11 June 1951, pursuant to notice previously issued, plaintiff appeared with witnesses before The North Carolina Board of Nurse Examiners and the Joint Committee on Standardization, and reported what progress had been made in meeting the criticisms of the Nursing Educational Consultant and gave assurance and promised to fully comply with these requirements insofar as was possible; that irrespective of the efforts that plaintiff had made to comply with the criticisms and requirements, as aforesaid, and its solemn sworn promise to comply with these requirements, defendants arbitrarily, and without giving plaintiff an opportunity to meet its alleged minimum requirements, issued a directive ordering that the Hamlet Hospital School of Nursing should be taken off the accredited list of schools of professional nursing in North Carolina, and no new certificates be issued after 30 June 1951. That . . . the votes of the members of the aforesaid Committee to deny plaintiff listing on the accredited list of Nursing Schools in North Carolina was by very small majority . . ."

5. "Plaintiff has now met all of the minimum requirements of defendants as set out in" the memorandum of deficiencies and criticisms previously served on the plaintiff.

6. "That the regulations promulgated by defendants under the division entitled, 'Accredited Schools of Nursing,' contain, among other things, the following: 'If the school meets the minimum requirements for accreditation, it shall be accredited for a period of one year. Accreditation shall be renewed annually, provided the school continues to meet the minimum requirements for approval'."

7. "That if plaintiff's school of nursing is removed from the accredited list of School of Nursing by defendants, the graduates of said school under the regulations promulgated by defendants, will not be permitted to take the examination for license to practice their profession in North Carolina, regardless of their education and other qualifications."

8. "If defendants are permitted to remove plaintiff's nursing school from the accredited list of nursing schools, as intended by defendants, such removal will make it impossible for the said nursing school to continue in operation and will make it impossible for student nurses, except seniors, to complete their training in said school and to take the examination for practice of their profession in North Carolina."

9. Plaintiff, having operated its training school for nurses for more than 35 years, has invested many thousands of dollars in buildings, laboratories, and other equipment in addition to employing instructors, supervisors, and assistants to operate and maintain, in connection with its hospital, its training school for nurses. If defendants are permitted to remove plaintiff's school from the accredited list of

nursing schools in North Carolina, plaintiff will suffer irreparable loss and damage for which it has no adequate remedy at law. . . .

Here, it is observed that the plaintiff does not challenge the legality of the exercise of the defendants' discretion in respect to the promulgation of any of the regulations setting the standards and minimum requirements for accreditation. Nor does the plaintiff question the validity of the anomalous rule under which accreditation automatically terminates at the end of the year unless in the meantime the accrediting agency takes affirmative action and renews the listing for another year. The plaintiff accepts the regulations and alleges full compliance. Specifically, it is alleged in the complaint that the plaintiff has corrected all the deficiencies and criticisms pointed out by the joint accrediting boards as being the particulars in which the plaintiff's school failed to comply with the requirements for approval. It is further alleged that the "plaintiff has now met all the minimum requirements" for accreditation. The complaint also sets out the regulation promulgated by the defendants under which it is specifically provided that "accreditation shall be renewed annually, provided the school continues to meet the minimum requirements for approval."

Taking the foregoing facts as true, as we are required to do on demurrer, the defendants' duty to approve plaintiff's school becomes purely ministerial and the duty to perform absolute. These allegations, with the further averments that the defendants have refused arbitrarily to approve the plaintiff's school of nursing and that plaintiff will suffer irreparable damage by removal of its school from the accredited list, are sufficient to show that the plaintiff is without other adequate remedy and has a clear, legal right to the relief by mandamus as sought. . . .

Upon this record, presented as it is by demurrer, we are constrained to the view that the plaintiff is entitled to be heard on the facts alleged. Therefore, the orders appealed from are affirmed. This necessitates a hearing on the plaintiff's allegations of full compliance with the minimum requirements for accreditation, and to that end the cause will be remanded by the court below to the Joint Committee on Standardization and The North Carolina Board of Nurse Examiners, the joint agency in which is vested the power to find the facts in the first instance, with direction that the plaintiff be given a hearing on the issue of compliance, after which the joint agency will report its findings and conclusions to the Superior Court of Richmond County for such further proceedings in the cause as may be appropriate, with the plaintiff's right to be heard in the Superior Court on the report being preserved. To the end that the decision here reached may be effectuated, the cause is

Remanded.

Barnhill, Justice (concurring).

The Act as amended, now General Statutes Ch. 90, Art. 9, which is at least indirectly the subject matter of this action, created two administrative agencies: (1) a board of nurse examiners and (2) a joint committee on standardization. These two agencies, together with the individual members thereof, are defendants herein. For the sake of brevity and convenience of discussion I shall hereinafter refer to them as the Board and the Joint Committee.

The Legislature is the policy-making agency of the State government. The law-making function is assigned exclusively to it, and it alone can prescribe standards of conduct which have the force and effect of law. This function, except when expressly authorized by the Constitution—as is the case in respect to counties, cities, and towns—cannot be delegated to any other authority or body.

While the Legislature may not delegate the power to make the law, it may create an administrative agency and authorize it to make rules and regulations to effect the operation and enforcement of a law within the general scope and expressed general purpose of the statute. This authority, when granted, must be limited to the right "to fill in the details" in respect to procedural and administrative matters. It cannot lawfully include the power to make the law, for neither urgency of necessity nor gravity of situation arising from economic or social conditions allows the Legislature to abdicate, transfer, or delegate its constitutional authority or duty to an administrative agency. Hence, an administrative agency has no power to create a duty where the law creates none. Motsinger v. Perryman, supra.

The Legislature has the authority to regulate the practice of the professions. This includes the authority to establish minimum requirements to be observed by the schools which undertake to prepare applicants for license to practice such professions. It may likewise create administrative agencies to administer and enforce such laws. But standards of conduct to be observed can be prescribed only by the law-making branch of the government. Therefore, an act, the purpose of which is to regulate a profession or school, must establish the standards and minimum requirements; that is, standards of conduct must be prescribed by the Legislature. Only the power to enforce standards thus established may be delegated to a governmental agency. Motsinger v. Perryman, supra. This rule is inflexible.

There is no direct attack—on constitutional grounds—upon the statute under which defendants acted or purported to act. Even so, it is alleged that the defendants, in withdrawing from plaintiff accreditation as a hospital school of nursing and refusing to place its name on the list of accredited schools for the year beginning 1 July 1951, was arbitrary and contrary to law. Therefore, if the Act prescribes no standards or minimum requirements for hospital schools of nursing in respect of the "deficiencies of Hamlet Hospital School of Nursing" listed by defendants as justification for their action in ordering "that the Hamlet Hospital School of Nursing not be listed on the said accredited list for the year beginning July 1, 1951, and ending July 30th, 1952," then their action was in fact arbitrary and contrary to law as alleged. This necessitates an examination of the statute to ascertain what standards, if any, are prescribed so as to determine whether said order of defendants is pursuant to and in furtherance of the enforcement of standards lawfully established. If not, the order is without force or effect and the restraining order was properly continued in force.

The Board is created by G.S. § 90–158 and is empowered to give examinations to applicants for license to practice nursing, G.S. § 90–162, on certain specified subjects, G.S. § 90–163. The "prerequisites for applicants" are listed in G.S. § 90–162. One of the requirements is that the applicant "shall have graduated from a school of nursing connected with a general hospital giving a three years' course of practical and theoretical instruction, which said hospital meets the minimum requirements and standards for the conduct of schools of nursing which may have been set up and established by the joint committee on standardization provided for in § 90–159."

The Act contains no specific standard to be observed or minimum requirement to be met by a hospital school of nursing. Instead, there is an attempt to delegate this law-making power to the Joint Committee. G.S. § 90–159. It is there provided that "The joint committee on standardization shall advise with the Board of Nurse Examiners herein created in the adoption of regulations governing the education of nurses, and shall jointly with the North Carolina Board of Nurse Examiners have power to establish standards and provide minimum requirements for the conduct of schools of nursing of which applicants for examination for nurse's license under this chapter must be graduates before taking such examination." This does not serve to establish standards or to vest valid authority in the Joint Committee to do so.

However, the Act, in my opinion, does establish, by necessary implication, two standards or requirements for the conduct of hospital schools of nursing.

The applicant for license must have graduated from a school of nursing giving a three-year course of practical and theoretical instruction, G.S. § 90–162, in specified subjects, G.S. § 90–163. It would seem to follow by necessary implication that the school must furnish a three-year course of instruction in the specified subjects. It may be the additional requirement that the school shall have a library containing approved reference books on the prescribed subjects of study and adequate laboratory facilities is likewise necessarily implied.

But the Act does not, either directly or indirectly, establish any standards or minimum requirements for the conduct of hospital schools of nursing in respect of the "records," "personal practices of nurses," absence on account of vacation or illness, hours of practical training, system of bookkeeping, reception room and bath tub facilities, or time for giving theoretical instruction, in respect to all of which it is charged plaintiff was deficient. No doubt the Legislature considered that these matters are best left to the hospitals themselves. The attempted delegation of authority to establish such requirements is without legal effect and any standards established by defendants in respect of such "deficiencies" are void. Any attempted enforcement thereof is of necessity arbitrary and in disregard of law. Therefore, the only course open to the court below was to continue the restraining order in full force and effect.

The objective of the law is to provide for a minimum standard of training for those who seek license as trained nurses and to ascertain by examination that such applicants possess the required degree of proficiency before being granted a license.

The duty of the defendant boards is to regulate, not eliminate—to enforce, not to establish—standards for the conduct of schools of nursing. And they must confine their activities to the enforcement of the standards established by the Legislature. Where there is no standard, they have no power to act.

No doubt the defendants have acted in absolute good faith. The statute purports to delegate to them the power to establish minimum requirements and standards for the conduct of hospital schools of nursing. This they undertook to do, believing no doubt, they had ample legal authority for their action. Even so, if some of the listed "deficiencies" of plaintiff are a fair indication of the "standards" prescribed by them, they have passed from the field of regulation into the hunting ground of unauthorized intermeddling. This is true notwithstanding their absolute good faith. The hours of active duty, the time for theoretical instruction, the personal conduct of trainee nurses while in school, and facilities for their entertainment are matters for the several schools to regulate, certainly in the absence of specific legislation to the contrary.

Likewise, in my opinion, the requirement that hospital schools of nursing must approach defendants each year, with hat in hand, and beg leave to be accredited once again for the ensuing year is arbitrary and unreasonable. As already noted, such schools must provide a three-year course of training. Therefore, when the name of a school is once placed on the accredited list—granting for the present that defendants have the right to require accreditation—its name should not be removed from such list except after notice and full opportunity to be heard.

The enforcement of regulations such as those herein indicated will inevitably culminate in the elimination of many of the smaller schools of nursing and centralize the training of student nurses in a few large institutions. Such is not the purpose and intent of the Act. Small colleges and professional training schools play a vital role in the life of our State and, within reasonable bounds, their continued existence must be fostered and encouraged.

So long as defendants direct their efforts to enforcement of standards adopted by the Legislature to give assurance that student nurses shall receive adequate training in their chosen profession they are rendering a fine and useful service for which they should be commended. In seeking to accomplish this objective, however, they should always keep in mind the fact that this statute was not enacted for the benefit of nurses or to create a guild having the legal right to limit or proscribe competition, either of nurses or of hospital schools of nursing. It was enacted to promote the good health and general welfare of the people at large. Benefits accruing to nurses and schools are purely incidental. The Act can be justified and sustained on no other grounds.

I concur in the direction that this cause be sent back to the Joint Committee to ascertain, upon hearing, whether plaintiff has now complied with the requirements of the Board which come within their legitimate field of action.

### ANALYSIS

1. Bear in mind that this decision was written in 1952. What were the statutory provisions for membership on the Board and Joint Commission on Standardization set forth in the case that are at variance with the position taken by the Legislative Committee of the American Nurses' Association?

2. What were the actual procedural steps in securing and maintaining accreditation of a school of nursing as set forth in the facts? Does the procedure in North Carolina follow the pattern in the regulations for accreditation in your state? Might there have been an interim step; if so, what?

3. What were the findings of the Joint Accrediting Board on which the denial of accreditation was based? In each instance support or deny that such a deficiency would have bearing on the quality of education offered.

4. In the meeting of June 11, 1951, between representatives of the board and the plaintiff, a not infrequent present-day attitude toward the purposes of accreditation in general was reflected. Discuss the points raised in that meeting as though you were a member of the Board. Discuss them as though you were a member of the faculty of a school of nursing, this particular school or another one.

5. The plea of the plaintiff sets forth penalties for loss of accreditation by a state agency that to some may seem harsh. What are the arguments in justification?

6. What was the decision on appeal?

7. In Justice Barnhill's concurring opinion, what statements does he make that reflect his philosophy of the boundaries of administrative law and the work of the administrative agency? Is this in accord with general practice? In the past and even now what would have been the effect on the quality of nursing education if boards were held to enforcement of standards established by the legislature and where, if there were no standard, they had no power to act in a given situation? If some of the deficiencies listed by the Board were a fair indication of the type of standard prescribed by them, do you believe that it meant that the board was passing from the field of regulation into "the hunting ground of unauthorized intermeddling"?

## CASES FOR FURTHER ANALYSIS

### *Craft v. Balderston,* 58 Id. 650, 78 P.2d 122 (1938)

This was an appeal by a physician for judicial review of a proceeding that resulted in the revocation of license.

The appellant had been indicted on twelve counts, to the effect that while serving as a medical examiner for the United States Veteran's Bureau, he had knowingly and wilfully made and presented for approval to the chief medical officer of the Bureau, fictitious and fraudulent accounts and claims against the United States, with the intent of cheating and defrauding the United States. To ten of these counts he entered pleas of guilty and was sentenced for a period of one year and a day on each count, the terms of imprisonment to run concurrently.

Until his conviction, appellant was duly licensed to practice medicine and surgery in the state of Idaho. Following conviction, a copy of the judgment of conviction was sent to an Idaho state law enforcement officer, who issued an order for him to appear in person or by attorney to show cause why his license should not be revoked for conviction of a felony. Appellant appeared with his attorney, and following the hearing, the license was revoked. The district court, upon review, affirmed the decision of the law enforcement officer. An appeal was then taken to the Supreme Court, and the appellant contended that his conviction did not disqualify him for the proper and successful practice of medicine. The statute controlling the practice of medicine gave as grounds for revocation the conviction of a felony or any crime involving moral turpitude.

The revocation of the license was affirmed.

### *Board of Governors of Registered Dentists v. Brown,* 182 Okla. 243, 76 P.2d 1074 (1937)

This was an appeal to the Supreme Court of Oklahoma from a decision of the Board of Registered Dentists suspending the license of W. K. Brown.

The controlling statute authorized the board to revoke a license upon receipt of a certified copy of a court record showing that a member had been convicted of a crime involving moral turpitude. The facts were that two years prior to the hearing Dr. Brown had been found guilty of second-degree manslaughter. Dr. Brown claimed self-defense and stated that the man he shot was burglarizing an office. The jury that assessed his punishment as a fine and jail sentence immediately recommended clemency, whereupon he was granted parole. After his conviction he continued the practice of his profession for eighteen months, maintaining the high standing of character that had been true of his twenty-three years of practice.

The court in its review noted that action had been taken without consideration of the fact that the appellant had re-established himself and ruled that the action of the Board of Registered Dentists was an abuse of discretionary power and reversed their decision.

### *Garlington v. Smith,* 63 Ariz. 460, 163 P.2d 685 (1945)

In this case, the court affirmed the revocation of a physician's license on the grounds that he had engaged in an offense involving moral turpitude when the facts showed that he had been convicted of violating the Harrison Antinarcotics Act by selling morphine to a person other than one of his patients. In affirming, the court quoted several cases to the effect that conviction under the narcotics statute does involve a crime of moral turpitude.

## Recommended Source Material

TEXTS

Landis, J., *The Administrative Process* (New Haven: Yale University Press, 1938).
Lesnik, M., and Anderson, B.,*Nursing Practice and the Law*, 56–105 (Philadelphia: J. B. Lippincott Co., 2nd ed., 1962).
Schwartz, B., *An Introduction to American Administrative Law* (New York: Isaac Pitman & Sons, 2nd ed., 1962).
Shartel, B., and Plant, M., *The Law of Medical Practice*, 195–238 (Springfield, Ill.: Charles C Thomas, Publisher, 1959).
Stetler, C., Stetler, J., and Moritz, A., *Doctor, Patient and the Law*, 13–36, 77–92 (St. Louis: C. V. Mosby Co., 4th ed., 1962).

PERIODICALS

Alexander, F., Mandatory v. Permissive Licensure for Nurses, *J.A.M.A.*, 195:496, 1966.

Connors, F., *Laws Regulating the Practice of Nursing*, 40 State Gov't. 30 (1967).

Dean, M., *The Opportunity to be Heard in Professional Licensing Process in Pennsylvania*, 67 Dick. L. Rev. 31 (1962).

Dixon, P., *"Disqualification" of Regulatory Agency Members : The New Challenge to the Administrative Process*, 25 Fed. B. J. 273 (1965).

Holmer, W., *The Role and Function of State Licensing Agencies*, 40 State Gov't. 34 (1967).

Loevinger, L., *The Administrative Agency as a Paradigm of Government—A Survey of the Administrative Process*, 40 Ind. L. J. 287 (1965).

Note, *Administrative Law—Constitutionality of Statutes Licensing Occupations*, 35 N.C. L. Rev. 473 (1957).

# Appendixes

# Appendix I

# Study Methods: Legal and Clinical Cases

The student of nursing is familiar with the case method of study. Her courses make her aware that a clinical nursing care plan starts with a life situation, and a description of what happened to the individual, the home, family, or community. The second step is to note why it happened and to identify those problems that were an outgrowth of the event. The third phase is the one in which the student seeks a solution and initiates some form of action to utilize the best efforts of herself and others to deal with the problem in the most effective way. As the nurse reads the cases presented in this book she can analyze them in the same way as she could a case in clinical nursing. The legal case presents a fact pattern of some form of deviant conduct which can be likened to the situation in a clinical nursing case. From this fact situation she identifies problems or issues and traces and analyzes the reasoning of the judicial decision.

Both forms of cases as described have another common characteristic and that is that they cannot be studied in a vacuum. The textual materials presented in this book will aid the nurse in understanding the law that entered into the analysis of the decision. More is required of the nurse, however, if she is to comprehend fully the implication for her practice of the pattern of facts which gave rise to litigation. She will need to bring to bear her knowledge of nursing science and nursing practice to properly explore and evaluate the conduct which led the participants to the courtroom. Each case is selected to present a realistic picture of nursing or medical practice in action, and to enable the reader to see that it is from common everyday experiences that litigation arises. A realization of the commonplace origin of most lawsuits should help the nurse to realize that being named as a party in a legal dispute is not an unfortunate and un-related event in the life of an unknown practitioner. Rather, it should lead her to appreciate that knowledge of the law will help her avoid those situations leading to litigation.

The cases in this text are followed by questions to assist the reader's analysis of the case; these questions are intended to be provocative and suggestive rather than comprehensive or conclusive. In reading the cases in the text, and also in reading the cases listed for further study, undergraduate, graduate, or continuing education students could endeavor to answer two questions—what theoretical knowledge did the nurse have, or what knowledge should she have had, to lead her to make the nursing judgment that she made or failed to make? Did her nursing judgment lead her to take appropriate action; if not, wherein was her judgment at fault?

Another exercise that should be made a part of case study is for the reader to assume that she is invited as a nurse clinician to come to X hospital to study the nursing service situation in which an injury to a patient occurred and which gave rise to the case. From the point of view of this consultant, study the facts of the case and seek the point or points at which the quality of care broke down and why. As consultant, write a report to the director of nursing service sufficiently comprehensive to be used by the members of the in-service program planning committee on "The Role of the Nurse Practitioner in the Prevention of Litigation."

The cases are designed to aid the student to read and understand in depth materials pertinent to the law underlying nursing practice. The decisions deal with topics of law and at the end of each chapter attention is called to legal writings related to the various topics which present differing and deeper analyses of significant aspects of the law.

As a further guide to case study, there is reprinted here a portion of an article guiding law school students in developing skill and understanding in the analysis of cases. The article should prove helpful to the nurse as well.

# Appendix II

# Studying Law Under the "Case Method" or "Case System"

KINYON, S., HOW TO STUDY LAW AND WRITE LAW EXAMINATIONS,
15–34 (St. Paul: West Publishing Co., 2nd ed., 1951)*

"CASES" AND "CASEBOOKS." Before you can properly read and "brief" the cases in your casebook, it is essential that you understand what they are, how they came to be written, where the author of your casebook got them, and what is in them. In some schools this is adequately explained when you start the first year's work. In others it is not, and therefore it is probably worthwhile to explain these things here briefly even though some of you may already know them. You obviously can't read cases intelligently unless you know what they are.

Cases, as we shall use the term in this discussion, are the published reports of controversies, which have come before the courts, including the court's decision and its reasons for the decision. These reports usually deal with the decisions and opinions of *appellate* courts (courts deciding cases appealed from lower courts). Trial court decisions (those rendered in the first court to which the controversy was taken) are not ordinarily recorded in printed volumes for public distribution, except in the Federal courts, New York, and a few other states. In most jurisdictions the pleadings, orders, verdicts, judgments, etc., in the trial courts are merely filed in bundles in the office of the clerk of the court, and the record of the proceedings at trial remains in shorthand in the court reporter's notebook unless a case is appealed. In that event, however, the appealing party has the record transcribed, printed and sent to the proper appellate court. Printed briefs are also usually submitted by each party to that court setting forth the arguments pro and con and the authorities relied on. Each party then has an opportunity for oral argument before the appellate court judges at a time prescribed by them. After the arguments have been heard, the judges meet in conference and come to some conclusion as to their decision. One of them is assigned the task of writing a statement of the decision and the court's reasons for making it. This is called the *opinion*, and when he has finished writing it he submits it to the other members of the court who either approve it, suggest changes, or dissent, in which case they may write a dissenting opinion of their own. After the majority of the

* Reprinted with permission of West Publishing Co.

judges have approved an opinion, it is "handed down" together with any dissenting opinions. That is, it is given out to the parties and made public in one way or another. Sometimes, as in the United States Supreme Court, the opinions are read from the bench by the judge writing them; sometimes they are merely given to the clerk of the appellate court, who makes copies and sends one to each party concerned. In any event, the clerk keeps the opinions in each case decided by the court until a number have accumulated, and then has them edited and published in a volume—ordinarily in the order in which they were handed down. These volumes, called the "state reports" where the decisions are those of state courts, are numbered consecutively. There is a series of reports published by the West Publishing Company, called the National Reporter System, which contains, in complete and accurate form, all state and federal decisions. Each unit of this system combines the opinions from a group of jurisdictions.* There are also several systems of reports which publish only those state or federal opinions considered to be of special significance. Thus, an opinion handed down by a state court in this country will be published in at least two sets of books, and sometimes in three or more. After they are published, these opinions or "cases" are customarily referred to or "cited" by giving the name of the case, the volume number, name and page of the state report in which it is published if it was decided by a state court, the volume number, name and page of the particular unit and series of the National Reporter System in which it is reported, the volume number,

---

\* Following is a list of the Reporters and the jurisdictions which they cover:

**Atlantic**

| | |
|---|---|
| Connecticut | New Hampshire |
| Delaware | New Jersey |
| Maine | Pennsylvania |
| Maryland | Rhode Island |
| | Vermont |

District of Columbia
(*Municipal Court of Appeals*)

**New York Supplement**
Court of Appeals
Appellate Divisions
Miscellaneous

**North Eastern**

| | |
|---|---|
| Illinois | Massachusetts |
| Indiana | New York |
| | Ohio |

**North Western**

| | |
|---|---|
| Iowa | Nebraska |
| Michigan | North Dakota |
| Minnesota | South Dakota |
| | Wisconsin |

**Pacific**

| | |
|---|---|
| Arizona | Nevada |
| California | New Mexico |
| Colorado | Oklahoma |
| Idaho | Oregon |
| Kansas | Utah |
| Montana | Washington |
| | Wyoming |

**South Eastern**

| | |
|---|---|
| Georgia | South Carolina |
| North Carolina | Virginia |
| | West Virginia |

**Southern**

| | |
|---|---|
| Alabama | Louisiana |
| Florida | Mississippi |

**South Western**

| | |
|---|---|
| Arkansas | Missouri |
| Kentucky | Tennessee |
| | Texas |

**Federal**
U.S. Courts of Appeals
U.S. Court of Customs
& Patent Appeals
U.S. Emergency Court
of Appeals

**Federal Supplement**
U.S. District Courts
U.S. Court of Claims

**Federal Rules Decisions**
U.S. District Courts

**U.S. Supreme Court**

name and page of any other selected case series in which it may have been published and the date it was decided. For example:

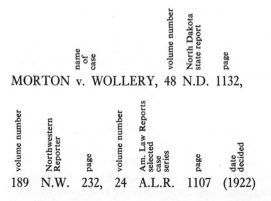

MORTON v. WOLLERY, 48 N.D. 1132,

189   N.W.   232,   24   A.L.R.   1107   (1922)

The citation of a case decided in a *federal* district court or court of appeals frequently will refer only to *one* set of reports—the Federal Supplement or the Federal Reporter—but will usually contain a reference, in connection with the date, to the particular federal court in which it was decided. For example:

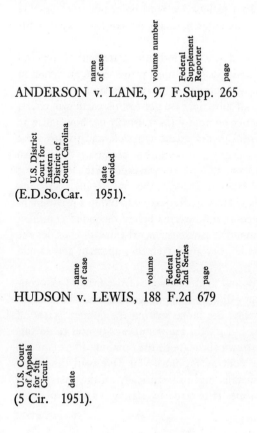

ANDERSON v. LANE, 97 F.Supp. 265

(E.D.So.Car.   1951).

HUDSON v. LEWIS, 188 F.2d 679

(5 Cir.   1951).

The "casebooks" which you use in school are made up principally of selected cases taken from these reports (or from English or British Empire reports) and arranged or grouped according to the type of controversy involved in the case. Sometimes the author of the casebook reproduces the whole opinion verbatim as originally published; sometimes he omits parts of it not regarded as significant, or substitutes a brief statement of his own as to some part which is omitted, but this is always indicated. Therefore, a case you read in your casebook is normally an exact copy of what some judge has written in explanation of his court's decision in a particular law suit brought to that court for decision.

READING CASES. Having briefly considered what these cases are, how they came to be written and where the authors of our casebooks found them, we are ready to tackle the problem of how to read them intelligently. No doubt you will be told that you must concentrate when you read, that you must read carefully and thoroughly, that you must try to understand what you read, that you must look up in the law dictionary the words you don't understand, and so forth and so on. Doing all those things is of course essential, but they alone won't make you an intelligent case reader or a good law student. The fundamental thing in reading cases is to know *what to look for*. Otherwise you may concentrate on the wrong thing or miss an important point.

Perhaps the best way to explain what to look for is to point out *what you can normally expect to find* in a case and what the judge normally puts or tries to put in his opinion.

1. The first thing you will usually find in a case is a brief statement of the kind of controversy involved. That is, whether it was a criminal prosecution, an action of tort for damages, an action for breach of contract, or to recover land, etc. This is usually accompanied by an explanation of how the case got to this particular court; whether it started there, or, if it is a matter on appeal (as it usually is), how and why it happened to get there, whether plaintiff or defendant appealed, and to just what action of the lower court the appealing party is objecting. For example: "This is an appeal by defendant from an adverse judgment," or "from an order of the lower court denying his motion for new trial," or "from an order of the lower court overruling his demurrer to the complaint," etc. These facts are frequently found in a preliminary paragraph prepared by the clerk of the court and inserted before the judge's opinion. Nevertheless, since they tell you just how that particular court came to consider the controversy and just what it had to decide, they are extremely important and should not be overlooked or passed over lightly.

2. The next thing you will usually find is a statement of the facts of the controversy—who the parties were, what they did, what happened to them, who brought the action and what he wanted. Normally, the judge writing the opinion starts off with a complete statement of the facts, but judges are not always careful to do this and you will frequently find the facts strewn throughout the opinion. Thus you can never be sure you know all about the controversy until you have read the whole opinion. Sometimes the statement of facts is made categorically on the basis of the court's or jury's *findings* of fact; sometimes it is made by stating what the plaintiff

and defendant *alleged* in their pleadings; and sometimes it is in the form of a *resumé* of the *evidence* produced at trial. Wherever they may appear, however, and in whatever form they may be stated, every case contains some statement of the facts and circumstances, out of which the controversy arose.

3. Next comes a statement of the question or questions the court is called upon to decide—the various "issues" (either of law or fact) which must be settled before a decision on the controversy can be reached. Any of you who have done any debating understand "issues"—the breaking up of a general problem into specific subproblems. Some judges are very careful to state the issues clearly; others will leave them to inference from the discussion, or else wander around from one thing to another and leave the precise questions they are deciding in doubt.

4. After the issues comes the argument on them—a discussion of the pros and cons. This is where logic comes into play. You'll recall that there are two main types of logical reasoning—inductive and deductive. Inductive reasoning involves the *formulation* of general propositions from a consideration of specific problems or observations; deductive reasoning involves the *application* of a general proposition already formulated to some specific situation or problem so that a conclusion can be drawn as to it. In each case the court, having these definite and specific issues or problems to decide, decides or purports to decide them by first concluding what the general rule or proposition of law is as to this type of issue, and then deducing the decision on that issue from the general rule. If there happens to be a statute or constitutional provision prescribing a general rule as to questions like those involved in the case, the judge has his major premise and will devote his argument to a consideration of its scope and applicability to the issues in the case. If there is no statute or other prescribed general rule, the judge will try by induction to derive one from the decisions and opinions in previous cases involving issues similar to those in the present case, or from general principles of fairness, policy and common sense, and then apply it to the issues at hand and deduce his conclusion.

5. Finally, after the argument on all the issues (and sometimes a good deal of irrelevant argument and discussion), the judge states the *general* conclusion to be drawn therefrom, and winds up the opinion with a statement of the court's decision. For example: "Judgment affirmed;" "Judgment reversed;" "Case remanded;" "New trial ordered;" etc.

It is to be remembered, of course, that legal opinions do not all follow the same order and are not all cut from the same pattern. They are written by many different judges, each of whom has his own style of writing and his own particular method of presenting a legal argument. Some opinions are not as easy to understand as others and it would be erroneous to assume in reading them that they are all perfect. Courts frequently disagree as to the principles that ought to be applied in certain types of controversy and occasionally the same court will change its view as to the law on a particular point. In reading these cases, you are not trying to find *the* ultimate and perfect rule, you are trying to learn by *inductive* reasoning from what various courts have actually decided in particular cases the rules and principles most frequently applied and most likely to be applied by them in future cases of that type.

Now, having in mind what you can expect to find in the cases, and also the fact that they are not necessarily perfect and seldom embody an unchanging principle or universal truth, you are in a position to read them intelligently. It's not a bad idea, however, to adopt a systematic method of reading them. The following has proved effective, and you might try it as a starter.

First, get a clear picture of the controversy involved. Get all the facts and issues straight. Consider the following:

> What kind of an action it is,
> Who the parties were,
> What they did and what happened to them,
> Who brought the action, what he wanted, what the defence was,
> What happened in the lower court (if it's a case on appeal),
> How the case got to this court,
> Just what this court had to decide.

At this point stop for a moment. Look at the problem, first from the plaintiff's point of view, then from the defendant's. Ask yourself how *you* would decide it, what *you* think the decision ought to be. Compare this case with others you have studied on the same topic. What result do *they* indicate ought to be reached here. By doing this you put yourself in a better position to read the court's argument critically, and spot any fallacies in it. We are all somewhat prone to accept what we read in print as the Gospel, and this little device of considering the problem in your own mind *before* reading the court's argument is a rather effective means of keeping a critical attitude.

Now read the argument and the court's conclusions. Consider the various rules and propositions advanced on each issue and the reasons given for adopting them. See whether the conclusions drawn follow logically from those rules. Then ask yourself whether you agree with the court, and if not, why not. Consider also how the result in this case lines up with other similar cases you have studied.

In thus analyzing the court's argument and conclusions it is important to distinguish carefully between the rules and propositions of law *actually relied upon by the court* in deciding the *issues involved in the case* (these are called *"holdings"*) and other legal propositions and discussion which you may find in the opinion but which are *not relevant nor applicable to the issues before the court* (these are called *"dicta"*). When the case was before the court, counsel for the opposing parties probably availed themselves of the opportunity to prepare fully and present to the court their arguments pro and con *upon the issues involved in it,* and the court thus had the opportunity to consider all aspects of each issue, choose the better result and "hold" with that view. *Dicta,* however, not being relevant to the issues before the court, was probably not argued by counsel nor thoroughly considered by the court. It was not *necessary* to the decision of the case and the court may have stated it casually without considering all aspects of the problem. Courts in each jurisdiction regard their own prior "holdings" as creating *binding precedents* which they feel obliged to follow in later cases involving the same issues. This is called the doctrine of *stare decisis* and makes for stability and predictability in the law. *Dicta,* on the other hand, being casual and not a matter of *actual decision*, is *not* regarded as establishing law which will be binding on the court in a subsequent case. Thus, the former case containing the *dictum* is not a controlling "authority" on the question although it may be followed in later decisions.

You may find it very helpful, in picking out the important matters in the cases and in weeding out the irrelevant, to keep a pen or pencil handy and *underline* all statements of pertinent facts, issues, rules, etc. as you read. (Do this only *in your own casebooks*, however. *Do not deface books in the library or elsewhere which are for common use ! ! !* )

Finally, study carefully the *notes* the author has appended to the case. They contain a good deal of valuable information about other similar cases and frequently suggest problems and criticisms which might not occur to you. There is an increasing tendency among the authors of casebooks to put in more collateral matter along with the cases in order to clarify their significance. This matter is there for your benefit; take advantage of it!

If you adopt some such method as the above in reading your cases and acquire the habit of following it, you are much more likely to get an accurate understanding of each case and are much less apt to overlook some important detail. Furthermore, if you get out of each case all the things mentioned above, you can feel reasonably well *prepared* for class discussion or lecture.

# Appendix III

# Constitution of the United States

Adopted September 17, 1787
Effective March 4, 1789

We the people of the United States, in order to form a more perfect union, establish justice, insure domestic tranquillity, provide for the common defense, promote the general welfare, and secure the blessings of liberty to ourselves and our posterity, do ordain and establish this Constitution for the United States of America.

## ARTICLE I

SECTION 1. All legislative powers herein granted shall be vested in a Congress of the United States, which shall consist of a Senate and House of Representatives.

SECTION 2. 1. The House of Representatives shall be composed of members chosen every second year by the people of the several States, and the electors in each State shall have the qualifications requisite for electors of the most numerous branch of the State legislature.

2. No person shall be a representative who shall not have attained to the age of twenty-five years, and been seven years a citizen of the United States, and who shall not, when elected, be an inhabitant of that State in which he shall be chosen.

3. Representatives and direct taxes shall be apportioned among the several States which may be included within this Union, according to their respective numbers, which shall be determined by adding to the whole number of free persons, including those bound to service for a term of years, and excluding Indians not taxed, three fifths of all other persons. The actual enumeration shall be made within three years after the first meeting of the Congress of the United States, and within every subsequent term of ten years, in such manner as they shall by law direct. The number of representatives shall not exceed one for every thirty thousand, but each State shall have at least one representative; and until such enumeration shall be made, the State of New Hampshire shall be entitled to choose three, Massachusetts eight, Rhode Island and Providence Plantations one, Connecticut five, New York six, New Jersey four, Pennsylvania eight, Delaware one, Maryland six, Virginia ten, North Carolina five, South Carolina five, and Georgia three.

4. When vacancies happen in the representation from any State, the executive authority thereof shall issue writs of election to fill such vacancies.

5. The House of Representatives shall choose their speaker and other officers; and shall have the sole power of impeachment.

SECTION 3. 1. The Senate of the United States shall be composed of two senators from each State, chosen by the legislature thereof, for six years; and each senator shall have one vote.

2. Immediately after they shall be assembled in consequence of the first election, they shall be divided as equally as may be into three classes. The seats of the senators of the first class shall be vacated at the expiration of the second year, of the second class at the expiration of the fourth year, and of the third class at the expiration of the sixth year, so that one third may be chosen every second year; and if vacancies happen by resignation, or otherwise, during the recess of the legislature of any State, the executive thereof may make temporary appointments until the next meeting of the legislature, which shall then fill such vacancies.

3. No person shall be a senator who shall not have attained to the age of thirty years, and been nine years a citizen of the United States, and who shall not, when elected, be an inhabitant of that State for which he shall be chosen.

4. The Vice President of the United States shall be President of the Senate, but shall have no vote, unless they be equally divided.

5. The Senate shall choose their other officers, and also a president *pro tempore*, in the absence of the Vice President, or when he shall exercise the office of the President of the United States.

6. The Senate shall have the sole power to try all impeachments. When sitting for that purpose, they shall be on oath or affirmation. When the President of the United States is tried, the chief justice shall preside: and no person shall be convicted without the concurrence of two thirds of the members present.

7. Judgment in cases of impeachment shall not extend further than to removal from office, and disqualifications to hold and enjoy any office of honor, trust or profit under the United States: but the party convicted shall nevertheless be liable and subject to indictment, trial, judgment and punishment, according to law.

SECTION 4. 1. The times, places, and manner of holding elections for senators and representatives, shall be prescribed in each State by the legislature thereof; but the Congress may at any time by law make or alter such regulations, except as to the places of choosing senators.

2. The Congress shall assemble at least once in every year, and such meeting shall be on the first Monday in December, unless they shall by law appoint a different day.

SECTION 5. 1. Each House shall be the judge of the elections, returns and qualifications of its own members, and a majority of each shall constitute a quorum to do business; but a smaller number may adjourn from day to day, and may be authorized to compel the attendance of absent members, in such manner, and under such penalties as each House may provide.

2. Each House may determine the rules of its proceedings, punish its members for disorderly behavior, and, with the concurrence of two thirds, expel a member.

3. Each House shall keep a journal of its proceedings, and from time to time publish the same, excepting such parts as may in their judgment require secrecy; and the yeas and nays of the members of either House on any question shall, at the desire of one fifth of those present, be entered on the journal.

4. Neither House, during the session of Congress, shall, without the consent of the other, adjourn for more than three days, nor to any other place than that in which the two Houses shall be sitting.

SECTION 6. 1. The senators and representatives shall receive a compensation for their services, to be ascertained by law, and paid out of the Treasury of the United States. They shall in all cases, except treason, felony, and breach of the peace, be privileged from arrest during their attendance at the session of their respective Houses, and in going to and returning from the same; and for any speech or debate in either House, they shall not be questioned in any other place.

2. No senator or representative shall, during the time for which he was elected, be appointed to any civil office under the authority of the United States, which shall have been created, or the emoluments whereof shall have been increased during such time; and no person holding any office under the United States shall be a member of either House during his continuance in office.

SECTION 7. 1. All bills for raising revenue shall originate in the House of Representatives; but the Senate may propose or concur with amendments as on other bills.

2. Every bill which shall have passed the House of Representatives and the Senate, shall, before it becomes a law, be presented to the President of the United States; if he approves he shall sign it, but if not he shall return it, with his objections to that House in which it shall have originated, who shall enter the objections at large on their journal, and proceed to reconsider it. If after such reconsideration two thirds of that House shall agree to pass the bill, it shall be sent, together with the objections, to the other House, by which it shall likewise be reconsidered, and if approved by two thirds of that House, it shall become a law. But in all such cases the votes of both Houses shall be determined by yeas and nays, and the names of the persons voting for and against the bill shall be entered on the journal of each House respectively. If any bill shall not be returned by the President within ten days (Sundays excepted) after it shall have been presented to him, the same shall be a law, in like manner as if he had signed it, unless the Congress by their adjournment prevent its return, in which case it shall not be a law.

3. Every order, resolution, or vote to which the concurrence of the Senate and the House of Representatives may be necessary (except on a question of adjournment) shall be presented to the President of the United States; and before the same shall take effect, shall be approved by him, or being disapproved by him, shall be repassed by two thirds of the Senate and House of Representatives, according to the rules and limitations prescribed in the case of a bill.

SECTION 8. The Congress shall have the power

1. To lay and collect taxes, duties, imposts, and excises, to pay the debts and provide for the common defense and general welfare of the United States; but all duties, imposts, and excises shall be uniform throughout the United States;

2. To borrow money on the credit of the United States;

3. To regulate commerce with foreign nations, and among the several States, and with the Indian tribes;

4. To establish a uniform rule of naturalization, and uniform laws on the subject of bankruptcies throughout the United States;

5. To coin money, regulate the value thereof, and of foreign coin, and fix the standard of weights and measures;

6. To provide for the punishment of counterfeiting the securities and current coin of the United States;

7. To establish post offices and post roads;

8. To promote the progress of science and useful arts, by securing for limited times to authors and inventors the exclusive right to their respective writings and discoveries;

9. To constitute tribunals inferior to the Supreme Court;

10. To define and punish piracies and felonies committed on the high seas, and offenses against the law of nations;

11. To declare war, grant letters of marque and reprisal, and make rules concerning captures on land and water;

12. To raise and support armies, but no appropriation of money to that use shall be for a longer term than two years;

13. To provide and maintain a navy;

14. To make rules for the government and regulation of the land and naval forces;

15. To provide for calling forth the militia to execute the laws of the Union, suppress insurrections and repel invasions;

16. To provide for organizing, arming, and disciplining the militia, and for governing such part of them as may be employed in the service of the United States, reserving to the States respectively, the appointment of the officers, and the authority of training the militia according to the discipline prescribed by Congress;

17. To exercise exclusive legislation in all cases whatsoever, over such district (not exceeding ten miles square) as may, by cession of particular States, and the acceptance of Congress, become the seat of the government of the United States, and to exercise like authority over all places purchased by the consent of the legislature of the State in which the same shall be, for the erection of forts, magazines, arsenals, dockyards, and other needful buildings; and

18. To make all laws which shall be necessary and proper for carrying into execution the foregoing powers, and all other powers vested by this Constitution in the government of the United States, or in any department or officer thereof.

SECTION 9. 1. The migration or importation of such persons as any of the States now existing shall think proper to admit, shall not be prohibited by the Congress prior to the year one thousand eight hundred and eight, but a tax or duty may be imposed on such importation, not exceeding ten dollars for each person.

2. The privilege of the writ of *habeas corpus* shall not be suspended, unless when in cases of rebellion or invasion the public safety may require it.

3. No bill of attainder or *ex post facto* law shall be passed.

4. No capitation, or other direct, tax shall be laid, unless in proportion to the census or enumeration hereinbefore directed to be taken.

5. No tax or duty shall be laid on articles exported from any State.

6. No preference shall be given by any regulation of commerce or revenue to the ports of one State over those of another: nor shall vessels bound to, or from, one State be obliged to enter, clear, or pay duties in another.

7. No money shall be drawn from the treasury, but in consequence of appropriations made by law; and a regular statement and account of the receipts and expenditures of all public money shall be published from time to time.

8. No title of nobility shall be granted by the United States: and no person holding any office of profit or trust under them, shall, without the consent of the Congress, accept of any present, emolument, office, or title, of any kind whatever, from any king, prince, or foreign State.

Section 10. 1. No State shall enter into any treaty, alliance, or confederation; grant letters of marque and reprisal; coin money; emit bills of credit; make anything but gold and silver coin a tender in payment of debts; pass any bill of attainder, *ex post facto law*, or law impairing the obligation of contracts, or grant any title of nobility.

2. No State shall, without the consent of the Congress, lay any imposts or duties on imports or exports, except what may be absolutely necessary for executing its inspection laws; and the net produce of all duties and imposts laid by any State on imports or exports, shall be for the use of the treasury of the United States; and all such laws shall be subject to the revision and control of the Congress.

3. No State shall, without the consent of the Congress, lay any duty of tonnage, keep troops, or ships of war in time of peace, enter into any agreement or compact with another State, or with a foreign power, or engage in war, unless actually invaded, or in such imminent danger as will not admit of delay.

## ARTICLE II

Section 1. 1. The executive power shall be vested in a President of the United States of America. He shall hold his office during the term of four years, and, together with the Vice President, chosen for the same term, be elected as follows:

2. Each State shall appoint, in such manner as the legislature thereof may direct, a number of electors, equal to the whole number of senators and representatives to which the State may be entitled in the Congress: but no senator or representative, or person holding an office of trust or profit under the United States, shall be appointed an elector.

The electors shall meet in their respective States, and vote by ballot for two persons, of whom one at least shall not be an inhabitant of the same State with themselves. And they shall make a list of all the persons voted for, and of the number of votes for each; which list they shall sign and certify, and transmit sealed to the seat of the government of the United States, directed to the president of the Senate. The president of the Senate shall, in the presence of the Senate and House of Representatives, open all the certificates, and the votes shall then be counted. The person having the greatest number of votes shall be the President, if such a number be a majority of the whole number of electors appointed; and if there be more than one who have such majority, and have an equal number of votes, then the House of Representatives shall immediately choose by ballot one of them for President; and if no person have a majority, then from the five highest on the list the said House shall in like manner choose the President. But in choosing the President, the votes shall be taken by States, the representation from each State having one vote; a quorum for this purpose shall consist of a member or members from two thirds of the States, and a majority of all the States shall be necessary to a choice. In every case, after the choice of the President, the person having the greatest number of votes of the electors shall be the Vice President. But if there should remain two or more who have equal votes, the Senate shall choose from them by ballot the Vice President.

3. The Congress may determine the time of choosing the electors, and the day on which they shall give their votes; which day shall be the same throughout the United States.

4. No person except a natural born citizen, or a citizen of the United States, at the time of the adoption of this Constitution, shall be eligible to the office of President; neither shall any person be eligible to that office who shall not have attained to the age of thirtyfive years, and been fourteen years a resident within the United States.

5. In case of the removal of the President from office, or of his death, resignation, or inability to discharge the powers and duties of the said office, the same shall devolve on the Vice President, and the Congress may by law provide for the case of removal, death, resignation, or inability, both of the President and Vice President, declaring what officer shall then act as President, and such officer shall act accordingly, until the disability be removed, or a President shall be elected.

6. The President shall, at stated times, receive for his services a compensation, which shall neither be increased nor diminished during the period for which he shall have been elected, and he shall not receive within that period any other emolument from the United States, or any of them.

7. Before he enter on the execution of his office, he shall take the following oath or affirmation:—"I do solemnly swear (or affirm) that I will faithfully execute the office of President of the United States, and will to the best of my ability, preserve, protect and defend the Constitution of the United States."

SECTION 2. 1. The President shall be commander in chief of the army and navy of the United States, and of the militia of the several States, when called into the actual service of the United States; he may require the opinion, in writing, of the principal officer in each of the executive departments, upon any subject relating to the duties of their respective offices, and he shall have power to grant reprieves and pardons for offenses against the United States, except in cases of impeachment.

2. He shall have power, by and with the advice and consent of the Senate, to make treaties, provided two thirds of the senators present concur; and he shall nominate, and by and with the advice and consent of the Senate, shall appoint ambassadors, other public ministers and consuls, judges of the Supreme Court, and all other officers of the United States, whose appointments are not herein otherwise provided for, and which shall be established by law: but the Congress may by law vest the appointment of such inferior officers, as they think proper, in the President alone, in the courts of law, or in the heads of departments.

3. The President shall have power to fill up all vacancies that may happen during the recess of the Senate, by granting commissions which shall expire at the end of their next session.

SECTION 3. He shall from time to time give to the Congress information of the state of the Union, and recommend to their consideration such measures as he shall judge necessary and expedient; he may, on extraordinary occasions, convenue both Houses, or either of them, and in case of disagreement between them with respect to the time of adjournment, he may adjourn them to such time as he shall think proper; he shall receive ambassadors and other public ministers; he shall take care that the laws be faithfully executed, and shall commission all the officers of the United States.

SECTION 4. The President, Vice President, and all civil officers of the United States, shall be removed from office on impeachment for, and conviction of, treason, bribery, or other high crimes and misdemeanors.

## ARTICLE III

SECTION 1. The judicial power of the United States shall be vested in one Supreme Court, and in such inferior courts as the Congress may from time to time ordain and establish. The judges, both of the Supreme and inferior courts, shall hold their offices during good behavior, and shall, at stated times, receive for their services, a compensation, which shall not be diminished during their continuance in office.

SECTION 2. 1. The judicial power shall extend to all cases, in law and equity, arising under this Constitution, the laws of the United States, and treaties made, or which shall be made, under their authority;—to all cases affecting ambassadors, other public ministers and consuls;—to all cases of admiralty and maritime jurisdiction;—to controversies to which the United States shall be a party;—to controversies between two or more States;—between a State and citizens of another State;—between citizens of different States;—between citizens of the same State claiming lands under grants of different States, and between a State, or the citizens thereof, and foreign States, citizens or subjects.

2. In all cases affecting ambassadors, other public ministers and consuls, and those in which a State shall be party, the Supreme Court shall have original juris-

diction. In all the other cases before mentioned, the Supreme Court shall have appellate jurisdiction, both as to law and to fact, with such exceptions, and under such regulations as the Congress shall make.

3. The trial of all crimes, except in cases of impeachment, shall be by jury; and such trial shall be held in the State where the said crimes shall have been committed; but when not committed within any State, the trial shall be at such place or places as the Congress may by law have directed.

SECTION 3. 1. Treason against the United States shall consist only in levying war against them, or in adhering to their enemies, giving them aid and comfort. No personal shall be convicted of treason unless on the testimony of two witnesses to the same overt act, or on confession in open court.

2. The Congress shall have power to declare the punishment of treason, but no attainder of treason shall work corruption of blood, or forfeiture except during the life of the person attained.

## ARTICLE IV

SECTION 1. Full faith and credit shall be given in each State to the public acts, records, and judicial proceedings of every other State. And the Congress may by general laws prescribe the manner in which such acts, records and proceedings shall be proved, and the effect thereof.

SECTION 2. 1. The citizens of each State shall be entitled to all privileges and immunities of citizens in the several States.

2. A person charged in any state with treason, felony, or other crime, who shall flee from justice, and be found in another State, shall on demand of the executive authority of the State from which he fled, be delivered up to be removed to the State having jurisdiction of the crime.

3. No person held to service or labor in one State under the laws thereof, escaping into another, shall, in consequence of any law or regulation therein, be discharged from such service or labor, but shall be delivered up on claim of the party to whom such service or labor may be due.

SECTION 3. 1. New States may be admitted by the Congress into this Union; but no new State shall be formed or erected within the jurisdiction of any other State; nor any State be formed by the junction of two or more States, or parts of States, without the consent of the legislatures of the States concerned as well as of the Congress.

2. The Congress shall have power to dispose of and make all needful rules and regulations respecting the territory or other property belonging to the United States; and nothing in this Constitution shall be so construed as to prejudice any claims of the United States, or of any particular State.

SECTION 4. The United States shall guarantee to every State in this Union a republican form of government, and shall protect each of them against invasion; and on application of the legislature, or of the executive (when the legislature cannot be convened) against domestic violence.

## ARTICLE V

The Congress, whenever two thirds of both Houses shall deem it necessary, shall propose amendments to this Constitution, or, on the application of the legislatures of two thirds of the several States, shall call a convention for proposing amendments, which in either case, shall be valid to all intents and purposes, as part of this Constitution when ratified by the legislatures of three fourths of the several States, or by conventions in three fourths thereof, as the one or the other mode of ratification may be proposed by the Congress; Provided that no amendment which may be made prior to the year one thousand eight hundred and eight shall in any manner affect the first and fourth clauses in the ninth section of the first article; and that no State, without its consent, shall be deprived of its equal suffrage in the Senate.

## ARTICLE VI

1. All debts contracted and engagements entered into, before the adoption of this Constitution, shall be as valid against the United States under this Constitution, as under the Confederation.

2. This Constitution, and the laws of the United States which shall be made in pursuance thereof; and all treaties made, or which shall be made, under the authority of the United States, shall be the supreme law of the land; and the Judges in every State shall be bound thereby, anything in the Constitution or laws of any State to the contrary notwithstanding.

3. The senators and representatives before mentioned, and the members of the several State legislatures, and all executive and judicial offices, both of the United States and of the several States, shall be bound by oath or affirmation to support this Constitution; but no religious test shall ever be required as a qualification to any office or public trust under the United States.

## ARTICLE VII

The ratification of the conventions of nine States shall be sufficient for the establishment of this Constitution between the States so ratifying the same.

Done in Convention by the unanimous consent of the States present the seventeenth day of September in the year of our Lord one thousand seven hundred and eighty-seven, and of the independence of the United States of America the twelfth. In witness whereof we have hereunto subscribed our names. [Names omitted]

Articles in addition to, and amendment of, the Constitution of the United States of America, proposed by Congress, and ratified by the legislatures of the several States pursuant to the fifth article of the original Constitution.

# Amendments

First Ten Amendments passed by Congress Sept. 25, 1789
Ratified by three-fourths of the States December 15, 1791

## ARTICLE I

Congress shall make no law respecting an establishment of religion, or prohibiting the free exercise thereof; or abridging the freedom of speech, or of the press; or the right of the people peaceably to assemble, and to petition the government for a redress of grievances.

## ARTICLE II

A well regulated militia, being necessary to the security of a free State, the right of the people to keep and bear arms, shall not be infringed.

## ARTICLE III

No soldier shall, in time of peace be quartered in any house, without the consent of the owner, nor in time of war, but in a manner to be prescribed by law.

## ARTICLE IV

The right of the people to be secure in their persons, houses, papers, and effects, against unreasonable searches and seizures, shall not be violated, and no warrants shall issue, but upon probable cause, supported by oath or affirmation, and particularly describing the place to be searched, and the persons or things to be seized.

## ARTICLE V

No person shall be held to answer for a capital, or otherwise infamous crime, unless on a presentment or indictment of a grand jury, except in cases arising in the land or naval forces, or in the militia, when in actual service in time of war or public danger; nor shall any person be subject for the same offense to be twice put in jeopardy of life or limb; nor shall be compelled in any criminal case to be a witness against himself, nor be deprived of life, liberty, or property, without due process of law; nor shall private property be taken for public use without just compensation.

## ARTICLE VI

In all criminal prosecutions, the accused shall enjoy the right to a speedy and public trial, by an impartial jury of the State and district wherein the crime shall have been committed, which district shall have been previously ascertained by law, and to be informed of the nature and cause of the accusation; to be confronted with the witnesses against him; to have compulsory process for obtaining witnesses in his favor, and to have the assistance of counsel for his defense.

## ARTICLE VII

In suits at common law, where the value in controversy shall exceed twenty dollars, the right of trial by jury shall be preserved, and no fact tried by a jury shall be otherwise reexamined in any court of the United States, than according to the rules of the common law.

## ARTICLE VIII

Excessive bail shall not be required, nor excessive fines imposed, nor cruel and unusual punishments inflicted.

## ARTICLE IX

The enumeration in the Constitution of certain rights shall not be construed to deny or disparage others retained by the people.

## ARTICLE X

The powers not delegated to the United States by the Constitution, nor prohibited by it to the States, are reserved to the States respectively, or to the people.

## ARTICLE XI

Passed by Congress March 5, 1794
Ratified January 8, 1798

The judicial power of the United States shall not be construed to extend to any suit in law or equity, commenced or prosecuted against one of the United States by citizens of another State, or by citizens or subjects of any foreign State.

## ARTICLE XII

Passed by Congress December 12, 1803
Ratified September 25, 1804

The electors shall meet in their respective States, and vote by ballot for President and Vice President, one of whom, at least, shall not be an inhabitant of the same State with themselves; they shall name in their ballots the person voted for as President, and in distinct ballots, the person voted for as Vice President, and they shall make distinct lists of all persons voted for as President and of all persons voted for as Vice President, and of the number of votes for each, which lists they shall sign and certify, and transmit sealed to the seat of the government of the United States, directed to the President of the Senate;—The President of the Senate shall, in the presence of the Senate and House of Representatives, open all the certificates and the votes shall then be counted;—The person having the greatest number of votes for President, shall be the President, if such number be a majority of the whole number of electors appointed; and if no person have such majority, then from the persons having the highest numbers not exceeding three on the list of those voted for as President, the House of Representatives shall choose immediately, by ballot, the President. But in choosing the President, the votes shall be taken by States, the representation from each State having one vote; a quorum for this purpose shall consist of a member or members from two thirds of the States, and a majority of all the States shall be necessary to a choice. And if the House of Representatives shall not choose a President whenever the right of choice shall devolve upon them, before the fourth day of March next following, then the Vice President shall act as President, as in the case of the death or other constitutional disability of the President. The person having the greatest number of votes as Vice President shall be the Vice President, if such number be a majority of the whole number of electors appointed, and if no person have a majority, then from the two highest numbers on the list, the Senate shall choose the Vice President; a quorum for the purpose shall consist of two thirds of the whole number of Senators, and a majority of the whole number shall be necessary to a choice. But no person constitutionally ineligible to the office of President shall be eligible to that of Vice President of the United States.

## ARTICLE XIII

Passed by Congress February 1, 1865
Ratified December 18, 1865

SECTION 1. Neither slavery nor involuntary servitude, except as punishment for crime whereof the party shall have been duly convicted, shall exist within the United States, or any place subject to their jurisdiction.

SECTION 2. Congress shall have power to enforce this article by appropriate legislation.

## ARTICLE XIV

Passed by Congress June 16, 1866
Ratified July 23, 1868

SECTION 1. All persons born or naturalized in the United States, and subject to the jurisdiction thereof, are citizens of the United States and of the State wherein they reside. No State shall make or enforce any law which shall abridge the privileges or immunities of citizens of the United States; nor shall any State deprive any person of life, liberty, or property, without due process of law; nor deny to any person within its jurisdiction the equal protection of the laws.

SECTION 2. Representatives shall be apportioned among the several States according to their respective numbers, counting the whole number of persons in each State, excluding Indians not taxed. But when the right to vote at any election for the choice of electors for President and Vice President of the United States, representatives in Congress, the executive and judicial officers of a State, or the members of the legislature thereof, is denied to any of the male inhabitants of such State, being twenty-one years of age, and citizens of the United States, or in any way abridged, except for participation in rebellion, or other crime, the basis of representation therein shall be reduced in the proportion which the number of such male citizens shall bear to the whole number of male citizens twenty-one years of age in such State.

SECTION 3. No person shall be a senator or representative in Congress, or elector of President and Vice President, or hold any office, civil or military, under the United States, or under any State, who having previously taken an oath, as a member of Congress, or as an officer of the United States, or as a member of any State legislature, or as an executive or judicial officer of any State, to support the Constitution of the United States, shall have engaged in insurrection or rebellion against the same, or given aid or comfort to the enemies thereof. But Congress may by a vote of two thirds of each House, remove such disability.

SECTION 4. The validity of the public debt of the United States, authorized by law, including debts incurred for payment of pensions and bounties for services in suppressing insurrection or rebellion, shall not be questioned. But neither the United States nor any State shall assume or pay any debt or obligation incurred in aid of insurrection or rebellion against the United States, or any claim for the loss or emancipation of any slave; but all such debts, obligations, and claims shall be held illegal and void.

SECTION 5. The Congress shall have power to enforce, by appropriate legislation, the provisions of this article.

## ARTICLE XV

Passed by Congress February 27, 1869
Ratified March 30, 1870

SECTION 1. The right of citizens of the United States to vote shall not be denied or abridged by the United States or by any State on account of race, color, or previous condition of servitude.

SECTION 2. The Congress shall have power to enforce this article by appropriate legislation.

# ARTICLE XVI

Passed by Congress July 12, 1909
Ratified February 25, 1913

The Congress shall have power to lay and collect taxes on incomes, from whatever source derived, without apportionment among the several States, and without regard to any census or enumeration.

# ARTICLE XVII

Passed by Congress May 16, 1912
Ratified May 31, 1913

The Senate of the United States shall be composed of two senators from each state, elected by the people thereof, for six years; and each senator shall have one vote. The electors in each State shall have the qualifications requisite for electors of the most numerous branch of the State legislature.

When vacancies happen in the representation of any State in the Senate, the executive authority of such State shall issue writs of election to fill such vacancies: *Provided*, That the legislature of any State may empower the executive thereof to make temporary appointments until the people fill the vacancies by election as the legislature may direct.

This amendment shall not be so construed as to affect the election or term of any senator chosen before it becomes valid as part of the Constitution.

# ARTICLE XVIII

Passed by Congress December 17, 1917
Ratified January 29, 1919

After one year from the ratification of this article, the manufacture, sale, or transportation of intoxicating liquors within, the importation thereof into, or the exportation thereof from the United States and all territory subject to the jurisdiction thereof for beverage purposes is hereby prohibited.

The Congress and the several States shall have concurrent power to enforce this article by appropriate legislation.

This article shall be inoperative unless it shall have been ratified as an amendment to the Constitution by the legislatures of the several States, as provided in the Constitution, within seven years from the date of the submission hereof to the states by Congress.

# ARTICLE XIX

Passed by Congress June 5, 1919
Ratified August 26, 1920

The right of citizens of the United States to vote shall not be denied or abridged by the United States or by any State on account of sex.

The Congress shall have power by appropriate legislation to enforce the provisions of this article.

## ARTICLE XX

Passed by Congress March 3, 1932
Ratified January 23, 1933

SECTION 1. The terms of the President and Vice President shall end at noon on the 20th day of January, and the terms of Senators and Representatives at noon on the 3d day of January, of the years in which such terms would have ended if this article had not been ratified; and the terms of their successors shall then begin.

SECTION 2. The Congress shall assemble at least once in every year, and such meeting shall begin at noon on the 3d day of January, unless they shall by law appoint a different day.

SECTION 3. If, at the time fixed for the beginning of the term of the President, the President-elect shall have died, the Vice President-elect shall become President. If a President shall not have been chosen before the time fixed for the beginning of his term, or if the President-elect shall have failed to qualify, then the Vice President-elect shall act as President until a President shall have qualified; and the Congress may by law provide for the case wherein neither a President-elect nor a Vice President-elect shall have qualified, declaring who shall then act as President, or the manner in which one who is to act shall be selected, and such person shall act accordingly until a President or Vice President shall have qualified.

SECTION 4. The Congress may by law provide for the case of the death of any of the persons from whom the House of Representatives may choose a President whenever the right of choice shall have devolved upon them, and for the case of the death of any of the persons from whom the Senate may choose a Vice President whenever the right of choice shall have devolved upon them.

SECTION 5. Sections 1 and 2 shall take effect on the 15th day of October following the ratification of this article.

SECTION 6. This article shall be inoperative unless it shall have been ratified as an amendment to the Constitution by the legislatures of three-fourths of the several States within seven years from the date of its submission.

## ARTICLE XXI

Passed by Congress February 20, 1933
Ratified December 5, 1933

SECTION 1. The Eighteenth Article of amendment to the Constitution of the United States is hereby repealed.

SECTION 2. The transportion or importation into any State, Territory, or possession of the United States for delivery or use therein of intoxicating liquors in violation of the laws thereof, is hereby prohibited.

SECTION 3. This article shall be inoperative unless it shall have been ratified as an amendment to the Constitution by conventions in the several States, as provided in the Constitution, within seven years from the date of the submission thereof to the States by the Congress.

## ARTICLE XXII

Passed by Congress March 12, 1947
Ratified February 26, 1951

No person shall be elected to the office of the President more than twice, and no person who has held the office of President, or acted as President, for more than two years of a term to which some other person was elected President shall be elected to the office of the President more than once.

But this article shall not apply to any person holding the office of President when this article was proposed by the Congress, and shall not prevent any person who may be holding the office of President, or acting as President, during the term within which this article becomes operative from holding the office of President or acting as President during the remainder of such term.

This article shall be inoperative unless it shall have been ratified as an amendment to the Constitution by the legislatures of three-fourths of the several states within seven years from the date of its submission to the states by the Congress.

## ARTICLE XXIII

Passed by Congress June 16, 1960
Ratified March 30, 1961

SECTION 1. The District constituting the seat of Government of the United States shall appoint in such manner as the Congress may direct:

A number of electors of President and Vice President equal to the whole number of Senators and Representatives in Congress to which the District would be entitled if it were a State, but in no event more than the least populous State; they shall be in addition to those appointed by the States, but they shall be considered, for the purposes of the election of President and Vice President, to be electors appointed by a State; and they shall meet in the District and perform such duties as provided by the twelfth article of amendment.

SECTION 2. The Congress shall have power to enforce this article by appropriate legislation.

## ARTICLE XXIV

Passed by Congress August 27, 1962
Ratified January 23, 1964

SECTION 1. The right of citizens of the United States to vote in any primary or other election for President or Vice President, for electors for President or Vice President, or for Senator or Representative in Congress, shall not be denied or abridged by the United States or any State by reason of failure to pay any poll tax or other tax.

SECTION 2. The Congress shall have power to enforce this article by appropriate legislation.

## ARTICLE XXV

Passed by Congress July 6, 1965
Ratified February 15, 1967

SECTION 1. In case of the removal of the President from office or of his death or resignation, the Vice President shall become President.

SECTION 2. Whenever there is a vacancy in the office of the Vice President, the President shall nominate a Vice President who shall take office upon confirmation by a majority vote of both Houses of Congress.

SECTION 3. Whenever the President transmits to the President pro tempore of the Senate and the Speaker of the House of Representatives his written declaration that he is unable to discharge the powers and duties of his office, and until he transmits to them a written declaration to the contrary, such powers and duties shall be discharged by the Vice President as Acting President.

SECTION 4. Whenever the Vice President and a majority of either the principal officers of the executive departments or of such other body as Congress may by law provide, transmit to the President pro tempore of the Senate and the Speaker of the House of Representatives their written declaration that the President is unable to discharge the powers and duties of his office, the Vice President shall immediately assume the powers and duties of the office as Acting President.

Thereafter, when the President transmits to the President pro tempore of the Senate and the Speaker of the House of Representatives his written declaration that no inability exists, he shall resume the powers and duties of his office unless the Vice President and a majority of either the principal officers of the executive department or of such other body as Congress may by law provide, transmit within four days to the President pro tempore of the Senate and the Speaker of the House of Representatives their written declaration that the President is unable to discharge the powers and duties of his office. Thereupon Congress shall decide the issue, assembling within forty-eight hours for that purpose if not in session. If the Congress, within twenty-one days after receipt of the latter written declaration, or, if Congress is not in session, within twenty-one days after Congress is required to assemble, determines by two-thirds vote of both Houses that the President is unable to discharge the powers and duties of his office, the Vice President shall continue to discharge the same as Acting President; otherwise, the President shall resume the powers and duties of his office.

# Appendix IV

# The Code for Nurses with Interpretive Statements

## INTRODUCTION

The development of a code of ethics is an essential characteristic of a profession, and provides one means whereby professional standards may be established, maintained, and improved. A code indicates a profession's acceptance of the responsibility and trust with which it has been invested. Each practitioner, upon entering a profession, inherits a measure of that responsibility and trust and the corresponding obligation to adhere to standards of ethical practice and conduct set by the profession.

*The Code for Nurses*, adopted by the American Nurses' Association in 1950 and revised in 1960 and 1968, is intended to serve the individual practitioner as a guide to the ethical principles that should govern her nursing practice, conduct, and relationships. The *Code* and the accompanying interpretive statements clarify the essential areas in which definite standards of practice and conduct are seen as essential to the full and ethical discharge of the nurse's responsibility to the public, to other groups with whom she may be associated, and to the profession of which she is a member. Each nurse has an obligation to uphold and adhere to the *Code* in her individual practice and to ensure that her colleagues do likewise.

Guidance and assistance in implementing the *Code* in local situations may be obtained from committees or councils on nursing practice of State Nurses Associations. Further information about the *Code* and its interpretation may be obtained from the ANA Nursing Practice Department.

## THE CODE FOR NURSES

1. The nurse provides services with respect for the dignity of man, unrestricted by considerations of nationality, race, creed, color, or status.

2. The nurse safeguards the individual's right to privacy by judiciously protecting information of a confidential nature, sharing only that information relevant to his care.

3. The nurse maintains individual competence in nursing practice, recognizing and accepting responsibility for individual actions and judgments.

4. The nurse acts to safeguard the patient when his care and safety are affected by incompetent, unethical, or illegal conduct of any person.

468

5. The nurse uses individual competence as a criterion in accepting delegated responsibilities and assigning nursing activities to others.

6. The nurse participates in research activities when assured that the rights of individual subjects are protected.

7. The nurse participates in the efforts of the profession to define and upgrade standards of nursing practice and education.

8. The nurse, acting through the professional organization, participates in establishing and maintaining conditions of employment conducive to high-quality nursing care.

9. The nurse works with members of health professions and other citizens in promoting efforts to meet health needs of the public.

10. The nurse refuses to give or imply endorsement to advertising, promotion, or sales for commercial products, services, or enterprises.

## [Interpretative Statements]

1. The nurse provides services with respect for the dignity of man, unrestricted by considerations of nationality, race, creed, color, or status.

The need for nursing care is universal, cutting across all national, ethnic, religious, cultural and economic differences, as does nursing's response to this fundamental human need. Whoever the individual and whatever his background and circumstances, his nursing care should be determined solely by his needs as a unique human being. Individual differences in background, customs, attitudes, and beliefs influence nursing practice only insofar as they represent factors that the nurse must understand, consider, and respect in tailoring care to personal needs and in maintaining the individual's self-respect and dignity. In whatever employment setting she may be, the nurse herself should adhere to this principle of nondiscriminatory, nonprejudical care and endeavor to promote its acceptance by others.

The nurse's respect for the worth and dignity of the individual human being extends throughout the entire life cycle, from birth to death, and is reflected in her care of the defective as well as the normal, the patient with a longterm in contrast to an acute illness, the young and the old, the recovering patient as well as the one who is terminally ill or dying. In the latter instance the nurse should use all the measures at her command to enable the patient to live out his days with as much comfort, dignity, and freedom from anxiety and pain as possible. His nursing care will determine, to a great degree, how he lives this final human experience and the peace and dignity with which he approaches death.

2. The nurse safeguards the individual's right to privacy by judiciously protecting information of a confidential nature, sharing only that information relevant to his care.

The nurse has a clear obligation to safeguard any confidential information about the patient that she may acquire from the patient himself or from any other source. The nurse-patient relationship is built on trust; this relationship could be destroyed and the patient's welfare and reputation jeopardized by the nurse's injudicious disclosure of confidential information.

In some instances, however, knowledge gained in confidence is relevant or essential in planning the patient's care. Under these circumstances, and guided by her professional judgment, the nurse may share the pertinent information with others who are directly concerned with the patient's care. But she discloses only the information relevant to the patient's welfare, and only to those who are responsible for maintaining and promoting it. The rights, well-being, and safety of the individual patient should be the determining factors in the decision to share this information.

Occasionally, the nurse may be obligated to give testimony in court in relation to confidential information about a patient. Under these circumstances, she should obtain legal counsel before testifying in order to be fully informed as to her rights and responsibilities in relation to both her patient and herself.

3. The nurse maintains individual competence in nursing practice, recognizing and accepting responsibility for individual actions and judgments.

The nature of nursing is such that inadequate or incompetent practice could result in the loss of health or even the life of the patient. Therefore, the maintenance of competence in practice is the personal responsibility of each individual practitioner. Over and above the moral obligation this imposes on the individual nurse, she can be held legally responsible—in the event of injury to a patient—if it is proved that she has failed to carry out the actions or to exercise the judgment that is considered standard nursing practice within the particular area and at the time of the injury. Neither physician's orders nor the employing agency's policies relieve the nurse of responsibility for her own nursing actions or judgments.

Competence is a relative term; and an individual's competence in any field may be diminished or otherwise affected by the passage of time and the emergence of new knowledge. This means that for the patient's optimum well-being and for the nurse's own professional development, her nursing care should reflect and incorporate new techniques and knowledge in health care as these develop, and especially as they relate to her particular field of practice.

Nursing knowledge, like that in the other health disciplines, is rendered rapidly obsolete by mounting technological and scientific advances, changing concepts and patterns in the provision of health services, and increasingly complex nursing responsibilities. The nurse must therefore be aware of the need for continuous updating and expansion of the body of knowledge on which her practice is based, and must keep her knowledge and skills current by whatever means are appropriate and available to her: inservice education, academic study, professional reading, conferences, workshops, and the like. Only by such continuing infusion of new knowledge and skills into her practice can the nurse maintain her individual competence and provide nursing care of high quality to the public.

4. The nurse acts to safeguard the patient when his care and safety are affected by incompetent, unethical, or illegal conduct of any person.

Inasmuch as the nurse's primary commitment is to the patient's care and safety, she must be alert to, and take appropriate action regarding, any instances of incompetent, unethical, or illegal practice by any member of the health care team, or any action on the part of others that is prejudicial to the patient's best interests.

"Appropriate action" may take the form of expressing her concern to the person carrying out the questionable practice and calling attention to the possible detrimental effect upon the patient's welfare. If indicated, the practice should be reported to the appropriate authority within the institutional or agency setting. It is highly desirable that there be an established mechanism for the reporting and handling of incompetent, unethical or illegal practice within the employment setting, so that such reporting can go through official channels and be done without fear of reprisal.

When incompetent, unethical, or illegal practice on the part of anyone concerned with the patient's care (nurses, ancillary workers, technical specialists, or members of other professional disciplines, for instance) is not corrected within the employment setting and continues to jeopardize the patient's care and safety, additional steps need to be taken. It should be reported to such other appropriate authorities as the practice committees of the various professional organizations, or the legally constituted bodies concerned with licensing of specific categories of health workers or professional practitioners. Some situations may warrant the concern and involvement of all these groups.

Reporting should be both factual and objective, and the nurse should be fully aware of the state laws governing practice in the health care field and of the employing institution's policies in relation to incompetent, unethical, or illegal practice. Whenever a practice threatens the patient's health, welfare, or safety, the nurse has no choice but to take appropriate action in his behalf.

5. The nurse uses individual competence as a criterion in accepting delegated responsibilities and assigning nursing activities to others.

Because of the increased complexity of health care, changing patterns in the delivery of health services, and continuing shortages in skilled health manpower, nurses are being requested or expected to carry out functions that have formerly been performed by physicians. In turn, nurses are assigning some former registered nurse functions to variously prepared ancillary personnel. In this gradual shift of functions, the nurse is the "middle man." It is fully as important that she exercise judgment in accepting responsibilities as in assigning responsibilities to others.

Medical and nursing practice acts are usually expressed in broad and general terms, and offer little guidance, direction, or protection to the nurse in relation to her acceptance or performance of specific delegated medical functions. A recognition by nurses of the need for a more definitive delineation of medical and nursing roles and responsibilities has resulted in collaborative efforts on the part of the official nursing, hospital, and medical organizations to develop joint policy statements. These statements specify the functions that are agreed upon as appropriate and proper for the nurse to perform. They include the circumstances under which she should and should not carry out these functions, and the required preparation in the skills and judgments necessary to perform the functions. Such statements represent a body of expert judgment that can be used as authority where responsibilities are not definitively outlined by legal statute. Similar formulations have been developed and made official policy within many individual health care agencies and institutions.

The nurse should look to such mutually agreed-upon policy statements for guidance and direction; but even where such statements exist, the individual nurse should also assess her personal competence carefully before accepting these responsibilities. If she does not consider herself competent or adequately prepared to carry out a specific function, she should feel free, without fear of censure, to refuse to do so; in so doing, she protects both the patient and herself.

The reverse of the coin is also true. The nurse should not accept delegated responsibilities that do not utilize her nursing skills and competencies or that prevent her from providing needed nursing care to patients.

Inasmuch as the nurse is responsible for the patient's total nursing care, she must also assess individual competence in assigning selected components of that care to other nursing service personnel. The nurse should not delegate to any member of the nursing team a function which that person has not been prepared for or is not qualified to perform.

Concern for the patient's welfare and safety is the nurse's primary consideration in both accepting and assigning these various responsibilities. Decisions in this area call for knowledge of, and adherence to, the joint policy statements and to the laws regulating medical and nursing practice, as well as for the exercise of informed, professional nursing judgment.

6. The nurse participates in research activities when assured that the rights of individual subjects are protected.

Nurses today find themselves increasingly involved in research activities, as members of many disciplines, including nursing, search for improved methods of patient care and treatment. Generally speaking, nurses in the research setting assume one of two roles: that of investigator, including membership on a research team; or that of practitioner, giving care to patients serving as subjects in a research study. The latter role may call for specified nursing performance as part of the research design and/or the gathering or reporting of specific data.

This item in the *Code* focuses on the role of the nurse as a practitioner in a research setting as guidelines for the nurse investigator have been delineated in the ANA publication *The Nurse in Research: ANA Guidelines on Ethical Values.*

The nurse practitioner is, first of all, responsible for rendering quality nursing to all patients entrusted to her care. Implicit in this care is the protection of the individual's rights as outlined in the above publication: privacy, self-determination, conservation of personal resources, freedom from arbitrary hurt and intrinsic risk of injury, and the special rights of minors and incompetent persons. While the research investigator assumes primary responsibility for the preservation of these rights, the individual nurse practitioner within the research setting should also be aware of them and of her share in this responsibility.

Research projects may call for specific observations, treatments, or care procedures that represent variations from the usual. The nurse participates in such research or experimental activity only with the assurance that the project has the official sanction of the research committee or other appropriate authority within the institutional or agency setting. For her own and the patient's protection, she needs sufficient knowledge of the research design to enable her to participate in the required activities in an informed, effective, and ethical fashion. With this knowledge, she is conscientious in carrying out her specific functions and responsibilities as outlined in the research design.

Investigational drugs, potentially harmful to the patient, may represent a special problem. The nurse administering such drugs should have basic information about them: method of administration, strengths, actions and uses, side effects, symptoms of toxicity, and so on.

Occasionally, the research may be of such a nature as to give rise to questions, and perhaps conflicts, for the nurse where it appears that the well-being and safety of the patient are adversely affected by procedures prescribed as part of the project. In such instances the nurse is obligated to voice her concern to appropriate persons in the agency. She should also bear in mind that participation in research activities does not relieve her of responsibility for her own acts and judgments.

Participation in research activities carries the implication that the nurse will want and is entitled to information about the study findings, and that she will utilize in her own practice appropriate findings from research studies related to nursing education and practice.

7. The nurse participates in the efforts of the profession to define and upgrade standards of nursing practice and education.

The professional association, through its membership, is responsible for determining standards of nursing practice and education. The key phrase "through its membership" means that each nurse should share in the activities that go into developing, evaluating, disseminating, and implementing these standards. These standards, furthermore, should be reflected in the individual nurse's preparation and practice. Standards represent not only professional goals but also a means of ensuring a high quality of nursing care for the public. As such, each nurse has a vested interest in developing and maintaining them.

Standards can never be static because of the constantly changing nature of health care and of educational patterns. As an active participant in the necessarily continuous process of defining, maintaining, and upgrading standards of nursing practice and education, the nurse must keep herself informed of present and projected standards. She should adhere to these standards in her own practice; help to disseminate them and provide for their implementation in the institution or agency with which she is associated; and take responsible and remedial action when standards are violated. Through the channels provided by her professional association, she should work to support the standards that have been adopted, or endeavor to revise or upgrade them as indicated.

8. The nurse, acting through the professional organization, participates in establishing and maintaining conditions of employment conducive to high-quality nursing care.

The nurse must be concerned with the conditions of economic and general welfare within her profession because these conditions are important determinants in the recruitment and retention of well-qualified personnel and in the opportunity for each nurse to function to her fullest potential in the working situation. If the needs and demands of society for both quantity and quality of nursing care are to be met, the professional association and the individual nurse must share in the effort to establish conditions that will make it possible to meet these needs.

An appropriate channel through which the nurse can work constructively, ethically, and with professional dignity to promote the employment conditions conducive to high-quality nursing care is the economic security program of her professional association. This program, encompassing commitment to the principle of collective bargaining, promotes the right and responsibility of the individual nurse to participate in determining the terms and conditions of her employment.

This participation, to be most productive, should be in the form of a group approach to economic action, through the channels provided by the professional organization and with that organization providing assistance and representation in nurses' collective negotiations with employers. In this way, the nurse can work most effectively to achieve working conditions that will be commensurate with her preparation, qualifications, functions, and responsibilities today and in so doing, will promote the welfare of the public.

9. The nurse works with members of health professions and other citizens in promoting efforts to meet health needs of the public.

It is increasingly recognized that society's need and mounting demand for comprehensive health services can be met only through a broad and intensive effort on the part of both the community and the health professions. The nurse, with her special knowledge and skills in the health field, her essential role in the provision of health services, and her traditional commitment to ever higher standards of health care, has an obligation to participate actively and responsibly in professional, interprofessional, and community endeavors designed to meet the health needs of the public.

She should involve herself in both the planning and implementation of the health services needed, maintaining open and constructive communication with the citizen and professional groups involved. Especially important in this process is the exploration by physician and nurse of their interdependent functions as these relate to the delivery of comprehensive health services. Such exploration calls for a continuous exchange of ideas between members of the two professions on local, state, regional, and national levels, the goal being closer liaison between the two groups in the interest of improved patient care.

A similar and continuing communication should also be carried on with representatives of the other disciplines in the health field—pharmacy, social service, nutrition, physical, occupational, and recreational therapy, hospital or agency administration—as well as with specialized technical groups providing various health services. Nurses must work together with representatives of these groups in defining, exploring, and enhancing the relationships created by their interaction and mutual concern with health care.

The nurse, because of her close and continuing contact with patients and families, and awareness of both individual and community health needs, has much to contribute to community planning for health services. By assuming an active and, on occasion, a leadership role in these activities, nurses can help to shape programs that will provide the public with care that takes full advantage of the resources of modern science.

10. The nurse refuses to give or imply endorsement to advertising, promotion, or sales for commercial products, services, or enterprises.

Over the years the public has learned to trust and respect the nurse and to have confidence in her judgment and advice. Very often, the individual nurse represents the entire profession to patients and others. This means that what one nurse says or does may be interpreted as reflecting the action, opinion, or judgment of the profession as a whole. Therefore, this favorable professional image should not be used in ways that might be misleading or harmful to the public and bring discredit upon the nurse and her profession. The nurse should not permit her name, title, professional status, or symbols—uniform, pin, or the letters "R.N.", for instance—to be used or associated with the promotion of any commercial product or service.

The right to use the title "Registered Nurse" is granted by state governments through licensure by examination for the protection of the public. Use of the title carries with it the responsibility to act in the public interest. This title, and other symbols of the profession, should not be used for the personal benefit of the nurse or those who may seek to exploit them for other purposes.

By permitting her professional self or the nursing profession's symbols or representations to be used in association with a particular product or service, the nurse places herself in the position of seeming to endorse, or recommend, or make the judgment that one among several similar and competing products is preferable to the others. She has neither the qualifications nor authority to make this judgment. The public, because of its tendency to identify the individual with the profession, may construe this individual action as reflecting endorsement or approval of a product or service by the profession as a whole. In some instances, such action on the part of an individual nurse could also be interpreted as a violation of the legal statutes forbidding nurses to make medical diagnosis or to prescribe medications or treatments.

Nursing symbols and representations of nurses may be used in advertisements directed to members of the health professions, but only in such advertisements, and never to imply medical diagnosis or prescription, or professional endorsement of commercial products.

The nurse may indicate the availability of her own services by listing herself in directories or professional publications available to the public. Properly used, such advertising may prove of benefit to the public in securing needed care. It is expected, however, that nurses will present the necessary information in a manner consistent with the dignity of the profession and in keeping with the general practices of other professional groups within the community.

Not only should the nurse herself adhere to the above principles; she should also be alert to any instances of their violation by others. She should report promptly, through appropriate channels, any advertisement or commercial which involves a nurse, implies her involvement, or in any way suggests nursing endorsement of a commercial product, service, or enterprise. The nurse who knowingly involves herself in such unethical activities negates her professional responsibility for personal gain, and jeopardizes the public confidence and trust in the nursing profession that have been created by generations of nurses working together in the public interest.

Prepared by ANA Committee on Ethical, Legal and Professional Standards. Elizabeth C. Stobo, chairman; Mary E. Macdonald, vice chairman; Lucy H. Conant; Rosamond C. Gabrielson; Barbara J. Horn; Mrs. Myra E. Levine; Mrs. Barbara W. Madden; Mrs. Geraldine Price; Dorothy M. Smith; Mrs. Henrietta Walsh.

# Appendix V

# Principles of Legislation Relating to the Practice of Nursing, American Nurses' Association*

Approved by the Board of Directors of the American Nurses' Association, September 1953.
Revised January 1958

| Principle | Reason |
|---|---|
| 1. The primary purpose of a licensing law for the control of the practice of nursing is to protect the health of the people by establishing minimum standards which qualified practitioners must meet. | It is recognized that licensure involves achievement, but it is a minimum of achievement which is deemed adequate to guarantee safe performance in any field of practice, including nursing. |
| 2. All persons who, for compensation, are engaged in the practice of nursing as defined in the law should be licensed. | Mandatory licensure for the practice of nursing is the goal towards which nursing should move. It is generally accepted in any field of practice that complete protection of the people is accomplished only if all who practice as defined in the law are licensed. The people should not be expected to have to differentiate between competent and incompetent practitioners. It should be the function of the nursing profession to fulfill its social responsibility by assisting the public to secure protection through the promotion of adequate nursing practice legislation. |
| 3. There should be one nursing practice act in a state with provisions for licensing the practitioners of nursing. | Since nursing is one occupational field the practice should be controlled by one licensing law. More than one law in a field with a fundamental core of principles basic to its practice creates problems in control which are confusing both to the public and to the practitioners. |

* Issued by the American Nurses' Association, 10 Columbus Circle, New York, N.Y., 10019.

477

| Principle | Reason |
| --- | --- |

4. There should be one licensing board for nursing in a state composed of licensed registered nurses qualified to carry out the functions of the board as provided in the law.

One nursing practice act necessitates only one licensing board. The major function of the board is to license qualified practitioners of nursing. This involves the evaluation of eligibility of candidates, the determination of type and scope of examinations and the testing of individual competency for licensure. The board is also required to accredit educational programs for the preparation of nursing practitioners. This involves the evaluation of all aspects of these educational programs—purpose, curriculum, faculty, students, facilities, organization and administration. In the interest of the public only those licensed registered nurses who are best qualified by general and professional educational preparation and educational experience should be appointed to the state licensing board for nurses.

5. All candidates for licensure should have completed an educational program for the preparation of nursing practitioners accredited by the board and should be required to pass a licensing examination before a license is granted.

The licensing examination should be taken after the legal completion of the program. The license should be issued after the candidate has fulfilled all the requirements of the law for demonstrating competency to practice.

6. Exceptions to, or waiver of, certain requirements for licensure should be provided for a limited period of time when new licensure requirements are first made effective or when they are made mandatory. However, all candidates for whom these requirements are waived should be required to demonstrate competence by passing an examination before a license is granted.

A law is unconstitutional which is retroactive and which legislates out of existence the right of livelihood of current practitioners who do not meet the requirements for licensure.

# Essential Considerations in Legislation Relating to the Practice of Nursing, American Nurses' Association

When drafting a bill relating to the practice of nursing in a state, it is essential that the principles to be incorporated in the law be clearly and briefly defined as well as generally acceptable to the groups most concerned.

The purpose of nursing licensure is the same as that of all other professional groups in that the nursing law is designed to protect the public by establishing certain requirements with which an individual must comply in order to engage in the practice of nursing. The nursing act, then, is concerned primarily with terms on which a license, or "formal permission from the proper authorities to perform certain acts,"* may be procured and retained in good standing.

It is also advised that the nursing practice act be decisively worded as to: "(a) the nature of the authority which licenses or authorizes action, (b) the purpose sought to be accomplished by the licensing authority, (c) the nature of the act to be performed, (d) the character, training and skill required for the proper performance of the act."†

In a sound nursing practice act, therefore, the authority to license will be delegated to the board of nursing. The major function of a board of nursing is to license qualified practitioners of nursing. To carry out this function, the board engages in such essential activities as:

1. Evaluation of the personal and educational qualifications of those applying for licensure,
2. Determination through examination of the individual's competency to practice,
3. Accrediting educational programs for the preparation of nursing practitioners.

To carry out these activities, board members must be professional nurses of broad educational background and experience in nursing who have a comprehensive understanding of current situations in nursing education.

The purpose of the law should also be clearly stated so there can be no question as to its intent. While it is true that nurses may benefit from licensing laws, the *primary* reason for the existence of such laws is public protection, rather than the establishment of the rights and privileges of any special group.

---

* "The Philosophy of Professional Licensure," an address delivered by Justin Miller, Dean, School of Law, Duke University, at the Thirtieth Annual Congress on Medical Education, Licensure and Hospitals, Chicago, February 12, 1934.

† Ibid.

Another essential characteristic of a good licensing law is a clear, concise definition of the practice it is expected to regulate. It is for this reason that the proposed definitions of professional and practical nursing are stated in terms of functions which the profession has agreed constitute the practice of nursing and which have been declared as such by action of the courts.

Of importance also is a definite statement in the law as to the minimum preparation which will be required of all applicants for licensure, although it is recommended that the nature of these requirements be designated by board rule in order to permit the necessary flexibility of standards without the costly and time-consuming process of amending an existing law or passing a new one.

It is recommended that the nursing practice act include only those provisions which are essential to the legal regulation of nursing without reference to the specialized area of practice for which the applicant may qualify. To set minimum standards which will insure safe practice in any and all areas of nursing is the function of the law. It is the function of the professional association to establish desirable qualifications for each area of practice, and to upgrade practice in each area above the minimum standards set by law.

There should not be fragmentation into specialized clinical areas in the basic preparation for the practice of nursing, nor in licensure for nursing practice. The preparation of both categories of nurses, professional and practical, should include the basic core of nursing knowledge, and the law should provide for licensure of only the two types of practitioners, each authorized to function in any area and only within the scope of the respective legal definition of either professional or practical nursing. No provision should be made in the law for identifying clinical specialists in professional nursing. Neither should the law provide separate licensure for supplementary personnel termed as "psychiatric aides," "psychiatric technicians," "tuberculosis nurses," or "baby nurses."

In its Platform, the American Nurses' Association is committed to "promote state laws which provide for mandatory licensure for the practice of professional nursing and for the practice of practical nursing." Accepting such a responsibility entails the closest possible cooperation between the state and district associations, based on a clear understanding of the essential principles to be included in a nursing practice act.

Belief in the principle of mandatory regulation of nursing practice underlies the statement in the Platform. This is the goal towards which nursing should move.

# Suggestions for Major Provisions to Be Included in a Nursing Practice Act Which Is Mandatory for Professional Nursing and for Practical Nursing, American Nurses' Association

| Model Act | Explanation |
|---|---|

### DESCRIPTION OF ACT

An act to provide for the regulation of the practice of nursing; to provide for a state board of nursing and to define the powers and duties of the board including licensure of practitioners of nursing and establishment of standards for educational programs preparing for nursing practice, and to prescribe penalties for violations of the provisions of this act.

The description of the act should include the major provisions in a condensed statement although a short title may be used for general reference, i.e. _____ Nursing Practice Act.
                              (state)

### SECTION I—PURPOSE

In order to safeguard life and health, any person practicing or offering to practice:

a. professional nursing; or

b. practical nursing

in this state for compensation, shall hereafter be required to submit evidence that he or she is qualified so to practice, and shall be licensed as hereinafter provided. After (date) it shall be unlawful for any person not licensed under the provisions of this act:

a. to practice or offer to practice professional nursing or practical nursing; or

b. to use any sign, card or device to indicate that such person is a professional registered nurse or a licensed practical nurse.

The purpose should be clearly stated so that the need for and the intent of the law will be definitely established. The effective date of the law should be far enough in the future to allow sufficient time for the board of nursing to:

a. Act upon applications which may be received under Sections IV and V.

b. Prepare minimum standards including curricula for educational programs for the preparation of nursing practitioners.

c. Prepare policies and rules for carrying out the provisions of this Act.

d. Survey existing and prospective nursing educational programs.

481

## Model Act

## Explanation

The purpose as stated makes licensure for both the practice of professional nursing and practical nursing mandatory. Under such a law persons must be licensed in order to practice professional nursing and practical nursing. The title "Registered Nurse" is protected in that no one who is not licensed as a professional registered nurse may use that title or its abbreviation, "R.N." or any other sign or device to represent himself as a "Registered Nurse." To use the title "Licensed Practical Nurse" or its abbreviation "L.P.N." one must also be licensed.

SECTION II—DEFINITIONS

As used in this Act:

a. Board—means the State Board of Nursing.

A board of nursing may be an autonomous agency of state government responsible directly to the governor of the state or it may be within a department of state government such as a department of occupational licensing or department of education.

When a board of nursing functions under a department of state government, it is advisable to define "department," "commissioner" or other title of the head of the department so that the terms "department" and "commissioner" or other title, may be used throughout the law without giving the complete name.

b. Practice of nursing

1. The practice of professional nursing means the performance for compensation of any acts in the observation, care and counsel of the ill, injured or infirm, or in the maintenance of health or prevention of illness of others, or in the supervision and teaching of other personnel, or the administration of medications and treatments, as prescribed by a licensed physician or dentist; requiring substantial specialized judgment and skill and based on knowledge and application of the principles of biological, physical and social science. The foregoing shall not be deemed to include acts of diagnosis or prescription of therapeutic or corrective measures.

The nursing practice act must contain a definition of the practice which it seeks to regulate. This definition must be stated in terms of the acts which persons licensed under the law are permitted to perform, and which in the interest of public health and safety all others are forbidden to perform.

For the purposes of the law, the definition of nursing practice should be stated in terms broad enough to permit flexibility in the utilization of nursing personnel within the bounds of safety. It must also permit changes in practice consistent with trends in the practice of nursing and related health professions.

In order that the interests of the public and the practitioner both be protected, the

Model Act

Explanation

definition of nursing practice in licensing law must clearly differentiate between those acts which are independent nursing functions, and those which are dependent upon the prescription of the physician or the dentist.

The Statements of Functions prepared and approved by the Sections of the American Nurses' Association are the principal authority for this legal definition of nursing practice. The definition reflects the essential and, for the most part, common elements of nursing practice described in the definitions of nursing functions adopted by the occupational groups represented in the sections of the professional organization.

Delegation by medical authority is provided for the circumscribed area of nursing practice where such delegation is required, namely for the administration of medications and treatments. For clarity, the definition includes a prohibition of acts of diagnosis and prescription of therapeutic or corrective measures.

Also provided are the elements of substantial specialized judgment and skill which characterize professional nursing, and the nature of the preparation required for the safe practice of professional nursing.

2. The practice of practical nursing means the performance for compensation of selected acts in the care of the ill, injured, or infirm under the direction of a registered professional nurse or a licensed physician or a licensed dentist; and not requiring the substantial specialized skill, judgment, and knowledge required in professional nursing.

Where the law seeks to regulate practical nursing, it must define a second level of practice and, in doing so, must differentiate between professional and practical nursing.

The definition provides for the essential differences in the two levels of nursing practice through requiring that the acts of nursing which may be performed by a practical nurse be selected by and performed under the direction of a professional person who is either a nurse, a physician or a dentist.

The Statement of Functions of the Licensed Practical Nurse approved by the American Nurses' Association and the National Federation of Licensed Practical Nurses is the principal authority by which this legal

## Model Act

## Explanation

definition of practical nursing is to be interpreted.

The law should not require the practical nurse to exercise the same degree of judgment and skill as is required for professional nursing as the nature of her preparation does not permit such a requirement.

SECTION III—BOARD OF NURSING

a. **Appointment, Term of Office and Removal from Office**

The governor shall appoint a board consisting of not less than ———— members. Provided however, that the present members of the (state) board holding office under the provisions of (identify act which is being amended or repealed) shall serve as members of said board until the expiration of their respective terms or until their successors have been appointed. The term of office for members of the board shall be ———— years. No member shall be appointed to more than two consecutive terms.

Since the law is not intended to prohibit gratuitous care of the sick by members of a patient's family or friends, it is necessary to include the consideration of compensation in the definition.

There may be some question as to the legality of a provision to continue the terms of board members who were appointed under a law which is being entirely repealed. In the event it is not possible to provide for the continuation of the current board in the new law, the necessary authorities should be alerted in advance to the need for the immediate appointment of the board members on the effective date of the law. In the event it is necessary to provide for the appointment of a completely new board, it is wise to provide for their appointment for varying lengths of time in order that the terms of all board members will not expire on the same date. It is also suggested that the terms of office be limited to two, thus affording the board members sufficient time to develop and contribute to the work of the board and yet not allow the board to be a self-perpetuating one. There should be some relationship between the number of board members and the terms of their office.

On expiration of the term of any member, the (state) nurses' association shall submit to the governor a list of its members qualified to serve, such list to contain in number at least twice the number of vacancies to be filled. Appointments shall be made from this list. Vacancies occurring on the board shall be filled for the

The state board of nursing is an agency of state government and its members are public officials who are held responsible by state government to act in the best interests of the public in implementing all provisions of the nursing practice act.

Inasmuch as the principle has been accepted that a profession should control its own

## Model Act

unexpired terms by appointments to be made by the governor from nominations submitted by the (state) nurses' association in the manner aforesaid.

On or before (date) of each year and at any other time when there is a vacancy the (state) nurses' association shall submit to the governor a list of its members qualified for appointment in number not less than twice the number of vacancies to be filled.

The governor may remove any member from the board for neglect of any duty required by law or for incompetency or unprofessional or dishonorable conduct.

### b. Qualifications of Board Members

Each member of the board shall be a citizen of the United States, a resident of

## Explanation

practice, only licensed registered nurses, who are best qualified by general and professional educational preparation and experience should be appointed to the state board of nursing.

In the interest of the public and adequate nursing standards provision should be made in the law to require that appointments be made by the governor from lists submitted by the state nurses' association.

As an additional safeguard, the qualifications of board members should be clearly stated in the law so there can be no question as to the preparation and experience considered necessary for board members to fulfill their responsibilities.

The general laws of the state controlling the removal from office of a public official should be followed in dismissing board members and should include a hearing.

In the event it seems desirable to have a regular channel for consulting with other groups, provision may be made in the law for an advisory council to which members would be appointed by the governor to represent such groups as: practical nurses; physicians; educators; registered nurses; hospital administrators, and the general public. Such a provision would be a means whereby these groups could discuss some of the crucial problems involved in the accreditation of nursing education programs and afford them an opportunity to express their views concerning nursing education requirements in an organized way. And, although such a council would function in an advisory capacity only, it could serve as a highly constructive force in establishing and maintaining standards of nursing education and licensure regulations in the interest of public protection.

The qualifications of board members stated here are deemed essential to the performance

## Model Act

this state, and shall file with the proper state authority the constitutional oath of office before beginning his or her term of office. Each member of the board shall possess these additional qualifications:

1. EDUCATION:
   (a) Graduation from a state-accredited educational program for the preparation of practitioners of professional nursing; and

   (b) Holds a graduate degree in nursing; and

2. LICENSURE:
   (a) Is a registered nurse in the state; and

3. EXPERIENCE:
   (a) Has had at least five years successful experience since graduation in administration or teaching in an educational program to prepare practitioners of nursing; and

   (b) Has been actively engaged in nursing for at least three years immediately preceding appointment or reappointment.

c. **Duties and Powers**

The board shall meet annually in the month of _____ and shall elect from its members a president and a secretary who shall also be the treasurer. It may hold such other meetings during the year as may be deemed necessary to transact its business. A majority of the board including one officer shall constitute a quorum at any meeting.

## Explanation

of the duties imposed by law upon members of the board. If possible it would be desirable to include among the qualifications, membership in the state nurses' association. It is also essential that the organization have well recognized criteria including personal qualifications by which individuals are selected for the list submitted to the governor.

Eligibility for appointment to the board should be based on the candidate's experience in nursing education which will best fit her to carry out the functions of the board rather than on representation from a clinical field or geographical area. The required experience might be in administration or teaching in any phase of an educational program to prepare practitioners of nursing.

The annual meeting of the board should be scheduled as near the beginning of the fiscal year as possible.

The duties and powers of the board of nursing should be so clearly stated in the law that there can be no question as to what the obligations of the board are, as well as additional functions it may assume.

When a board functions under a department of state government all fees would be paid

## Model Act

## Explanation

to the department and a treasurer would not be needed. Some of the other powers and duties of the board would also probably be the responsibility of the department.

The board is authorized to:

1. Adopt and, from time to time, revise such rules and regulations not inconsistent with the law, as may be necessary to enable it to carry into effect the provisions of this act;

2. Prescribe standards and approve curricula for educational programs preparing persons for licensure under this act;

3. Provide for surveys of such programs at such times as it may deem necessary;

4. Accredit such programs as meet the requirements of this act and of the board;

5. Deny or withdraw accreditation from educational programs for failure to meet prescribed standards;

6. Examine, license, and renew the licenses of duly qualified applicants;

7. Conduct hearings upon charges calling for discipline of a licensee or revocation of a license;

There may be some states in which the legal process referred to in 7 and 8 is otherwise provided for.

8. Have the power to issue subpoenas, compel the attendance of witnesses, and administer oaths to persons giving testimony at hearings;

9. Cause the prosecution of all persons violating this act and have power to incur such necessary expenses therefor;

10. Keep a record of all its proceedings;

11. Make an annual report to the governor;

| Model Act | Explanation |
|---|---|

12. Appoint and employ a qualified person who shall not be a member of the board to serve as executive officer to the board;

13. Define the duties and fix the compensation for the executive officer; and

14. Employ such other persons as may be necessary to carry on the work of the board.

The executive officer shall meet all the qualifications for board members and shall, in addition:

1. Have had at least eight years experience since graduation, five years of which shall have been in teaching or in administration of a program preparing nursing practitioners or in a combination thereof; and

2. Have been actively engaged in nursing education for at least five years immediately preceding appointment.

It is believed the executive officer should not be a member of the board in order that she may be unhampered in her capacity as an administrator in carrying out the policies of the board. It is further suggested that the qualifications of the executive officer should extend beyond those of the board members for reasons of mutual respect and understanding. It is assumed that if the board has the power to appoint additional professional personnel, it will define their qualifications according to the needs of the position.

In states where state board personnel are covered by civil service, the language of this section will have to be adjusted accordingly.

### d. Compensation

Each member of the board shall receive traveling, hotel and other necessary expenses incurred while actually engaged in the discharge of official duties.

Careful consideration should be given to the advisability of fixing compensation for board members by law. There are justifiable reasons for not offering compensation to board members beyond their actual expenses; however, if compensation is paid, the amounts should be commensurate with that offered to members of other professional boards for like services.

SECTION IV—REGISTERED NURSE

### a. Qualifications of Applicants

An applicant for a license to practice professional nursing shall submit to the board written evidence, verified by oath, that said applicant:

The qualifications for applicants should include only those which are essential to a safe performance and should be specifically stated. Since safe performance cannot be

| Model Act | Explanation |
|---|---|

1. Is of good moral character; and

2. Has completed an approved high school course of study or the equivalent thereof as determined by the appropriate educational agency; and

3. Has completed the required accredited professional nursing education program and holds a diploma.

guaranteed by such factors as age and citizenship, these requirements have not been included in this form. It is also considered impractical to require that an applicant be in good physical and mental health unless a workable plan could be instituted for determining the status of each person's health.

## b. License

1. By examination:

The applicant shall be required to pass a written examination in such subjects as the board may determine. Each written examination may be supplemented by an oral examination. Upon successfully passing such examination, the board shall issue to the applicant a license to practice professional nursing as a registered nurse.

A statement such as this should enable the board to use any type of examination considered desirable and to determine what shall constitute a passing score. Percent or letter grades have not been included since in granting or denying a license the variations of performance have no meaning once the passing score is determined.

2. By endorsement:

The board may issue a license to practice professional nursing as a registered nurse by endorsement to an applicant who has been duly licensed as a registered nurse under the laws of another state, territory or foreign country, if, in the opinion of the board, the applicant meets the qualifications required of registered nurses in this state at the time of graduation.

The term "by endorsement" is used in preference to "reciprocity" and other terms which have resulted in considerable confusion. Since there actually are no standing reciprocal agreements between states, each person's qualifications for licensure must be evaluated on an individual basis and the procedure, therefore, is one of endorsement or approval of the previous state's action, rather than acceptance by reciprocity.

3. By Waiver:

Application for license under this provision must be made before (date). The board may issue a license to practice as a registered nurse to any person who shall submit to the board written evidence, verified by oath, that said applicant:

When preparing a bill for either mandatory or permissive licensure of a group for the first time, from the standpoint of constitutional law, it is considered advisable to include a waiver provision for those persons who are practicing in the field at that time. It is generally recommended that the waiver be limited to a period of not more than two

| Model Act | Explanation |
|---|---|
| (a) Is of good moral character; and | years, depending on the time required by the board to prepare for and administer that portion of the act. |
| (b) Has practiced professional nursing in this state at least _____ years within the five-year period immediately preceding the effective date of this act; and | |
| (c) Has completed a professional nursing education program which was accredited by the board at the time of completion and which would have enabled such person to take an examination and be licensed as a registered nurse under any act relating to nursing heretofore approved by the (insert title of the state legislature); and | In the main, the purpose of the waiver clause is to provide the means by which the persons who can submit evidence that they are qualified to give safe nursing care may become licensed, although they may not possess the educational requirements specified for recent graduates of accredited nursing education programs. |
| (d) Has passed an examination to be administered by the board of nursing, wholly or in part in writing. | |

## c. Fee

| | |
|---|---|
| The applicant applying for a license to practice as a registered nurse shall pay a fee of $_____ to the board. A fee of $_____ is required for each re-examination. | It is recommended that the fee for the examination be sufficient to cover the cost of those functions under the law which are related to accreditation and original licensure only. It is recommended that charges not be made for surveys of educational programs, verification of credentials to other states and other services performed by the board. Provisions for a fee for re-examination will need to be in line with regulations relating to such fees in other agencies of the state government. |

## d. Title and Abbreviation

| | |
|---|---|
| Any person who holds a license to practice professional nursing in this state shall have the right to use the title "Registered Nurse" and the abbreviation "R.N." No other person shall assume such title or use such abbreviation or any | This clause is considered advisable not only to protect the title of registered nurse but also to provide an adequate basis for filing charges in the event that a person who is not privileged to do so represents himself as a registered nurse. |

| Model Act | Explanation |
|---|---|

other words, letters, signs, or devices to indicate that the person using the same is a registered nurse.

### e. Nurses Registered Under a Previous Law

Any person holding a license or certificate of registration to practice nursing as a registered nurse issued by the board which is valid on (date this Act is to take effect) shall thereafter be deemed to be licensed as a registered nurse under the provisions of this Act.

If the previous law is to be repealed, this provision is necessary or advisable in order to make certain that licenses issued under previous Acts will be considered valid under the new law.

SECTION V—LICENSED PRACTICAL NURSE

### a. Qualifications of Applicants

An applicant for a license to practice practical nursing shall submit to the board evidence, verified by oath, that the applicant:

1. Is of good moral character; and

2. Has completed an approved high school course of study or the equivalent thereof as determined by the appropriate educational agency.

3. Has completed a prescribed curriculum in a state accredited program for the preparation of practical nurses and holds a diploma or certificate therefrom.

The same remarks as those listed for qualifications of applicants for registered nurse licensure apply here.

### b. License

1. By examination:

The applicant shall be required to pass a written examination in such subjects as the board may determine. Each written examination may be supplemented by an oral or practical

Comparable to that given for registered nurse licensure.

| Model Act | Explanation |
|---|---|

examination. Upon successful completion of such examination the board shall issue to the applicant a license to practice as a licensed practical nurse.

2. By endorsement:

| | |
|---|---|
| The board may issue a license to practice practical nursing by endorsement to any applicant who has been duly licensed or registered as a licensed practical nurse or a person entitled to perform similar services under a different title, under laws of another state, territory or foreign country, if, in the opinion of the board, the applicant meets the requirements for licensed practical nurses in this state at the time of graduation. | Comparable to that given for registered nurse licensure. A license to practice practical nursing by endorsement should be issued on the basis of graduation from an approved school of practical nursing. |

3. By Waiver:

| | |
|---|---|
| Application for license under this provision must be made before (date). The board may issue a license to practice as a licensed practical nurse to any person who shall submit to the board written evidence, verified by oath, that said applicant: | Recommendations comparable to those which refer to registered nurse licensure apply here. |

(a) Is of good moral character; and

(b) Has practiced practical nursing in this state at least _____ years within the five-year period immediately preceding the effective date of this act; and

(c) Has passed an examination to be administered by the Board of Nursing, wholly or in part in writing.

c. **Fee**

| | |
|---|---|
| The applicant applying for a license to practice as a licensed practical nurse shall pay a fee of $_____ to the board. A fee | Same as that given for registered nurse licensure. |

| Model Act | Explanation |
|---|---|

of $_____ shall be paid for each re-examination.

### d. Title and Abbreviation

Any person who holds a license to practice practical nursing in this state shall have the right to use the title "Licensed Practical Nurse" and the abbreviation "L.P.N." No other person shall assume such title or use such abbreviation or any other words, letters, signs or devices to indicate that the person using the same is a licensed practical nurse.

This clause provides protection of the title "Licensed Practical Nurse." In the event another title is used for practical nurse in the law, this provision will have to be altered accordingly.

### e. Persons Licensed Under Previous Law

Any person holding a license to practice as a practical nurse issued by the board and which is valid on (date this act is to take effect) shall hereinafter be deemed to be licensed as a practical nurse under provisions of this Act.

If the previous law is to be repealed this provision is necessary or advisable in order to make certain that licenses issued under previous Acts will be considered valid under the new law.

#### SECTION VI—RENEWAL OF LICENSE

The license of every person licensed under the provisions of this Act shall be renewed annually, except as hereinafter provided. On or before (date) the board shall mail an application for renewal of license to every person to whom a license was issued or renewed during the current year. The applicant shall fill in the application blank and return it to the board with a renewal fee of (amount) before (date). Upon receipt of the application and fee the board shall verify the accuracy of the application and issue to the applicant a certificate of renewal for the current year beginning _____ (date) and expiring _____ (date). Such renewal shall

It is recommended that licenses be renewed annually in the interest of a more accurate roster; also that provision be made for exempting inactive nurses from paying the annual renewal fee.

Model Act

Explanation

render the holder thereof a legal practitioner of nursing for the period stated on the renewal form.

Any licensee who allows his or her license to lapse by failing to renew the license as provided above may be reinstated by the board on satisfactory explanation for such failure to renew his license and on payment of the renewal fee.

Any person practicing nursing during the time his or her license has lapsed shall be considered an illegal practitioner and shall be subject to the penalties provided for violations of this Act.

A nurse who does not engage in nursing in the state during the succeeding year shall not be required to pay the renewal fee as long as she remains inactive. Should she wish to resume nursing at some future time she shall so notify the board and remit the renewal fee for the current annual period.

SECTION VII—DISPOSITION OF FUNDS

All fees received by the board and monies collected under this Act shall be paid to the treasurer of the board who shall deposit the same at the end of each month, with the state treasurer.

All amounts paid into this fund shall be held subject to the order of the board to be used only for the purpose of meeting necessary expenses incurred in the performance of the purpose of this Act, and the duties imposed thereby.

All funds which may have accumulated to the credit of the board under the Act which is now repealed shall be continued for use by the Board of Nursing in the administration of this Act.

As has been elsewhere stated, it is felt that the fees provided for under this Act should be commensurate with the cost of administering the law. The budget of the board, therefore, would be determined by the income from the licensure of nurses including the annual renewal fees. Since it is recommended that the functions of the board be limited to the examination and licensing of nurses and accreditation of nursing education programs, the budget need only provide adequate funds for the administration of those duties. It is felt that the responsibility for the promotion of nursing education and nursing service should not be assumed by the board but should rather be borne by the nursing organizations, local, state and national.

## Model Act

**Explanation**

SECTION VIII—NURSING EDUCATION
PROGRAMS

### a. Application for Accreditation

An institution desiring to conduct a nursing education program to prepare professional or practical nurses shall apply to the board and submit evidence that:

1. It is prepared to carry out a program in professional nursing education or a program in practical nurse training, as the case may be; and

2. It is prepared to meet such standards as shall be established by this law and by the board.

The term "nursing education program" is preferred to "school of nursing" since one program may involve the facilities of several different agencies. Some institutions use terms other than "school of nursing" to describe their programs. It is important that the requirements to be met by the accredited programs be made a matter of board rules and regulations in order that the standards may be revised in accordance with current trends in nursing education without necessitating a change in the law.

### b. Survey

A survey of the institution and its entire nursing education program shall be made by the executive officer or other authorized employee of the board, who shall submit a written report of the survey to the board. If, in the opinion of the board, the requirements for an accredited nursing education program are met, such program shall be accredited as a nursing education program for professional or practical nurses.

From time to time as deemed necessary by the board, it shall be the duty of the board, through its executive officer or other authorized representative of the board, to survey all nursing education programs in the state. Written reports of such surveys shall be submitted to the board. If the board shall determine that any accredited nursing education program is not maintaining the standards required by the statutes and by the board, notice thereof in writing specifying the defect or defects shall be immediately given to the institution conducting the program.

It is recommended that surveys of nursing education programs be made at the discretion of the board rather than at intervals stated in the law.

| Model Act | Explanation |
|---|---|

A program which fails to correct these conditions to the satisfaction of the board within a reasonable time shall be discontinued after a hearing.

SECTION IX—DISCIPLINARY PROCEEDINGS

## a. Grounds for Discipline

The board shall have power to deny, revoke, or suspend any license to practice nursing issued by the board or applied for in accordance with the provisions of this Act, or to otherwise discipline a licensee upon proof that the person:

This section is necessary to establish a means of barring from practice those individuals who are considered unsafe to practice nursing.

1. Is guilty of fraud or deceit in procuring or attempting to procure a license to practice nursing; or

2. Is guilty of a crime or gross immorality; or

3. Is unfit or incompetent by reason of negligence, habits or other causes; or

4. Is habitually intemperate or is addicted to the use of habit-forming drugs; or

5. Is mentally incompetent; or

6. Is guilty of unprofessional conduct; or

7. Has willfully or repeatedly violated any of the provisions of this Act.

## b. Proceedings

Upon filing of a sworn complaint with the board, charging a person with having been guilty of any of the actions specified as a ground for disciplinary action, the executive officer of the board shall fix a time and place for a hearing and shall

If other proceedings are used in a state, it is recommended that the same proceedings be adopted for nursing as for other professions.

## Model Act

cause a copy of the charges, together with a notice of the time and place fixed for the hearing to be served on the accused at least ten days prior thereto. When personal service cannot be effected and such fact is certified on oath by any person duly authorized to make legal service, the executive secretary of the board shall cause to be published, twice in each of two successive weeks, a notice of the hearing in a newspaper published in the county in which the accused last practiced according to the records of the board and shall mail a copy of the charges and of such notice to the accused at his or her last known address.

When publication of the notice is necessary, the date of the hearing shall not be less than ten days after the last date of the notice. The attendance of witnesses and the production of books, papers, and documents at the hearing may be compelled by subpoenas issued by the board, which shall be served in accordance with the law. At the hearing the board shall administer oaths as may be necessary for the proper conduct of the hearing. The board shall not be bound by strict rules of procedure or by the laws of evidence in the conduct of its proceedings, but the determination shall be based upon sufficient legal evidence to sustain it. At the hearing the accused shall have the right to appear either personally or by counsel, or both, to produce witnesses or evidence on his or her own behalf, to cross-examine witnesses and to have subpoenas issued by the board. If the accused shall be found guilty of the charges, the board may refuse to issue a license to the applicant or may revoke, suspend or otherwise discipline a licensee. A revoked or suspended license may be reissued after one year, in the discretion of the board.

## Explanation

Provision for investigation of the charge by two or more board members may be inserted under "proceedings" in order to discourage irresponsible or spite charges.

| Model Act | Explanation |
|---|---|

SECTION X—EXCEPTIONS

This Act does not prohibit:

a. The furnishing of nursing assistance in an emergency.

b. The practice of nursing which is incidental to their program of study by students enrolled in nursing education programs accredited by the board.

c. The practice of any legally qualified nurse of another state who is employed by the United States Government or any bureau, division or agency thereof, while in the discharge of his or her official duties.

Only those exemptions which are essential to protect persons practicing in unusual circumstances should be made to the provisions of the law. It is not necessary, for instance, to exempt from the law the giving of incidental care by domestic servants, since, if these persons are not practicing nursing within the meaning of the law, they would not be subject to its provisions. Neither should it be necessary to exempt other groups, or persons, whose practice is not that of nursing as it is defined in the law.

Care should be taken in drafting this section of the law to prevent the inclusion of any provision which would defeat the purpose of the law by permitting persons to practice who have not met the requirements of the law.

Boards of nursing should provide for the examination of applicants at frequent intervals. This would preclude having recent graduates wait long periods of time between their graduation and the granting of their licenses.

SECTION XI—VIOLATION OF
ACT—PENALTIES

It shall be a misdemeanor for any person (including any corporation, association or individual) to:

a. Sell or fraudulently obtain or furnish any nursing diploma, license, renewal or record or aid or abet therein; or

b. Practice nursing as defined by this Act under cover of any diploma, license, or record illegally or fraudulently obtained or signed or issued unlawfully or under fraudulent representation; or

c. Practice professional nursing or practical nursing as defined by this Act unless duly licensed to do so under the provisions of this Act; or

The violations as well as the penalties for such misdemeanors should be clearly defined in the Act in order that it may be effective.

## Model Act

d. Use in connection with his or her name any designation tending to imply that he or she is a licensed registered nurse or a licensed practical nurse unless duly licensed so to practice under the provisions of this Act; or

e. Practice professional nursing or practical nursing during the time his or her license issued under the provisions of this Act shall be suspended or revoked; or

f. Conduct a nursing education program for the preparation of professional or practical nurses unless the program has been accredited by the board; or

g. Otherwise violate any provisions of this Act. Such misdemeanor shall be punishable by a fine of not less than $_____ for a first offense. Each subsequent offense shall be punishable by a fine of $_____ or by imprisonment of not more than _____ or by such fine and imprisonment.

Courts of original criminal jurisdiction (insert names of specific local courts) are hereby empowered to hear, try and determine such misdemeanor without indictment and to impose in full the punishment or imprisonment and fines herein prescribed. It shall be necessary to prove in any prosecution or hearing under this article only a single act prohibited by law or a single holding out or an attempt without proving a general course of conduct, in order to constitute a violation.

Such misdemeanors shall be prosecuted by the Attorney General in the name of the People of the State of _____; provided, however, that nothing in this section shall be interpreted to prevent or impede the prosecution of such proceedings by the district attorney of any county when such proceedings shall have been initiated by him.

## Explanation

## Model Act

### SECTION XII—INJUNCTIVE RELIEF

The practice of professional nursing or practical nursing by any person who has not been issued a license under the provisions of this Act, or whose license has been suspended or revoked, or has expired, is hereby declared to be inimical to the public welfare and to constitute a public nuisance. The Board of Nursing may, in the name of the People of the State of _____, through the Attorney General of the State of _____, apply for an injunction in any court of competent jurisdiction to enjoin any person who has not been issued a license or whose license has been suspended or revoked or expired, from practicing professional nursing or practical nursing; and, upon the filing of a verified petition in such court, the court or any judge thereof, if satisfied by affidavit, or otherwise, that such person is or has been practicing professional nursing or practical nursing without having been issued a license, or after his license has been suspended or revoked or expired, may issue a temporary injunction, without notice or bond, enjoining the defendant from further practicing professional nursing or practical nursing. A copy of said verified petition shall be served upon the defendant and the proceedings shall thereafter be conducted as in other civil cases. If it be established that said defendant has been or is practicing professional nursing or practical nursing without having been issued a license or has been or is practicing professional or practical nursing after his license has been suspended or revoked, or expired, the court, or any judge thereof, may enter a decree perpetually enjoining said defendant from further practicing professional nursing or practial nursing. In case of violation of any injunction issued under the provisions of this section, the court, or any judge thereof, may summarily try and punish the offender for contempt of court. Such injunction proceed-

The additional protection of injunction proceedings is provided here. It is recommended that this clause be included in order that unlicensed persons can be enjoined from practice pending a hearing.

| Model Act | Explanation |
|---|---|
| ing shall be in addition to, and not in lieu of, all penalties and other remedies in this Act provided. | |

### SECTION XIII—REPEAL

| Model Act | Explanation |
|---|---|
| The (identify present nursing practice act or appropriate section) is herewith repealed. | Although it may be interpreted that the most recently enacted law takes precedence over previous laws of the same nature, it is considered wise to include a section to repeal the former nursing act or the portion which is being revised. |

### SECTION XIV—PROTECTION OF ACT

| Model Act | Explanation |
|---|---|
| If any provision of this Act, or the application of such provision to any person or circumstance, shall be held invalid, the remainder of this Act or the application of such provision to persons or circumstances, other than those to which it is held invalid, shall not be affected thereby. | This section might also be entitled "Partial Invalidity" in that it merely protects the remainder of the Act should any portion of it be held invalid. |

### SECTION XV—EFFECTIVE DATE OF ACT

| Model Act | Explanation |
|---|---|
| This Act shall take effect (date). | This section is essential in order to avoid any possible confusion regarding the effective date of the Act. In some instances it may be desirable to add an emergency clause which makes such legislation effective immediately when signed by the Governor. Emergency legislation may require a majority vote of both branches of the state legislature, however, and unless the legislation is exceedingly urgent, it is recommended that it be allowed to progress in the usual way. The effective date of the Act is ordinarily the first day of the next fiscal year unless there appears to be need for delaying it to permit further preparation for its effectiveness. It may be necessary and permitted in some instances to add provisions for an appropriation of money to be used by the board in carrying new provisions of the law into effect. |

## ESSENTIAL DIFFERENCES BETWEEN MANDATORY AND PERMISSIVE NURSING PRACTICE ACTS

There are three types of nursing practice acts.

1. An act which is mandatory for the practice of both professional and practical nursing.

2. An act which is mandatory for the practice of professional nursing and permissive for practical nursing.

3. An act which is permissive for the practice of both professional and practical nursing.

The essential differences in these various types of nursing practice acts are contained in Sections I, Purpose; X, Exceptions; XI, Violations; and XII, Injunctive Relief of the suggested form for an act developed by the American Nurses' Association.

In a mandatory act, *Section I, Purpose*, must be worded as to make it unlawful for anyone to practice professional or practical nursing without being licensed in that state, the only exceptions being those set forth in *Section X, Exceptions*. Great caution should be exercised to omit any exceptions, or anything that might be interpreted as an exception, elsewhere in the law.

A permissive bill should provide the same minimum standards for licensure and accreditation, but such an act merely protects the title "registered nurse" or "licensed practical nurse." Therefore, the practice of either level of nursing is not prohibited in a permissive act, but a person might not represent himself as a registered nurse or as a practical nurse or use the letters "R.N." or "L.P.N." after his name without being duly licensed under the law.

In a permissive act, then, there is no need for a section to list exceptions, since licensure is optional and a person may continue to practice nursing without a license as long as he does not misrepresent himself under the law. The section on violations and injunctive relief in the permissive act should be worded so as to agree with the purpose of the Act.

Other sections of an act will be the same as they appear in *Suggestions for Major Provisions To Be Included in a Nursing Practice Act Which Is Mandatory for Professional Nursing and for Practical Nursing* regardless of the type of statute that regulates nursing practice.

On the following pages, those sections which differ in the three types of nursing practice acts are compared.

# A Comparison of Suggested Provisions to Be Included in Three Types of Nursing Practice Acts, American Nurses' Association *

| For an Act Which Is Mandatory for Both Professional and Practical Nursing | For an Act Which Is Mandatory for Professional Nursing and Permissive for Practical Nursing | For an Act Which Is Permissive for Both Professional and Practical Nursing |
| --- | --- | --- |
| SECTION I—PURPOSE | SECTION I—PURPOSE | SECTION I—PURPOSE |
| In order to safeguard life and health, any person practicing or offering to practice: | In order to safeguard life and health, any person practicing or offering to practice: | In order to safeguard life and health, any person practicing or offering to practice: |
| a. professional nursing; or | a. professional nursing; or | a. professional nursing as a professional registered nurse; or |
| b. practical nursing | b. practical nursing as a licensed practical nurse | b. practical nursing as a licensed practical nurse |
| in this state for compensation, shall hereafter be required to submit evidence that he or she is qualified so to practice, and shall be licensed as hereinafter provided. After (date) it shall be unlawful for any person not licensed under the provisions of this act: | in this state for compensation, shall hereafter be required to submit evidence that he or she is qualified so to practice, and shall be licensed as hereinafter provided. After (date) it shall be unlawful for any person not licensed under the provisions of this act: | in this state for compensation, shall hereafter be required to submit evidence that he or she is qualified so to practice, and shall be licensed as hereinafter provided. After (date) it shall be unlawful for any person not licensed under the provisions of this act: |
| a. to practice or offer to practice professional nursing or practical nursing; or | a. to practice or offer to practice professional nursing in this state; or | a. to practice or offer to practice as a professional registered nurse or as a licensed practical nurse; or |

* All provisions other than those cited here remain the same in each type of law.

| For an Act Which Is Mandatory for Both Professional and Practical Nursing | For an Act Which Is Mandatory for Professional Nursing and Permissive for Practical Nursing | For an Act Which Is Permissive for Both Professional and Practical Nursing |
|---|---|---|
| b. to use any sign, card or device to indicate that such person is a professional registered nurse or a licensed practical nurse. | b. to practice or offer to practice as a licensed practical nurse; or<br><br>c. to use any sign, card or device to indicate that such person is a professional registered nurse or a licensed practical nurse. | b. to use any sign, card or device to indicate that such person is a professional registered nurse or a licensed practical nurse. |
| SECTION X—EXCEPTIONS | SECTION X—EXCEPTIONS | SECTION X—EXCEPTIONS |
| This Act does not prohibit:<br>a. The furnishing of nursing assistance in an emergency.<br><br>b. The practice of nursing which is incidental to their program of study by students enrolled in nursing education programs accredited by the board.<br><br>c. The practice of any legally qualified nurse of another state who is employed by the United States government or any bureau, division or agency thereof, while in the discharge of his or her official duties. | Same as Column 1 | *Omit* altogether |

## SECTION XI—VIOLATIONS OF ACT PENALTIES

It shall be a misdemeanor for any person (including any corporation, association or individual) to:

a. Sell or fraudulently obtain or furnish any nursing diploma, license, renewal, or record or aid or abet therein; or

b. Practice nursing as defined by this Act under cover of any diploma, license or record illegally or fraudulently obtained or signed or issued unlawfully or under fraudulent representation; or

c. Practice professional or practical nursing as defined by this Act unless duly licensed to do so under the provisions of this Act; or

d. Use in connection with his or her name any designation tending to imply that he or she is a licensed registered nurse or a licensed practical nurse unless duly licensed so to practice under the provisions of this Act; or

e. Practice professional or practical nursing during the time his or her license issued under the provisions of this Act shall be suspended or revoked.

## SECTION XI—VIOLATIONS OF ACT PENALTIES

It shall be a misdemeanor for any person (including any corporation, association or individual) to:

a. Sell or fraudulently obtain or furnish any nursing diploma, license, renewal, or record or aid or abet therein; or

b. Practice nursing as defined by this Act under cover of any diploma, license or record illegally or fraudulently obtained or signed or issued unlawfully or under fraudulent representation; or

c. Practice professional nursing as defined by this Act unless duly licensed to do so under the provisions of this Act; or

d. Practice nursing as a licensed practical nurse unless duly licensed to do so under the provisions of this Act; or

e. Use in connection with his or her name any designation tending to imply that he or she is a licensed registered nurse or a licensed practical nurse unless duly licensed so to practice under the provisions of this Act; or

f. Practice professional nursing or practice as a licensed practical nurse during the time his or her license issued under the provisions of this Act shall be suspended or revoked.

## SECTION XI—VIOLATIONS OF ACT PENALTIES

It shall be a misdemeanor for any person (including any corporation, association or individual) to:

a. Sell or fraudulently obtain or furnish any nursing diploma, license, renewal, or record or aid or abet therein; or

b. Practice nursing as defined by this Act under cover of any diploma, license or record illegally or fraudulently obtained or signed or issued unlawfully or under fraudulent representation; or

c. Practice nursing as a registered nurse or as a licensed practical nurse unless duly licensed to do so under the provisions of this Act; or

d. Use in connection with his or her name any designation tending to imply that he or she is a licensed registered nurse or a licensed practical nurse unless duly licensed so to practice under the provisions of this Act; or

e. Practice as a registered nurse or a licensed practical nurse during the time his or her license issued under the provisions of this Act shall be suspended or revoked.

## For an Act Which Is Mandatory for Both Professional and Practical Nursing

### SECTION XII—INJUNCTIVE RELIEF

The practice of professional nursing or practical nursing by any person who has not been issued a license under the provisions of this Act, or whose license has been suspended or revoked, or has expired, is hereby declared to be inimical to the public welfare and to constitute a public nuisance. The Board of Nursing may, in the name of the People of the State of _____, through the Attorney General of the State of _____, apply for an injunction in any court of competent jurisdiction to enjoin any person who has not been issued a license or whose license has been suspended or revoked or expired, from practicing professional nursing or practical nursing; and, upon the filing of a verified petition in such court, the court or any judge thereof, if satisfied by affidavit, or otherwise, that such person is or has been practicing professional nursing or practical nursing without having been issued a license, or after his license has been suspended or revoked or expired, may issue a temporary injunction, without notice or bond, enjoining the defendant from further practicing professional nursing or practical nursing. A copy of said verified petition shall be

## For an Act Which Is Mandatory for Professional Nursing and Permissive for Practical Nursing

### SECTION XII—INJUNCTIVE RELIEF

The practice of professional nursing, or the practice of nursing as a licensed practical nurse, by any person who has not been issued a license to do so under the provisions of this Act, or whose license has been suspended or revoked, or has expired, is hereby declared to be inimical to the public welfare and to constitute a public nuisance. The Board of Nursing may, in the name of the People of the State of _____, through the Attorney General of the State of _____, apply for an injunction in any court of competent jurisdiction to enjoin any person who has not been issued a license or whose license has been suspended or revoked or expired, from practicing professional nursing or from practicing nursing as a licensed practical nurse; and, upon the filing of a verified petition in such court, the court or any judge thereof, if satisfied by affidavit or otherwise, that such person is or has been practicing professional nursing, or is or has been practicing nursing as a licensed practical nurse, without having been issued a license to do so, or after his license has been suspended or revoked or expired, may issue a temporary injunction, without notice or

## For an Act Which Is Permissive for Both Professional and Practical Nursing

### SECTION XII—INJUNCTIVE RELIEF

The practice of nursing as a registered nurse, or as a licensed practical nurse by any person who has not been issued a license to do so under the provisions of this Act, or whose license has been suspended or revoked, or has expired, is hereby declared to be inimical to the public welfare and to constitute a public nuisance. The Board of Nursing may, in the name of the People of the State of _____, through the Attorney General of the State of _____, apply for an injunction to enjoin any person who has not been issued a license or whose license has been suspended or revoked or expired, from practicing nursing as a registered nurse or as a licensed practical nurse; and upon the filing of a verified petition in such court, the court or any judge thereof, if satisfied by affidavit, or otherwise, that such person is or has been practicing nursing as a registered nurse or as a licensed practical nurse without having been issued a license to do so, or after his license has been suspended or revoked or expired, may issue a temporary injunction, without notice or bond, enjoining the defendant from further practicing nursing as a registered nurse or as a licensed served upon the defendant and the proceedings shall thereafter be conducted as in other civil cases. If it be established that said defendant has been, or is practicing professional nursing or practical nursing without having been issued a license or has been or is practicing professional nursing or practical nursing after his license has been suspended or revoked, or expired, the court, or any judge thereof, may enter a decree perpetually enjoining said defendant from further practicing professional nursing or practical nursing. In case of violation of any injunction issued under the provisions of this section, the court, or any judge thereof, may summarily try and punish the offender for contempt of court. Such injunction proceeding shall be in addition to, and not in lieu of, all penalties and other remedies in this Act provided.

bond, enjoining the defendant from further practicing professional nursing or from further practicing nursing as a licensed practical nurse. A copy of said verified petition shall be served upon the defendant and the proceedings shall thereafter be conducted as in other civil cases. If it be established that said defendant has been or is practicing professional nursing, or has been or is practicing nursing as a licensed practical nurse, after his license has been suspended or revoked, or expired, the court, or any judge thereof, may enter a decree perpetually enjoining said defendant from further practicing nursing as a licensed practical nurse. In case of violation of any injunction issued under the provisions of this section, the court, or any judge thereof, may summarily try and punish the offender for contempt of court. Such injunction proceeding shall be in addition to, and not in lieu of, all penalties and other remedies in this Act provided.

practical nurse. A copy of said verified petition shall be served upon the defendant and the proceedings shall thereafter be conducted as in other civil cases. If it be established that said defendant has been or is practicing nursing as a registered nurse or as a licensed practical nurse after his license has been suspended or revoked, or expired, the court, or any judge thereof, may enter a decree perpetually enjoining said defendant from further practicing nursing as a registered nurse or as a licensed practical nurse. In case of violation of any injunction issued under the provisions of this section, the court, or any judge thereof, may summarily try and punish the offender for contempt of court. Such injunction proceeding shall be in addition to, and not in lieu of, all penalties and other remedies in the Act provided.

# Glossary

*Admission.* A concession as to the truth or falsity of a particular proposition, or the existence or nonexistence of a particular fact or set of facts.

*Affirmative defense.* Matter that, if proved, means that the plaintiff cannot recover in his suit. The phrase applies to matters unrelated to the primary claim that offer independent reasons why plaintiff may not recover.

*Appeal.* A presentation to a higher court, with the power to set aside, modify, or affirm a judgment of a lower court.

*Appellate court.* The court that sits in review of the decisions of a lower court.

*Burden of proof.* The obligation of a party to produce evidence establishing his contention. The term is used in several senses, the primary ones being the burden to produce a preponderance of the evidence in civil cases, or the burden to offer evidence countering evidence offered by the opponent.

*Certiorari.* A procedural device to obtain review when normal channels are not available.

*Complaint.* In a legal sense, a formal document filed in court describing an alleged wrong done to the plaintiff.

*Confession.* An admission of guilt, usually used in a formal sense.

*Culpable.* Responsible for; liable for.

*Decree.* A judgment of a court, in a written form, specifying what the parties to a lawsuit must do or not do.

*Defendant.* One who is accused of crime by the state, or one against whom suit is brought by a private litigation, in which complaint is made that the defendant violated his duty or is responsible for a breach of duty or for negligence.

*Demurrer.* A procedural device used to raise the defense or claim that, even assuming all the facts alleged by a plaintiff were true, there would be no right to legal relief based on those facts.

*Deposition.* A proceeding whereby questions are asked of a person, relating to the subject matter of a lawsuit, and in advance of trial, and the questions and answers are recorded in written form.

*Directed verdict.* A verdict given by a judge rather than a jury, in a jury trial, on the grounds that the evidence is so clear that only one result would be permitted.

*Discovery—discovery proceedings.* Full procedures of asking oral and written questions, and providing oral and written answers, as well as giving another party access to relevant documents and things, all undertaken prior to a trial.

*Due process of law.* A phrase used to describe the right of every person to be convicted of a crime, or have his property taken, only after the state has acted in a fair and proper way.

508

*Eleemosynary.* Charitable, or in the public interest.

*Evidence.* The data offered to establish the existence or nonexistence of a proposition or a fact.

*Felony.* A serious crime, the commission of which results in severe penalties. In the ancient common law a felony resulted in complete forfeiture of the felon's property, and perhaps capital punishment or imprisonment as well.

*Fraud.* Misstatements of fact, which are intended to and do deceive another person to his damage.

*Hearsay evidence.* Evidence of an out-of-court statement, written or oral, that is not subject to cross-examination and that is offered to prove the truth of the matter asserted.

*Homicide.* The killing of a human being.

*Impeachment.* Demonstration that testimony or statements made are false or substantially inaccurate.

*Incest.* Sexual intercourse or cohabitation among family members.

*Indictment.* A written accusation prepared and filed by the state making an accusation of the commission of the crime against one or more particular persons.

*Injunction.* A decree of the court prohibiting the doing of certain acts.

*Judgment notwithstanding the verdict.* A decision by a trial judge that the verdict reached by a jury was erroneous and should not be allowed to stand.

*Jurisdiction.* The authority given to courts to decide cases. Sometimes, jurisdiction is limited and courts can decide only particular kinds of cases.

*Legal remedy.* A means provided by law for the redress of a wrong committed; generally implies a court proceeding.

*Litigant.* A party to a lawsuit.

*Manslaughter.* The intentional taking of a human life without malice or premeditation.

*Misdemeanor.* A crime less serious than a felony and not resulting in severe penalties.

*Negligence per se.* Conduct that the actor cannot claim to be other than negligent; often applied to violations of criminal law.

*Nonsuit.* A dismissal of an action without determination of the merits.

*Penal system.* The system of prisons, probation departments, and formal state organizations designed to implement the imposition of sanctions in the criminal law.

*Plaintiff.* One who initiates a lawsuit and claims that he has a right to recover from the defendant.

*Prima facie.* A Latin phrase meaning "on the first appearance." It usually used to mean the state of a lawsuit where, if no further evidence is introduced, one party or another has presented sufficient evidence to prevail.

*Privilege.* The right given to persons dealing with certain professions not to have the matters they discuss with the members of those professions disclosed in court; also used to describe the right to remain silent in criminal cases.

*Remand.* An order given by an appellate court sending a case back to the trial court for further action.

*Sanction.* A penalty or punishment established by the state imposed upon a person after the commission of a crime.

*Sine qua non.* A Latin phrase meaning "without which not." It is used to describe an absolutely necessary prerequisite to the occurrence of an event.

*Solvent.* Financially responsible; able to pay.

*Stare decisis.* A Latin phrase meaning to abide by decided cases. The phrase is used to describe the policy of courts to decide cases in a manner consistent with the way similar cases have been decided in the past.

*Statute.* An act of the legislature set forth in writing that declares, requires, or prohibits certain conduct.

*Statute of limitations.* An enactment of the legislature stating that after the lapse of a certain period of time, a lawsuit cannot be brought for a wrong.

*Subpoena.* A paper issued by a judge or the clerk of a court requiring a person to attend to give testimony.

*Substantive law.* That portion of the law which deals with matters of substance rather than matters of procedure; substantive law deals with the definition and regulation of rights and duties. Its opposite is "adjective" law, which deals with the legal remedies and modes of procedure for obtaining redress for the violation of rights or the breaches of duties.

*Summary judgment.* An adjudication of a lawsuit on the merits prior to trial, on the grounds that no trial is necessary because there is no genuine issue of material fact present.

*Testimony.* Oral statement, made under oath at a trial.

*Tortfeasor.* One who commits a tort.

*Transcript of proceeding.* A written record which records verbatim testimony and statements made in a proceeding.

*Trier of fact.* The decision-making body with respect to disputed testimony and matters of fact as opposed to decisions of law. The trier of fact may be either the judge, in a case where no jury is impaneled, or a jury, when the jury exists.

*Wanton conduct.* Conduct undertaken in reckless disregard of the consequences.

*Writ of mandamus.* A procedural device for obtaining review of a lower court's decision when ordinary channels of review are not available or are too slow.

# Index

(Numbers in *italics* indicate references to cases.)